Calculations of Analytical Chemistry

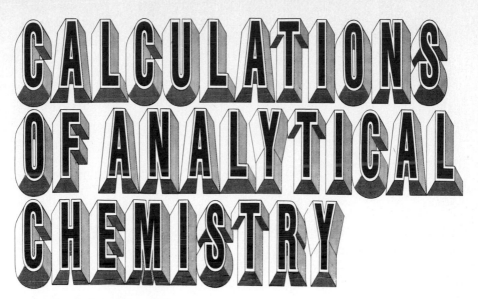

CALCULATIONS OF ANALYTICAL CHEMISTRY

Leicester F. Hamilton, S.B.
Professor of Analytical Chemistry, Emeritus
Massachusetts Institute of Technology

Stephen G. Simpson, Ph.D.
Associate Professor of Analytical Chemistry, Emeritus
Massachusetts Institute of Technology

David W. Ellis, Ph.D.
Associate Professor of Chemistry
University of New Hampshire

Seventh Edition

McGraw-Hill Book Company
New York   St. Louis   San Francisco   Toronto   London   Sydney

Preface

The greatest change in this edition from that preceding it is the considerable amount of added material covering so-called "instrumental" methods of analysis. Topics in this field that were previously given, such as those pertaining to various electrochemical methods, have been revised and expanded, and many modern optical and specialized methods have been introduced. In the discussions of these methods, emphasis has been directed to the mathematical aspects of their application to quantitative chemical analysis. As in the case of the topics covering conventional noninstrumental methods, illustrative discussions are followed by numerical problems, and answers are given to most of the problems relating to this added material. A chapter has also been added on the application of conventional analytical methods to the determination of organic functional groups.

Throughout the book the signs of the numerical values of electrode potentials have been changed from those given in the preceding edition, and most half-cell reactions are expressed as reductions rather than as oxidations. These conventions now seem to be favored by most analytical chemists.

Credit for most of the added instrumental methods should be given to the junior author, Professor Ellis, and thanks are due Professor Daggett of the University of New Hampshire for numerous suggestions in this field.

Leicester F. Hamilton
Stephen G. Simpson
David W. Ellis

Contents

ONE
General
Analysis

Mathematical Operations

1-1 Divisions of Analytical Chemistry

Analytical chemistry is ordinarily divided into qualitative analysis and quantitative analysis. A compound or mixture is analyzed by the methods of qualitative analysis to determine what constituents or components are present; a compound or mixture is analyzed by the methods of quantitative analysis to determine the proportions in which the constituents or components are present.

Calculations in qualitative analysis are limited mostly to those pertaining to equilibrium constants and simple weight and volume relationships. Calculations in quantitative analysis are more extensive and are based on numerical data obtained from careful measurements of masses and volumes of chemical substances.

1-2 Errors in Quantitative Measurements

In quantitative analysis, as in other fields of science, numerical data and numerical results obtained from them are subject to errors, and independent measurements of the same quantity, even when made under apparently identical conditions, usually differ to some extent.

Errors can be classed as *determinate errors* and *random errors.*

Determinate errors are errors that persist in a definite way and to a fixed degree from one determination to another and are of such nature that their magnitudes can be determined and their effects eliminated or at least greatly reduced. They include (1) *instrumental errors,* an example of which is the error caused by the use of a balance with arms of unequal lengths; (2) *personal errors,* an example of which is the error caused by consistently establishing a color change too late; (3) *methodic errors*, an example of which is the error caused by the presence of a foreign substance in a weighed precipitate. Determinate errors can usually be corrected for by calibration or by other experimental means.

Random errors are errors that are more or less beyond the control of the observer and that have signs and magnitudes determined solely by chance. They may be caused by such factors as fluctuations in temperature and pressure, inability of the observer to estimate correctly fractional parts of marked divisions, and general fatigue of the eye. They are characterized by the fact that positive and negative errors are equally likely to occur. For this reason, the arithmetical mean of the numerical results of a series of similar observations subject only to random errors can be taken as the most probable value.

1-3   Precision and Accuracy

The *precision* of a numerical value is the degree of agreement between it and other values obtained under substantially the same conditions. The *accuracy* of a numerical value is the degree of agreement between it and the true value. Since the true value is never known except within certain limits, the accuracy of a value is never known except within those limits. A numerical result may have a high degree of precision and yet have a low degree of accuracy because of the effect of one or more determinate errors that have not been established and corrected for.

The difference between two numerical values can be expressed as the *absolute difference* or as the *relative difference* (the latter usually in parts per thousand). The absolute difference between the values 2.431 and 2.410 is 0.021; the relative difference is $\dfrac{0.021}{2.4\cdots} \times 1{,}000 = 8.7$ parts per thousand ($=8.7$ p.p.t.).

The absolute difference between a numerical result and the true value is the *absolute error* of the result; the relative difference between a numerical result and the true value is the *relative error* of the result. In the case just cited, if 2.431 is the true value, the absolute error of the value 2.410 is 0.021 and its relative error is 8.7 p.p.t.

1-4   Precision Measures

In a series of independent determinations of a given quantity, if determinate errors have been effectively eliminated or corrected for, the average, or *mean*, of the numerical values obtained can be taken as the most probable value of the series, and a measure of the degree of precision of this mean value can be considered as a measure of the limiting degree to which the result is likely to differ from the unknown true value. It is, therefore, a measure of the *reliability* of the result.

Suppose in a series of independent determinations of a given quantity the errors are essentially random ones, and suppose the following nine values are obtained:

31.62	31.76	31.60
31.47	31.71	31.60
31.64	31.53	31.71

The mean value ($\overline{X}$) is obtained by dividing the sum of the individual values by the number of measurements (n) made. In the case of a large number of values, it is permissible to express the mean to one more significant figure than is given in the individual values. In the above case, the mean is 31.627. The difference between any one of the values and this mean is the deviation (x_i) of that value from the mean. In the above case, the deviations (without regard to sign) are as follows:

0.007	0.133	0.027
0.157	0.083	0.027
0.013	0.097	0.083

The *average deviation (d) of a single measurement* is the mean of the deviations of all the individual measurements:

$$d = \frac{\Sigma x_i}{n}$$

where Σx_i denotes the sum of the individual deviations from the mean. In this case the average deviation is 0.070 and represents the amount by which an average independent measurement of the series is likely to differ from the most probable value.

It is often more important, however, to know the precision or reliability of the mean than that of the component measurements. It can be shown that the *average deviation (D) of the mean* is numerically equal to the average deviation of a single measurement divided by the square root of the number of measurements made:

$$D = \frac{d}{\sqrt{n}}$$

In the above case, the average deviation of the mean is $0.070/\sqrt{9} = 0.023$.

The *standard deviation* is often used as a precision measure and is considered to be a more reliable measure than the average deviation. The *standard deviation (s) of a single measurement*[1] is found by extracting

---

[1] In discussions of statistical methods, the symbol μ is used for the mean value of an *infinite* series of measurements, δ for the corresponding average deviation, and σ for the corresponding standard deviation.

the square root of the quotient obtained by dividing the sum of the squares of the individual deviations by one less than the number of measurements made:

$$s = \sqrt{\frac{\Sigma(x_i)^2}{n-1}}$$

In the case cited, the standard deviation of a single measurement is $\sqrt{\dfrac{(0.007)^2 + (0.157)^2 + \cdots}{8}} = 0.091$, and the *standard deviation (S) of the mean* is $0.091/\sqrt{9} = 0.030$. This number serves to give an indication of the reliability of the mean and does not imply that the true value must necessarily fall within the limits of $31.627 - 0.030$ and $31.627 + 0.030$. Many writers in this field take twice the value of the standard deviation of the mean as an indication of the "reasonable" limits within which the true value is likely to be. According to this convention, in the case cited (and in the absence of determinate errors) the true value can be expected to fall within the limits of $31.627 - 0.060$ ($=31.567$) and $31.627 + 0.060$ ($=31.687$).

In a series of measurements of the same quantity, the *median value* is sometimes taken instead of the mean value to represent the most probable value. The median or median value of a series of readings is the reading of such magnitude that the number of readings having a greater numerical value is equal to the number having a lesser value. It is the value halfway in a series arranged in ascending or descending order. In the series of nine values given in the first part of this section, 31.62 is the median, since there are four values greater than 31.62 and four values less than 31.62. In a series containing an even number of values, the mean of the two "middle values" is taken as the median.

1-5 Rejection of Measurements

In a series of similar measurements it sometimes happens that one (or more) of the numerical values stands out as being considerably different from the others, and the temptation is to reject it in establishing the mean value. Several rules have been proposed for determining whether or not such a rejection is justified from the point of view of mathematical probability.

One rule is as follows: Omit the doubtful value, and determine in the usual way the mean and the average deviation of the retained values. The rejection can be considered as mathematically justified if the deviation of the suspected value from the mean is at least four times the average deviation of the retained values, that is, if

$$x_i \geq 4d$$

Many writers advocate the stricter requirement of $x_i \geq 2\frac{1}{2}d$, but this rule will not be used in this book.   In either case, the error of the rejected value is called a *huge error*.

As an example, suppose that a tenth value in the series given in the preceding section were 31.34.   The deviation of this suspected low value from the mean is $31.627 - 31.34 = 0.287$.   This is more than four times 0.070, and the rejection is justified.

1-6   Rules Governing the Proper Retention of Significant Figures

In most routine chemical analyses relatively few independent readings or determinations are made, so that numerical precision measures are not often used.   In such cases the precision of a numerical value is best indicated by the number of significant figures used in expressing that value.   This gives only a rough idea of the precision of the result but is nevertheless important.

The following definitions and rules are applicable to all calculations in analytical chemistry.

A *number* is an expression of quantity.

A *figure*, or *digit*, is any one of the characters 0, 1, 2, 3, 4, 5, 6, 7, 8, 9 which, alone or in combination, serves to express a number.

A *significant figure* is a digit that denotes the amount of the quantity in the place in which it stands.   In the case of the number 243, the figures signify that there are two hundreds, four tens, and three units and are therefore all significant.   The character 0 is used in two ways.   It may be used as a significant figure, or it may be used merely to locate the decimal point.   It is a significant figure when it indicates that the quantity in the place in which it stands is known to be nearer zero than to any other value.   Thus, the weight of a crucible may be found to be 10.603 g, in which case all five figures, including the zeros, are significant.   If the weight in grams of the crucible is found to be 10.610, meaning that the weight as measured is nearer to 10.610 than to 10.609 or 10.611, both zeros are significant.

By analysis, the weight of the ash of a certain quantitative filter paper is found to be 0.00003 g.   Here the zeros are not significant but serve merely to show that the figure 3 belongs in the fifth place to the right of the decimal point.   Any other characters except digits would serve the purpose as well.   The same is true of the value 356,000 in. when signifying the distance between two given points as measured by instruments that are accurate to three figures only.   The zeros are not significant.   In order to avoid confusion, this value should be written 3.56×10^5 in.   If the distance has been measured to the nearest 100 in., it should be written 3.560×10^5 in.

Rule 1.   Retain as many significant figures in a result and in data in general as will give only one uncertain figure.   (For very accurate work involving lengthy computations, two uncertain figures may sometimes be retained.)   Thus, the value 25.34, representing the reading of an ordinary buret, contains the proper number of significant figures, for the digit 4 is obtained by estimating an ungraduated scale division and is doubtless uncertain.

Rule 2.   In rejecting superfluous and inaccurate figures, increase by 1 the last figure retained if the following rejected figure is 5 or over. Thus, in rejecting the last figure of the number 16.279, the new value becomes 16.28.

Rule 3.   In adding or subtracting a number of quantities, extend the significant figures in each term and in the sum or difference only to the point corresponding to that uncertain figure occurring farthest to the left relative to the decimal point.

For example, the sum of the three terms 0.0121, 25.64, and 1.05782, on the assumption that the last figure in each is uncertain, is

$$
\begin{array}{r}
0.01 \\
25.64 \\
\underline{1.06} \\
26.71
\end{array}
$$

Rule 4.   In multiplication or division, the percentage precision of the product or quotient cannot be greater than the percentage precision of the least precise factor entering into the computation.   Hence, in computations involving multiplication or division, or both, retain as many significant figures in each factor and in the numerical result as are contained in the factor having the largest percentage deviation.   In most cases, as many significant figures can be retained in each factor and in the result as are contained in the factor having the least number of significant figures.

For example, the product of the three terms 0.0121, 25.64, and 1.05782, on the assumption that the last figure in each is uncertain, is

$$0.0121 \times 25.6 \times 1.06 = 0.328$$

for, if the first term is assumed to have a possible variation of 1 in the last place, it has an actual deviation of 1 unit in every 121 units and its percentage deviation would be $\frac{1}{121} \times 100 = 0.8$.   Similarly, the possible percentage deviation of the second term would be $\frac{1}{2,564} \times 100 = 0.04$, and that of the third term would be $\frac{1}{105,782} \times 100 = 0.0009$.   The first term, having the largest percentage deviation, therefore governs the number of significant figures that can be properly retained in the product, for the product cannot have a precision greater than 0.8%. That is, the product may vary by 0.8 part in every 100 or by nearly 3 parts in every 328. The last figure in the product as expressed with three significant figures above is therefore doubtful, and the proper number of significant figures has been retained.

Rule 5.   Computations involving a precision not greater than 0.25% can be made with a 10-in. slide rule. For greater precision, logarithm tables should be used.

Rule 6.   In carrying out the operations of multiplication or division by the use of logarithms, retain as many figures in the mantissa of the logarithm of each factor as are properly contained in the factors themselves under rule 4. Thus, in the solution of the example given under rule 4, the logarithms of the factors are expressed as follows:

$$
\begin{aligned}
\log 0.0121 &= 8.083 - 10 \\
\log 25.64 &= 1.409 \\
\log 1.05782 &= \underline{0.024} \\
& 9.516 - 10 = \log 0.328
\end{aligned}
$$

In this case the same numerical result is obtained with a 10-in. slide rule.

1-7   Conventions Regarding the Solution of Numerical Problems

In the calculation of numerical results from chemical data that have been obtained under known conditions and by known methods, little difficulty should be experienced in forming an approximate estimate of the precision of the various factors and of the results obtained. In the case of numerical problems that are unaccompanied by any data to show the conditions under which the various measurements were made or the precision of the values given, the retention of the proper number of significant figures in the final computed results may be a matter of considerable judgment. In such cases the rules listed above are subject to modification, but in any case the need for a certain amount of common sense and judgment in using them in no way detracts from their value.

In the solution of problems in this book, it can be assumed that the given data conform to rule 1 above. In problems containing such expressions as "a 2-g sample," "a 25-ml pipetful," or "a tenth-normal solution," it may be assumed that the weight of the sample, the volume of the pipet, and the normality of the solution are known to a precision at least as great as that of the other factors involved in the problem.

It should also be remembered that the atomic weights of the elements are known only to a limited number of significant figures, and in the absence of further data, it may be assumed that the values ordinarily given in atomic-weight tables conform to rule 1 above, in that the last figure in each is doubtful. It follows, therefore, that the same attention should be paid to the precision of the atomic and formula weights involved in computations as to that of any other data.

It often happens that independent calculations from given data give results which disagree by one or two units in the last significant figure retained. This is usually due to the fact that figures have been rejected at different stages of the operations involved, but this is usually of no importance, since, when properly expressed, the last significant figure in the result is doubtful anyway.

Analytical determinations are usually done in duplicate or triplicate. In most of the problems in this book, however, data apparently covering only one determination are given. It may be assumed that such values represent mean values obtained from multiple determinations.

PROBLEMS

(Problems to which answers are given in Part IX are denoted by asterisks.)

*1-1.   How many significant figures are implied in each of the following values: (a) 2.20×10^{-9}, (b) 5,000.002, (c) 2.010×10^5?

*1-2.   Give the f. wt. of $OsCl_4$ to as high a degree of precision as is warranted by the at. wts. involved.

*1-3   Express the velocity of light, 186,000 miles/sec, in such a way as to indicate that it has been measured to the nearest 100 miles/sec.

*1-4.   An ore contains 33.79% Fe_2O_3. Duplicate detns. give 33.80 and 34.02%, and the mean of these is reported. (a) By how many p.p.t. do the duplicate values differ from each other? (b) What is the mean value? (c) What is the absolute error? (d) What is the relative error in p.p.t.?

*1-5.   Two analysts separately analyze in duplicate a certain steel for the percentage of sulfur. Each uses 3.5-g samples weighed to the nearest 0.1 g. One analyst reports 0.042 and 0.041 for the duplicate values; the other reports 0.04199 and 0.04101. (a) By how many p.p.t. do the duplicate percentages agree in each case? (b) Is the second analyst justified in his report?

*1-6.   What is the lower of two values if the higher value is 168.1 and the relative difference between them is 6.5 p.p.t.?

*1-7.   The following six independent results were obtained for the normality of a soln.: 0.2562, 0.2566, 0.2565, 0.2560, 0.2568, and 0.2566. A seventh value, lower than the others, was justifiably rejected according to the rule given in the text for determining a huge error. (a) What is the highest value that the rejected result could have? (b) What is the average deviation of the retained results? (c) What is the standard deviation of the mean of the retained results? (d) By how many p.p.t. does the mean differ from the median?

*1-8.   Eleven analysts, using the same method, reported the percentage of protein in a certain cereal product.   The values reported were as follows: 22.62, 22.73, 22.75, 22.78, 22.79, 22.83, 22.84, 22.87, 22.87, 22.92, 22.94, and these were examined with a view of establishing the most probable value.   (*a*) According to the criterion given in the text, is the rejection of the first value (22.62) justifiable on the basis that it involves a huge error?   (*b*) What are the two deviation measures that establish this decision?   (*c*) What is the mean value of the 11 results?   (*d*) What is the average deviation of the mean?   (*e*) What is the standard deviation of the mean?   (*f*) What is the median value?   (*g*) What is the relative difference between the lowest and highest reported values?   (*h*) Assuming the mean to be the true value, what is the relative error of the lowest reported value?

*1-9.   It is necessary to solve the following:

$$(1.276 \times 0.00047) + (1.7 \times 10^{-4}) - (0.0021764 \times 0.0121)$$

each term being uncertain in the last significant figure.   (*a*) Should one use arithmetic, logarithms, or a slide rule in the multiplications?   (*b*) What is the numerical answer?

*1-10.   A value which has been found by duplicate analyses to be 0.1129 and 0.1133, respectively, is to be multiplied by 1.36 (last figure doubtful), and the product is to be subtracted from the value 0.93742, which has been very accurately measured.   Express the result with the proper no. of significant figures.

1-11.   How many significant figures are implied in each of the following values: (*a*) 16×10^3, (*b*) 16.00×10^3, (*c*) 1.60×10^{-2}?

1-12.   In the following multiplication the last figure in each of the three factors is uncertain: $2.0000 \times 0.30 \times 500 = 300.00$.   (*a*) How many figures in the product as given should be rejected as superfluous?   (*b*) Express the result in such a way as to indicate the correct no. of significant figures.

1-13.   Give the f. wt. of $Pd(NH_3)_2(OH)_2$ to as high a degree of precision as is warranted by the at. wts. involved.

1-14.   A book on astronomy gives the polar diameter of the earth as 7,900.0 miles.   (*a*) To what precision of measurement does this value imply?   (*b*) If the measurement had been made only to the nearest 10 miles, how should the value be expressed to indicate this fact?

1-15.   Assuming each term to be uncertain in the last figure, solve the following and express the answer to the correct no. of significant figures: $(1.586 \div 29.10) + [162.22(3.221 \times 10^{-4})] - 0.00018$.

1-16.   A sample of $BaCl_2$ containing 65.97% Ba is given for analysis.   One analyst obtains 65.68, 65.79, and 65.99 for triplicate detns. and reports the mean value. (*a*) By how many p.p.t. does each value differ from the mean?   (*b*) What is the absolute error of the mean?   (*c*) What is the relative error of the median?

1-17.   A steel is found by analysis to contain 0.42% carbon.   The calculations involve only multiplication and division.   To how many decimal places should one weigh a 1-g sample in order to duplicate the result?

1-18.   A sample of limonite was analyzed by 12 students.   The values obtained for the percentage of Fe were 34.62, 34.42, 34.60, 34.48, 33.71, 34.50, 34.50, 34.22, 34.41, 35.00, 34.65, and 34.44.   (*a*) What are the mean value, the average deviation of a single result, and the deviation of the mean?   (*b*) What is the median value, and what is its standard deviation?   (*c*) If the true percentage is 34.75, what is the absolute error and what is the relative error of the mean?

1-19.   A sample of material was sent to two chemists.   Each used the same method and reported the results of four analyses as follows: Chemist A: 30.15, 30.15, 30.14, 30.16; Chemist B: 30.251, 30.007, 30.101, 30.241.   Find in each case the mean value and its deviation measure.   Other conditions being equal, which mean value is the more reliable?

1-20.   The relative difference between two values is 12 p.p.t.   What is the absolute difference, and what is the higher value if the lower is 233.6?

1-21.   The following four independent results were obtained for a certain instrumental reading: 3.685, 3.689, 3.681, and 3.692.   A fifth reading, higher than the others, was justifiably rejected according to the rule given in the text for determining a huge error.   (*a*) What is the lowest value that the rejected reading could have? (*b*) What is the average deviation of the mean of the retained results?   (*c*) What is the standard deviation of the mean of the retained results?   (*d*) What is the median value?

1-22.   A student obtained the following values for the normality of a solution: 0.6143, 0.6153, 0.6148, 0.6142, 0.6146, 0.6154.   (*a*) What is the mean value? (*b*) What is the average deviation of a single determination?   (*c*) What is the average deviation of the mean?   (*d*) What is the standard deviation of the mean? (*e*) What is the absolute difference between the mean and the median?   (*f*) Another value obtained for the normality was 0.6164, but this was rejected on the basis that it involved a huge error.   Show why this rejection was or was not justified, and give the two deviation measures involved.   (*g*) If the true value for the normality is 0.6145, what is the relative error of the rejected value?

1-8   The Use of Logarithms

It is assumed that the student is sufficiently familiar with the theory and use of logarithms to be able to use them in simple calculations, especially those involving multiplication and division, and that he appreciates the fact that the use of logarithms saves him a great deal of time and effort in making such calculations.

The precision of ordinary chemical analytical work is seldom great enough to warrant the retention of more than four significant figures in the numerical data obtained and in the calculations made from such data.   Hence a four-place logarithm table is entirely adequate.   To use the logarithm table given in the Appendix for the purpose of finding the mantissa (i.e., the decimal part) of the common logarithm of a number, proceed as follows: First find the first two digits of the number in the column headed "natural numbers," then go to the right until the column is reached which has the third digit of the number as a heading. To the number thus found, add the number which is in the same horizontal line at the right-hand side of the table and in the column of proportional parts headed by the fourth significant figure of the number. Thus, the mantissa of log 236.8 is $3729 + 15 = 3744$, and the logarithm is 2.3744.

Antilogarithms can be looked up in the antilogarithm table in the same way. Only the mantissa is used in looking up the number; the characteristic is used merely to locate the decimal point. Thus, the sequence of digits in the number having a logarithm of 1.8815 is

$$7603 + 9 = 7612$$

and the actual number is 76.12 as determined by the given characteristic of the logarithm.

In actual calculations from analytical data the essential purpose of the characteristic in a logarithm is to locate the position of the decimal point in the final numerical value obtained. Since in most cases a very rough mental calculation is all that is needed to establish the position of the decimal point, the use of characteristics can usually be dispensed with. The retention of characteristics is, however, helpful in serving as a check on the other method.

Example 1   Calculate by logarithms $\dfrac{9.827 \times 0.5062}{0.005164 \times 136.59}$.

Solution

$$
\begin{array}{rl}
\log 9.827 = 0.9924 & \qquad \text{or} \qquad 0.9924 \\
\log 0.5062 = \bar{1}.7044 & \qquad 9.7044 - 10 \\
\text{colog } 0.005164 = 2.2871 & \qquad 2.2871 \\
\text{colog } 136.59 = \bar{3}.8646 & \qquad 7.8646 - 10 \\
\text{Sum} = 0.8485 & \qquad 20.8485 - 20 \\
\text{antilog} = 7.055 & \qquad \textit{Ans.}
\end{array}
$$

As previously mentioned, much time is saved by omitting all characteristics in the solution of the above problem and merely writing the mantissas of each logarithm or cologarithm.[1] The location of the decimal point is then determined by a simple mental calculation on the original expression. Thus, inspection shows that the two factors in the numerator of the above expression give a result approximating 5 and that the factors in the denominator give a result approximating 0.7. The

---

[1] The mantissa of the cologarithm can be expressed as quickly as that of the logarithm merely by mentally subtracting each digit from 9 except the last nonzero digit, which is subtracted from 10. For example, mantissa of log $17.50 = 2430$; mantissa of colog $17.50 = 7570$.

answer must therefore be in the neighborhood of 7, which establishes the position of the decimal point.

1-9   Use of the Slide Rule

The slide rule is essentially a logarithm table mechanically applied.   On the scales used for multiplication and division, the numbers are stamped on the rule in positions proportionate to their logarithms.   Multiplication by means of the rule is merely a mechanical addition of two logarithms; division is a mechanical subtraction of two logarithms.   Manuals covering the proper use of a slide rule are readily obtainable.

The student of quantitative analysis should be proficient in the use of a slide rule, particularly in the processes of multiplication and division. The slide rule saves a great deal of time in making minor calculations and is an excellent means of checking calculations made by logarithms. Although the precision of the ordinary 10-in. slide rule is limited to three significant figures, it is suggested that slide-rule accuracy be permitted in solving quiz problems and home problems, even though the data given may theoretically require four-significant-figure accuracy.   The purpose of the problems is more to make sure that the methods of calculation are understood than to give practice in fundamental mathematical operations.

Most laboratory calculations, however, require four-significant-figure accuracy, and four-place logarithms are necessary.

1-10   Nomographs

A nomograph is a device by means of which the numerical result of a given calculation can be read directly from a previously drawn scale or series of scales.   It is roughly comparable to a slide rule in fixed position but has the advantage of being equally applicable to formulas and equations containing additive and subtractive terms.   The scales are drawn on a plain surface and are so constructed that a straightedge, applied one or more times, connects the points corresponding to the given numerical data to the point corresponding to the desired numerical answer.   Since a separate nomograph is needed for each formula to be solved, nomographs are of practical use only when the same type of calculation is made repeatedly.   A typical nomograph is shown in Fig. 2, which accompanies Sec. 8-7, and its use is discussed in that section.

PROBLEMS

*1-23. Using four-place logarithms, determine the following: (*a*) log 387.6, (*b*) log 0.0009289, (*c*) colog 52.61, (*d*) colog 0.06003, (*e*) antilog 2.4474, (*f*) antilog $\overline{4}$.1733, (*g*) antilog 7.2068 − 10.

*1-24. Using four-place logarithms, calculate the following: (*a*) 226.3 × 0.00002591, (*b*) 0.05811 ÷ 64.53, (*c*) fourth power of 0.3382, (*d*) cube root of 0.09508. Check these to three significant figures with a slide rule.

*1-25. Using four-place logarithms, find the value of the following:

$$\frac{0.0046191 \times 287.7}{51.42 \times 0.84428}$$

Locate the position of the decimal point by mental arithmetic and also by the proper use of characteristics. Also check the answer to three significant figures with a slide rule.

1-26. Using four-place logarithms, determine the following: (*a*) log 67.84, (*b*) log 0.005903, (*c*) colog 0.9566, (*d*) colog 718.1, (*e*) antilog 3.6482, (*f*) antilog $\overline{2}$.0696, (*g*) antilog 6.0088 − 10.

1-27. Using four-place logarithms, calculate the following: (*a*) 33.81 × 0.0009915, (*b*) 0.1869 ÷ 362.4, (*c*) cube of 0.09279, (*d*) square root of 0.5546. Check these to three significant figures with a slide rule.

1-28. Using four-place logarithms, find the numerical value of the following expression:

$$\frac{5,987.9 \times 0.006602}{1.864 \times 0.4617 \times 1,053.3}$$

Locate the position of the decimal point by the proper use of characteristics, and check by mental arithmetic. Also check the answer to three significant figures by means of a slide rule.

Chemical Equations

2-1 Purpose of Chemical Equations

When the nature and composition of the initial and final products of a chemical reaction are known, the facts can be symbolized in the form of a chemical equation. When properly written, the equation indicates (1) the nature of the atoms and the composition of the molecules taking part in the reaction, (2) the relative number of atoms and molecules of the substances taking part in the reaction, (3) the proportions by weight of the interacting and resulting substances, and (4) the proportions by volume of all gases involved. These four principles, applied to reactions which go to completion, serve as the foundation of quantitative chemical analysis. Before the calculation of a chemical analysis can be made, it is important to understand the chemistry involved and to be able to express the reactions in the form of balanced equations.

2-2 Types of Chemical Equations

The determination of the nature of the products formed by a given reaction requires a knowledge of general chemistry which, it is assumed, has already been acquired from previous study, but the ability to write and balance equations correctly and quickly is acquired only by considerable practice. The following discussion is given to help the student attain this proficiency, especially with regard to equations involving oxidation and reduction, which usually give the most trouble to the beginner.

With equations expressing the reactions of (1) combination, (2) decomposition, and (3) metathesis, it is seldom that much difficulty is experienced in bringing about equality between the atoms and molecules of the reacting substances and those of the products, for little more is involved than purely mechanical adjustment of the terms and an elementary knowledge of valence. As examples of the above types of chemical change in the order given, the following equations may be cited:

$$2H_2 + O_2 \longrightarrow 2H_2O \tag{1}$$
$$2HgO \longrightarrow 2Hg + O_2 \tag{2}$$
$$3CaCl_2 + 2Na_3PO_4 \longrightarrow Ca_3(PO_4)_2 + 6NaCl \tag{3}$$

Equations expressing reactions of oxidation and reduction, although usually somewhat more complicated, offer little additional difficulty, provided the principles underlying these types of chemical change are understood.

The above equations are molecular equations. For reactions taking place in aqueous solution (such as the third case above), equations are usually better written in the ionic form. To do so correctly requires a knowledge of the relative degrees of ionization of solutes and the correct application of a few simple rules.

2-3   Ionization of Acids, Bases, and Salts

Although the theory of ionization should be familiar to the student from his previous study of general chemistry, the following facts should be kept in mind because they are particularly important in connection with writing equations:

"Strong" (i.e., highly ionized) acids include such familiar acids as HCl, HBr, HI, H_2SO_4, HNO_3, $HClO_3$, $HBrO_3$, HIO_3, $HClO_4$, and $HMnO_4$. These acids in solution are completely ionized, although at ordinary concentrations interionic effects may give conductivities corresponding to an apparent degree of ionization a little less than 100%. In ionic equations (see below) strong acids are written in the form of ions.

"Strong" bases include $NaOH$, KOH, $Ba(OH)_2$, $Sr(OH)_2$, and $Ca(OH)_2$. These bases in solution are completely ionized and in ionic equations are written as ions.

Salts, with few exceptions, are completely dissociated in solution and give relatively high concentrations of simple metal ions. Two exceptions frequently encountered in analytical chemistry are lead acetate and mercuric chloride.

Many acids and bases are ionized in solution to only a slight degree at ordinary concentrations. Table 11 in the Appendix lists most of such acids and bases ordinarily encountered in analytical chemistry, and the student should familiarize himself with the names of these substances and have at least a general idea of the magnitude of the degree of ionization in the case of the more common ones.

Certain acids contain more than one hydrogen replaceable by a metal (*polybasic or polyprotic acids*).   It will be noted that these acids ion-ize in steps, and the degree of ionization of the first hydrogen is invari-ably greater than that of the others.   Phosphoric acid, for example, is about 30% ionized in tenth-molar solution to give H^+ and $H_2PO_4^-$ ions, but the concentration of $HPO_4^=$ ions is much less, and that of PO_4^{3-} ions is very small.   Sulfuric acid at low concentrations is completely ionized into H^+ and HSO_4^- ions, but the bisulfate ion is moderately ionized further to give H^+ ions and $SO_4^=$ ions.

2-4   Ionic Equations Not Involving Oxidation

Most of the reactions of analytical chemistry are reactions between ions in aqueous solution.   For this reason, although the molecular type of equation is serviceable as a basis for quantitative analytical calculations, the so-called ionic equation is usually easier to write and is generally preferable.

In writing ionic equations, the following basic rules should be observed:

1. *Include in the equation only those constituents actually taking part in the chemical reaction.*

Example 1   The addition of a solution of sodium hydroxide to a solution of ferric nitrate results in a precipitation of ferric hydroxide (or, strictly speaking, hydrated ferric oxide, $Fe_2O_3 \cdot xH_2O$).   The simplified ionic equa-tion is

$$Fe^{3+} + 3OH^- \longrightarrow \underline{Fe(OH)_3}^*$$

The sodium ions from the sodium hydroxide and the nitrate ions from the ferric nitrate do not enter into the reaction and hence are not repre-sented in the equation.

2. *In cases where a reactant or product exists in equilibrium with its constituent ions, express in the equation that species present in greatest amount.*

It follows that weak acids and weak bases should be written in the molecular form.   Substances of this type most often encountered in ana-lytical chemistry are the following: H_2O, $HC_2H_3O_2$, NH_4OH, H_2S, H_2CO_3, HNO_2, HF, HCN, H_3PO_4, $H_2C_2O_4$, and H_2SO_3 (see Table 11, Appendix). The last three of these are borderline cases, since at concentrations

---

* It is desirable to underline formulas of precipitates.   The use of downward-pointing arrows is equally satisfactory.   If desired, formulas of gases can be overbarred or denoted by upward-pointing arrows.   The symbols s and g to denote "solid" and "gas," respectively, are also in common use.   Such a symbol is added in parentheses after the formula of the sub-stance to which it applies.   This method will be used in later chapters.

ordinarily encountered in analytical work they are ionized to a moderate degree to give hydrogen ions and $H_2PO_4^-$, $HC_2O_4^-$, and HSO_3^- ions, respectively.

The salts lead acetate and mercuric chloride are dissociated into complex ions [$Pb(C_2H_3O_2)^+$ and $HgCl^+$] but are ionized relatively little to give the metal ions.   In equations they should therefore be expressed as complex ions.

Example 2   The addition of an aqueous solution of ammonium hydroxide to a solution of ferric nitrate results in a precipitation of ferric hydroxide.   The ionic equation can be written simply as follows:

$$Fe^{3+} + 3NH_4OH \longrightarrow \underline{Fe(OH)_3} + 3NH_4^+$$

In this case, although ammonium hydroxide is ionized into ammonium ions and hydroxyl ions, the ionization is comparatively slight and only the undissociated ammonium hydroxide molecules are expressed in the equation.[1]

Example 3   The addition of a solution of hydrogen sulfide to an acid solution of copper sulfate gives a precipitate of copper sulfide:

$$Cu^{++} + H_2S \longrightarrow \underline{CuS} + 2H^+$$

The fact that the original solution is acid does not require that hydrogen ions be on the left-hand side of the equation.   The equation merely indicates that the acidity of the solution increases.

Example 4   When a solution containing lead nitrate is treated with sulfuric acid, a white precipitate of lead sulfate is obtained.   This precipitate dissolves in a solution of ammonium acetate, and the addition of a solution of potassium chromate then causes a yellow precipitate to appear.   The ionic equations for these reactions are

$$Pb^{++} + HSO_4^- \longrightarrow \underline{PbSO_4} + H^+$$
$$PbSO_4 + C_2H_3O_2^- \longrightarrow Pb(C_2H_3O_2)^+ + SO_4^=$$
$$Pb(C_2H_3O_2)^+ + CrO_4^= \longrightarrow \underline{PbCrO_4} + C_2H_3O_2^-$$

Example 5   Silver chloride dissolves in an aqueous solution of ammonia. The equation is written as follows (see Example 2 and the footnote to it):

---

[1] As a matter of fact, it is not certain that an appreciable concentration of NH_4OH exists at all. The equilibrium existing in an aqueous solution of ammonia can be expressed as follows:

$$NH_3 + H_2O \rightleftharpoons [NH_4OH(?)] \rightleftharpoons NH_4^+ + OH^-$$

Here again, the concentration of OH^- is relatively low, and the equation for the above reaction can therefore be written

$$Fe^{3+} + 3NH_3 + 3H_2O \longrightarrow \underline{Fe(OH)_3} + 3NH_4^+$$

$$AgCl + 2NH_4OH \longrightarrow Ag(NH_3)_2^+ + Cl^- + 2H_2O$$

or

$$AgCl + 2NH_3 \longrightarrow Ag(NH_3)_2^+ + Cl^-$$

The silver ammino ion, like most complex ions, is only very slightly dissociated into its constituents: $Ag(NH_3)_2^+ \rightleftharpoons Ag^+ + 2NH_3$.

Example 6   A nitric acid solution of ammonium molybdate $[(NH_4)_2MoO_4]$ added to a solution of phosphoric acid results in the precipitation of ammonium "phosphomolybdate," the formula of which is written here in simplified form:

$$12MoO_4^= + H_3PO_4 + 3NH_4^+ + 21H^+ \longrightarrow (NH_4)_3PO_4 \cdot 12MoO_3 \cdot H_2O + 11H_2O$$

For every 12 molybdate ions only 3 of the corresponding 24 ammonium ions present enter into the reaction.   The nitrate ions, of course, take no part in the reaction.

2-5   Oxidation Number

Although the term *valence* usually refers to the degree of combining power of an atom or radical, it is likely to be applied somewhat differently in the various branches of chemistry.   For this reason, in inorganic chemistry the term *oxidation number* is usually to be preferred in expressing state of oxidation.

The oxidation number of an element is often expressed by writing the appropriate Roman numeral after the name or formula of the element, thus, Fe(II), chromium(III).

It is assumed that the student is already familiar with the combining power of the elements he has thus far studied.   It will be recalled that (1) the oxidation number of all free elements is zero, (2) the oxidation number of hydrogen in its compounds is $+1$ (except in the case of the relatively rare hydrides), (3) the oxidation number of sodium and potassium in their compounds is $+1$, and (4) the oxidation number of oxygen in its compounds is -2 (with few exceptions).

Since the algebraic sum of the oxidation numbers of the elements of a given compound is zero, the oxidation number of any element in a compound can usually be readily calculated from those of the other elements making up the compound.   Thus, the oxidation number of Cl in $HClO_3$ is $+5$, since $1 + 5 + [3 \times (-2)] = 0$.   In this case the oxidation number of the ClO_3 *radical* is -1, since it is combined with the $+1$ hydrogen.   The oxidation number of S_2 in $Na_2S_2O_7$ is $+12$, since $Na_2 = +2$ and 7 oxygen atoms $= -14$.   Each sulfur atom therefore has an oxidation number of $+6$.

The oxidation number of an ion is the same as the charge it bears.

Thus, the oxidation number of the nitrate ion (NO_3^-) is -1, that of the sulfate ion ($SO_4^=$) is -2, and that of the phosphate ion (PO_4^{3-}) is -3.

A compound like Fe_3O_4 shows an apparent fractional oxidation number for the metal constituent—in this case $2\frac{2}{3}$. Actually two of the iron atoms have an oxidation number of $+3$, and one iron atom has an oxidation number of $+2$. This is called a *mixed oxide* ($FeO \cdot Fe_2O_3$). A similar case is the salt $Na_2S_4O_6$; the *average* oxidation number of each sulfur atom is $2\frac{1}{2}$.

2-6   Ionic Redox Equations

In the case of equations involving oxidation and reduction (redox equations), the two rules given in Sec. 2-4 should also be observed. It will be found convenient in most cases to write balanced equations systematically according to the following steps:

1. *Write the formula of the oxidizing agent and of the reducing agent on the left-hand side of the equation. These should conform to rules 1 and 2.*

2. *Write the formulas of the resulting principal products on the right-hand side of the equation. These should likewise conform to rules 1 and 2.*

3. *Under the formula of the oxidizing substance, write the number expressing the total change in oxidation number of all its constituent elements. Under the formula of the reducing substance, write the number expressing the total change in oxidation number of its constituent elements.*

4. *Use the number under the formula of the oxidizing agent in the equation as the coefficient for the reducing substance; use the number under the formula of the reducing agent in the equation as the coefficient for the oxidizing substance.*

5. *Insert coefficients for the principal products to conform to the preceding step.*

6. *If possible, divide all the coefficients by the greatest common divisor, or if necessary, clear of fractions by multiplying all the coefficients by the necessary factor.*

7. *If the reaction takes place in acid solution, introduce the formulas H_2O and H^+ (or H_3O^+) in amounts necessary to balance the atoms of oxygen and hydrogen on the two sides of the chemical equation. If the reaction takes place in alkaline solution, introduce the formulas H_2O and OH^- in amounts necessary to balance the atoms of oxygen and hydrogen.*

8. *Check the equation by determining the total net ionic charge on each of the two sides of the equation. They should be the same.*

Example 1   When a solution of chlorine water is added to a sulfuric acid solution of ferrous sulfate, the iron is oxidized. The step-by-step formulation of the equation for this reaction is as follows:

Step	Result
1, 2	$Fe^{++} + Cl_2 \longrightarrow Fe^{3+} + Cl^-$
3	$Fe^{++} + Cl_2 \longrightarrow Fe^{3+} + Cl^-$
	$\quad\;\; 1 \qquad 2$
4, 5	$2Fe^{++} + Cl_2 \longrightarrow 2Fe^{3+} + 2Cl^-$
6	None
7	None
8	$4+ \; = 4+$

Example 2   When a dilute nitric acid solution of stannous chloride is treated with a solution of potassium dichromate, tin is oxidized (from 2 to 4) and chromium is reduced (from 6 to 3).   Neglecting the partial formation of complex ions (for example, $SnCl_{\overline{6}}$), the development of the equation is as follows:

Step	Result
1, 2	$Sn^{++} + Cr_2O_{\overline{7}} \longrightarrow Sn^{4+} + Cr^{3+}$
3	$Sn^{++} + Cr_2\mathbf{O_{\overline{7}}} \longrightarrow Sn^{4+} + Cr^{3+}$
	$\qquad\quad 2 \quad\;\; 3+3$
4, 5	$6Sn^{++} + 2Cr_2O_{\overline{7}} \longrightarrow 6Sn^{4+} + 4Cr^{3+}$
6	$3Sn^{++} + Cr_2O_{\overline{7}} \longrightarrow 3Sn^{4+} + 2Cr^{3+}$
7	$3Sn^{++} + Cr_2O_{\overline{7}} + 14H^+ \longrightarrow 3Sn^{4+} + 2Cr^{3+} + 7H_2O$
8	$18+ \; = 18+$

Note that in writing this equation in the molecular form, one would be at a loss to express the products correctly.   The question would arise whether to write stannic chloride and chromic nitrate or stannic nitrate and chromic chloride. As a matter of fact, none of these is formed since the salts are completely ionized in dilute solution.

Example 3   When hydrogen sulfide is bubbled into a dilute sulfuric acid solution of potassium permanganate, the latter is reduced (to manganous salt) and a white precipitate of free sulfur is obtained.

Step	Result
1, 2	$MnO_4^- + H_2S \longrightarrow Mn^{++} + \underline{S}$
3	$\underset{5}{MnO_4^-} + \underset{2}{H_2S} \longrightarrow Mn^{++} + \underline{S}$
4, 5	$2MnO_4^- + 5H_2S \longrightarrow 2Mn^{++} + 5\underline{S}$
6	None
7	$2MnO_4^- + 5H_2S + 6H^+ \longrightarrow 2Mn^{++} + 5\underline{S} + 8H_2O$
8	$4+ = 4+$

Example 4 In the presence of sulfuric acid an excess of potassium permanganate solution will oxidize a chromic salt to dichromate.

Step	Result
1, 2	$Cr^{3+} + MnO_4^- \longrightarrow Cr_2O_7^= + Mn^{++}$
3	$\underset{3}{Cr^{3+}} + \underset{5}{MnO_4^-} \longrightarrow Cr_2O_7^= + Mn^{++}$
4, 5	$5Cr^{3+} + 3MnO_4^- \longrightarrow 2\frac{1}{2}Cr_2O_7^= + 3Mn^{++}$
6	$10Cr^{3+} + 6MnO_4^- \longrightarrow 5Cr_2O_7^= + 6Mn^{++}$
7	$10Cr^{3+} + 6MnO_4^- + 11H_2O \longrightarrow 5Cr_2O_7^= + 6Mn^{++} + 22H^+$
8	$24+ = 24+$

Example 5 When metallic aluminum is added to an alkaline solution of a nitrate, the latter is reduced and ammonia gas is evolved.

Step	Result
1, 2	$\underline{Al} + NO_3^- \longrightarrow AlO_2^- + \overline{NH_3}$
3	$\underset{3}{\underline{Al}} + \underset{8}{NO_3^-} \longrightarrow AlO_2^- + \overline{NH_3}$
4, 5	$8\underline{Al} + 3NO_3^- \longrightarrow 8AlO_2^- + \overline{3NH_3}$
6	None
7	$8\underline{Al} + 3NO_3^- + 5OH^- + 2H_2O \longrightarrow 8AlO_2^- + \overline{3NH_3}$
8	$8- = 8-$

Example 6 Solid cuprous sulfide is oxidized by hot concentrated nitric acid, forming a cupric salt, sulfate, and NO_2 gas.

Step	Result
1, 2	$\underline{Cu_2S} + NO_3^- \longrightarrow Cu^{++} + SO_4^= + \overline{NO_2}$
3	$\underset{1+1+8}{\underline{Cu_2S}} + \underset{1}{NO_3^-} \longrightarrow Cu^{++} + SO_4^= + \overline{NO_2}$
4, 5	$\underline{Cu_2S} + 10NO_3^- \longrightarrow 2Cu^{++} + SO_4^= + 10\overline{NO_2}$
6	None
7	$\underline{Cu_2S} + 10NO_3^- + 12H^+ \longrightarrow 2Cu^{++} + SO_4^= + 10\overline{NO_2} + 6H_2O$
8	$2+ = 2+$

Another method of writing balanced redox equations is shown in Sec. 6-4.

PROBLEMS

*2-1.   What is the (average) oxidation no. of each of the elements (other than H and O) in each of the following: (a) N_2O_3, (b) SbS_3^{3-}, (c) $H_4P_2O_5$, (d) $K_2Pt(NO_2)_4$, (e) S_8, (f) $Co(NH_3)_6^{3+}$, (g) $Cu_3[Fe(CN)_6]_2$, (h) HCOONa, (i) $(VO)_3(PO_4)_2$, (j) $CdS_2O_6 \cdot 6H_2O$, (k) $(UO_2)(ClO_4)_2 \cdot 4H_2O$?

2-2.   What is the (average) oxidation no. of each of the elements (other than H and O) in each of the following: (a) N_2, (b) N_2O, (c) $Na_2U_2O_7$, (d) $(BiO)_2SO_4$, (e) $HC_2O_4^-$, (f) $Pd(OH)_2(NH_3)_2$, (g) $Na_2S_4O_6$, (h) $HgI_2 \cdot HgINI\,I_2$, (i) $B_4O_7^=$, (j) FeS_2, (k) HN_3, (l) $V_3[Fe(CN)_6]_2$, (m) $NaMg(UO_2)_3(C_2H_3O_2)_9 \cdot 6H_2O$?

2-3.   The following unbalanced equations do not involve oxidation and reduction. Convert them to complete, balanced ionic equations.   Introduce H_2O and other permissible constituents if necessary.   Substances are in soln. unless underlined.

(a) $AlCl_3 + NaOH \longrightarrow NaAlO_2 + NaCl$
(b) $Fe_2(SO_4)_3 + NH_4OH \longrightarrow \underline{Fe(OH)_3} + (NH_4)_2SO_4$
(o) $CuSO_4 + NH_4OH \longrightarrow [Cu(NH_3)_4]SO_4$
(d) $K_2[Cd(CN)_4]$ (neutral soln.) $+ H_2S \longrightarrow \underline{CdS}$
(e) $\underline{Pb(OH)_2} + KOH \longrightarrow K_2PbO_2$
(f) $HgCl_2 + NH_4OH \longrightarrow \underline{HgClNH_2}$
(g) $Na_3AsS_4 + H_2SO_4 \longrightarrow \underline{As_2S_5} + H_2S + Na_2SO_4$
(h) $Bi_2O_2SO_4$ (acid soln.) $+ H_2S \longrightarrow \underline{Bi_2S_3}$
(i) $(NH_4)_2U_2O_7 + HCl \longrightarrow UO_2Cl_2$
(j) $HC_2H_3O_2 + \underline{PbO} \longrightarrow Pb(C_2H_3O_2)_2$
(k) $Pb(C_2H_3O_2)_2 + K_2CrO_4 \longrightarrow \underline{PbCrO_4} + KC_2H_3O_2$
(l) $Hg(NO_3)_2 + KI \longrightarrow K_2HgI_4$
(m) $UO_2SO_4 + KOH \longrightarrow K_2U_2O_7$

2-4.   Balance the following redox equations:

(a) $Fe^{++} + ClO_3^- + H^+ \longrightarrow Fe^{3+} + Cl^- + H_2O$
(b) $Mo^{3+} + Ce^{4+} + H_2O \longrightarrow MoO_4^= + Ce^{3+} + H^+$
(c) $MnO_4^- + Cl^- + H^+ \longrightarrow Mn^{++} + \overline{Cl_2} + H_2O$
(d) $Sn^{++} + BrO_3^- + Cl^- + H^+ \longrightarrow SnCl_6^= + Br^- + H_2O$
(e) $IO_3^- + I^- + H^+ \longrightarrow I_3^- + H_2O$
(f) $SeO_4^= + I^- \longrightarrow \underline{Se} + I_3^-$
(g) $Cr_2O_7^= + H_2S + H^+ \longrightarrow Cr^{3+} + \underline{S} + H_2O$
(h) $\underline{Zn} + OH^- \longrightarrow ZnO_2^= + H_2$
(i) $H_3AsO_4 + \underline{Zn} + H^+ \longrightarrow \overline{AsH_3} + Zn^{++} + H_2O$
(j) $NO_2^- + \underline{Al} + OH^- + H_2O \longrightarrow \overline{NH_3} + AlO_2^-$
(k) $Cr^{3+} + NO_2 + OH^- \longrightarrow CrO_4^= + \overline{NO} + H_2O$
(l) $\underline{Fe_3P} + NO_3^- + H^+ \longrightarrow Fe^{3+} + H_2PO_4^- + NO + H_2O$
(m) $\underline{FeS_2} + NO_3^- + H^+ \longrightarrow Fe^{3+} + SO_4^= + \overline{NO_2} + H_2O$
(n) $\underline{Na_2FeO_4} + H_2O \longrightarrow \underline{Fe(OH)_3} + \overline{O_2} + Na^+ + OH^-$

2-5. The following unbalanced redox equations represent reactions taking place in acid soln.   Convert them to balanced ionic equations, introducing H^+ and H_2O wherever necessary.

(a) $Cr_2O_7^= + NO_2^- \longrightarrow Cr^{3+} + NO_3^-$

(b) $Cr^{3+} + S_2O_8^= \longrightarrow Cr_2O_7^= + SO_4^=$

(c) $MnO_4^- + H_2O_2 \longrightarrow Mn^{++} + \overline{O_2}$

(d) $Mn^{++} + \underline{BiO_2} \longrightarrow MnO_4^- + BiO^+$

(e) $VO^{++} + MnO_4^- \longrightarrow HVO_3 + Mn^{++}$

(f) $UO_2^{++} + \underline{Zn} \longrightarrow U^{4+} + Zn^{++}$

(g) $Cr^{3+} + MnO_4^- \longrightarrow Cr_2O_7^= + Mn^{++}$

(h) $MnO_4^- + H_2C_2O_4 \longrightarrow \overline{CO_2} + Mn^{++}$

(i) $S_2O_3^= + I_3^- \longrightarrow S_4O_6^= + I^-$

(j) $UO_5^= + H^+ \longrightarrow UO_2^{++} + \overline{O_2}$

(k) $\underline{Hg_2Cl_2} + IO_3^- + Cl^- \longrightarrow HgCl^+ + ICl_2^-$

(l) $\underline{AlCl_3} + Na_2S_2O_3 \longrightarrow \underline{Al(OH)_3} + \underline{S} + SO_2$

(m) $SbCl_4^- + \underline{Zn} \longrightarrow \overline{SbH_3} + Zn^{++}$

2-6. The following molecular equations involve oxidation and reduction, and the reactions take place in the presence of acid unless otherwise specified.   Convert the equations to balanced ionic equations.   Introduce H^+, OH^-, H_2O, and other permissible constituents wherever necessary.

(a) $\underline{FeCl_3} + H_2SO_3 \longrightarrow FeCl_2 + H_2SO_4$

(b) $K_2Cr_2O_7 + HI + HCl \longrightarrow CrCl_3 + KCl + I_3^-$

(c) $\underline{Zn} + HNO_3 \text{ (very dil.)} \longrightarrow Zn(NO_3)_2 + NH_4NO_3$

(d) $\underline{Fe_2Si} + HNO_3 \longrightarrow Fe(NO_3)_3 + H_2SiO_3 + \overline{NO}$

(e) $Co(NH_3)_6Cl_3 + HCl \longrightarrow CoCl_2 + \overline{Cl_2} + NH_4Cl$

(f) $H_3PO_3 + HgCl_2 \longrightarrow Hg_2Cl_2 + H_3PO_4 + HCl$

(g) $\underline{K_2Na[Co(NO_2)_6]} + KMnO_4 \longrightarrow KNO_3 + NaNO_3 + Co(NO_3)_2 + Mn(NO_3)_2$

(h) $\underline{Sn} + HNO_3 \longrightarrow H_2SnO_3 + \overline{NO}$

(i) $\underline{Ag_3AsO_4} + Zn + H_2SO_4 \longrightarrow \overline{AsH_3} + \underline{Ag} + ZnSO_4$

(j) $Se_2Cl_2 + H_2O \longrightarrow H_2SeO_3 + \underline{Se}$

(k) $\underline{Ce(IO_3)_4} + H_2C_2O_4 \longrightarrow Ce_2(C_2O_4)_3 + I_3^- + \overline{CO_2}$

(l) $CoCl_2 + KNO_2 + HC_2H_3O_2 \longrightarrow \underline{K_3Co(NO_2)_6} + \overline{NO}$

(m) $\underline{Bi(OH)_3} + SnO_2^= \text{ (alkaline soln.)} \longrightarrow \underline{Bi} + SnO_3^=$

(n) $NaCrO_2 \text{ (alkaline soln.)} + \underline{Na_2O_2} \longrightarrow Na_2CrO_4$

(o) $KOCl \text{ (alkaline soln.)} + KAsO_2 \longrightarrow K_3AsO_4 + KCl$

2-7. Write balanced ionic equations for the following reactions (taking place in acid soln. unless otherwise indicated).   Introduce H^+ ions, OH^- ions, and H_2O wherever necessary.   (a) Dichromate reduced by sulfurous acid to give chromic salt and sulfate, (b) chromic salt oxidized by chlorine to give dichromate and chloride, (c) chromite ions in alkaline soln. oxidized by hydrogen peroxide to chromate, (d) cobalt(II) salt treated with $NaOH + Na_2O_2$ to give cobalt(III) oxide ppt., (e) manganous ions + chlorate ions to give chlorine dioxide gas and a ppt. of manganese dioxide, (f) nitrate + metallic aluminum in the presence of NaOH to give

aluminate ions + hydrogen gas + ammonia gas, (g) dichromate + hydrogen peroxide to give chromic salt + oxygen gas, (h) cupric sulfate + potassium iodide to
give a ppt. of cuprous iodide and triiodide ions, (i) manganous salt + potassium
permanganate in alkaline soln. to give a ppt. of manganese dioxide, (j) cerium(III)
chloride + hydrogen peroxide in the presence of alkali to give a ppt. of Ce(VI) oxide.

2-8.   Complete and balance the following molecular equations, which represent
fusions and reactions taking place in concentrated soln.   Introduce H_2O and other
constituents wherever necessary.

(a) $\underline{Cu} + H_2SO_4 \text{ (concd.)} \longrightarrow CuSO_4 + \overline{SO_2}$

(b) $\underline{Fe(CrO_2)_2} + Na_2CO_3 + \overline{O_2} \longrightarrow Fe_2O_3 + Na_2CrO_4 + \overline{CO_2}$

(c) $\underline{Cr_2(SO_4)_3} + Na_2O_2 \longrightarrow Na_2CrO_4$

(d) $\underline{TiO_2} + K_2S_2O_7 \longrightarrow Ti(SO_4)_2$

(e) $\underline{KAlSi_3O_8} + CaCO_3 + \underline{NH_4Cl} \longrightarrow CaSiO_3 + \underline{Ca(AlO_2)_2} + \underline{KCl} + \overline{CO_2} +$
$\underline{NH_3} + H_2O$

(f) $\underline{FeS_2} + Na_2O_2 \longrightarrow Na_2FeO_4 + Na_2SO_4$

(g) $\underline{MnO_2} + \underline{KNO_3} + \underline{KOH} \longrightarrow K_2MnO_4 + \underline{KNO_2}$

3 Calculations Based on Formulas and Equations

3-1 Mathematical Significance of a Chemical Formula

The law of definite proportions states that in any pure compound the proportions by weight of the constituent elements are always the same. A chemical formula therefore not only is a shorthand method of naming a compound and of indicating the constituent elements of the compound but also shows the relative masses of the elements present.

Thus the formula Na_2SO_4 (molecular weight = 142.04) indicates that in every 142.04 g of pure anhydrous sodium sulfate there are $2 \times 22.99 = 45.98$ g of sodium, 32.06 g of sulfur, and $4 \times 16.00 = 64.00$ g of oxygen. The proportion of sodium in pure anhydrous sodium sulfate is therefore

$$\frac{2 \times 22.99}{142.04} \times 100 = 32.37\%$$

3-2 Formula Weights

A *gram-molecular weight* of a substance is its molecular weight expressed in grams. Thus, a gram-molecular weight (or *gram mole* or simply *mole*) of Na_2SO_4 is 142.04 g. A mole of nitrogen gas, N_2, is 28.014 g of the element.

A *formula weight* (f. wt.) is that weight in grams corresponding to the formula of the substance as ordinarily written. In most cases it is identical with the gram-molecular weight, but occasionally the true molecular weight of a compound is a multiple of the weight expressed by the formula as ordinarily written in a chemical equation. In practically all the reactions of analytical chemistry, however, it can be assumed that the value of the formula weight and that of the mole are the same.

The *gram atom* or *gram-atomic weight* is the atomic weight of the element expressed in grams (for example, 40.08 g of calcium, 14.007 g of nitrogen).   A *gram ion* is the atomic or formula weight of an ion expressed in grams (for example, 40.08 g of Ca^{++}, 62.007 g of NO_3^-).

A *millimole* is one-thousandth of a mole; a *milligram atom* is one-thousandth of a gram atom.

A formula weight of hydrated ferric sulfate, $Fe_2(SO_4)_3 \cdot 9H_2O$, for example, is 562.0 g of the salt.   It contains 2 g atoms of iron ($= 111.7$ g), 21 g atoms of oxygen ($= 336$ g), 9 f. wts. of water, and 3,000 mg atoms of sulfur and in solution gives 3 g ions of sulfate.

3-3   Mathematical Significance of a Chemical Equation

A chemical equation not only represents the chemical changes taking place in a given reaction but also expresses the relative quantities of the substances involved.   Thus, the molecular equation

$$H_2SO_4 + BaCl_2 \longrightarrow \underline{BaSO_4} + 2HCl$$

not only states that sulfuric acid reacts with barium chloride to give barium sulfate and hydrochloric acid but also expresses the fact that every 98.08 parts by weight of hydrogen sulfate react with 208.25 parts of barium chloride to give 233.40 parts of barium sulfate and $2 \times 36.46 = 72.92$ parts of hydrogen chloride, these numerical values being the molecular weights of the respective compounds.   These are relative weights and are independent of the units chosen.   If a weight of any one of the above four substances is known, the weight of any or all of the other three can be calculated by simple proportion.   This is the basis of analytical computations.

Example 1   A sample of pure lead weighing 0.500 g is dissolved in nitric acid according to the equation

$$3\underline{Pb} + 8HNO_3 \longrightarrow 3Pb(NO_3)_2 + 2\overline{NO} + 4H_2O$$

How many grams of pure HNO_3 are theoretically required?   How many grams of $Pb(NO_3)_2$ could be obtained by evaporating the resulting solution to dryness?   How many grams of NO gas are formed in the above reaction?

Solution

At. wt. of Pb $= 207$; mol. wt. of $HNO_3 = 63.0$; mol. wt. of $Pb(NO_3)_2 = 331$; mol. wt. of NO $= 30.0$
$3 \times 207 = 621$ g of Pb reacts with $8 \times 63.0 = 504$ g of HNO_3
$3 \times 207 = 621$ g of Pb would form $3 \times 331 = 993$ g of $Pb(NO_3)_2$ and $2 \times 30.0 = 60.0$ g of NO

Hence 0.500 g of Pb would require

0.500 × $\frac{504}{621}$ = 0.406 g HNO_3 *Ans.*

and would form

0.500 × $\frac{993}{621}$ = 0.800 g $Pb(NO_3)_2$ *Ans.*

and

0.500 × $\frac{60}{621}$ = 0.0483 g NO   *Ans.*

Example 2   How many grams of H_2S would theoretically be required to precipitate the lead as lead sulfide from the above solution?   How many milliliters of H_2S under standard temperature and pressure would theoretically be required for the precipitation?   (A gram-molecular weight of a gas under standard conditions occupies 22.4 liters.   See Sec. 31-3.)

Solution

$Pb^{++} + \overline{H_2S} \longrightarrow \underline{PbS} + 2H^+$
At. wt. of Pb = 207; mol. wt. of H_2S = 34.1
207 g of Pb^{++} requires 34.1 g of H_2S
Hence 0.500 g of Pb^{++} requires 0.500 × 34.1/207 = 0.0824 g of H_2S
34.1 g of H_2S occupies 22,400 ml under standard conditions
Volume of H_2S = (0.0824/34.1) × 22,400 = 54.1 ml   *Ans.*

Example 3   In the reaction expressed by the equation

$2\underline{Ag_2CO_3} \longrightarrow 4\underline{Ag} + \overline{O_2} + 2\overline{CO_2}$

(*a*) how many gram atoms of silver can be obtained from 1.00 f. wt. of silver carbonate, (*b*) how many gram atoms of silver can be obtained from 1.00 g of silver carbonate, (*c*) how many grams of silver carbonate are required to give 3.00 g of oxygen gas, (*d*) how many moles of gas ($CO_2 + O_2$) are produced from 50.0 g of silver carbonate, and (*e*) when measured under standard conditions, how many milliliters of dry gas are produced from 1.00 millimole of silver carbonate?

Solution

(*a*) 2.00 f. wts. of Ag_2CO_3 gives 4.00 g atoms of Ag
       1.00 f. wt. of Ag_2CO_3 gives 2.00 g atoms of Ag   *Ans.*
(*b*) Mol. wt. of Ag_2CO_3 = 276
       1.00 g of Ag_2CO_3 = 1.00/276 = 0.00362 f. wt. of Ag_2CO_3
       0.00362 × 2 = 0.00724 g atom of Ag   *Ans.*
(*c*) 2.00 moles of Ag_2CO_3 (= 552 g) gives 1.00 mole of O_2 (= 32.0 g)
       3.00 g of O_2 = 3.00 × 552/32.0 = 51.8 g of Ag_2CO_3 *Ans.*
(*d*) 2.00 moles of Ag_2CO_3 (= 552 g) gives 3.00 moles of $O_2 + CO_2$
       50.0 g of Ag_2CO_3 gives 3.00 × 50.0/552 = 0.272 mole of gas   *Ans.*

(e) 1.00 millimole of Ag_2CO_3 gives 1.50 millimoles of gas
1.50 millimoles of gas occupies $1.50 \times 22.4 = 33.8$ ml   *Ans.*

Example 4   In the reaction expressed by the equation

$$MnO_2 + 2NaCl + 3H_2SO_4 \longrightarrow MnSO_4 + 2NaHSO_4 + \overline{Cl_2} + 2H_2O$$

(a) how many gram ions of Mn^{++} can be obtained from 100 millimoles of MnO_2; (b) how many grams of $MnSO_4$ can be obtained from 5.00 g of MnO_2; (c) how many millimoles of MnO_2 are required to give 100 ml of Cl_2 (standard conditions); and (d) if 1.00 g of MnO_2, 1.00 g of NaCl, and 5.00 g of H_2SO_4 are used, which is the limiting reagent and how many milliliters of dry Cl_2 (standard conditions) are evolved?

Solution

(a) 1 mole $MnO_2 \longrightarrow$ 1 g ion Mn^{++}

   1 millimole $MnO_2 \longrightarrow$ 0.001 g ion Mn^{++} *Ans.*

(b) 1 mole MnO_2 (= 86.9 g) $\longrightarrow$ 1 mole $MnSO_4$ (= 151 g)

   5.00 g $MnO_2 \longrightarrow 5.00 \times \dfrac{151}{86.9} = 8.69$ g $MnSO_4$ *Ans.*

(c) 100 ml $Cl_2 = \dfrac{100}{22.4} = 4.46$ millimoles Cl_2

   1 millimole $Cl_2 \leftrightharpoons$ 1 millimole MnO_2

   100 ml $Cl_2 \leftrightharpoons$ 4.46 millimoles MnO_2 *Ans.*

(d) 1.00 g $MnO_2 = \dfrac{1.00}{MnO_2} = \dfrac{1.00}{86.9} = 0.0115$ mole

   1.00 g NaCl $= \dfrac{1.00}{NaCl} = \dfrac{1.00}{58.5} = 0.0171$ mole

   5.00 g $H_2SO_4 = \dfrac{5.00}{H_2SO_4} = \dfrac{5.00}{98.1} = 0.0510$ mole

According to the equation, these substances react in the molar ratio of 1:2:3, or 0.0115:0.0230:0.0345. The NaCl is therefore the limiting reagent, and the other two are in excess.

   2 moles NaCl $\longrightarrow$ 1 mole $Cl_2 = 22,400$ ml Cl_2

   0.0171 mole NaCl $\longrightarrow \dfrac{0.0171}{2} \times 22,400 = 192$ ml Cl_2 *Ans.*

3-4   Gas Laws

In some of the examples above and in several problems and examples to be encountered in subsequent sections, familiarity with the simple laws of gases is assumed. These fundamental gas laws are covered in Chap. 31. This subject matter can, if desired, be taken up at this point.

PROBLEMS

*3-1.   How many g of potassium and of carbon are contained in (a) 0.211 g of $K_4Fe(CN)_6 \cdot 3H_2O$, (b) 1.00 f. wt. of $KHC_4H_4O_6$?

*3-2.   A certain wt. of $Pb_3(PO_4)_2$ contains 0.100 g of lead.   (a) How many g of phosphorus are present?   (b) What is the wt. of the $Pb_3(PO_4)_2$?   (c) What is the percentage of oxygen present?

*3-3.   (a) How many g of oxygen are present in 1.00 g of $Fe(NO_3)_3 \cdot 6H_2O$?   (b) What is the percentage of sulfur in $K_2SO_4 \cdot Al_2(SO_4)_3 \cdot 24H_2O$?

*3-4.   Ignition of magnesium ammonium phosphate forms magnesium pyrophosphate according to the equation $2MgNH_4PO_4 \longrightarrow Mg_2P_2O_7 + 2\overline{NH_3} + \overline{H_2O}$.   Calculate (a) no. of f. wts. of $Mg_2P_2O_7$ produced from 1.00 f. wt. of $MgNH_4PO_4$, (b) no. of g of NH_3 produced at the same time, (c) no. of ml of NH_3 (standard conditions) accompanying the formation of 1.00 millimole of $Mg_2P_2O_7$.

*3-5.   Calculate the no. of lb of materials theoretically required for the preparation of (a) 1.00 lb of KOH from CaO and K_2CO_3, (b) 1.00 lb of $BaSO_4$ from $Na_2SO_4 \cdot 10H_2O$ and $Ba_3(PO_4)_2$.

*3-6.   Balance the following equation (representing a soln. reaction) and also write it as a balanced ionic equation: $Al_2(SO_4)_3 + BaCl_2 \longrightarrow AlCl_3 + BaSO_4$.   Calculate from it the following: (a) no. of g ions of Al^{3+} contained in 1.00 g mole of $Al_2(SO_4)_3$, (b) no. of g ions of Ba^{++} reacting with 1.00 g of Al^{3+}, (c) no. of g of $BaSO_4$ obtainable from 2.00 g of $Al_2(SO_4)_3 \cdot 18H_2O$, (d) no. of g of $BaSO_4$ produced by mixing a soln. contg. 3.00 g of $Al_2(SO_4)_3$ with one contg. 4.00 g of $BaCl_2$.

*3-7.   From the reaction $4FeS_2 + 11\overline{O_2} \longrightarrow 2Fe_2O_3 + 8\overline{SO_2}$, calculate the following: (a) no. of moles of FeS_2 required to form 1.00 f. wt. of Fe_2O_3, (b) no. of g of O_2 required to react with 2.00 moles of FeS_2, (c) no. of millimoles of SO_2 equivalent to 0.320 g of O_2, (d) vol. of SO_2 (standard conditions) accompanying the formation of 0.160 g of Fe_2O_3.

*3-8.   Complete and balance the following ionic equation taking place in the presence of H_2SO_4: $Fe^{++} + MnO_4^- \longrightarrow Fe^{3+} + Mn^{++}$.   Calculate from it the following: (a) no. of g ions of Mn^{++} produced from 1.00 g ion of Fe^{++}; (b) no. of millimoles of $Fe_2(SO_4)_3 \cdot 9H_2O$ obtainable from the reduction of 1.00 millimole of $KMnO_4$; (c) decrease in the no. of g ions of H^+ accompanying the formation of 1.00 g of Fe^{3+}; (d) no. of g of $Fe_2(SO_4)_3$ obtainable from the soln. made by mixing separate solns. contg. 1.00 g of $FeSO_4 \cdot 7H_2O$, 0.100 g of $KMnO_4$, and 1.00 g of H_2SO_4, respectively.

*3-9.   (a) How many g of Cl are in the $CrCl_3$ that could be obtained from 100 mg of $K_2Cr_2O_7$ after reduction by H_2S in the presence of HCl ($Cr_2O_7^= + 3H_2S + 8H^+ \longrightarrow 2Cr^{3+} + 3\underline{S} + 7H_2O$)?   (b) How many g and how many ml (standard conditions) of H_2S gas would be required?

3-10.   (a) How many g of chromium are present in 0.250 g of $K_2Cr_2O_7$, and (b) what is the percentage of potassium in this compound?

3-11.   (a) What wt. of alum, $K_2SO_4 \cdot Al_2(SO_4)_3 \cdot 24H_2O$, contains 0.200 g of aluminum?   (b) What is the percentage of oxygen in the alum?

3-12. What wt. of sulfur is present in an amt. of $Na_2S_2O_3 \cdot 5H_2O$ that contains (*a*) 318 mg of sodium, (*b*) 1.00 g atom of oxygen?

3-13. Ignition of bismuth basic carbonate takes place according to the following equation: $2BiOHCO_3 \longrightarrow Bi_2O_3 + 2\overline{CO_2} + \overline{H_2O}$. Calculate the following: (*a*) no. of f. wts. of Bi_2O_3 produced from 1.00 f. wt. of the carbonate, (*b*) no. of millimoles of CO_2 accompanying the formation of 1.00 g of Bi_2O_3, (*c*) vol. of dry CO_2 (standard conditions) formed from 0.0200 g of $BiOHCO_3$, (*d*) vol. of gas (CO_2 + water vapor) measured at 110°C and 770 mm pressure accompanying the formation of 1.00 milli-mole of Bi_2O_3 (see Secs. 31-1 and 31-2).

3-14. Convert the following to a balanced ionic equation: $FeCl_3 + AgNO_3 \longrightarrow Fe(NO_3)_3 + AgCl$. Calculate from it the following: (*a*) no. of f. wts. of AgCl obtain-able from 1.00 f. wt. of $FeCl_3$, (*b*) no. of g ions of Fe^{3+} produced per millimole of AgCl, (*c*) no. of g of $Fe(NO_3)_3 \cdot 6H_2O$ obtainable if 1.00 mole of $AgNO_3$ is used up, (*d*) no. of g of AgCl obtained by mixing 0.700 g of dissolved $FeCl_3$ and 0.600 g of dissolved $AgNO_3$. (*e*) How many g of which reactant are left over?

3-15. Convert the following to a balanced molecular equation: $Fe(CrO_2)_2 + Na_2CO_3 + NaNO_3 \longrightarrow Na_2FeO_4 + \overline{N_2} + \overline{CO_2}$. From it calculate the no. of milli-moles and the no. of ml of gas (standard conditions) that are formed from that wt. of $Fe(CrO_2)_2$ contg. (*a*) 1.00 g atom of Cr, (*b*) 1.00 g of Cr.

3-16. Balance the following equation: $MnO_4^- + Fe^{++} + H^+ \longrightarrow Mn^{++} + Fe^{3+} + H_2O$, and calculate from it the no. of g of $FeSO_4 \cdot 7H_2O$ required to reduce that wt. of $KMnO_4$ that contains 0.250 g of Mn.

3-17. Balance the following equation: $Cr_2O_7^= + Fe^{++} + H^+ \longrightarrow Cr^{3+} + Fe^{3+} + H_2O$. If 1.00 g mole of K_2CrO_4 is dissolved in water and the soln. acidified ($2CrO_4^= + 2H^+ \longrightarrow Cr_2O_7^= + H_2O$), how many g of $FeSO_4 \cdot (NH_4)_2SO_4 \cdot 6H_2O$ would be required to reduce the Cr in the resulting soln.?

Concentrations of Solutions

4-1 Concentration Units

Solution reagents used in analytical chemistry are usually either (1) laboratory reagents, the concentrations of which need be known only approximately, or (2) titration reagents, the concentrations of which must be known to a high degree of accuracy. In analytical work, concentrations are expressed, directly or indirectly, as the weight (in grams) of solute in a unit volume (usually 1 liter or 1 ml) of solution. Methods of expressing concentration in terms of "packaged" units such as the gram mole or the gram-equivalent weight in a unit volume of solution are favored in cases where calculations of volume relationships are involved.

4-2 Grams per Unit Volume

By this method a concentration is expressed in terms of the number of grams (or milligrams) of solute in each liter (or milliliter) of solution. A 5 g/liter solution of sodium chloride is prepared by dissolving 5 g of the salt in water and diluting to 1 liter (*not* by adding 1 liter of water to the salt).

    This method is simple and direct, but it is not convenient from a stoichiometric point of view, since solutions of the same concentration bear no simple relation to each other as far as volumes involved in chemical reactions are concerned.

4-3 Percentage Composition

This method is on a percentage-by-weight basis and expresses concentration in terms of number of grams of solute per 100 g of solution. A 5% solution of sodium chloride is made by dissolving 5 g of the salt in 95 g of water.

4-4   Specific Gravity

The specific gravity of the solution of a single solute is a measure of the concentration of the solute in the solution.   Although occasionally used in analytical chemistry, it is a cumbersome method, since it necessitates consulting a table in order to determine the percentage-by-weight composition.   Tables of specific gravities of common reagents are found in the handbooks and other reference books of chemistry.   Tables covering common acids and bases are also in the Appendix of this text.   Here it will be found, for example, that hydrochloric acid of specific gravity 1.12 contains 23.8 g of hydrogen chloride in 100 g of solution.

4-5   Volume Ratios

Occasionally in analytical work the concentration of a mineral acid or of ammonium hydroxide is given in terms of the volume ratio of the common concentrated reagent and water.   Thus HCl (1:3) signifies a solution made by mixing one volume of common *concentrated* hydrochloric acid (sp. gr. about 1.20) with three volumes of water.   This method of expressing concentrations is cumbersome, particularly in work where subsequent calculations involving the solutions are to be made.

4-6   Molar and Formal Solutions

A *molar solution* is one containing a gram mole of substance dissolved in a liter of *solution*.   This is usually identical with a *formal solution,* which contains a formula weight of substance in a liter of solution (see Sec. 3-2). A gram-molecular weight of substance dissolved in a liter of *water* does not constitute a molar solution, for the resulting solution does not occupy a volume of exactly a liter.[1]   A liter of molar (M) sulfuric acid solution contains 98.08 g of H_2SO_4; a liter of half-molar ($\frac{1}{2}M$, 0.5 M, or $M/2$) sulfuric acid solution contains 49.04 g of H_2SO_4.   In this particular case, 98.08 g of H_2SO_4 does not mean 98.08 g of the ordinary *concentrated* sulfuric acid but of hydrogen sulfate.   The concentrated acid contains about 96% of the latter.   A liter of half-formal (0.5 F) sulfuric acid solution contains 49.04 g of H_2SO_4.

Since 1 mole of hydrochloric acid reacts with 1 mole of sodium hydroxide, a certain volume of sodium hydroxide solution will be exactly neutralized by an equal volume of hydrochloric acid of the same molar concentration or twice the volume of hydrochloric acid of one-half the molar concentration of the sodium hydroxide.   One molecule of hydrogen sulfate will react with two molecules of sodium hydroxide:

---

[1] Solutions containing a gram-molecular weight of substance dissolved in 1,000 g of water are useful in computations involving certain physicochemical phenomena.   Such solutions are referred to as *molal* solutions, but this standard is not used in general analytical work.

$$H_2SO_4 + 2NaOH \longrightarrow Na_2SO_4 + 2H_2O$$

To neutralize a certain volume of sodium hydroxide solution, only one-half that volume of sulfuric acid of the same molar concentration would be required. Volumetric calculations are therefore greatly simplified when concentrations are expressed in terms of moles of substance per unit volume of solution, for, when so expressed, the volumes of reacting solutions of the same molar concentration, although not necessarily equal, bear simple numerical relationships to each other.

Example 1   What volume of 0.6380 M potassium hydroxide solution will neutralize 430.0 ml of 0.4000 M sulfuric acid?

Solution

1 mole $H_2SO_4 \rightleftharpoons$ 2 moles KOH

430.0 ml of 0.4000 M soln. contains (430.0/1,000) $\times$ 0.4000
$$= 0.1720 \text{ mole } H_2SO_4$$

0.1720 mole $H_2SO_4 \rightleftharpoons$ 0.3440 mole KOH

1.000 ml KOH soln. contains 0.0006380 mole KOH

Vol. required $= \dfrac{0.3440}{0.0006380} = 539.2$ ml   *Ans.*

4-7   Equivalent Weight and Normal Solution

The *equivalent weight* of an element or compound is that weight which in a given reaction has the total reactive power equal to that of one atomic weight of hydrogen. The *milliequivalent weight* is one-thousandth of the equivalent weight. The *gram-equivalent* weight is the equivalent weight expressed in grams; the *gram-milliequivalent weight* is the milliequivalent weight expressed in grams.[1] The application of gram-equivalent weights to various types of chemical reactions will be taken up in detail in Part III, but simple cases, applying particularly to qualitative analysis, will be considered briefly here.

The gram-equivalent weight of an acid, base, or salt involved in a simple metathesis such as a neutralization or precipitation is that weight in grams of the substance equal in total neutralizing or precipitating power to 1 g ion of hydrogen (that is, 1.008 g of H^+). It is also equivalent to 17.008 g of OH^-.

A *normal solution* contains 1 gram-equivalent weight of solute in 1 liter of solution, or 1 gram-milliequivalent weight in 1 ml of solution.

---

[1] The equivalent weight of a substance, like the atomic or molecular weight, is merely a number without a unit of weight; the gram-equivalent weight is a definite number of grams. However, when the connotation is clear, the terms *equivalent weight* and *milliequivalent weight* are frequently used to signify gram-equivalent weight and gram-milliequivalent weight, respectively.

The *normality* of a solution is its numerical relationship to a normal solution. A half-normal solution therefore contains in a unit volume one-half the weight of solute contained in its normal solution, and this concentration can be expressed as $0.5\ N$, $\frac{1}{2}\ N$, or $N/2$.

Since the concentrations of solutions used in precise volumetric analysis are usually found experimentally, the concentrations cannot often be expressed by whole numbers or by simple fractions. They are more likely to be expressed as decimal fractions, for example, $0.1372\ N$.

4-8 Simple Calculations Involving Equivalents, Milliequivalents, and Normality

The use of equivalents, milliequivalents, and normality is so extensive in analytical chemistry and the terms are so fundamental that a clear understanding of them is essential at this time. More detailed discussions applying particularly to quantitative analysis will be given in Part III.

Let us consider here only the simplest reactions among common acids, bases, and salts, and as an example let us take sulfuric acid. The molecular weight of H_2SO_4 is 98.08. A mole, or gram-molecular weight, of H_2SO_4 is 98.08 g, and a molar solution of the acid therefore contains that amount of pure hydrogen sulfate in a liter of solution. Since 98.08 g of H_2SO_4 has a neutralizing power equivalent to 2 g atoms (2.016 g) of hydrogen as an ion, the gram equivalent of H_2SO_4 as an acid is $98.08/2 = 49.04$ g, which is equivalent in neutralizing power to a gram atom (1.008 g) of hydrogen as an ion. The gram-milliequivalent weight is 0.04904 g. A normal solution of sulfuric acid therefore contains 49.04 g of H_2SO_4 in a liter of solution, or 0.04904 g of H_2SO_4 in a milliliter of solution. A $1\ M$ solution of sulfuric acid is $2\ N$; a $1\ N$ solution of sulfuric acid is $\frac{1}{2}\ M$.

Sodium hydroxide is a base with a molecular weight of 40.00. The gram-equivalent weight of NaOH is 40.00 g, since that amount is neutralized by 1.008 g of H^+ (or will furnish 17.008 g of OH^-). A normal solution of NaOH contains 40.00 g in a liter of solution and is also both a molar solution and a formal solution.

The gram-equivalent weight of a simple salt is determined in the same way as that of an acid or base, namely, by reference to 1.008 g of H^+ as a standard. In the case of the salt of a metal, the equivalent weight is ordinarily the molecular weight of the salt divided by the total oxidation number represented by the atoms of metal in the formula.

The equivalent weights of a few acids, bases, and salts are shown in Fig. 1. *Since these amounts are equivalent to the same standard, they are mutually equivalent to one another.*

In each case the specified amount, when dissolved in 1 liter of solution, will produce a $1\ N$ solution.

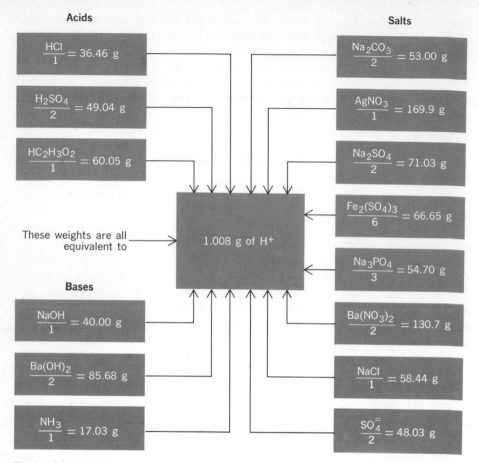

Acids

$$\frac{HCl}{1} = 36.46 \text{ g}$$

$$\frac{H_2SO_4}{2} = 49.04 \text{ g}$$

$$\frac{HC_2H_3O_2}{1} = 60.05 \text{ g}$$

These weights are all equivalent to → 1.008 g of H⁺

Bases

$$\frac{NaOH}{1} = 40.00 \text{ g}$$

$$\frac{Ba(OH)_2}{2} = 85.68 \text{ g}$$

$$\frac{NH_3}{1} = 17.03 \text{ g}$$

Salts

$$\frac{Na_2CO_3}{2} = 53.00 \text{ g}$$

$$\frac{AgNO_3}{1} = 169.9 \text{ g}$$

$$\frac{Na_2SO_4}{2} = 71.03 \text{ g}$$

$$\frac{Fe_2(SO_4)_3}{6} = 66.65 \text{ g}$$

$$\frac{Na_3PO_4}{3} = 54.70 \text{ g}$$

$$\frac{Ba(NO_3)_2}{2} = 130.7 \text{ g}$$

$$\frac{NaCl}{1} = 58.44 \text{ g}$$

$$\frac{SO_4^=}{2} = 48.03 \text{ g}$$

Fig. 1   Gram-equivalent weights of some acids, bases, and salts.

It follows that 1 liter of 1 N HCl will neutralize 1 liter of 1 N NaOH, 1 liter of 1 N Ba(OH)$_2$, or 1 liter of *any* 1 N base. One liter of 1 N H$_2$SO$_4$ will also neutralize 1 liter of any 1 N base. More generally, a certain volume of any acid will neutralize the same volume of any base of the same normality.

Similarly, 1 liter of 1 N AgNO$_3$ will precipitate the chloride from 1 liter of 1 N NaCl or 1 liter of 1 N BaCl$_2$, and the latter will just precipitate the sulfate from 1 liter of 1 N Na$_2$SO$_4$ or 1 liter of 1 N Fe$_2$(SO$_4$)$_3$.

We found that when two solutions of equal *molarity* react, the volumes are in simple ratio to each other.   But when two solutions of equal *normality* react, the volumes of the solutions are *equal.*

Since volumes of reagents in analytical chemistry are usually measured in milliliters rather than in liters, it is more convenient to consider a normal solution as containing 1 g meq. wt./ml.   Hence the number of gram-milliequivalent weights present in a solution can be found from the simple relationship:

Number of milliliters $\times$ normality = number of gram-milliequivalent weights

or

ml $\times N$ = no. of meq. wts.   (see footnote, Sec. 4-7)

Thus, 2.00 ml of 6.00 N HCl contains 12.0 meq. wts., or $12.0 \times \dfrac{HCl}{1,000} =$ 0.438 g of hydrogen chloride.   This will exactly neutralize 12.0 meq. of any base, for example, 4.00 ml of 3.00 N NaOH, 4.00 ml of 3.00 N Na_2CO_3, or 80.0 ml of 0.150 N $Ba(OH)_2$.

It follows that when solutions A and B mutually interact to a complete reaction,

$$ml_A \times N_A = ml_B \times N_B$$

Example 1   What is the approximate molarity and normality of a 13.0% solution of H_2SO_4?   To what volume should 100 ml of the acid be diluted in order to prepare a 1.50 N solution?

Solution   From specific gravity table in the Appendix, the specific gravity of the acid is 1.090.

1 liter weighs 1,090 g and contains $1,090 \times 0.130 = 142$ g H_2SO_4
1 mole $H_2SO_4 = 98.08$ g
Molarity of soln. = $142/98.08 = 1.45$ M *Ans.*
1 g equiv. $H_2SO_4 = H_2SO_4/2 = 49.04$ g
Normality of soln. = $142/49.04 = 2.90$ N *Ans.*
100 ml contains 290 meq. H_2SO_4
After dilution, x ml of 1.50 N contains 290 meq.
$x \times 1.50 = 290$
$\quad\quad x = 193$ ml*   *Ans.*

Example 2   A solution contains 3.30 g of $Na_2CO_3 \cdot 10H_2O$ in each 15.0 ml.   What is its normality?   What is its molarity?   With how many milliliters of 3.10 N acetic acid, $HC_2H_3O_2$, will 25.0 ml of the carbonate react according to the equation $2H^+ + CO_3^= \longrightarrow H_2O + \overline{CO_2}$?   With how many milliliters of 3.10 N H_2SO_4 will 25.0 ml of the carbonate react?

---

* The dilution is therefore made by adding 93 ml of water.   However, the volume of a liquid obtained by mixing measured volumes of different solutions or of a solution and water is not always precisely the sum of the component volumes, although in cases involving dilute aqueous solutions the error introduced by assuming volumes to be additive is usually negligible in three-significant-figure calculations.

Solution

Mol. wt. $Na_2CO_3 \cdot 10H_2O = 286$

Equiv. wt. $Na_2CO_3 \cdot 10H_2O = \dfrac{286}{2} = 143$

Meq. wt. $= 0.143$

Soln. contains $\dfrac{3.30}{15.0} = 0.220$ g/ml

A normal soln. would contain 0.143 g/ml

Normality $= \dfrac{0.220}{0.143} = 1.54\ N$ *Ans.*

Molarity $= \dfrac{0.220}{0.286} = 0.77\ M$ *Ans.*

$x \times 3.10 = 25.0 \times 1.54$

$x = 12.4$ ml $HC_2H_3O_2$ *Ans.*

$= 12.4$ ml H_2SO_4 *Ans.*

Example 3   (*a*) A 0.100 *M* solution of aluminum sulfate, $Al_2(SO_4)_3$, would be of what normality as an aluminum salt? (*b*) What normality as a sulfate? (*c*) How many milliequivalents of the salt are contained in each milliliter? (*d*) What volume of 6.00 *N* NH_4OH would be required to react with the aluminum in 35.0 ml of the salt solution according to the equation $Al^{3+} + 3NH_4OH \longrightarrow Al(OH)_3 + 3NH_4^+$? (*e*) What volume of 6.00 *N* $BaCl_2 \cdot 2H_2O$ solution would be required to precipitate the sulfate from 35.0 ml of the solution? (*f*) How many grams of $BaCl_2 \cdot 2H_2O$ are contained in each milliliter of the above solution?

Solution

(*a*) 1 mole $Al_2(SO_4)_3 = 6$ equiv. $(2\ Al^{3+} \backsim 6H^+)$

0.100 $M = 0.600\ N$ as Al salt   *Ans.*

(*b*) $= 0.600\ N$ as sulfate   *Ans.*

(*c*) 0.600 meq./ml   *Ans.*

(*d*) $ml_A \times N_A = ml_B \times N_B$

$x \times 6.00 = 35.0 \times 0.600$

$x = 3.50$ ml   *Ans.*

(*e*) $ml_A \times N_A = ml_B \times N_B$

$x \times 6.00 = 35.0 \times 0.600$

$x = 3.50$ ml   *Ans.*

(*f*) $6.00 \times \dfrac{BaCl_2 \cdot 2H_2O}{2,000} = 0.733$ g   *Ans.*

PROBLEMS

*4-1. What fraction of the mol. wt. represents the meq. wt. (*a*) of the acid SO_2 (assuming complete neutralization), (*b*) of the base Ag_2O, and (*c*) of the salt $Zn_3(AsO_4)_2$?

*4-2. (*a*) How many g of K_2SO_4 are contained in 50.0 ml of 0.200 N soln.? (*b*) How many millimoles of K_2SO_4 are present?

*4-3. (*a*) What is the normality of a soln. of NH_4OH having a sp. gr. of 0.900? (*b*) How many ml of 13.0 N H_2SO_4 would be neutralized by 15.0 ml of the NH_4OH? (*c*) To what vol. should 250 ml of the 13.0 N H_2SO_4 be diluted to make a soln. that is 5.00 M? (*d*) What is the approx. sp. gr. of the diluted H_2SO_4?

*4-4. A 30% soln. of H_3PO_4 has a sp. gr. of 1.180. (*a*) What is its normality as an acid assuming action with a base to form $HPO_4^=$? (*b*) What is its molar concn.?

*4-5. (*a*) How many g of $SrCl_2 \cdot 6H_2O$ are required to prepare 500 ml of 0.550 N soln.? (*b*) What is the formal concn. of the soln., and how many ml of 1.00 M $AgNO_3$ would be required to ppt. all the chloride from 20.0 ml of the soln.?

*4-6. (*a*) To what vol. should 50.0 ml of a 0.400 N soln. of $Cr_2(SO_4)_3 \cdot 18H_2O$ be diluted in order to prepare a soln. of the salt that is 0.0500 M? (*b*) How many ml of 0.200 N NH_4OH would be required to ppt. all the Cr as $Cr(OH)_3$ from 20.0 ml of the original undiluted soln.?

*4-7. A 6.00 N soln. of H_2SO_4 has a density of 1.18 g/ml. (*a*) What is the molar concn., and (*b*) what is the mol*al* concn. of the soln. (see footnote, Sec. 4-6)?

*4-8. A piece of metallic Al weighing 2.70 g is treated with 75.0 ml of H_2SO_4 (sp. gr. 1.18, contg. 24.7% H_2SO_4 by wt.). After the metal is dissolved ($2\ \underline{Al} + 6H^+ \longrightarrow 2Al^{3+} + 3\overline{H_2}$), the soln. is diluted to 400 ml. Calculate (*a*) normality of the resulting soln. in free H_2SO_4, (*b*) normality of the soln. with respect to the Al salt it contains, (*c*) total vol. of 6.00 N NH_4OH required to neutralize the acid and ppt. all the Al as $Al(OH)_3$ from 50.0 ml of the soln., (*d*) vol. of 0.100 N $BaCl_2$ soln. required to ppt. all the sulfate from another 50.0-ml portion of the soln.

4 9. What fraction of the mol. wt. represents the equiv. wt. (*a*) of the base Ce_2O_3, (*b*) of the salt $Ca_3(PO_4)_2$, and (*c*) of the acid As_2O_5 (assuming reaction with a base to the formation of $H_2AsO_4^-$)?

4-10. (*a*) How many ml of 2.30 M H_2SO_4 would be neutralized by 15.8 ml of 3.20 M NaOH? (*b*) How many ml of 0.0460 N $H_2C_2O_4 \cdot 2H_2O$ (oxalic acid) soln. would be neutralized by 10.0 ml of 0.0510 N NaOH and by 10.0 ml of 0.0510 N $Ba(OH)_2$? (*c*) How many ml of 0.0460 N $HC_2H_3O_2$ (acetic acid) and how many ml of 0.0460 N H_2SO_4 would be neutralized by 10.0 ml of 0.510 N NaOH?

4-11. (*a*) To what vol. must 25.0 ml of HCl (sp. gr. 1.100) be diluted in order to make a soln. of HCl with a sp. gr. of 1.040? (*b*) How many ml of 0.0500 N $Ba(OH)_2$ would be required to neutralize 4.00 ml of the resulting diluted soln.?

4-12.   Given a 12.0% soln. of $H_2C_2O_4 \cdot 2H_2O$ (sp. gr. = 1.04).   (a) What is the normality of the soln. as an acid, and (b) how many ml of 3.00 M KOH would be neutralized by 18.0 ml of the acid?

4-13.   (a) How many ml of 0.500 N $BaCl_2$ soln. would be required to ppt. all the sulfate from 10.0 millimoles of $FeSO_4 \cdot (NH_4)_2SO_4 \cdot 6H_2O$?   (b) How many ml of 0.100 N $AgNO_3$ would be required to ppt. all the chloride from 8.30 ml of the $BaCl_2$ soln.?

4-14.   A 4.10 mol*al* soln. of H_2SO_4 has a density of 1.21 g/ml.   (a) What is the mol*ar* concn., and (b) what is the normality of the soln.?

4-15.   What is the approx. normality of a soln. marked "HNO_3 1:4"?   (Ordinary concd. HNO_3 has a sp. gr. of 1.42 and contains approx. 70% HNO_3 by wt.)

4-16.   A soln. of H_3PO_4 contains 0.500 millimole/ml.   (a) How many ml of 1.20 N KOH would be required to convert 5.00 ml of the acid to $H_2PO_4^-$?   (b) To what vol. must 25.0 ml of the original acid be diluted in order to make the soln. 1.10 N as a phosphate?

4-17.   (a) How many g of $FeCl_3$ are contained in 25.0 ml of 0.520 N soln. of $FeCl_3 \cdot 6H_2O$?   (b) How many millimoles of $FeCl_3 \cdot 6H_2O$ could be obtained by evaporating the soln. to dryness?   (c) How many ml of 0.200 N NH_4OH are required to react with 25.0 ml of the ferric soln. to ppt. all the Fe as $Fe(OH)_3$?   (d) What is the formal concn. of the original soln.?

4-18.   16 millimoles of Cr metal is dissolved in a soln. of 44.0 millimoles of H_2SO_4 in H_2O ($2\underline{Cr} + 6H^+ \longrightarrow 2Cr^{3+} + 3\overline{H_2}$), and the soln. is then diluted to 250 ml. Calculate (a) the normality of the resulting soln. in free H_2SO_4, (b) the normality of the soln. in terms of the chromic salt it contains, (c) the no. of ml of 3.00 N $BaCl_2$ required to ppt. all the sulfate from one-half of the soln., and (d) the total no. of ml of 3.00 N NH_4OH required to neutralize the acid and ppt. all the chromic salt [as $Cr(OH)_3$] from the other half of the soln.

Reaction and Equilibrium Constants

(See Chap. 28 for discussions on the kinetics of chemical reactions.)

5-1 Thermochemical Equations

Chemical reactions almost invariably take place with either the evolution of heat (*exothermic reactions*) or the absorption of heat (*endothermic reactions*). The unit of heat is the *calorie.* Although a very exact definition of the calorie can be given in terms of electrical energy, the calorie can be simply defined as the quantity of heat required to raise the temperature of one gram of liquid water through one degree centigrade. One kilogram-calorie (kg-cal) [or kilo-calorie (kcal)] is equal to 1,000 calories.

In writing a thermochemical equation, one adds algebraically to the right-hand side of the equation the number of calories or kilogram-calories representing the heat evolved (with a positive sign) or the heat absorbed (with a negative sign). The temperature of the initial substances should ordinarily be the same as those of the products and should be specified, and the physical state of each substance should be indicated. In this book, a temperature of 25°C may be assumed unless otherwise specified, and the symbols *g*, *l*, and *s* will be used to denote a gas, liquid, and solid, respectively. In addition, the symbol *aq* indicates an aqueous solution so dilute as to give no appreciable heat effect on further addition of water.

When thermochemical equations are added or subtracted algebraically to obtain a new equation, the thermal values should be similarly treated. When equations are thus combined, the quantitative heat effects of reactions can be determined in cases where such heat effects are not easily determined directly by experimental means. The *law of Hess* applies here. It states that at constant pressure the overall heat of a chemical reaction is independent of the intermediate steps involved. The following are illustrative thermochemical equations of various types. The heat values correspond to the number of gram moles of substances shown in the indicated equation.

Heat of fusion of ice:

$$H_2O(s) \xrightarrow{0°C} H_2O(l) - 1{,}436 \text{ cal}$$

Heat of vaporization of water:

$$H_2O(l) \xrightarrow{100°C} H_2O(g) - 9{,}710 \text{ cal}$$

Heat of transition of sulfur:

$$S(s, \text{ monoclinic}) \xrightarrow{95°C} S(s, \text{ rhombic}) + 93 \text{ cal}$$

Heat of combustion of methane:

$$CH_4(g) + 2O_2(g) \xrightarrow{25°C} CO_2(g) + 2H_2O(l) + 212.8 \text{ kg-cal}$$

Heat of formation of water:

$$H_2(g) + \tfrac{1}{2}O_2(g) \xrightarrow{25°C} H_2O(l) + 68.3 \text{ kg-cal}$$

Heat of neutralization of strong acids with strong bases:

$$H^+(aq) + OH^-(aq) \xrightarrow{25°C} H_2O(l) + 13{,}600 \text{ cal}$$

Reference books of chemistry give in tabular form the molar heat effects of many reactions of various types. It should be noted, however, that a heat-effect value such as a heat of formation or a heat of combustion is likely to be expressed as a change in heat *content,* and this is symbolized as ΔH. The sign of this value is the opposite of that used as a part of an equation. Thus, in the reaction expressed by the equation $C(s) + O_2(g) \longrightarrow CO_2(g) + 94.0$ kg-cal, the ΔH value is -94.0 kg-cal, since the product CO_2 has a lower heat content than the reactants have.

It should be remembered that when it is necessary to multiply an equation by a factor, the heat value must be similarly multiplied.

Example 1   Calculate the heat of hydrogenation of ethylene, C_2H_4, according to the equation

$$C_2H_4(g) + H_2(g) \longrightarrow C_2H_6(g) + x \text{ kg-cal}$$

from the following data:

$$C_2H_4(g) + 3O_2(g) \longrightarrow 2CO_2(g) + 2H_2O(l) + 337.2 \text{ kg-cal}$$
$$2C_2H_6(g) + 7O_2(g) \longrightarrow 4CO_2(g) + 6H_2O(l) + 745.6 \text{ kg-cal}$$
$$H_2(g) + \tfrac{1}{2}O_2(g) \longrightarrow H_2O(l) + 68.3 \text{ kg-cal}$$

Solution   By reversing the second equation and dividing it by 2, we obtain

$$2CO_2(g) + 3H_2O(l) \longrightarrow C_2H_6(g) + 3\tfrac{1}{2}O_2(g) - 372.8 \text{ kg-cal}$$

Adding this to the sum of the other two equations, we obtain

$$C_2H_4(g) + H_2(g) \longrightarrow C_2H_6(g) + 32.7 \text{ kg-cal} \qquad Ans.$$

The quantitative heat effect of reactions can be found from the heats of formation of their component parts. Such heats of formation for many compounds are listed in handbooks and represent the heats of formation of the compounds from their constituent elements. In this connection, the chemical elements in their ordinary state are assumed to have a zero heat of formation.

Example 2   Given the following heats of formation:

$$Fe(s) + \tfrac{1}{2}O_2(g) \longrightarrow FeO(s) + 64.3 \text{ kg-cal} \qquad \Delta H = -64.3 \text{ kg-cal}$$
$$2Fe(s) + \tfrac{3}{2}O_2(g) \longrightarrow Fe_2O_3(s) + 198.5 \text{ kg-cal} \qquad \Delta H = -198.5 \text{ kg-cal}$$

complete the following equation:

$$2FeO(s) + \tfrac{1}{2}O_2(g) \longrightarrow Fe_2O_3(s) + x \text{ kg-cal}$$

Is the reaction exothermic or endothermic?

Solution

$$2FeO = 2 \times 64.3 = 128.6 \text{ kg-cal}$$
$$\tfrac{1}{2}O_2 = 0 \text{ kg-cal}$$
$$Fe_2O_3 = 198.5 \text{ kg-cal}$$
$$x = 198.5 - 128.6 = 69.9 \text{ kg-cal} \qquad \Delta H = -69.9 \text{ kg-cal} \qquad Ans.$$
Reaction is exothermic (loss in heat content).   *Ans.*

Example 3   Solve the problem given in Example 1 from the following molar heats of formation:

$$C_2H_4(g) \qquad \Delta H = +11.8 \text{ kg cal}$$
$$C_2H_6(g) \qquad \Delta H = -20.2 \text{ kg-cal}$$

Solution

$$\underset{+11.8}{C_2H_4(g)} + \underset{0}{H_2(g)} \longrightarrow \underset{-20.2}{C_2H_6(g)} + x \text{ kg-cal}$$

Decrease in heat content $= 11.8 - (-20.2) = 32.0 \text{ kg-cal}$
$x = $ heat evolved $= 32.0 \text{ kg-cal} \qquad Ans.$

(*Note:* Calculated values of heats of formation of compounds from their constituent elements are not highly precise. Heats of reaction calculated from these values are likely to differ somewhat from those calculated from heats of combustion.   The difference is usually within 5%, however.)

PROBLEMS

*5-1.   Given the following three thermochemical equations, find the value of x in the last one: $2CO(g) + O_2(g) \longrightarrow 2CO_2(g) + 136.0$ kg-cal; $C(s) + O_2(g) \longrightarrow CO_2(g) + 94.0$ kg-cal; $2C(s) + O_2(g) \longrightarrow 2CO(g) + x$ kg-cal.

*5-2.   If the combustion in O_2 of 1.00 g of Al evolves 7.101 kg-cal and the combustion of 1.00 g of C in a limited vol. of O_2 to form CO evolves 2.160 kg-cal, find the value of x in the equation representing the reduction of 1 mole of Al_2O_3: $Al_2O_3(s) + 3C(s) \longrightarrow 2Al(s) + 3CO(g) + x$ kg-cal.

*5-3.   Given the thermochemical equations involving propylene, C_3H_6, and propane, C_3H_8: $C_3H_6(g) + 4\frac{1}{2}O_2(g) \longrightarrow 3CO_2(g) + 3H_2O(l) + 490.2$ kg-cal; $C_3H_8(g) + 5O_2(g) \longrightarrow 3CO_2(g) + 4H_2O(l) + 526.3$ kg-cal; $H_2(g) + \frac{1}{2}O_2(g) \longrightarrow H_2O(l) + 68.3$ kg-cal.   (a) Combine them so as to obtain the value of x in the equation $C_3H_6(g) + H_2(g) \longrightarrow C_3H_8 + x$ kg-cal.   (b) Also calculate the value of x from the heats of formation of C_3H_8 ($\Delta H = -24.82$ kg-cal) and of C_3H_6 ($\Delta H = +4.88$ kg-cal).

*5-4.   The molar heat of combustion of ethylene, C_2H_4, is shown in the equation $C_2H_4(g) + 3O_2(g) \longrightarrow 2CO_2(g) + 2H_2O(l) + 331.6$ kg-cal.   Similarly, $C(s) + O_2(g) \longrightarrow CO_2(g) + 94.0$ kg-cal and $H_2(g) + \frac{1}{2}O_2(g) \longrightarrow H_2O(l) + 68.3$ kg-cal. Calculate from these data the ΔH value for the molar heat of formation of ethylene from its constituent elements.

*5-5.   The ΔH value for the molar heat of formation of liquid n-propyl alcohol, $C_2H_5CH_2OH$, is -71.87 kg-cal.   The heat evolved in the combustion of a g atom of graphite to form CO_2 is 94.0 kg-cal, and the heat evolved in the combustion of a mole of H_2 is 68.3 kg-cal.   Find from these data the heat of combustion of liquid $C_2H_5CH_2OH$.

*5-6.   The heat of solution of 1 mole of HCl gas in an infinite vol. of water in terms of ΔH is -17.53 kg-cal.   The heat of formation of HCl gas is indicated by the thermochemical equation $H_2(g) + Cl_2(g) \longrightarrow 2HCl(g) + 44.12$ kg-cal.   Find the value of x in the following: $\frac{1}{2}H_2 + \frac{1}{2}Cl_2 + aq \longrightarrow HCl(aq) + x$ kg-cal.

5-7.   Calculate the value of x in the thermochemical equation $N_2(g) + 3H_2(g) \longrightarrow 2NH_3(g) + x$ cal from the following: $4NH_3(g) + 3O_2(g) \longrightarrow 2N_2(g) + 6H_2O(l) + 364{,}000$ cal; $H_2(g) + \frac{1}{2}O_2(g) \longrightarrow H_2O(l) + 68{,}300$ cal.

5-8.   If the combustion in O_2 of 1.00 g of Fe to form Fe_2O_3 evolves 2,840 cal and the combustion of 1.00 g of C in a limited vol. of O_2 to form CO evolves 2,160 cal, (a) find the value of x in the equation representing the reduction of 1 mole of Fe_2O_3: $Fe_2O_3(s) + 3C(s) \longrightarrow 2Fe(s) + 3CO(g) + x$ cal.   (b) Is the reaction exothermic or endothermic?

5-9.   The ΔH value for the molar heat of formation of $C_2H_5OH(l)$ from its constituent elements is -66.4 kg-cal.   The heat evolved in the combustion of a g atom of C(s) to $CO_2(g)$ is 94.0 kg-cal, and that of a mole of H_2 is 68.3 kg-cal. Find from these data the heat of combustion of C_2H_5OH.

5-10. Consult a standard handbook of chemistry for the appropriate heats of formation, and calculate from them the heat of reaction of $PbS(s) + 2PbO(s) \longrightarrow 3Pb(s) + SO_2(g)$.

5-11. Given the following thermochemical equations: $HCl(g) + aq \longrightarrow HCl(aq) + 36.0$ kg-cal; $Zn(s) + 2HCl(aq) \longrightarrow ZnCl_2(aq) + H_2 + 44.0$ kcal; $H_2(g) + Cl_2(g) \longrightarrow 2HCl(g) + 17.0$ kg-cal. Find the value of x in the equation $Zn(s) + Cl_2(g) + aq \longrightarrow ZnCl_2(aq) + x$ kg-cal.

5-12. The heat of formation of HBr(g) is listed in terms of ΔH as -8.66 kg-cal. The heat of solution of 1 mole of HBr(g) in 200 moles of H_2O is given in terms of ΔH as -19.88 kg-cal. Find the value of x in the equation $H_2(g) + Br_2(g) + 200H_2O \longrightarrow 2HBr(200H_2O) + x$ kg-cal.

5-2 Effect of Concentration on Reaction Rate

Although most reactions encountered in analytical chemistry take place very rapidly, a few take appreciable time for their completion. In the field of organic chemistry, most reactions are slow. Many factors such as temperature, pressure, exposed surface, and the presence of catalysts influence reaction rate, but a very important factor is concentration.

It is logical to assume that in order for molecules or ions to react, they must first collide with sufficient kinetic energy and that the rate of reaction must be proportional to the number of reactant molecules of each type present in a unit volume. Since rate is proportional to the concentration of each reactant, it is proportional to the product of the concentrations of all of them. In mathematical expressions of rate, concentrations of dissolved substances are conventionally expressed in moles per liter. In reactions of gaseous substances, partial pressures are used. It should be clear that during the progress of a reaction, the concentrations of the reacting substances are continually decreasing, and the rate at any moment is governed by the concentrations at that moment.

5-3 First-order Reactions

When a reaction is expressed in the form of a chemical equation, the order of the reaction is indicated by the number of molecules of reacting substance which change during the reaction. In a first-order reaction, the concentration of only one substance decreases. It is typified by the general equation $A \longrightarrow B + C$. An example is the decomposition of dimethyl ether: $CH_3OCH_3 \longrightarrow CH_4 + CO + H_2$.

Another example is the hydrolysis of sucrose (cane sugar) to glucose and fructose: $C_{12}H_{22}O_{11} + H_2O \longrightarrow C_6H_{12}O_6 + C_6H_{12}O_6$. In this reaction, although water is one of the reacting substances, its concentration does not change appreciably, since the reaction takes place in dilute aqueous solution.   Under constant conditions of acidity and volume, the concentration of sucrose will decrease at a rate proportional to its prevailing concentration, or, in general for a first-order reaction involving the decomposition of substance A,

$$-\frac{d[A]}{dt} = k[A]$$

The molar concentration of A is here expressed by enclosing its formula in brackets.   The expression at the left of the equality sign is the conventional mathematical way of denoting rate (i.e., the change in concentration of A with time t), and the negative sign indicates a decreasing rate.

The expression of reaction rate can also be in terms of the products of the reaction.   In the sugar hydrolysis reaction, if C_0 denotes the initial concentration of sucrose and C the concentration of the products,

$$\frac{dC}{dt} = k(C_0 - C)$$

By applying the calculus, this equation can be converted to the equation

$$2.303 \log \frac{1}{1 - x} = kt$$

in which x is the fraction of reacting substance (that is, $x = C/C_0$) in time t.   The number 2.303 is the factor which converts a natural logarithm to a common logarithm and can be incorporated in the constant k to give the simple but useful formula

$$\log \frac{1}{1 - x} = Kt$$

Such an expression makes possible the calculation of the time required for the formation of a desired quantity of product or the extent of decomposition at the end of a given time.

Example 1   If under a certain condition of acidity, a 0.44 M solution of sucrose shows 23.7% hydrolysis at the end of 8.00 hr, what is its concentration at the end of 35.0 hr, and how long a time will be required for the concentrations of the three sugars to be the same?

Solution   At the end of 8.00 hr, fraction decomposed $= x = 0.237$

$$\log \frac{1}{1-x} = Kt$$

$$\log \frac{1}{1-0.237} = K \times 8.00$$

Solving,

$$K = 0.01475$$

At the end of 35.0 hr,

$$\log \frac{1}{1-x} = 0.01475 \times 35.0$$

Solving,

$$x = 0.696$$

$$0.696 \times 0.44 = 0.306 \; M \qquad Ans.$$

Concentrations of sucrose, glucose, and fructose are equal when one-half of the sucrose has hydrolyzed.   Therefore,

$$\log \frac{1}{1-0.50} = 0.01475 \times t$$

Solving,

$$t = 20.3 \text{ hr} \qquad Ans.$$

The decay of a radioactive element is an example of a reaction of the first order, since each nucleus of radioactive element decomposes independently of the presence of other atoms.   The term *half-life* is frequently applied to radioactive elements and occasionally to other reactions.   It is merely the time required for one-half of a reactant to decompose.

Example 2   If 0.100% of a sample of radium decomposes in $2\frac{1}{2}$ years, what is the half-life of radium?

Solution

$$\log \frac{1}{1-0.00100} = K \times 2\frac{1}{2}$$

Solving for K and substituting its value in the equation

$$\log \frac{1}{1-0.50} = Kt$$

we obtain

$$t = 1,744 \text{ years} \qquad \textit{Ans.}$$

It is not always possible to predict the order of a reaction from the overall equation representing it. The overall reaction may consist of a slow, rate-determining reaction of the first order combined with a fast secondary reaction. For example, the general reaction $2A \longrightarrow 4C + D$ could be a first-order rather than a second-order reaction, for it might consist of the slow first-order reaction $A \longrightarrow B + C$ followed by the fast reaction $2B \longrightarrow 2C + D$. The combination of these two equations (after multiplying the first by 2) gives the equation for the overall reaction, but the rate of the latter is controlled by the first-order reaction.

5-4   Second-order Reactions

A second-order reaction can be of either the type $2A \longrightarrow$ products or $A + B \longrightarrow$ products. The rate of the first reaction at any moment is proportional to the square of the prevailing concentration of A; the rate of the second is proportional to the product of the prevailing concentrations of A and B.

An illustration of the first type is the decomposition of hydrogen peroxide ($2H_2O_2 \longrightarrow 2H_2O + O_2$), although this occurs as a second-order reaction only under special circumstances. An illustration of the second type is the saponification of an organic ester such as ethyl acetate ($CH_3COOC_2H_5 + NaOH \longrightarrow C_2H_5OH + CH_3COONa$). When, as in the last case, the two reactants are different substances, we shall consider only the simple case where the concentrations of the two reactants are the same.

If the concentration of the reactant (or of each of the two reactants) is C_0 and that of one of the products is C, then

$$\frac{dC}{dt} = k(C_0 - C)^2$$

Integrating this, we obtain

$$\frac{C}{C_0(C_0 - C)} = kt$$

and if we denote by x the fraction decomposed ($x = C/C_0$), we obtain

$$\frac{x}{1 - x} = ktC_0$$

By combining the constants k and C_0, we obtain the useful formula

$$\frac{x}{1 - x} = Kt$$

Example 1   In the second-order decomposition of H_2O_2 according to the equation $H_2O_2 \longrightarrow 2H_2O + O_2$, if 43.7% decomposition and the evolution of 18.0 ml of O_2 occur after 9.2 min, what volume of O_2 has been evolved at the end of 30.8 min?

Solution

$$\frac{0.437}{1 - 0.437} = K \times 9.2$$

$$K = 0.0843$$

$$\frac{x}{1 - x} = 0.0843 \times 30.8$$

$$x = \frac{2.60}{3.60} = 0.723$$

$$\frac{72.3}{43.7} \times 18.0 = 29.8 \text{ ml} \qquad Ans.$$

As stated under the discussion of first-order reactions, it is not always possible to predict the order of a reaction from the equation representing the overall reaction.   The equation for the reduction of hydrogen peroxide by hydroiodic acid is formulated: $H_2O_2 + 2H^+ + 2I^- \longrightarrow 2H_2O + I_2$.   This would appear at first sight to be a reaction of the fifth order, implying that the reaction proceeds only when the hydrogen peroxide molecule, two iodide ions, and two hydrogen ions collide simultaneously.   Actually, the reaction is one of the second order.   This is explained by assuming that the following three reactions occur:

$$H_2O_2 + I^- \xrightarrow{\text{slow}} H_2O + IO^-$$

$$H^+ + IO^- \xrightarrow{\text{fast}} HIO$$

$$HIO + H^+ + I^- \xrightarrow{\text{fast}} H_2O + I_2$$

The net equation is the sum of these three, but the first one controls the rate of the overall reaction.

5-5   Reactions of Higher Order

The mathematics involved in third-order reactions, especially in cases where the reacting components are at different concentrations, is complicated and will not be covered in this book.   Reactions of an order greater than three are practically nonexistent, for the probability of simultaneous collisions among four or more different molecules or ions is very small.

5-6   Effect of Temperature on Reaction Rate

Since the rate of a reaction is governed by the number of collisions per unit time between moving molecules or ions, and since kinetic theory indicates that molecular movement is greater at higher temperatures, it follows that chemical reactions are hastened by an increase in temperature.   Mathematical relationships have been developed for various types of reactions, but they are rather involved.   For the practical chemist, it is helpful to know that, for a majority of reactions at ordinary temperatures, each 10°C rise in temperature approximately doubles the rate of reactions.

5-7   Effect of a Catalyst on Reaction Rate

A catalyst is a substance which hastens (or sometimes retards) a reaction without being used up in the reaction.   In most of the cases encountered in analytical chemistry, the mechanism of the speeded reaction involves a step in which the catalyst reacts in some way with a reactant and another step in which it is regenerated.   For example, the velocity of decomposition of hydrogen peroxide is greatly increased by the presence of a small amount of hydrobromic acid, and the mechanism is probably as indicated by the equations

$$H_2O_2 + 2H^+ + 2Br^- \longrightarrow Br_2 + 2H_2O$$
$$Br_2 + H_2O_2 \longrightarrow O_2 + 2H^+ + 2Br^-$$

In the case of a solid catalyst, one or more of the reactants may be adsorbed on the surface of the solid to give a localized high concentration favorable to fast reaction.   In any case, final states of equilibrium, and hence the numerical values of equilibrium constants, are not affected by the presence of catalysts.

PROBLEMS

*5-13.   In the first-order reaction A $\longrightarrow$ B + C, if 60 min is required to convert 25% of A to its products, how much longer must the action continue to convert 75% of A?

*5-14.   A certain gas decomposes to two gaseous products according to the first-order reaction typified by the general equation A $\longrightarrow$ B + C.   If the original gas is in a closed system at a pressure of 100 mm of Hg, (*a*) what would be the pressure when the reaction is 50% complete?   (*b*) 100% complete?   (*c*) If 10 min is required for 50% decomposition, what would be the pressure of the system at the end of 30 min?

*5-15.   A sample of methyl acetate was hydrolyzed in approx. 1 *N* HCl at 25°C ($CH_3COOCH_3 + H_2O \longrightarrow CH_3OH + CH_3COOH$).   Small equal aliquot portions were removed at intervals and titrated with NaOH.   The following vols. of NaOH were required at different time intervals: 25.74 ml at 0 sec, 26.34 ml at 339 sec, 39.81 ml at completion of reaction.   How many ml of the NaOH would have been required for an aliquot portion at the end of 45 min?

*5-16.   (a) In a second-order reaction of the type 2A $\longrightarrow$ B + C, if it takes 10.0 min to bring about 25% decomposition of the initial substance, what total time is required to decompose 75% of it?   (b) Answer the above for a first-order reaction of the type A $\longrightarrow$ B + C.

*5-17.   Radium spontaneously decomposes by a reaction of the first order.   If it takes $25\frac{1}{3}$ years for a 1% decomposition of radium, what is its half-life?

*5-18.   A certain substance A is mixed with an equimolar quantity of substance B. At the end of 60 min, 75% of A has reacted.   What percentage will not have reacted at the end of 120 min if the reaction is (a) first order in A and independent of B, (b) first order in A and first order in B?

*5-19.   The decomposition of dimethyl ether [$CH_3OCH_3(g)$ $\longrightarrow$ $CH_4(g) + CO(g) + H_2(g)$] is a first-order reaction.   The ether is in a closed system at 100 mm of Hg pressure.   If A min is required to bring the total gas pressure in the system to 200 mm, what total time (in terms of A) would be required to bring the pressure to (a) 250 mm; (b) 298 mm?

*5-20.   A soln. of a certain organic acid contains an inert mineral acid, the latter serving as a catalyst.   The organic acid decomposes to a neutral product by a first-order reaction.   At intervals, small equal portions are titrated with standard alkali. At the very start the portion requires 19.04 ml of the alkali.   At the end of 76.0 min a portion requires 16.90 ml.   At the completion of the reaction a portion requires 10.71 ml.   What vol. of alkali would have been used for a portion after 204 min?

*5-21.   An aq. soln. of H_2O_2 decomposes under the action of iodide catalyst according to the overall equation $2H_2O_2$ $\longrightarrow$ $2H_2O + O_2$, but because of side reactions, the reaction is one of the first order.   If it takes 40.0 min for the no. of moles of O_2 formed to equal the no. of moles of H_2O_2 remaining undecomposed, how many min would be required to decompose one-quarter of the H_2O_2?

*5-22.   The progress of the hydrolysis of sucrose (see text) can be quantitatively followed by measuring the angle of rotation of a beam of polarized light passing through a column of the soln.   In such a series of measurements in a certain acid soln. of sucrose at 30°C, the angle of rotation before hydrolysis starts is +57.90°; the angle of rotation of the completely hydrolyzed sucrose is −15.45°.   After 4.0 hr of hydrolysis, the angle is 48.50°   What would be the angle of rotation at the end of 40 hr?

*5-23.   The solubility of $PbCl_2$ at a certain temp. is 38.66 millimoles/liter.   When excess solid $PbCl_2$ is shaken with a liter of water, 6.14 millimoles dissolves in 10.25 min and 24.58 millimoles dissolves in 60.0 min.   Show mathematically that this conforms to a first-order reaction, and determine how many min are required to dissolve 90% of the salt under the same conditions.

5-24. If the first-order reaction A $\longrightarrow$ B + C is started at noon and 80% of A has been converted to its products at 2:00 P.M. of the same day, at what time was 10% of A converted?

5-25. In a first-order reaction of the type A $\longrightarrow$ B + C, if it takes 20 min to bring about decomposition of 30% of the initial substance, what total time would be required to decompose (a) 60% of it, (b) all of it? (c) Answer the above also for a second-order reaction of the type 2A $\longrightarrow$ B + C.

5-26. Under certain conditions of temp. and catalytic action, a soln. of H_2O_2 in quinoline decomposes: $2H_2O_2 \longrightarrow O_2 + 2H_2O$. At the point of half decomposition, 20.6 ml (standard conditions) of O_2 has been formed. In 9.2 min, 0.00161 mole of H_2O_2 has been decomposed; in 30.8 min, 30.2 ml of O_2 has been formed. (a) Show from the respective values of the rate constant that the decomposition conforms to a second-order reaction but not to a first-order reaction. (b) Find the time required to reach 80% decomposition.

5-27. Equimolar amts. of A and B are mixed and dissolved. They interact slowly, and after 1 hr, 60% of A has been used up. What percentage of A will be used up at the end of 3 hr if the reaction is (a) first order in A and independent of B, (b) first order in A and first order in B?

5-28. Dimethyl ether gas is in a closed system at a pressure of 100 mm of Hg. It decomposes by the first-order reaction $CH_3OCH_3(g) \longrightarrow CH_4(g) + CO(g) + H_2(g)$. If A min is required to bring the total gas pressure to 125 mm, what total time would be required to bring the pressure to 280 mm?

5-29. From the data given in Prob. 5-22, (a) determine the fraction of the original sucrose that has hydrolyzed when the angular rotation is zero, and (b) find the time required to reach this point.

5-30. What is the approx. numerical ratio between the half-life of a substance which decomposes by a first-order reaction and the time required for one-thousandth of it to decompose?

5-31. The oxidation of Mn^{++} by $S_2O_8^{=}$ to form permanganate and sulfate ions takes place only in the presence of silver ions. Assuming that the catalytic action is due to the intermediate oxidation of Ag^+ to Ag^{++} and that the latter oxidizes the manganous ions, write a balanced equation for the overall reaction, and show how it results by combining two equations expressing the intermediate steps.

5-32. The rate of hydrolysis of a 17% soln. of sucrose in 0.099 N HCl at 35°C was measured. In 9.82 min, 93.18% of the original sucrose remained; in 93.18 min, 71.0% remained; in 589.4 min, 11.1% remained. (a) Under these conditions how many min are required for half of the sucrose to decompose? (b) What proportionate increase would you expect if the temp. were 65 instead of 35°C?

5-33. In aq. soln. in the presence of iodide ions H_2O_2 decomposes: $2H_2O_2 \longrightarrow 2H_2O + O_2$. Because the reaction actually takes place in two steps of which the first step is a slow, rate-controlling, first-order reaction, the overall decomposition is of the first order. (a) Show mathematically that this is true from the experimental fact that the H_2O_2 is one-third decomposed in 15.0 min, and half decomposed in 25.5 min. (*b*) Find the time required to reach the point where the no. of moles of O_2 formed just equals the no. of moles of H_2O_2 remaining undecomposed.

5-8   Principle of Mass Action

Many reactions encountered in analytical chemistry are reversible ones. This means that the products of a given reaction interact, at least to some extent, to give the initial substances. Consider a general reversible reaction between substances A and B at a given temperature to give substances C and D according to the following equation:

$$A + B \rightleftharpoons C + D$$

At the start of the reaction, only substances A and B are present. These react at a certain rate to give C and D, and as the latter are produced, the concentrations of A and B decrease. As indicated in Sec. 5-2, the rate of reaction between A and B at any given moment is proportional to the prevailing effective concentrations of A and B at that moment. The rate of forward reaction is expressed as follows:

$$-\frac{d[A]}{dt} = -\frac{d[B]}{dt} = k'[A][B]*$$

where [A] and [B] are the prevailing effective molar concentrations of A and B, respectively, and k' is a constant at a given temperature. As the concentrations of substances C and D increase, these substances in turn react at a constantly increasing rate to produce A and B. The rate of this reaction at any moment is proportional to the product of the prevailing concentrations of C and D.

$$\frac{d[C]}{dt} = \frac{d[D]}{dt} = k''[C][D]$$

When equilibrium has been established, these two rates are equal. Hence,

$$\frac{[C][D]}{[A][B]} = \frac{k'}{k''} = K$$

In the reaction $A + 2B \rightleftharpoons C + D$, the rate of reaction between A and B is proportional to the concentration of A and to the *square* of the concentration of B. Hence, at equilibrium,

---

* For the student who has not had differential calculus, it may be explained that an expression like dx/dt means merely "the rate of change of x with time t." A negative sign preceding the expression signifies a decreasing rate.

$$\frac{[C][D]}{[A][B]^2} = K$$

More generally, in the reaction $wA + xB + \cdots \rightleftharpoons yC + zD + \cdots$, the equilibrium constant is expressed as follows:

$$\frac{[C]^y[D]^z}{[A]^w[B]^x} = K$$

Since the rates of the forward and backward reactions are usually not affected to the same degree by a change in temperature, the equilibrium constant K is likely to be a function of temperature.

Although this kind of constant is often referred to as a mass-action constant and the principle underlying its application is called the mass-action principle, the term is somewhat of a misnomer, for concentrations rather than masses are the contributing factors.

The principle of "mass action" applies to gases as well as to substances in solution, and in such cases the partial pressure of a gas rather than its concentration is used to express its quantitative effect on an equilibrium. In analytical chemistry, however, the principle is applied mostly to aqueous solutions. In this connection, as indicated in Sec. 5-15, for precise results in mathematical calculations, activities rather than molar concentrations should be used in formulating equilibrium constants. However, when applied to the dilute solutions ordinarily encountered in analytical chemistry, only a small sacrifice in accuracy results in the use of concentrations expressed as moles of solute per liter of solution. Since this method of expressing concentrations is consistent with that used as a basis for other types of analytical calculations, it is so used in this book.

In general, if a solid substance is involved in a chemical equilibrium, its concentration is not included in the formulation of the constant, since the concentration of the solid is itself essentially a constant and its activity is taken as unity. The same is true of water in an equilibrium pertaining to dilute aqueous solutions. Thus, the constant for the equilibrium

$$CO_3^= + H_2O \rightleftharpoons HCO_3^- + OH^-$$

is simply

$$\frac{[HCO_3^-][OH^-]}{[CO_3^=]} = K$$

5-9   Ion Product Constant of Water

Water dissociates slightly into hydrogen ions[1] and hydroxyl ions as follows:

$$H_2O \rightleftharpoons H^+ + OH^-$$

The mass-action expression for this dissociation is simply

$$[H^+][OH^-] = K_w$$

since the concentration of undissociated H_2O in dilute aqueous solutions is essentially a constant and, as stated above, is omitted from mass-action expressions.   In any aqueous solution, therefore, the product of the molar hydrogen-ion concentration and the molar hydroxyl-ion concentration is a constant at a given temperature.   This constant is called the *ion product constant* of water and at 25°C has the value of 1.0×10^{-14}.

$$
\begin{aligned}
[H^+][OH^-] = K_w &= 1.0 \times 10^{-14} \quad &\text{at } 25°C \\
&= 1.2 \times 10^{-15} \quad &\text{at } 0°C \\
&= 5.8 \times 10^{-13} \quad &\text{at } 100°C
\end{aligned}
$$

In pure water the hydrogen-ion and the hydroxyl-ion concentrations are equal; at 25°C each has the value 1.0×10^{-7} M.

5-10   pH Value

It is often convenient to express hydrogen-ion concentrations in terms of the pH value.   The pH value as originally formulated by Sörensen is simply the common logarithm of the reciprocal of the hydrogen-ion concentration:

$$pH = \log \frac{1}{[H^+]} = -\log [H^+]$$

More accurately, it is the negative logarithm of the hydrogen-ion *activity*:

$$pH = -\log a[H^+]$$

Since in the problems of this book we are in general neglecting activity values (see Sec. 5-15), the original formulation can be applied to advantage without much sacrifice of accuracy.   Similarly the pOH value, although less often used, is the negative logarithm of the hydroxyl-ion

---

[1] The hydrogen ion exists as a series of hydrates but is often expressed as the monohydrate H_3O^+.   This ion is called the *hydronium ion* and is formed by the union of a proton with a molecule of the solvent.   Since the use of this symbol offers no particular advantages in analytical computations, the simpler symbol H^+ is used in this text.   The same simplification is made in the case of several other hydrated ions.

concentration. The pH value of pure water at 25°C is 7.0. The pH value of acid solutions is less than 7.0; the pH value of alkaline solutions is greater than 7.0. In general, at 25°C,

$$pH + pOH = 14.0$$

Example 1 What is the pH value and what is the hydroxyl-ion concentration of a solution that is 0.0010 M in HCl (effective ionization = 100%)?

Solution

$$[H^+] = 0.0010 = 1.0 \times 10^{-3}$$
$$pH = -\log(1.0 \times 10^{-3}) = 3.0 \qquad Ans.$$
$$pOH = 14.0 - 3.0 = 11.0$$
$$[OH^-] = 1.0 \times 10^{-11} \qquad Ans.$$

Example 2 The hydrogen-ion concentration in a certain dilute solution of sulfuric acid is 2.0×10^{-5} M. What is the pH value? What is the pOH value?

Solution

$$pH = -\log(2.0 \times 10^{-5}) = -(\log 2.0 + \log 10^{-5})$$
$$= -(0.30 - 5) = 4.70 \qquad Ans.$$
$$pOH = 14.0 - 4.70 = 9.30 \qquad Ans.$$

Example 3 The pH value of a certain solution is 5.92. What are the pOH value, the hydrogen-ion concentration, and the hydroxyl-ion concentration?

Solution

$$pH + pOH = 14.0$$
$$pOH = 14.0 - 5.92 = 8.08 \qquad Ans.$$
$$[H^+] = 10^{-5.92} = 10^{+0.08} \times 10^{-6} = 1.20 \times 10^{-6} \ M \qquad Ans.$$
$$[H^+][OH^-] = 1.0 \times 10^{-14}$$
$$[OH^-] = \frac{1.0 \times 10^{-14}}{1.20 \times 10^{-6}} = 8.3 \times 10^{-9} \ M \qquad Ans.$$

PROBLEMS

(Temperatures are 25°C.)

*5-34. (a) What is the pH value of a soln. of which the hydrogen-ion concn. is 2.8×10^{-3} M? Is the soln. acid or alkaline? (b) What is the hydrogen-ion concn. of a soln. with a pOH value of 4.17? Is the soln. acid or alkaline?

*5-35. What is the pH value of (a) 0.010 M HCl (100% effective ionization), (b) 0.30 M NaOH (90% effective ionization), (c) a soln. of HCl in which the hydrogen-ion concn. is 8.0 M?

*5-36. What is the hydrogen-ion concn. of a soln. of which the pH value is −0.55?

*5-37. (a) Given pH = 10.46, calculate [H$^+$], [OH$^-$], and pOH. (b) Given [OH$^-$] = 5.6 × 10^{-2}, calculate [H$^+$], pH, and pOH.

5-38. (a) What is the pOH value of a soln. of which the hydrogen-ion concn. is 5.3 × 10^{-4} M? Is the soln. acid or alkaline? (b) What is the hydroxyl-ion concn. of a soln. of which the pH value is 9.27? Is the soln. acid or alkaline?

5-39. What is the pH value of (a) 0.050 M HNO$_3$ (100% ionized), (b) 0.80 M KOH (85% effective ionization), (c) a soln. of HCl in which the hydrogen-ion concn. is 5.0 M?

5-40. What is the hydroxyl-ion concn. of a soln. in which pOH = −0.27?

5-41. (a) Given pOH = 5.80, calculate [H$^+$], [OH$^-$], and pH. (b) Given [H$^+$] = 3.1 × 10^{-9} M, calculate [OH$^-$], pH, and pOH.

5-11   Ionization Constant

The mass-action principle can be applied to the equilibrium in dilute solution between the molecules of a weak acid or weak base and its ions. Thus, acetic acid, $HC_2H_3O_2$,* is partially ionized in solution as follows:

$$HC_2H_3O_2 \rightleftharpoons H^+ + C_2H_3O_2^-$$

Therefore,

$$\frac{[H^+][C_2H_3O_2^-]}{[HC_2H_3O_2]} = K_{HC_2H_3O_2}$$

That is, in a solution containing acetic acid, the total molar concentration of hydrogen ions (from whatever source) multiplied by the total molar concentration of acetate ions (from whatever source) divided by the molar concentration of un-ionized acetic acid is a constant at a given temperature. This value is called the ionization constant of acetic acid. Its value at 25°C is 1.86 × 10^{-5}.

A similar expression can be set up for the ionization of a solution of ammonia in water. Here ammonium hydroxide molecules are presuma-

* The structural formula of acetic acid is C $\overset{\overset{\displaystyle CH_3}{|}}{\underset{\underset{\displaystyle O \quad H}{}}{\diagup}} \overset{\displaystyle O}{}$, and the organic chemist usually expresses

the straight-line formula as CH_3COOH. The abbreviations HAc and AcOH are frequently used for the acid, and Ac$^-$ and AcO$^-$ for the acetate ion.

bly formed, which, in turn, dissociate partially into ammonium ions and hydroxyl ions.

$$NH_4OH \rightleftharpoons NH_4^+ + OH^-$$

The ionization constant is therefore expressed as

$$\frac{[NH_4^+][OH^-]}{[NH_4OH]} = K_{NH_4OH}$$

Since ammonium hydroxide molecules (if they exist at all) are in equilibrium with ammonia and water, the equilibrium is more generally expressed as

$$NH_3 + H_2O \rightleftharpoons (NH_4OH) \rightleftharpoons NH_4^+ + OH^-$$

and the ionization constant is written

$$\frac{[NH_4^+][OH^-]}{[NH_3]} = K_{NH_4OH}$$

In either case the *total* concentration of NH_3, either dissolved as such or combined as NH_4OH, is used in the denominator of the fraction, so the numerical value of the constant is the same in the two cases. At 25°C it is 1.75×10^{-5}.

The ionization constants of a few weak acids and bases are given in the Appendix. Such ionization constants are commonly expressed by the general symbols K_a and K_b, respectively.

Just as it is often convenient to express hydrogen-ion concentrations in terms of pH values, ionization constants of acids and bases (K_a and K_b) can be similarly expressed as logarithmic functions:

$$pK_a = -\log K_a$$
$$pK_b = -\log K_b$$

Example 1 What are the ionization constant and the pK_a value of acetic acid at a certain temperature if in tenth-molar solution it is 1.3% ionized?

$$HC_2H_3O_2 \rightleftharpoons H^+ + C_2H_3O_2^-$$

Solution If 0.10 mole of $HC_2H_3O_2$ were completely ionized, it would give 0.10 mole (or 0.10 g ion) of H^+ and 0.10 mole of $C_2H_3O_2^-$. Being only 1.3% ionized, it gives $0.10 \times 0.013 = 0.0013$ mole of H^+ and 0.0013 mole of $C_2H_3O_2^-$, leaving 0.0987 mole of undissociated $HC_2H_3O_2$ molecules. The molar concentrations are therefore as follows:

$$[H^+] = 0.0013$$
$$[C_2H_3O_2^-] = 0.0013$$
$$[HC_2H_3O_2] = 0.0987$$

Substituting these in the above expression for the ionization constant of acetic acid, we find

$$\frac{(0.0013)(0.0013)}{0.0987} = K_a$$

$K_a = 1.7 \times 10^{-5}$ Ans.

$pK_a = -\log(1.7 \times 10^{-5}) = 4.77$ Ans.

Example 2   At a certain temperature the pK_b value of NH_4OH is 4.70. What is the pH value of a 0.20 M solution of NH_4OH at that temperature?

Solution

$K_b = 10^{-4.70} = 10^{0.30} \times 10^{-5} = 2.0 \times 10^{-5}$

Let x = molar concn. of OH^- and of NH_4^+

$0.20 - x$ = molar concn. of NH_3

$$K_b = \frac{[NH_4^+][OH^-]}{[NH_3]} = 2.0 \times 10^{-5}$$

$$= \frac{x^2}{0.20 \quad x} = 2.0 \times 10^{-5}$$

$x = [OH^-] = 2.0 \times 10^{-3}$

$[H^+] = 5.0 \times 10^{-12}$

$pH = -\log(5.0 \times 10^{-12}) = 11.30$ *Ans.*

Numerical values in mass-action expressions need not be expressed to more than two or, at the most, three significant figures.   Therefore simplifying assumptions can often be made.   In the above fractional equation, the value of x is so small compared with the value 0.20 from which it is subtracted that it is well within the limit of precision to write

$$\frac{(x)(x)}{0.20} = 1.86 \times 10^{-5}$$

and thus avoid solving a quadratic equation.[1]

5-12   Common-ion Effect. Buffered Solution

Suppose into a dilute solution of acetic acid is dissolved a considerable quantity of sodium acetate, i.e., a highly ionized salt of acetic acid.   The total acetate-ion concentration is greatly increased, but since the equilib-

---

[1] In cases where such simplifying assumptions cannot be made, the formula for solving the general equation $ax^2 + bx + c = 0$ is

$$x = \frac{-b \pm \sqrt{b^2 - 4ac}}{2a}$$

rium constant $\dfrac{[H^+][C_2H_3O_2^-]}{HC_2H_3O_2} = K_a$ must be maintained, the greater part of the hydrogen ions present must unite with acetate ions to form more of the undissociated acetic acid molecules. In other words, the equilibrium reaction $HC_2H_3O_2 \rightleftharpoons H^+ + C_2H_3O_2^-$ must go to the left to a degree sufficient to reestablish the numerical value of the constant. The solution therefore becomes much less acidic, with a hydrogen-ion concentration only slightly greater than that of pure water.

A similar case is one in which an ammonium salt is added to a solution of ammonium hydroxide. The common ion NH_4^+ represses the ionization $NH_3 + H_2O \rightleftharpoons (NH_4OH) \rightleftharpoons NH_4^+ + OH^-$ to a very great extent, for in order to maintain the equilibrium constant $\dfrac{[NH_4^+][OH^-]}{[NH_3]} = K_b$, the hydroxyl-ion concentration must be greatly decreased. The hydroxyl-ion concentration of the resulting solution is only slightly greater than that of pure water.

In each of the above two cases the solution is said to be *buffered* by the common ion added. The acetic acid–sodium acetate combination, for example, has a low hydrogen-ion concentration which is little affected by the addition of small amounts of even a strong acid or alkali. In the former case the added hydrogen ions merely unite with the acetate ions (still present in excess) to give more acetic acid, the ionization of which is repressed by the acetate. Similarly, the basicity of a buffered ammonium hydroxide solution is not much affected by the addition of small amounts of even a strong alkali like sodium hydroxide or a strong acid like hydrochloric acid. These facts are illustrated in Example 1 following and in Probs. 5-54 and 5-71.

Buffered solutions are much used both in qualitative and quantitative analysis to effect certain separations of elements where a carefully controlled hydrogen-ion or hydroxyl-ion concentration is essential.

Example 1   What is the hydrogen-ion concentration in 500 ml of a 0.100 M solution of acetic acid at 25°C if the solution contains an additional 2.00 g of acetate ions added in the form of sodium acetate ($K_{HC_2H_3O_2} = 1.86 \times 10^{-5}$)? What is the hydrogen-ion concentration if 4 millimoles of NaOH and if 4 millimoles of HCl are introduced into the buffered solution? What is the pH value in each of the three cases?

Solution

2.00 g $C_2H_3O_2^-$ per 500 ml = 0.0678 mole/liter

Let

$$x = \text{concn. of } H^+ \text{ ions}$$

Then

$$x + 0.0678 = \text{concn. of } C_2H_3O_2^- \text{ ions}$$

and

$$0.100 - x = \text{concn. of un-ionized } HC_2H_3O_2$$

Therefore,

$$\frac{(x)(x + 0.0678)}{(0.100 - x)} = 1.86 \times 10^{-5}$$

or, since x is small,

$$\frac{(x)(0.0678)}{0.100} \cong 1.86 \times 10^{-5}$$

Solving,

$$x = 2.74 \times 10^{-5} M \qquad \textit{Ans.}$$
$$pH = -\log(2.74 \times 10^{-5}) = 4.56 \qquad \textit{Ans.}$$

After adding 4 millimoles ($= 8$ millimoles/liter) of OH^-,

$$HC_2H_3O_2 + OH^- \longrightarrow C_2H_3O_2^- + H_2O$$

New concn. of $HC_2H_3O_2 = 0.100 - 0.008 = 0.092 M$

New concn. of $C_2H_3O_2^- = 0.0678 + 0.008 = 0.076 M$

$$\frac{[H^+](0.076)}{0.092} = 1.86 \times 10^{-5}$$

$$[H^+] = 2.25 \times 10^{-5} M \qquad \textit{Ans.}$$
$$pH = -\log(2.25 \times 10^{-5}) = 4.65 \qquad \textit{Ans.}$$

After adding 8 millimoles/liter of H^+,

$$C_2H_3O_2^- + H^+ \longrightarrow HC_2H_3O_2$$

New concn. of $C_2H_3O_2^- = 0.0678 - 0.008 = 0.060 M$

New concn. of $HC_2C_3O_2 = 0.100 + 0.008 = 0.108 M$

$$\frac{[H^+](0.060)}{0.108} = 1.86 \times 10^{-5}$$

$$[H^+] = 3.35 \times 10^{-5} M \qquad \textit{Ans.}$$
$$pH = -\log(3.35 \times 10^{-5}) = 4.47 \qquad \textit{Ans.}$$

5-13   Le Châtelier's Principle

In general terms, the Le Châtelier principle or theorem states that when substances are in equilibrium, a change in any of the conditions or factors involved will cause a shift in the equilibrium in a direction which tends to offset the change and restore the original conditions.   In the case of solutions, the common-ion effect just discussed bears out the Le Châtelier principle, for an ionic reaction is displaced in the direction which maintains its ionization constant.   In an equilibrium reaction indicated by the general equation $A + B \rightleftharpoons C + D$, an increase in the concentration of substance C or of substance D or a decrease in the concentration of A or of B displaces the reaction to the left.

The principle applies also to gas pressures.   If in the reaction just cited substance C is a gas, an increase in pressure on the system would displace the reaction to the left.   Furthermore, the principle applies to changes in temperature.   If the reaction is exothermic ($A + B \rightleftharpoons C + D + x$ cal), an increase in temperature would cause the reaction, as written, to go to the left; if the reaction is endothermic, an increase in temperature would cause the reaction to go more nearly to completion.

5-14   Ionization of Polybasic Acids. Simultaneous Equilibria

Polybasic (or polyprotic) acids have more than one replaceable hydrogen, and it is characteristic of them that they ionize in steps, each step to a lesser degree than the preceding one.   Thus, the primary ionization of carbonic acid is

$$H_2CO_3 \rightleftharpoons H^+ + HCO_3^- \qquad K_1 = \frac{[H^+][HCO_3^-]}{[H_2CO_3]} = 3.3 \times 10^{-7}$$

The secondary ionization is

$$HCO_3^- \rightleftharpoons H^+ + CO_3^= \qquad K_2 = \frac{[H^+][CO_3^=]}{[HCO_3^-]} = 5.0 \times 10^{-11}$$

It is, of course, also true that

$$H_2O \rightleftharpoons H^+ + OH^- \qquad K_w = [H^+][OH^-] = 1.0 \times 10^{-14}$$

The first reaction above is the main one, for its ionization constant is about 10,000 times that of the second reaction.   The concentrations of H^+ and HCO_3^- are therefore approximately the same, and the concentrations of $CO_3^=$ and OH^- are very small indeed.

In a solution of $NaHCO_3$ the various equilibria coexisting are as follows:

$$HCO_3^- \rightleftharpoons H^+ + CO_3^= \qquad K = K_2 = \frac{[H^+][CO_3^=]}{[HCO_3^-]}$$
$$= 5.0 \times 10^{-11} \tag{1}$$

$$HCO_3^- + H_2O \rightleftharpoons OH^- + H_2CO_3 \qquad K = \frac{K_w}{K_1} = \frac{[OH^-][H_2CO_3]}{[HCO_3^-]}$$
$$= 3.0 \times 10^{-8} \tag{2}$$

$$2HCO_3^- \rightleftharpoons H_2CO_3 + CO_3^= \qquad K = \frac{K_2}{K_1} = \frac{[H_2CO_3][CO_3^=]}{[HCO_3^-]^2}$$
$$= 1.5 \times 10^{-4} \tag{3}$$

$$H_2O \rightleftharpoons H^+ + OH^- \qquad K_w = [H^+][OH^-] = 1.0 \times 10^{-14} \tag{4}$$

Of these reactions the third one has a much larger equilibrium constant and therefore represents the main reaction. The hydrogen-ion concentration of a 0.10 M solution of $NaHCO_3$ can therefore be found from Eqs. (3) and (1) above as follows:

$$\frac{[H_2CO_3][CO_3^=]}{[HCO_3^-]^2} = \frac{[CO_3^=]^2}{(0.10)^2} = 1.5 \times 10^{-4}$$

$$[CO_3^=] = 1.2 \times 10^{-3}$$

Substituting in the equation for the equilibrium constant of (1), we obtain

$$\frac{[H^+](1.2 \times 10^{-3})}{0.10} = 5.0 \times 10^{-11}$$

$$[H^+] = 4.0 \times 10^{-9}$$

$$pH = -\log(4.0 \times 10^{-9}) = 8.4$$

In a solution of Na_2CO_3, the main reaction is one of hydrolysis and is represented by the equation

$$CO_3^= + H_2O \rightleftharpoons HCO_3^- + OH^- \qquad K = \frac{K_w}{K_2} = 2.0 \times 10^{-4}$$

The hydrolysis reaction

$$CO_3^= + 2H_2O \rightleftharpoons H_2CO_3 + OH^- \qquad K = \frac{(K_w)^2}{K_1 K_2} = 6.0 \times 10^{-12}$$

would be negligible, for its equilibrium constant is comparatively small.

An important polybasic acid in analytical chemistry is hydrogen sulfide. Its primary ionization results in the formation of H^+ and HS^-, and the ionization constant is

$$\frac{[H^+][HS^-]}{[H_2S]} = K_1 = 9.1 \times 10^{-8}$$

The HS^- ions are further ionized into H^+ and $S^=$, in which case

$$\frac{[H^+][S^=]}{[HS^-]} = K_2 = 1.2 \times 10^{-15}$$

Multiplying the two equations one by the other gives

$$\frac{[H^+]^2[S^=]}{[H_2S]} = K = 1.1 \times 10^{-22}$$

A *saturated* solution of H_2S is about 0.10 M, and $[H_2S] = 0.10$. Therefore in cases where metallic elements are precipitated by saturating their solutions with H_2S, $[H^+]^2[S^=] = 1.1 \times 10^{-23}$.

It is seen that the primary ionization of H_2S is much greater than the secondary ionization and that the ionization cannot be correctly expressed by the equation $H_2S \rightleftharpoons 2H^+ + S^=$. The concentration of H^+ ions in a solution of H_2S is not twice that of the $S^=$ ions. The primary ionization of any polybasic acid is much greater than the secondary ionization.

Example 1   What is the approximate hydrogen-ion concentration in a solution of hydrogen sulfide which is 0.07 M in H_2S?

Solution   In solving this problem, the expression $\dfrac{[H^+]^2[S^=]}{[H_2S]} = 1.1 \times 10^{-22}$ cannot be used, since neither $[H^+]$ nor $[S^=]$ is known and there is no simple relation between them. On the other hand, although H_2S is ionized in two steps, the first ionization is so much greater than the second ionization that, for the purpose of obtaining an approximate answer, the latter can be considered negligible. In other words, practically all the hydrogen ions can be considered to come from the ionization of H_2S into H^+ and HS^-. Therefore $[H^+]$ and $[HS^-]$ are practically equal in value and

$$\frac{[H^+][HS^-]}{[H_2S]} = 9.1 \times 10^{-8}$$

or

$$\frac{(x)(x)}{0.07} = 9.1 \times 10^{-8}$$

$$x = 8 \times 10^{-5} \text{ mole/liter} \qquad Ans.$$

Example 2   What is the concentration of $S^=$ ions in 200 ml of a solution that is 0.050 M in H_2S and that by the addition of HCl contains a total of 0.12 equivalent of H^+ ions?

Solution   Let

$$x = \text{molar concn. of } S^= \text{ ions}$$

$$0.050 - x = \text{approx. } 0.050 = \text{concn. of undissociated } H_2S$$

$$0.12 \times 5 = 0.60 = \text{concn. of } H^+ \text{ ions}$$

$$\frac{(0.60)^2(x)}{0.050} = K = 1.1 \times 10^{-22}$$

$$x = 1.5 \times 10^{-23} \text{ mole/liter} \qquad Ans.$$

5-15   Activity and Activity Coefficients

In analytical chemistry, mass-action calculations are usually applied to equilibria involving electrolytes in solution.   As solutions of electrolytes are made progressively more concentrated, the quantitative effect on such properties as conductivity and freezing-point lowering becomes progressively less than that calculated solely from the net change in molar concentration.   This is likewise true of mass-action equilibria.   This phenomenon was formerly explained by assuming that electrolytes are less completely ionized in more concentrated solutions, that the degree of ionization approaches 100% only as dilution approaches infinity.   A more satisfactory explanation is based on the assumption that most salts and the so-called strong acids and bases are practically completely ionized in all aqueous solutions but that the effective concentration, or *activity,* of the ions is decreased because of forces between the positive and negative ions.   These forces become less at higher dilutions, since the ions are farther apart.

In mass-action expressions, therefore, activities or effective concentrations, rather than molar concentrations, should be used for accurate results.   The activity a of an ion or molecule can be found by multiplying its molar concentration c by an activity coefficient f.

$$a = fc$$

An *activity coefficient* is therefore a factor which converts a molar concentration to a value which expresses quantitatively the true mass-action effect.   Thus, the ionization constant of acetic acid is correctly expressed as

$$\frac{f_1[\text{H}^+] \times f_2[\text{C}_2\text{H}_3\text{O}_2^-]}{f_3[\text{HC}_2\text{H}_3\text{O}_2]} = K$$

where f_1, f_2, and f_3 are the activity coefficients of the hydrogen ion, the acetate ion, and the acetic acid molecule, respectively.

Activity coefficients vary with temperature and, in general, decrease with increasing concentration.   The activity coefficient of 0.01 M HCl is 0.92, that of 0.05 M HCl is 0.86, and that of 0.10 M HCl is 0.82.   In general, too, under the same conditions of concentration and temperature, the activity coefficients of electrolytes of the valence type A^+B^- are greater than those of the types $(\text{A}^+)_2\text{B}^=$ and $\text{A}^{++}(\text{B}^-)_2$ and are still greater than those of the type $\text{A}^{++}\text{B}^=$.   For example, the activity coefficient of 0.01 M BaCl$_2$ is 0.72; that of 0.01 M MgSO$_4$ is 0.40.   The activity of a given electrolyte is also influenced by the presence of other electrolytes in the solution.

In general, it is difficult to determine, experimentally or otherwise, the numerical values of activity coefficients under any but the simplest conditions, but in the case of relatively dilute solutions (for example, 0.01 F or less) and particularly where univalent ions are involved, activity coefficients are not far from unity and so no great error is introduced when molar concentrations are used in place of activities. Since concentrations in most analytical operations are relatively low and since a high degree of precision is seldom required in analytical computations involving equilibrium constants, activity coefficients can be omitted without much error. They are therefore not included in the calculations in this book.

5-16   Dissociation Constants of Complex Ions

A complex ion is one that is in equilibrium with its constituents. These constituents are ordinarily a simple positive ion and either a neutral molecule or a negative ion. The mass-action principle can be applied to dilute solutions of such ions. Thus the copper ammino (or copper ammonio) ion, $Cu(NH_3)_4^{++}$, ionizes slightly as follows:

$$Cu(NH_3)_4^{++} \rightleftharpoons Cu^{++} + 4NH_3$$

Its dissociation constant is therefore expressed as follows:

$$\frac{[Cu^{++}][NH_3]^4}{[Cu(NH_3)_4^{++}]} = K \qquad (= 4.6 \times 10^{-14})$$

This means that in a dilute solution containing the complex ion, the total molar concentration of the simple cupric ions present multiplied by the fourth power of the total molar concentration of ammonia ($NH_3 + NH_4OH$) divided by the molar concentration of the undissociated complex ion is a constant at a given temperature.

Complex ions of this type frequently encountered in analytical chemistry are $Ag(NH_3)_2^+$, $Cu(NH_3)_4^{++}$, $Cd(NH_3)_4^{++}$, $Ni(NH_3)_4^{++}$, $CO(NH_3)_6^{3+}$, and $Zn(NH_3)_4^{++}$.

Important cyanide complexes include $Fe(CN)_6^{4-}$, $Fe(CN)_6^{3-}$, $Ag(CN)_2^-$, $Cd(CN)_4^=$, $Cu(CN)_3^=$, $Hg(CN)_4^=$, $Co(CN)_6^{3-}$, and $Ni(CN)_4^=$. Halide complexes like $SnCl_6^=$ and $HgI_4^=$ and oxalate complexes like $Mg(C_2O_4)_2^=$ are also common.

Example 1   What is the molar concentration of mercuric ions and of cyanide ions in a 0.10 M solution of $K_2Hg(CN)_4$? [Dissociation constant of $Hg(CN)_4^= = 4.0 \times 10^{-42}$.]

Solution

$$\frac{[Hg^{++}][CN^-]^4}{[Hg(CN)_4^=]} = 4.0 \times 10^{-42}$$

Let x = concentration of Hg^{++} in the dissociation:

$$Hg(CN)_4^= \rightleftharpoons Hg^{++} + 4CN^-$$

Then

$$4x = \text{concn. of } CN^-$$

$$0.10 - x = 0.10 \text{ (approx.)} = \text{concn. of } Hg(CN)_4^=$$

$$\frac{(x)(4x)^4}{0.10} = 4.0 \times 10^{-42}$$

$$x = 1.1 \times 10^{-9} \; M \; Hg^{++} \qquad Ans.$$

$$4x = 4.4 \times 10^{-9} \; M \; CN^- \qquad Ans.$$

Example 2   What is the dissociation constant of $Ag(NH_3)_2^+$ if a solution of 0.020 f. wt. of AgCl, in sufficient excess NH_4OH to give a total ammonia concentration of 2.0 M and a total volume of 1 liter, has a silver-ion concentration of only 0.000037 mg/liter?

Solution

$$\frac{[Ag^+][NH_3]^2}{[Ag(NH_3)_2^+]} = K$$

$$[Ag^+] = \frac{0.000037 \times 10^{-3}}{108} = 3.4 \times 10^{-10} \text{ mole/liter}$$

$$[NH_3] = 2.0$$

$$[Ag(NH_3)_2^+] = 0.020 \text{ (approx.)}$$

$$\frac{(3.4 \times 10^{-10})(2.0)^2}{0.020} = K$$

$$= 6.8 \times 10^{-8} \qquad Ans.$$

PROBLEMS

(See Appendix for ionization constants and dissociation constants for the following problems. Temperatures are 25°C unless otherwise specified.)

*5-42.   A certain organic acid has one replaceable hydrogen and in 0.010 M aq. soln. is 0.18% ionized.   (*a*) What is the ionization const. of the acid?   (*b*) What is its pK_a value?

*5-43.   Lactic acid is a monobasic acid with a pK_a value of 3.80.   What is the lactate-ion concn. in a 0.50 M soln. of the acid?

*5-44.   What is the molar concn. of each of the three constituents of acetic acid in 0.050 M soln.?

*5-45.   What is the concn. of a soln. of NH_4OH if it is (*a*) 3.0% ionized, (*b*) 0.50% ionized?

*5-46.   Formic acid is a monobasic acid that at a certain temp. is 3.2% ionized in 0.20 M soln.   (a) What is the ionization const. of formic acid at that temp., and what is its percentage ionization in 0.050 M soln.?   (b) What is the pK_a value of the acid?

*5-47.   What is the hydrogen-ion concn. in a 0.10-M soln. of acetic acid contg. sufficient dissolved sodium acetate to give a total acetate-ion concn. of 0.85 mole/liter?

*5-48.   Calculate the percentage ionization of pyridine in a 0.100 M soln. of that monoacidic base from its pK_b value of 8.64.

*5-49.   (a) What is the pH value of 0.30 M NH$_4$OH soln.?   (b) What is the pH value of 0.30 M NH$_4$OH contg. sufficient dissolved NH$_4$Cl to give an ammonium-ion conc. of 1.2 moles/liter?

*5-50.   Approx. how many g of acetate ions should be dissolved in a liter of 0.10 M acetic acid in order to cut down the hydrogen-ion concn. one-hundredfold?

*5-51.   The equilibrium in the system containing the gases N$_2$, H$_2$, and NH$_3$ is expressed by the equation $N_2(g) + 3H_2(g) \rightleftharpoons 2NH_3(g) + 22,000$ cal.   Would the equilibrium yield of NH$_3$ increase or decrease (a) with increasing temp., (b) with increasing pressure?

*5-52.   In a soln. of NaH$_2$PO$_4$ the following equilibria occur: (a) $H_2O \rightleftharpoons H^+ + OH^-$; (b) $H_2PO_4^- \rightleftharpoons H^+ + HPO_4^=$; (c) $H_2PO_4^- + H_2O \rightleftharpoons H_3PO_4 + OH^-$; (d) $2H_2PO_4^- \rightleftharpoons H_3PO_4 + HPO_4^=$; (e) $H_2PO_4^- \rightleftharpoons 2H^+ + PO_4^{3-}$.   (f) From the ionization consts. of H$_3$PO$_4$ (see Appendix), find the equilibrium const. of each of these reactions.   Which is the main reaction?

*5-53.   To what vol. should 100 ml of any weak 0.30 M monobasic acid be diluted in order to triple its percentage ionization?

*5-54.   Calculate the pH value of each of the following aq. solns. made by taking or mixing the indicated ingredients and diluting to 1 liter with H$_2$O.   The symbol HX represents the abbreviated formula of a certain weak monobasic acid having an ionization const. of 1.00×10^{-5}.   NaX is the corresponding salt.   (a) 1.00 ml of 10.0 M HCl, (b) 1.00 ml of 10.0 M NaOH, (c) 100 ml of 1.00 M HX, (d) 100 ml of 1.00 M HX + 1.00 mole of NaX, (e) 100 ml of 1.00 M HX + 1.00 mole of NaX + 1.00 ml of 10.0 M HCl, (f) 100 ml of 1.00 M HX + 1.00 mole of NaX + 1.00 ml of 10.0 M NaOH.

*5-55.   What is the approx. concn. of S$^=$ ions and of HS$^-$ ions in 0.070 M H$_2$S soln.?   (Assume that practically all the H$^+$ ions come from the primary ionization.)

*5-56.   Calculate the concn. of S$^=$ ions in a soln. that is 0.080 M in H$_2$S and contains sufficient HCl to give a pH value of 3.40.

*5-57.   What is the approx. molar concn. of Ag$^+$ and of CN$^-$ in a 0.10 M soln. of KAg(CN)$_2$?

*5-58.   What are the approx. molar concns. of Na$^+$, Cd^{++}, CN$^-$, and Cd(CN)$_4^=$ in a soln. made by dissolving 0.020 mole of Na$_2$Cd(CN)$_4$ in H$_2$O and diluting to 1 liter?

*5-59. If 100 mg of AgCl is dissolved in excess NH_4OH to give 500 ml of soln. and the total concn. of dissolved NH_3 is 0.30 M, what is the silver-ion concn.?

*5-60. What is the concn. of Cd^{++} in a soln. of 0.040 M in $Cd(NH_3)_4^{++}$ and 1.5 M in NH_3?

5-61. A certain organic amine acts as a monoacidic base in aq. soln. A 0.050 M soln. has a hydroxyl-ion concn. of 7.5×10^{-5} M. (a) What is the pH value of the soln., and (b) what is the ionization const. of the base? (c) What is its pK_b value?

5-62. Lactic acid is a monobasic acid with an ionization const. of 1.6×10^{-4}. In a liter of a 0.10 M soln. how may g of lactic acid is in the un-ionized form?

5-63. (a) What are the molar concns. of the three constituents in a 0.080 M soln. of benzoic acid? (b) What is the pH value of the soln.?

5-64. What is the molarity of a soln. of acetic acid if the acid is 2.0% ionized?

5-65. Ethylamine is a derivative of ammonia and in aq. soln. is a monoacidic base. At a certain temp. a 0.30 M soln. of ethylamine has a pH value of 12.11. (a) What is the ionization const. of ethylamine at that temp., and (b) what is the percentage ionization in 0.20 M soln.?

5-66. (a) What is the cyanide-ion concn. of a 0.030 M soln. of hydrocyanic acid? (b) What percentage of the acid is not ionized?

5-67. (a) Calculate the H^+ concn. of a soln. contg. 25.0 ml of 4.00 N acetic acid in a total vol. of 1,200 ml. (b) Calculate the H^+ concn. in the same soln. after adding 15.0 sodium acetate (effective ionization − 85%). (c) What is the pH value in each case?

5-68. To what vol. should 50 ml of any weak 0.200 M monobasic acid be diluted in order to double its percentage ionization?

5-69. Approx. how many g of NH_4^+ ions should be introduced into a liter of 0.20 M NH_4OH in order to cut down the concn. of OH^- ions to one-fiftieth of its previous value?

5-70. Given a soln. of 0.25 N acetic acid. By how many units does the pH value of the soln. change by dissolving in it sufficient sodium acetate to give an acetate-ion concn. of 2.0 moles /liter?

5-71. Calculate the pH value of each of the following aq. solns. made by taking or mixing the indicated ingredients and diluting to 1,000 ml with H_2O. The symbol XOH represents the abbreviated formula of a certain weak organic monoacidic base having an ionization const. of 2.00×10^{-5}. XCl is the corresponding salt. (a) 100 ml of 2.00 M XOH, (b) 100 ml of 2.00 M XOH + 15 millimoles of NaOH, (c) 100 ml of 2.00 M XOH + 15 millimoles of HCl, (d) 100 ml of 2.00 M XOH + 2.00 moles of XCl, (e) 100 ml of 2.00 M XOH + 2.00 moles of XCl + 15 millimoles of NaOH, (f) 100 ml of 2.00 M XOH + 2.00 moles of XCl + 15 millimoles of HCl.

5-72. The equilibrium in the system containing the gases NO, N_2, and O_2 is expressed by the equation $N_2(g) + O_2(g) \rightleftharpoons 2NO - 43.2$ kg-cal. Would the equilibrium yield of NO increase or decrease (*a*) with increasing temp., (*b*) with increasing pressure?

5-73. (*a*) Calculate the pK_b value of methyl amine from the ionization const. given in the Appendix, and (*b*) calculate the pH value of a 0.0100 M soln. of a certain monobasic acid which has a pK_a value of 6.75.

5-74. A certain base has the general formula ROH (in which R is an organic radical), and its pK_b value is 3.36.   A dil. aq. soln. is A molar in ROH and $1\frac{1}{2}A$ molar in the ionized salt RCl.   What is the pOH value of the soln.?

5-75. Write equations for the equilibria that can coexist in a soln. of Na_2HPO_4, and from the ionization consts. of H_3PO_4 (see Appendix) find the equilibrium const. of each.   Which of the equilibria represents the main reaction?

5-76. What are the approx. concns. of HCO_3^- and $CO_3^=$ in a 0.0010 M soln. of carbonic acid?   (Assume that practically all the H^+ ions come from the primary ionization of the acid.)

5-77. What is the sulfide-ion concn. of a soln. 0.090 M in H_2S and contg. sufficient HCl to give a pH value of 4.50?

5-78. What are the molar concns. of the four ionic species present in a soln. made by dissolving 0.010 f. wt. of K_2HgI_4 in water and diluting to 1 liter?

5-79. If 50 mg of AgCl is dissolved in excess NH_4OH [(AgCl + $2NH_4OH \longrightarrow Ag(NH_3)_2^+ + Cl^- + 2H_2O$)] and the resulting soln. is 0.50 F in NH_3 and has a vol. of 500 ml, what is the molar concn. of Ag^+ ions?

5-80. (*a*) What is the cyanide-ion concn. of an aq. soln. contg. 0.020 mole of $K_2Ni(CN)_4$ per 500 ml?   (*b*) What is the concn. of Ni^{++} in such a soln. if sufficient additional KCN is present to give a total cyanide-ion concn. of 0.10 M?

5-81. If 0.10 f. wt. of $Hg(NO_3)_2$ is treated with excess Na_2S + NaOH soln., the ppt. of HgS that first forms dissolves to give $HgS_2^=$ ions.   If the sulfide-ion concn. of the soln. is 2.0 M and the final vol. of the soln. is 500 ml, what is the concn. of Hg^{++} ions?

5-82. A mixt. of 40.0 ml of 1.00 M $BaAc_2$ and 50.0 ml of 0.400 M H_2SO_4 is diluted to 100 ml. $BaSO_4$ ppts. essentially completely.   Calculate to two significant figures the resulting molar concns. of the following constituents: (*a*) hydrogen ion, (*b*) acetate ion, (*c*) un-ionized HAc, (*d*) barium ion, (*e*) hydroxyl ion.

5-83. A certain organic monobasic acid has a K_a value of 2.0×10^{-5}.   What is the pH value of a soln. obtained by mixing 25.0 ml of 0.400 M soln. of the acid and 10.0 ml of 0.200 N NaOH soln. and then diluting to 100 ml?

5-17   Solubility Product

A very important equilibrium constant applies to a saturated solution of a slightly soluble, completely ionized salt.   Most of the precipitates encountered in analytical chemistry belong to this category.

Consider the simple case of a saturated solution of silver chloride in equilibrium with some of the undissolved salt.   What little silver chloride is in solution is completely ionized, and the equilibrium can be written

$$AgCl(s) \rightleftharpoons Ag^+ + Cl^-$$

The mass-action equilibrium constant is expressed simply as

$$[Ag^+][Cl^-] = K_{AgCl}$$

or more accurately as

$$f_1[Ag^+] \times f_2[Cl^-] = K_{AgCl}$$

where f_1 and f_2 are the respective activity coefficients of the two ions (see Sec. 5 15).   These coefficients are usually only slightly less than 1.00 in value.

This constant, applying as it does to a saturated solution of a slightly soluble salt, is called a *solubility product* or a *solubility product constant* (K_{SP}).   Its numerical value in the case of silver chloride at 25°C is 1.0×10^{-10}.   This means that in a solution saturated with silver chloride at this temperature the total molar concentration of silver ions in the solution multiplied by the total molar concentration of chloride ions equals 1.0×10^{-10}.   Conversely, when the product of the total concentration of silver ions and the total concentration of chloride ions in any solution exceeds this value, a precipitate of silver chloride is obtained under conditions of stable equilibrium.

Lead chloride ionizes as follows:

$$PbCl_2 \rightleftharpoons Pb^{++} + 2Cl^-$$

Its solubility product is therefore

$$[Pb^{++}][Cl^-]^2 = K_{SP}$$

Here the square of the total chloride-ion concentration must be used. In terms of activities, the solubility product is

$$f_1[Pb^{++}] \times f_2^2[Cl^-]^2 = K_{SP}$$

In most mass-action calculations two significant figures are all that are warranted by the precision of the data and of the constant itself. The precision is much less in calculations involving the solubilities and solubility products of the more insoluble hydroxides and sulfides.   These values are usually known only very approximately, for the composition of a precipitate of this type may be quite variable.   In addition, in the case of insoluble salts of weak polybasic acids like H_2S and H_3PO_4, conditions are complicated by hydrolysis effects.   Thus, sulfide ions are in equilibrium with bisulfide ions (HS^-), and phosphate ions hydrolyze to give $HPO_4^=$ and $H_2PO_4^-$ ions.   Numerical values obtained in simple calculations that neglect such side reactions can be considered as only approximate.   They are nevertheless helpful in showing relative magnitudes of effects.

A solubility product, like a hydrogen-ion concentration and an ionization constant, can be expressed as a logarithmic function:

$$pK_{SP} = -\log K_{SP}$$

Example 1   What is the solubility product and the pK_{SP} value of silver sulfate, Ag_2SO_4 (f. wt. = 312), if the solubility of the salt is 5.7×10^{-3} g/ml?

Solution

$$5.7 \times 10^{-3} \text{ g/ml} = 5.7/312 = 1.8 \times 10^{-2} \text{ mole/liter}$$

The salt is ionized as follows:

$$\underline{Ag_2SO_4} \longrightarrow 2Ag^+ + SO_4^=$$

Therefore,

$[Ag^+] = 2 \times 1.8 \times 10^{-2}$
$[SO_4^=] = 1.8 \times 10^{-2}$
$\quad K_{SP} = [Ag^+]^2[SO_4^=] = (3.6 \times 10^{-2})^2(1.8 \times 10^{-2}) = 2.3 \times 10^{-5}$ *Ans.*
$\quad pK_{SP} = -\log (2.3 \times 10^{-5}) = 4.64$ *Ans.*

Example 2   The pK_{SP} value of thorium fluoride, ThF_4 (f. wt. = 308), is 18.89.   How many grams of Th^{4+} is present in 500 ml of a saturated solution of ThF_4?   How many grams of $ThCl_4$ (f. wt. = 374) can theoretically be dissolved in 500 ml of a solution containing 9.5 g of fluoride ions?

Solution

$$K_{SP} = 10^{-18.89} = 10^{0.11} \times 10^{-19} = 1.3 \times 10^{-19}$$

Let

$\quad x = $ molar concn. of Th^{4+}

Then

$4x = $ molar concn. of F^-
$(x)(4x)^4 = 1.3 \times 10^{-19}$
$\quad\quad x = 5.5 \times 10^{-5}$ mole/liter
$[Th^{4+}] = 5.5 \times 10^{-5} \times \frac{1}{2} \times 232 = 6.4 \times 10^{-3}$ g/500 ml   *Ans.*
9.5 g F^- per 500 ml = 1 g atom F^- per liter
$\quad\quad (x)(1)^4 = 1.3 \times 10^{-19}$
$\quad\quad\quad x = 1.3 \times 10^{-19}$ mole Th^{4+} per liter
$\quad\quad\quad = 1.3 \times 10^{-19}$ mole $ThCl_4$ per liter
$1.3 \times 10^{-19} \times 374 \times \frac{1}{2} = 2.4 \times 10^{-17}$ g $ThCl_4$ per 500 ml   *Ans.*

Example 3   What is the hydroxyl-ion concentration in a solution of sodium hydroxide having a pH value of 11.6? How many grams of magnesium could remain dissolved in 500 ml of such a solution [solubility product of $Mg(OH)_2 = 3.4 \times 10^{-11}$]?

Solution

$$[H^+] = 10^{-11.6} = 10^{(-12+0.4)} \text{ or } 10^{\overline{12}.4}$$

$$= 2.5 \times 10^{-12} \qquad \text{(since antilog } 0.4 = 2.5)$$

$$[OH^-] = \frac{1.0 \times 10^{-14}}{2.5 \times 10^{-12}} = 4.0 \times 10^{-3} \qquad Ans.$$

$$[Mg^{++}][OH^-]^2 = 3.4 \times 10^{-11}$$

$$[Mg^{++}] = \frac{3.4 \times 10^{-11}}{(4.0 \times 10^{-3})^2} = 2.1 \times 10^{-6} \text{ mole/liter}$$

$$= 2.6 \times 10^{-5} \text{ g/500 ml} \qquad Ans.$$

The determination of a solubility product from other equilibrium constants is a matter of multiplying and dividing the given constants so as to cancel out extraneous concentration factors in the accompanying equilibria equations and thus arrive at the desired result.

Example 4   At a certain temperature the solubility product of $PbSO_4$ is 1.1×10^{-8} and the equilibrium constants of the following three reactions are as indicated: $PbSO_4(s) + 2I^- \rightleftharpoons PbI_2(s) + SO_4^=$ ($K_1 = 4.6 \times 10^{-1}$); $PbI_2(s) + CrO_4^= \rightleftharpoons PbCrO_4(s) + 2I^-$ ($K_2 = 4.3 \times 10^{12}$); $PbS(s) + CrO_4^= \rightleftharpoons PbCrO_4(s) + S^=$ ($K_3 = 7.5 \times 10^{-8}$). Calculate from these data the solubility product of PbS.

Solution   The constants for the above equilibria, in the order stated, are

$$[Pb^{++}][SO_4^=] = 1.1 \times 10^{-8} \tag{1}$$

$$\frac{[SO_4^=]}{[I^-]^2} = 4.6 \times 10^{-1} \tag{2}$$

$$\frac{[I^-]^2}{[CrO_4^=]} = 4.3 \times 10^{12} \tag{3}$$

$$\frac{[S^=]}{[CrO_4^=]} = 7.5 \times 10^{-8} \tag{4}$$

Combining these equations, (1) ÷ (2) ÷ (3) × (4) gives

$$[Pb^{++}][S^=] = 4.2 \times 10^{-28} \qquad Ans.$$

Example 5   From the appropriate ionization constants and solubility products given in the Appendix, find the equilibrium constant for (a) $Ag_2SO_4(s) + 2Cl^- \rightleftharpoons 2AgCl(s) + SO_4^=$; (b) $NH_4^+ + Bz^-$(benzoate) $+ H_2O \rightleftharpoons NH_4OH + HBz$.

Solution

(a) $\dfrac{[Ag^+]^2[SO_4^=]}{[Ag^+]^2[Cl^-]^2} = \dfrac{7.0 \times 10^{-5}}{(1.0 \times 10^{-10})^2} = 7.0 \times 10^{15}$ *Ans.*

(b) $\dfrac{[NH_4^+][OH^-]}{[NH_4OH]} = 1.75 \times 10^{-5} = K_1$

$\dfrac{[H^+][Bz^-]}{[HBz]} = 6.5 \times 10^{-5} = K_2$

$[H^+][OH^-] = 1.0 \times 10^{-14} = K_w$

The required $\dfrac{[NH_4OH][HBz]}{[NH_4^+][Bz^-]}$ is found by dividing K_w by the product $K_1 \times K_2$.

$\dfrac{K_w}{K_1K_2} = \dfrac{1.0 \times 10^{-14}}{(1.75 \times 10^{-5})(6.5 \times 10^{-5})} = 8.8 \times 10^{-6}$ *Ans.*

5-18   Fractional Precipitation

Ordinarily when a precipitating agent is added slowly to a solution containing two ions capable of being precipitated by the agent, the substance with the lesser solubility will precipitate first. The point at which the second substance will precipitate can be determined from the solubility products of the two precipitates.

Suppose to a solution 0.10 M in Ba^{++} and 0.10 M in Sr^{++} is added gradually and in very minute quantities a solution of Na_2SO_4. Insoluble $BaSO_4$ ($K_{BaSO_4} = 1.1 \times 10^{-10}$) precipitates first; then $SrSO_4$ ($K_{SrSO_4} = 2.8 \times 10^{-7}$) begins to precipitate. The ratio of the two solubility products is as follows:

$$\frac{[Ba^{++}][SO_4^=]}{[Sr^{++}][SO_4^=]} = \frac{1.1 \times 10^{-10}}{2.8 \times 10^{-7}}$$

Therefore, when both precipitates are present,

$$\frac{[Ba^{++}]}{[Sr^{++}]} = 0.00039$$

At the point where $SrSO_4$ just *begins* to precipitate (and the concentration of Sr^{++} is still 0.10 M), the barium-ion concentration will have been reduced to 0.000039 M, since

$$\frac{[Ba^{++}]}{0.10} = 0.00039$$

Separation of the two cations is therefore nearly complete at this point. In qualitative analysis the preparation of a solution of a water-insoluble salt for the anion tests is usually made by metathesis of the solid with a solution of Na_2CO_3. The extent of metathesis can be determined, roughly at least, from the solubility product of the original salt and that of the insoluble compound of the metal formed by the metathesis.

Example 1   If barium fluoride, BaF_2, is boiled with a solution of Na_2CO_3 which is 2.0 M in carbonate ions, the insoluble BaF_2 is converted to the more insoluble $BaCO_3$. Assuming that sufficient BaF_2 is present to give equilibrium conditions between the two substances and that at the temperature of the treatment the solubility of BaF_2 is 1.65 g/liter and that of $BaCO_3$ is 0.0206 g/liter, what would be the molar concentration of fluoride ions in the resulting solution?

Solution

$$\text{Molar soly. BaF}_2 = \frac{1.65}{175} = 9.43 \times 10^{-3}$$

$$\text{Molar soly. BaCO}_3 = \frac{0.0206}{197} = 1.05 \times 10^{-4}$$

$$\frac{[Ba^{++}][F^-]^2}{[Ba^{++}][CO_3^=]} = \frac{(9.43 \times 10^{-3})(2 \times 9.43 \times 10^{-3})^2}{(1.05 \times 10^{-4})(1.05 \times 10^{-4})}$$

$$\frac{[F^-]^2}{2.0} = 304$$

$$[F^-] = 24.7 \ M \qquad Ans.$$

This concentration is so large that it indicates that with an initial moderate amount of barium fluoride the salt would be completely metathesized before the equilibrium condition could be reached.

PROBLEMS

(Temperatures are 25°C unless otherwise specified. A table of solubility products is given in the Appendix.)

*5-84.   A satd. soln. of BaF_2 is 7.5×10^{-3} M. What is the soly. product of BaF_2?

*5-85.   Calculate the pK_{SP} value of $Ce(IO_3)_3$ (f. wt. = 665) from the fact that its solubility is 1.10 mg/ml.

*5-86.   Calculate the molar soly. of CaF_2 from the fact that its pK_{SP} value is 10.40.

*5-87.   A satd. soln. of BaF_2 is 7.5×10^{-3} M. What are the soly. product and the pK_{SP} value of BaF_2?

*5-88.   What are the K_{SP} value and the pK_{SP} value of $Pb(IO_3)_2$ if a satd. soln. of the salt contains 1.0×10^{-2} g of iodate ions per liter?

*5-89.   If 0.050 millimole of $Pb(NO_3)_2$ and 0.100 millimole of KIO_3 are mixed and diluted with water to 50.0 ml, what percentage of the total lead present would be in the form of pptd. $Pb(IO_3)_2$? ($pK_{SP} = 12.60$.)

*5-90. If 0.11 mg of AgBr dissolves in 1 liter of H_2O at a certain temp., what is the soly. product of AgBr at that temp.?

*5-91. (a) If the soly. product of calcium iodate, $Ca(IO_3)_2$ (f. wt. = 390), is 6.4×10^{-9}, how many mg will dissolve in 500 ml of H_2O? (b) How many mg of Ca^{++} can remain dissolved in 500 ml of a soln. that is 0.20 M in iodate ions?

*5-92. From the soly. product of PbI_2, calculate (a) the no. of g of Pb^{++} ions and of I^- ions that are contained in each ml of a satd. soln. of PbI_2, (b) the molarity and the normality of the soln.

*5-93. A satd. soln. of K_2PtCl_6 contains 11 mg of the salt in each ml. (a) What is the soly. product of the salt? (b) How many mg of Pt can remain dissolved (as $PtCl_6^=$) in each ml of a soln. contg. 3.9 g of K^+ per liter?

*5-94. Mercurous bromide, Hg_2Br_2, dissociates into Hg_2^{++} and $2Br^-$. Its soly. is 0.039 mg/liter. What is its soly. product?

*5-95. What is the soly. product of $Pb(IO_3)_2$ if a satd. soln. of the salt contains 1.0×10^{-2} g of iodate ions per liter?

*5-96. Excess CaF_2 is boiled with a soln. of Na_2CO_3 that is 2.0 M in $CO_3^=$ ions. Very small amts. of $CaCO_3$ and F^- are formed. If the soly. product of $CaCO_3$ is A and the molar soly. of CaF_2 is B, what (in terms of A and B) is the molar concn. of F^- ions in the resulting soln. after equilibrium has been reached?

*5-97. The concn. of a satd. soln. of Ag_2SO_4 is 0.052 N. What is the soly. product of Ag_2SO_4?

*5-98. If A moles of Ag_3PO_4 dissolve in 500 ml of water, express in terms of A the soly. product of Ag_3PO_4 and the normality of its satd. soln. Neglect hydrolysis effects.

*5-99. If the soly. product of $Ca_3(PO_4)_2$ is A, express in terms of A the normality of a satd. soln. of the salt. Neglect hydrolysis effects.

*5-100. How many mg of Mn^{++} can remain in 100 ml of a soln. of pH 8.6 [i.e., without pptg. $Mn(OH)_2$]?

*5-101. From the soly. product of $Fe(OH)_3$, calculate the wt. of Fe^{3+} in mg that must be present in a liter of soln. in order to cause precipitation of the hydroxide if the OH^--ion concn. is 8.0×10^{-5} M.

*5-102. Given K_{SP} $MgCO_3 = 2.6 \times 10^{-5}$; K_{SP} $CaCO_3 = 1.7 \times 10^{-8}$. In a soln. 0.20 M in Ca^{++} and 0.20 M in Mg^{++} and with a vol. of 250 ml, approx. how many mg of which cation would still remain in soln. when, on the slow addition of Na_2CO_3, the other cation just starts to ppt.?

*5-103. From the appropriate ionization consts. and soly. products (see Appendix), find the equilibrium const. for each of the following reactions: (a) $PbCl_2(s) + 2F^- \rightleftharpoons$ $PbF_2(s) + 2Cl^-$; (b) $NH_4^+ + Ac^- + H_2O \rightleftharpoons NH_4OH + HAc$; (c) $H_2SeO_3 +$ $2NH_4OH \rightleftharpoons 2NH_4^+ + SeO_3^= + 2H_2O$; (d) $Mg(OH)_2(s) + 2HAc \rightleftharpoons Mg^{++} + 2Ac^- +$ $2H_2O$.

*5-104.   The soly. product of AgCl is 1.0×10^{-10}.   The equilibrium const. of the reaction $AgCl(s) + Br^- \rightleftharpoons AgBr(s) + Cl^-$ is 2.0×10^2; that of the reaction $2AgBr(s) + S^= \rightleftharpoons Ag_2S(s) + 2Br^-$ is 1.6×10^{24}.   Find from these data the soly. product of Ag_2S.

*5-105.   Given the soly. product of $Ba(IO_3)_2 = 6.0 \times 10^{-10}$ and the indicated equilibrium consts. of the following reactions, find from them the soly. product of $BaCrO_4$; $Ba(IO_3)_2(s) + 2F^- \rightleftharpoons BaF_2(s) + 2IO_3^-$ $(K = 3.53 \times 10^{-4})$; $BaCrO_4(s) + SO_4^= \rightleftharpoons BaSO_4(s) + CrO_4^=$ $(K = 2.73)$; $BaF_2(s) + SO_4^= \rightleftharpoons BaSO_4(s) + 2F^-$ $(K = 1.55 \times 10^4)$.

*5-106.   (a) What are the soly. products of BaF_2 and $BaSO_4$ at a certain temp. if the solubilities at that temp. are 1.3 and 0.0025 g/liter, respectively?   (b) A soln. has a vol. of 100 ml and contains 0.010 mole of Na_2SO_4 and 0.020 mole of NaF. If $BaCl_2$ is slowly added, which anion will ppt. first and how many mg of this ion will still remain in soln. when the other ion just begins to ppt.?

5-107.   What is the soly. product of MgF_2 if its satd. soln. is 1.2×10^{-3} M?

5-108.   (a) What are the soly. products of $CaSO_4$ and CaF_2 if the solubilities are 1.1 and 0.016 mg/ml, respectively?   (b) How many mg of Ca^{++} can remain in 100 ml of a soln. that is 0.50 M in F^- ions?

5-109.   If the K_{SP} values of BaC_2O_4 and $Ba(IO_3)_2$ are 1.7×10^{-7} and 6.0×10^{-10}, respectively, what is the soly. of each salt in mg per liter?

5-110.   How many mg of Hg_2I_2 dissolve in 250 ml if it dissociates into Hg_2^{++} and $2I^-$ and its soly. product is 1.2×10^{-28}?

5-111.   The normality of a satd. soln. of cerous iodate, $Ce(IO_3)_3$, is 5.7×10^{-3}. What is the soly. product of the salt, and how many mg of cerous ions can remain dissolved in 500 ml of a soln. that is 0.30 M in IO_3^- ions?

5-112.   If A g of $Ba_3(AsO_4)_2$ dissolves in 500 ml, express in terms of A the soly. product of $Ba_3(AsO_4)_2$ and the normality of its satd. soln.   Neglect hydrolysis effects.

5-113.   If the soly. product of $Ag_2Cr_2O_7$ is 2.7×10^{-11}, how many mg of Ag^+ will be present in soln. when excess salt is shaken with 250 ml of H_2O?

5-114.   Calculate the soly. of Ag_2SO_4 (f. wt. $= 312$) in mg per ml from its pK_{SP} value of 4.80.

5-115.   A reference book gives the soly. at 25°C of ZrF_4 as 1.39 g/100 ml.   What is the pK_{SP} value of the salt?

5-116.   The mercurous ion exists as Hg_2^{++}.   Calculate the molar soly. of mercurous chloride (f. wt. $= 472$) from its pK_{SP} value of 18.00.

5-117.   A soln. contains 10.0 millimoles of $Pb(NO_3)_2$.   What percentage of the total lead is pptd. as $PbCl_2$ if 10.0 ml of 0.800 M HCl is added and the mixt. diluted to 100 ml?   ($pK_{SP} = 3.62$.)

5-118.   If a satd. soln. of $Pb_3(PO_4)_2$ is A N, what (in terms of A) is the soly. product of $Pb_3(PO_4)_2$?

5-119.   (*a*) If the soly. product of Ag_2CrO_4 is A, what (in terms of A) is the normality of a satd. soln. of $AgCrO_4$?   (*b*) How many g of Cr can remain dissolved (as $CrO_4^=$) in 500 ml of a soln. that is B M in Ag^+ ions?

5-120.   Mercurous chloride ionizes as follows: $Hg_2Cl_2 \longrightarrow Hg_2^{++} + 2Cl^-$. If its soly. product is 1.1×10^{-18}, how many g of mercurous mercury can remain dissolved in 2.00 ml of a soln. that contains 1.00 g-meq. wt. of Cl^- ions?

5-121.   How many g of $FeCl_3$ could be present in 200 ml of an acid soln. with a pH value of 3.0 without causing a ppt. of $Fe(OH)_3$ to form?

5-122.   (*a*) Show by calculation from the soly. product of Ag_2SO_4 whether or not that compd. would be suitable as a final ppt. in the detection or detn. of Ag. (*b*) What would the concn. of $SO_4^=$ theoretically have to be so that not more than 30 mg of Ag would remain unprecipitated in 500 ml of soln.?

5-123.   From the appropriate ionization consts. and soly. products (see Appendix), find the equilibrium const. for each of the following reactions: (*a*) $Ca(IO_3)_2(s) + 2F^- \rightleftharpoons CaF_2(s) + 2IO_3^-$; (*b*) $NH_4^+ + HCOO^- \cdot$(formate) $+ H_2O \rightleftharpoons NH_4OH + HCOOH$; (*c*) $2NH_4OH + H_2SO_3 \rightleftharpoons 2NH_4^+ + SO_3^= + 2H_2O$; (*d*) $Zn(OH)_2(s) + 2HAc \rightleftharpoons Zn^{++} + 2Ac^- + 2H_2O$.

5-124.   The soly. product of $BaSO_4$ is 1.1×10^{-10}. The equilibrium const. of the reaction $BaSO_4(s) + CrO_4^= \rightleftharpoons BaCrO_4(s) + SO_4^=$ is 0.37; that of the reaction $BaCrO_4(s) + 2F^- \rightleftharpoons BaF_2(s) + CrO_4^=$ is 1.8×10^{-4}. Find from these data the soly. product of BaF_2.

5-125.   Given the soly. product of $CaF_2 = 3.2 \times 10^{-11}$ and the indicated equilibrium consts. of the following reactions, find from them the soly. product of $Ca(IO_3)_2$: $Ca(IO_3)_2(s) + CrO_4^= \rightleftharpoons CaCrO_4(s) + 2IO_3^-$ $(K = 2.8 \times 10^{-7})$; $CaF_2(s) + SO_4^= \rightleftharpoons CaSO_4(s) + 2F^-$ $(K = 5.0 \times 10^{-7})$; $CaSO_4(s) + CrO_4^= \rightleftharpoons CaCrO_4(s) + SO_4^=$ $(K = 2.8 \times 10^{-3})$.

5-126.   What is the ratio of the concns. of Br^- and Cl^- in a soln. in which sufficient $AgNO_3$ has been added to cause ppt. of both halides?

5-127.   Calculate the no. of mg of $BaSO_4$ converted under equilibrium conditions to $BaCO_3$ by 20 ml of a soln. of Na_2CO_3 which is 2.0 N in $CO_3^=$ ions at a temp. at which the soly. products are 1.0×10^{-10} and 8.0×10^{-9} for $BaSO_4$ and $BaCO_3$, respectively.

5-128.   (*a*) Show from the appropriate soly. products which cation would ppt. first on the slow addition of K_2CrO_4 to 500 ml of a soln. 0.10 M in Sr^{++} and 0.10 M in Ba^{++}.   (*b*) How many mg of this cation would still remain in soln. when the other cation just starts to ppt.?

5-129.   (*a*) What are soly. products of $CaSO_4$ and of CaF_2 if the solubilities are 1.1 and 0.016 g/liter, respectively?   (*b*) If a soln. has a vol. of 250 ml and contains 0.020 mole of Na_2SO_4 and 0.030 mole of NaF, which anion will ppt. first on the slow addition of $CaCl_2$?   (c) How many mg of this ion will still remain in soln. when the other ion just begins to ppt.?

5-130.   The soly. of $SrCO_3$ is A mg/ml; the soly. product of SrF_2 is B.   Assuming that when $SrF_2(s)$ is boiled with a soln. of Na_2CO_3 that is C M in $CO_3^=$ ions, a very small amt. of the SrF_2 is metathesized, express in terms of A, B, and C the molar concn. of F^- ions in the resulting soln. after equilibrium is reached.

5-19   Application of Buffered Solutions in Analytical Separations

Buffered solutions are frequently used in both qualitative and quantitative analyses to effect certain separations of elements.   A familiar case is one in which a solution is buffered, usually either with $NH_4OH + NH_4Cl$ or with $HC_2H_3O_2 + NH_4C_2H_3O_2$, and the pH value thus brought to such a value that the solubility product of the hydroxide of an element (or the hydroxides of a group of elements) is greatly exceeded but the solubility products of other hydroxides are not reached.

The composition of many insoluble hydroxides is somewhat variable, and they are perhaps more properly called "hydrous oxides."   Their solubility products are not known accurately, and numerical values obtained from them should therefore be considered as showing only relative orders of magnitude.

Example 1   The solubility product of $Mg(OH)_2$ at a certain temperature is 3.4×10^{-11}; that of $Fe(OH)_3$ is 1.1×10^{-36}.   At that temperature (a) how many grams of Mg^{++} and of Fe^{3+} can remain dissolved in 100 ml of $M/10$ NH_4OH (ionization constant $= 1.75 \times 10^{-5}$), (b) how many grams of Mg^{++} and of Fe^{3+} can remain dissolved in 100 ml of $M/10$ NH_4OH containing a sufficient amount of dissolved NH_4Cl to make the ammonium-ion concentration 2.0 M?

Solution

(a) $NH_4OH \rightleftharpoons NH_4^+ + OH^-$

$$\frac{[NH_4^+][OH^-]}{[NH_4OH]} = 1.75 \times 10^{-5}$$

Let x = concn. of OH^- = concn. of NH_4^+

Then

$0.10 - x =$ concn. of undissociated NH_4OH

$$\frac{(x)(x)}{0.10 - x} = 1.75 \times 10^{-5}$$

$$\frac{(x)(x)}{0.10} \cong 1.75 \times 10^{-5} \qquad \text{since } x \text{ is small compared with } 0.10$$

$x = 1.3 \times 10^{-3}$ mole/liter

$$[Mg^{++}][OH^-]^2 = 3.4 \times 10^{-11}$$

$$[Mg^{++}](1.3 \times 10^{-3})^2 = 3.4 \times 10^{-11}$$

$$[Mg^{++}] = 2.0 \times 10^{-5} \text{ mole/liter}$$

$$= 2.0 \times 10^{-5} \times \tfrac{1}{10} \times 24.3$$

$$= 4.9 \times 10^{-5} \text{ g/100 ml} \qquad Ans.$$

$$[Fe^{3+}][OH^-]^3 = 1.1 \times 10^{-36}$$

$$[Fe^{3+}](1.3 \times 10^{-3})^3 = 1.1 \times 10^{-36}$$

$$[Fe^{3+}] = \frac{1.1 \times 10^{-36}}{(1.3 \times 10^{-3})^3} \times \frac{1}{10} \times 55.8$$

$$= 2.8 \times 10^{-27} \text{ g/100 ml} \qquad Ans.$$

(b) $\dfrac{[NH_4^+][OH^-]}{[NH_4OH]} = 1.75 \times 10^{-5}$

$$\frac{(2.0)(x)}{0.10} = 1.75 \times 10^{-5}$$

$$x = 8.8 \times 10^{-7}$$

$$[Mg^{++}](8.8 \times 10^{-7})^2 = 3.4 \times 10^{-11}$$

$$[Mg^{++}] = \frac{3.4 \times 10^{-11}}{(8.8 \times 10^{-7})^2} \times \frac{1}{10} \times 24.3$$

$$= 106 \text{ g/100 ml} \qquad Ans.$$

$$[Fe^{3+}](8.8 \times 10^{-7})^3 = 1.1 \times 10^{-36}$$

$$[Fe^{3+}] = \frac{1.1 \times 10^{-36}}{(8.8 \times 10^{-7})^3} = \frac{1}{10} \times 55.8$$

$$= 9.0 \times 10^{-18} \text{ g/100 ml} \qquad Ans.$$

5.20   Control of Acidity in Hydrogen Sulfide Precipitations

The separation of certain elements by precipitation from acid solution with H_2S is effectively used in analytical chemistry, particularly in qualitative analysis. Probably the most important factor influencing the effectiveness of the separation is the sulfide-ion concentration and its control by the regulation of the hydrogen-ion concentration. The concentration of the sulfide ion can be regulated to such a point that the solubility products of certain sulfides are greatly exceeded while the solubility products of other sulfides are not reached. The quantitative effect of the presence of acid on the ionization of H_2S and the calculation of the sulfide-ion concentration have been illustrated in Examples 1 and 2 of Sec. 5-14 and should be reviewed at this time.

Solubility products of sulfides are not known precisely, and hydrolysis effects and rates of precipitation influence the quantitative aspect of the separation of sulfides. Therefore, in the following example and problems of a similiar nature, the calculated values may not agree well with corresponding values determined experimentally, but they do show relative orders of magnitude and are useful only in this connection.

Example 1   How many grams of Zn^{++} and how many grams of Cd^{++} can remain dissolved in 200 ml of the solution of H_2S + HCl mentioned in Example 2 of Sec. 5-14 (solubility product of ZnS = 1.2×10^{-23}; solubility product of CdS = 3.6×10^{-29})?

Solution

$$[S^=] = 1.5 \times 10^{-23} \qquad \text{as calculated}$$

$$[Zn^{++}][S^=] = 1.2 \times 10^{-23}$$

$$[Zn^{++}] = \frac{1.2 \times 10^{-23}}{1.5 \times 10^{-23}} = 0.80 \text{ mole/liter}$$

$$= 0.80 \times 65 \times \tfrac{1}{5} = 10 \text{ g/200 ml} \qquad \textit{Ans.}$$

$$[Cd^{++}][S^=] = 3.6 \times 10^{-29}$$

$$[Cd^{++}] = \frac{3.6 \times 10^{-29}}{1.5 \times 10^{-23}}$$

$$= 2.4 \times 10^{-6} \text{ mole/liter}$$

$$= 2.4 \times 10^{-6} \times 112 \times \tfrac{1}{5}$$

$$= 5.4 \times 10^{-5} \text{ g/200 ml} \qquad \textit{Ans.}$$

5-21   Separations by Means of Complex-ion Formation

Certain separations in analytical chemistry are effected by making use of the equilibrium that exists between a complex ion and its constituents. The following cases illustrate the two general ways in which this is applied.

1.   When an ammoniacal solution of silver nitrate containing a carefully controlled excess of ammonia is added to a mixture of iodide and chloride, only silver iodide is precipitated, since most of the silver in the solution is as the ammino complex, $Ag(NH_3)_2^+$, and the concentration of Ag^+ is too small to exceed the solubility product of AgCl but is great enough to exceed the solubility product of the more insoluble AgI.

2.   When potassium cyanide is added to an ammoniacal solution of copper and cadmium salts, the two ions $Cu(CN)_3^=$ and $Cd(CN)_4^=$ are formed. When hydrogen sulfide is passed into the solution, only cadmium sulfide is precipitated, since the degree of dissociation of the copper complex is much less than that of the cadium complex.   A sufficiently high concentration of Cd^{++} is present to exceed the solubility product of CdS, but the concentration of Cu^+ is too low to exceed the solubility product of Cu_2S.

Example 1   How many grams of silver bromide (f. wt. $= 188$) will dissolve in 1 liter of NH_4OH if the resulting solution is 2.0 M in NH_3?

Solution

$$[Ag^+][Br^-] = 5.0 \times 10^{-13} \qquad \text{(see Appendix)}$$

$$\frac{[Ag^+][NH_3]^2}{[Ag(NH_3)_2^+]} = 6.8 \times 10^{-8} \qquad \text{(see Appendix)}$$

Let

$$x = \text{moles of AgBr dissolved} = [Br^-] = [Ag(NH_3)_2^+]$$

$$\frac{5.0 \times 10^{-13}}{x} = [Ag^+]$$

$$\frac{(5.0 \times 10^{-13}/x)(2.0)^2}{x} = 6.8 \times 10^{-8}$$

Solving,

$$x = 5.4 \times 10^{-3} \, M$$

$$5.4 \times 10^{-3} \times 188 = 1.0 \, \text{g} \qquad Ans.$$

Example 2   A solution 0.10 M in Cu^{++} and 0.10 M in Cd^{++} is treated with NH_4OH and KCN, forming $Cu(CN)_3^=$ and $Cd(CN)_4^=$. The solution is 0.020 M in excess CN^- ions. If H_2S is passed into the solution to give a sulfide-ion concentration of 0.010 M, show whether Cu_2S or CdS will precipitate.

Solution

$$\frac{[Cu^+][CN^-]^3}{[Cu(CN)_3^=]} = 5.0 \times 10^{-28} \qquad \text{(See Appendix)}$$

$$\frac{[Cu^+](0.020)^3}{0.10} = 5.0 \times 10^{-28}$$

$$[Cu^+] = 6.2 \times 10^{-24}$$

Therefore,

$$[Cu^+]^2[S^=] = (6.2 \times 10^{-24})^2(0.01)$$

$$= 3.8 \times 10^{-49}$$

The solubility product of Cu_2S ($= 1.0 \times 10^{-46}$) is greater than this value. Hence Cu_2S will not precipitate.   *Ans.*

$$\frac{[Cd^{++}][CN^-]^4}{[Cd(CN)_4^=]} = 1.4 \times 10^{-17}$$

$$\frac{[Cd^{++}](0.020)^4}{0.10} = 1.4 \times 10^{-17}$$

$$[Cd^{++}] = 8.7 \times 10^{-12}$$

Therefore,

$$[Cd^{++}][S^=] = (8.7 \times 10^{-12})(0.01)$$
$$= 8.7 \times 10^{-14}$$

The solubility product of CdS ($= 3.6 \times 10^{-29}$) is less than this value. Hence CdS will precipitate.   *Ans.*

PROBLEMS

(See Appendix for solubility products and ionization constants.   Neglect hydrolysis effects of sulfides.   Make the necessary simplifying assumptions to avoid quadratic equations as in the example in Sec. 5-19.)

*5-131.   How many g of Mg^{++} could remain dissolved [i.e., unprecipitated as $Mg(OH)_2$] in a liter of 0.20 M NH_4OH, and how many g of Mg^{++} could remain dissolved in a liter of 0.20 M NH_4OH contg. enough dissolved NH_4Cl to make the ammonium-ion concn. 1.0 M?

*5-132.   How many mg of Fe^{3+} could remain dissolved [i.e., unprecipitated as $Fe(OH)_3$] in 100 ml of a soln. 2.0 N in acetic acid and contg. sufficient sodium acetate to make the acetate-ion concn. 0.15 M?

*5-133.   Calculate the no. of g of Zn^{++} and of Cd^{++} that can remain dissolved in 1,500 ml of a soln. contg. 0.050 mole of dissolved H_2S and 0.30 N in H^+ ions.

*5-134.   By saturating with H_2S 350 ml of a soln. that is 0.010 M in a certain tripositive element and 1.0 M in H^+ ions, all but 12 millimoles of the element ppts. as sulfide.   What is the approx. soly. product of the sulfide of the element?

*5-135.   How many f. wts. of Cl^- must be introduced into a liter of 0.10 M $NaAg(CN)_2$ in order for AgCl to start to ppt.?

*5-136.   How many f. wts. of AgI will dissolve in a liter of NH_4OH that is 6.0 M in NH_3?   (*Hint:* In the resulting soln. $[Ag(NH_3)_2^+] = [I^-]$.)

*5-137.   A soln. 0.080 M in $AgNO_3$ is treated with $Na_2S_2O_3$, which converts practically all the Ag^+ into $Ag(S_2O_3)_2^{\equiv}$.   If sufficient excess thiosulfate is present to make the soln. 0.20 M in $S_2O_3^{\equiv}$, how many g per liter of I^- could be present without causing pptn. of AgI?

*5-138.   What is the max. molar concn. of sulfide ion in a soln. 0.20 M in $Cd(NH_3)_4Cl_2$ and 2.0 M in NH_3 without forming a ppt. of CdS?

5-139.   (*a*) What must be the max. pH value of a soln. in order that 0.50 g of Mg^{++} in 100 ml will remain unprecipitated as $Mg(OH)_2$?   (*b*) How many g of Fe^{3+} could remain dissolved in such a soln.?

5-140.   (*a*) How many mg of Mn^{++} could remain unprecipitated as $Mn(OH)_2$ in 500 ml of 0.10 M NH_4OH, and (*b*) how many mg of Mn^{++} could remain dissolved in 500 ml of 0.10 M NH_4OH contg. sufficient dissolved NH_4Cl to make the ammonium-ion concn. 2.0 M?

5-141.   How many mg of Fe^{3+} could remain unprecipitated as $Fe(OH)_3$ in 250 ml of a soln. 1.5 M in acetic acid and buffered by that amt. of dissolved sodium acetate that makes the acetate-ion concn. 0.20 M?

5-142.   What wt. of Bi^{3+} must be present in a liter of soln. to cause pptn. of Bi_2S_3 if the soln. is made 0.10 M in H_2S and 0.010 M in H^+?

5-143.   What is the max. pH value that 100 ml of a soln. contg. 0.0050 g of $PbCl_2$ can have so that on making the soln. 0.10 M in H_2S no PbS will ppt.?

5-144.   A soln. of 1.2 g of $ZnSO_4 \cdot 7H_2O$ in 500 ml of dil. acid is satd. with H_2S. The resulting soln. is found to be 0.10 M in H_2S and 0.050 M in H^+ ions.   (*a*) What fraction of the Zn has been pptd. as ZnS?   (*b*) What max. pH value should the soln. have in order for no ppt. to form if the concns. of Zn salt and H_2S are as above?

5-145.   (*a*) If 50 ml of 0.010 M $AgNO_3$ and 50 ml of 3.0 M NH_4OH are mixed, what is the resulting concn. of Ag^+ ions?   (*b*) How many moles of Cl^- would have to be introduced before pptn. of AgCl would take place?

5-146.   If a soln. is 0.050 M in K_2HgI_4 and 1.5 M in I^-, show by calculation whether or not pptn. of HgS would be expected if the soln. is made 1.0×10^{-15} M in sulfide ions.

5-147.   How many g of $S^=$ can be present in a liter of a soln. contg. 0.10 mole of $Cd(NH_3)_4Cl_2$ and 1.5 moles of NH_3 without forming a ppt. of CdS?

5-148.   How many g of AgBr will dissolve in 1 liter of NH_4OH which is 1.5 M in NH_3?   (*Hint:* In the resulting soln. $[Ag(NH_3)_2^+] = [Br^-]$.)

Redox Potentials

6-1 Relation of the Electric Current to Oxidation-Reduction ("Redox") Reactions

In the light of the concept of the structure of atoms, oxidation and reduction can be defined in terms of transfer of electrons. An element is oxidized when it loses electrons; an element is reduced when it gains electrons.

Redox reactions can be brought about by the application of an electric current; conversely, an electric current can be obtained from oxidation-reduction processes. The electrolysis of a solution of sodium chloride is an example of the first class. At the anode, negative chloride ions are oxidized to free chlorine gas; at the cathode, positive hydrogen ions from the water are reduced to free hydrogen gas. The voltaic cell is an example of the second class.

6-2 Standard Electrode Potentials

Suppose we have on the end of a platinum wire a platinum foil covered with platinum black. Suppose further that the foil is immersed in a solution of sulfuric acid having hydrogen ions at unit activity (H^+-ion concentration approximately $1\ M$; see Sec. 5-15) and that pure hydrogen gas at 1 atm pressure continually bubbles over the foil. Such a setup is called a *normal hydrogen electrode*. It can be represented graphically thus:

$$Pt\,|\,H_2(1\ atm),\ H^+(1\ M)$$

The platinum is chemically inert, but an equilibrium exists between the hydrogen gas and the hydrogen ions; thus, $2H^+ + 2e \rightleftharpoons H_2$, the symbol e representing an electron with its unit negative charge. An equation of this type represents what is known as a *half reaction*, or *half-cell reaction*.

Suppose now we have a strip of metallic zinc immersed in a solution of zinc sulfate with the zinc ions at unit activity. Equilibrium exists between the metal and its ions as represented by the half reaction $Zn^{++}(1\ M) + 2e \rightleftharpoons Zn$. If the two electrodes are connected by means of a wire and the two solutions connected by means of a capillary tube containing a solution of an electrolyte (for example, K_2SO_4), a current will flow through the wire and solution. Its initial potential will be 0.763 volt.

In this system, the flow of electrons in the wire is from the zinc electrode to the hydrogen electrode. In the solution, the negative sulfate ions of the electrolyte pass from the solution containing the sulfuric acid to that containing the zinc sulfate, and the charges on these transported ions just balance the charges gained or lost at the electrodes. At the same time, metallic zinc is oxidized and hydrogen ions are reduced, the net reaction being represented by the equation $\underline{Zn} + 2H^+ \longrightarrow Zn^{++} + H_2$. We therefore have a voltaic cell made up of two half-cells, and the entire system can be represented thus:

$Pt\,|\,H_2(1\ atm),\ H^+(1\ M)\|Zn^{++}(1\ M)\,|\,Zn$

When cells are represented in this way, a single line represents a junction between an electrode and a solution. A double line denotes a junction between two solutions, and it is assumed that the small potential difference between the solutions has been corrected for in formulating the total emf of the cell.

It should be noted that oxidation always takes place at the anode and reduction always takes place at the cathode. The passage of electrons through the wire is from anode to cathode.

In similar fashion, a copper electrode dipping in a solution of copper sulfate having copper ions at unit activity can be connected to a normal hydrogen electrode. A current having a potential of 0.337 volt will be generated. The passage of electrons in the wire is from the hydrogen electrode to the copper electrode.

If now we connect the above copper half-cell with the above zinc half-cell, we obtain a voltaic cell that is represented thus:

$Cu\,|\,Cu^{++}(1\ M)\|Zn^{++}(1\ M)\,|\,Zn$

It will be found that a current with a potential of 1.100 volts will be generated. The passage of electrons in the wire is from the zinc to the copper. At the same time metallic zinc is oxidized to zinc ions and the copper ions are reduced to metallic copper, the net reaction being

$\underline{Zn} + Cu^{++} \longrightarrow \underline{Cu} + Zn^{++}$

It is difficult to determine absolute potential differences between electrodes and solutions, but since we are usually concerned only with differences of potential, we can refer electrode potentials to some common standard. The normal hydrogen electrode is arbitrarily given the value of zero, and other electrode potentials are referred to it. The standard electrode potential of zinc (i.e., the potential, relative to the hydrogen potential, between metallic zinc and a solution of zinc ions at unit activity) is -0.763 volt; the standard potential of copper is $+0.337$ volt. Giving the zinc potential a negative sign and the copper potential a positive sign is again purely arbitrary, but this seems to be favored by most analytical chemists. Some chemists use the opposite sign convention.

In this book, standard potentials will be denotated by the symbol E^0, and a table of such potentials is given in the Appendix. When applied to an active metallic electrode, the numerical value refers to the potential at 25°C between the metal and a solution of its ions at unit activity, relative to the potential between hydrogen gas at 1 atm pressure and hydrogen ions at unit activity. As indicated in the table, half reactions will in general be expressed as reduction processes with the symbol of the constituent in its higher oxidation state, together with the appropriate number of electron symbols, on the left-hand side of the equation, and the reduced form expressed on the right-hand side. The corresponding standard potentials therefore can also be called reduction potentials.

The emf of a cell is the difference between the potentials of its two half-cells, or $E = E_1 - E_2$. In the case of the above-mentioned cell, $E = E^0_{Cu} - E^0_{Zn} = +0.337 - (-0.763) = 1.100$ volts.

Electrode potentials are not limited to those between elements and their ions. They apply also to potentials between ions at two states of oxidation. For example, as shown in the potential table in the Appendix, the standard potential between ferric and ferrous ions ($Fe^{3+} + e \rightleftharpoons Fe^{++}$) is $+0.771$ volt, indicating that a current having a potential of 0.771 volt would flow through the following cell:

Pt$|$H$_2$(1 atm), H$^+$(1 M)$\|$Fe^{3+}(1 M), Fe^{++}(1 M)$|$Pt

The positive sign of the voltage indicates that electrons would pass through the outer wire from left to right as written above (i.e., from the hydrogen electrode to the ferric-ferrous half-cell). Ferric ions would be reduced to ferrous ions; hydrogen gas would be oxidized to hydrogen ions.

Similarly, the standard potential between dichromate ions and chromic ions in the presence of acid ($Cr_2O_7^= + 14H^+ + 6e \rightleftharpoons 2Cr^{3+} + 7H_2O$) is $+1.33$ volts. The numerical value 1.33 represents the voltage of the following cell:

Pt$|$H$_2$(1 atm), H$^+$(1 M) $\left\|\begin{array}{c} Cr^{3+}(1\ M) \\ Cr_2O_7^=(1\ M) \\ H^+(1\ M) \end{array}\right|$ Pt

The positive sign indicates a behavior similar to that of the preceding case. Dichromate ions are reduced during the operation of the cell.

The emf of the following cell,

$$\text{Pt} \left| \begin{array}{l} \text{Cr}^{3+}(1\ M) \\ \text{Cr}_2\text{O}_7^=(1\ M) \\ \text{H}^+(1\ M) \end{array} \right| \left| \begin{array}{l} \text{Fe}^{3+}(1\ M) \\ \text{Fe}^{++}(1\ M) \end{array} \right| \text{Pt}$$

is the algebraic difference between the potentials of the two half-cells comprising it, or $+0.771 - (+1.33) = -0.56$ volt. The negative sign indicates that the passage of electrons through the outer wire is from right to left as written above. Dichromate ions are reduced and ferrous ions are oxidized during the action of the cell. The overall reaction is

$$6\text{Fe}^{++} + \text{Cr}_2\text{O}_7^= + 14\text{H}^+ \longrightarrow 6\text{Fe}^{3+} + 2\text{Cr}^{3+} + 7\text{H}_2\text{O}$$

6-3   Formal Potentials

Numerical values obtained in calculations in which standard potentials are used are sometimes in error because of the effect of the formation of complex ions with cations or anions. Because of such complex formation, the actual electrode potential in a given case may differ somewhat from the listed standard potential. For example, the standard electrode potential of $\text{Ce}^{4+} + e \rightleftharpoons \text{Ce}^{3+}$ is $+1.61$ volts, and in $1\ F\ \text{HNO}_3$ solution the experimentally determined potential agrees well with this value. But in $1\ F\ \text{HClO}_4$ the effective ceric-cerous potential is $+1.70$, and in $1\ F\ \text{H}_2\text{SO}_4$ it is $+1.44$. These experimentally determined values are referred to as *formal potentials*. In most cases the variations are not great. In order to avoid complications, minor complexing effects will be neglected, and, except in cases where formal potentials are definitely specified, standard potentials will be used in the problems given in this book.

6-4   Rules for Writing Equations for Half-cell Reactions

In writing and balancing equations for half-cell reactions, the following steps should be taken:

1. Write the oxidized form of the element that changes its oxidation number on the left-hand side of the equation; write the reduced form on the right-hand side. If necessary, balance the number of atoms of the element by inserting the proper coefficients.

2. On the left-hand side of the equation, introduce that number of electron symbols equal to the total change in oxidation number of the element.

3. If necessary, introduce sufficient hydrogen ions (if the reaction takes place in acid solution) or hydroxyl ions (if the reaction takes place in alkaline solution) to balance the electrical charges.   Remember that each electron symbol represents a negative charge.

4. If necessary, introduce water molecules into the equation to balance the hydrogen and oxygen atoms.

Example 1   Write balanced half-cell reactions for the following changes: (a) $VO_3^- \longrightarrow VO^{++}$ (acid solution); (b) $Cr_2O_7^= \longrightarrow Cr^{3+}$ (acid solution); (c) $\underline{MnO_2} \longrightarrow Mn^{++}$ (alkaline solution).

Solution   Following the above four steps, the results in each case are as follows:

(a) 1. $VO_3^- \longrightarrow VO^{++}$
   2. $VO_3^- + e \longrightarrow VO^{++}$ (change $= 5 - 4 = 1$)
   3. $VO_3^- + 4H^+ + e \longrightarrow VO^{++}$
   4. $VO_3^- + 4H^+ + e \longrightarrow VO^{++} + 2H_2O$

(b) 1. $Cr_2O_7^= \longrightarrow 2Cr^{3+}$
   2. $Cr_2O_7^= + 6e \longrightarrow 2Cr^{3+}$ (change $= (6 - 3) \times 2 = 6$)
   3. $Cr_2O_7^= + 14H^+ + 6e \longrightarrow 2Cr^{3+}$
   4. $Cr_2O_7^= + 14H^+ + 6e \longrightarrow 2Cr^{3+} + 7H_2O$

(c) 1. $\underline{MnO_2} \longrightarrow Mn^{++}$
   2. $\underline{MnO_2} + 2e \longrightarrow Mn^{++}$
   3. $\underline{MnO_2} + 2e \longrightarrow Mn^{++} + 4OH^-$
   4. $\underline{MnO_2} + 2H_2O + 2e \longrightarrow Mn^{++} + 4OH^-$

6-5   Redox Equations in Terms of Half-cell Reactions

In order to write an ordinary redox equation in terms of half-cell reactions, the appropriate couples are written one below the other and subtracted in algebraic fashion.   Since electron symbols should not appear in the net equation, it is frequently necessary to multiply one or both half-cell equations by a factor in order that the electron symbols will "cancel out."   This is illustrated in the following examples.   Obviously the potential of the half-cell reaction is not affected by such multiplication.

The oxidation of ferrous ions by chlorine can be written

(1) $Cl_2 + 2e \rightleftharpoons 2Cl^-$ $E_1^0 = +1.359$
      $Fe^{3+} + e \rightleftharpoons Fe^{++}$ $E_2^0 = +0.771$

(2) $2Fe^{3+} + 2e \rightleftharpoons 2Fe^{++}$

(1) − (2) $2Fe^{++} + Cl_2 \rightleftharpoons 2Fe^{3+} + 2Cl^-$

The oxidation of ferrous ions by dichromate in the presence of acid can be written

(1) $Cr_2O_7^= + 14H^+ + 6e \rightleftharpoons 2Cr^{3+} + 7H_2O$ $E_1^0 = +1.33$

(2) $6Fe^{3+} + 6e \rightleftharpoons 6Fe^{++}$ $E_2^0 = +0.771$

(1) − (2) $6Fe^{++} + Cr_2O_7^= + 14H^+ \rightleftharpoons 6Fe^{3+} + 2Cr^{3+} + 7H_2O$

The oxidation of stannous ions by permanganate in the presence of acid can be written

(1) $2MnO_4^- + 16H^+ + 10e \rightleftharpoons 2Mn^{++} + 8H_2O$ $E_1^0 = +1.51$
(2) $5Sn^{4+} + 10e \rightleftharpoons 5Sn^{++}$ $E_2^0 = +0.15$
(1) $-$ (2) $5Sn^{++} + 2MnO_4^- + 16H^+ \rightleftharpoons 5Sn^{4+} + 2Mn^{++} + 8H_2O$

If the activities are all 1 M, the net potentials in the above three examples are the algebraic differences between the standard potentials corresponding to the two half-cell reactions; namely,

$E = E_1^0 - E_2^0 = +1.359 - (+0.771) = +0.589$ volt
$E = E_1^0 - E_2^0 = +1.33 - (+0.771) = +0.56$ volt
$E = E_1^0 - E_2^0 = +1.51 - (+0.15) = +0.36$ volt

In cases like the above, if the algebraic difference between the electrode potentials, as written, is positive, the net reaction can be expected to go as written (i.e., from left to right). If the algebraic difference is negative, the reaction will not go as written but can be expected to go from right to left.

(1) $I_2 + 2e \rightleftharpoons 2I^-$ $(+0.536)$
(2) $2Fe^{3+} + 2e \rightleftharpoons 2Fe^{++}$ $(+0.771)$
(1) $-$ (2) $2Fe^{++} + I_2 \rightleftharpoons 2Fe^{3+} + 2I^-$
                                $(+0.536) - (+0.771) = -0.235$ volt

This reaction at 1 M activities will therefore not take place from left to right as written, but it will go in the opposite direction ($2Fe^{3+} + 2I^- \longrightarrow 2Fe^{++} + I_2$).

The behavior of metals with acids can be treated in the same way. Metallic zinc dissolves in 1 M HCl:

(1) $2H^+ + 2e \rightleftharpoons H_2$ (0.00)
(2) $Zn^{++} + 2e \rightleftharpoons Zn$ (-0.763)
(1) $-$ (2) $Zn + 2H^+ \longrightarrow Zn^{++} + H_2$ $(+0.763$ volt$)$

Metallic copper does not dissolve in HCl:

(1) $2H^+ + 2e \rightleftharpoons H_2$ (0.00)
(2) $Cu^{++} + 2e \rightleftharpoons Cu$ $(+0.337)$
(1) $-$ (2) $Cu + 2H^+ \longleftarrow Cu^{++} + H_2$ $(-0.337$ volt$)$

Both zinc and copper dissolve in 1 M HNO$_3$. In this acid two oxidizing agents are present, namely, H^+ and NO_3^-, but the nitrate ion has the greater oxidizing effect:

(1) $2NO_3^- + 8H^+ + 6e \rightleftharpoons 2NO + 4H_2O$ $(+0.96)$
(2) $3Cu^{++} + 6e \rightleftharpoons Cu$ $(+0.337)$
(1) $-$ (2) $3Cu + 2NO_3^- + 8H^+ \longrightarrow 3Cu^{++} + 2NO + 4H_2O$
                                $(+0.96) - (+0.337) = +0.62$ volt

The potential table therefore shows relative tendencies for substances to gain or lose electrons. Substances at the top left of the table gain electrons most readily and are therefore the strongest oxidizing agents. Substances at the bottom right of the table lose electrons most readily and are therefore the strongest reducing agents.

Such predictions as given above must be applied cautiously. In a few cases, reactions that should proceed according to the relative positions in the potential series do so at such a slow rate that they are almost negligible. More important still, as shown in Sec. 6-7, the concentration of each component of an oxidation-reduction equilibrium affects the value of the potential. A substance may be present that is capable of forming a complex ion with one of the components of the half-cell equilibrium and thus reduces the concentration of that component to a point where it no longer reacts. Thus, the potential of the equilibrium $Sn^{4+} + 2e \rightleftharpoons$ Sn^{++} is greatly affected by the presence of chloride ions which form $SnCl_6^=$ ions with the stannic tin. In a few cases, precipitation effects interfere in the same way. For example, according to the table, iodide ions should reduce silver ions to metallic silver ($2Ag^+ + 2I^- \longrightarrow$ $2Ag + I_2$). Actually, a precipitation of silver iodide takes place instead ($Ag^+ + I^- \longrightarrow AgI$), and the concentration of Ag^+ in the residual solution is made too small to be affected by excess iodide. In the case of a few metals, passivity effects may occur. Pure aluminum should dissolve readily in nitric acid ($Al + NO_3^- + 4H^+ \longrightarrow Al^{3+} + NO + 2H_2O$). It does not do so, however, probably because of the formation of a protective coating of oxide on the surface of the metal.

6-6   Calculation of an Electrode Potential from Other Electrode Potentials

In the preceding section it was shown that equations for electrode reactions can be added and subtracted to obtain equations for completed redox reactions and that the corresponding electrode potentials can be similarly added or subtracted. It is only necessary to combine the reactions in such a way as to cancel out the electrons. If, however, electrode reactions (written as reductions and usually involving a single element) are simply added, a new electrode reaction is obtained; thus,

$$
\begin{array}{ll}
Fe^{++} + 2e \rightleftharpoons Fe & E_1^0 = -0.440 \\
\underline{Fe^{3+} + e \rightleftharpoons Fe^{++}} & E_2^0 = +0.771 \\
Fe^{3+} + 3e \rightleftharpoons Fe &
\end{array}
$$

From considerations of free energy it can be shown that the resulting electrode potential is not the sum of the potentials of the separate reactions (that is, $+0.331$ volt in this case). Each potential must be multiplied by the number of electrons indicated in the equation and the algebraic sum divided by the number of electrons in the resultant electrode reaction equation.   In the above case, the electrode potential of the resultant reaction is

$$\frac{(2)(-0.440) + (+0.771)}{3} = -0.0363 \text{ volt}$$

6-7   Relation between Electrode Potential and Concentration

When the prevailing activities are not $1\ M$, the electrode potentials differ from the standard electrode potentials but can be calculated from them. From considerations of free energy it can be shown that, at 25°C, electrode potentials can be calculated from the following formula, which is often referred to as the *Nernst equation:*

$$E = E^0 + \frac{0.0591}{n} \log \frac{Q_{\text{oxid}}}{Q_{\text{red}}} \text{ *}$$

where E^0 = standard electrode potential (reduction potential)

$\quad\quad n$ = number of faradays involved in the change.   It is also the number of electrons expressed in the half-cell reaction equation

$\quad \log$ = common logarithm

Q_{oxid} = product of the prevailing molar activities of the components of that part of the half-reaction equation which contains the principal substance in its oxidized state, each activity being raised to a power equal to the coefficient of the corresponding component in the equation

Q_{red} = product of the prevailing molar activities of the components of that part of the half-reaction equation which contains the principal substance in its reduced state, each activity being raised to a power equal to the coefficient of the corresponding component in the equation

As in the case of equilibrium constants (Sec. 5-8), concentrations of water and of relatively insoluble substances are omitted from the Q ratio, and the activities of gases are expressed as partial pressures (in atmospheres).

In calculations of electrode potentials, as in the calculations of equilibrium constants, activities rather than concentrations should be used for precise results (see Sec. 5-15).   Values of standard electrode potentials should therefore be for unit activity rather than for unit molar concentration.   Analytical calculations in this particular field, however,

---

* As stated in Sec. 6-2, in some tables of electrode potentials, oxidation potentials are used, and the signs are opposite to those given in this book.   If this alternative system is used, the plus sign in the Nernst formula as given above must be changed to a minus sign.

seldom require a precision greater than two significant figures, and the use of activities and activity coefficients (which are not always easily determined) can ordinarily be dispensed with.   Therefore, in numerical problems given in this book, a constituent which, for example, is stated to be at 0.1 M concentration will be considered to have a molar activity essentially equal to this value.

Example 1   Find the emf at 25°C of the cell

$$\text{Pt} \begin{vmatrix} Fe^{3+}(1.0\ M) \\ Fe^{++}(0.010\ M) \end{vmatrix} \begin{vmatrix} Ce^{4+}(0.00010\ M) \\ Ce^{3+}(0.10\ M) \end{vmatrix} \text{Pt}$$

Solution

(1) $Fe^{3+} + e \rightleftharpoons Fe^{++}$ $E_1 = E_1^0 + \dfrac{0.0591}{1} \log \dfrac{[Fe^{3+}]}{[Fe^{++}]}$

$$= +0.771 + 0.0591 \log 100$$

$$= +0.889$$

(2) $Ce^{4+} + e \rightleftharpoons Ce^{3+}$ $E_2 = E_2^0 + \dfrac{0.0591}{1} \log \dfrac{[Ce^{4+}]}{[Ce^{3+}]}$

$$= +1.61 + 0.0591 \log 10$$

$$= +1.43$$

Subtracting (2) from (1),

$$Ce^{3+} + Fe^{3+} \rightleftharpoons Ce^{4+} + Fe^{++}$$

$$E = E_1 - E_2 = +0.889 - (+1.43) = -0.54$$
$$\text{emf} = 0.54 \text{ volt} \qquad Ans.$$

The negative sign of the derived value shows that the corresponding derived equation proceeds from *right* to *left*.   The ceric ions are reduced and the ferrous ions are oxidized ($Ce^{4+} + Fe^{++} \longrightarrow Ce^{3+} + Fe^{3+}$) until concentrations are such that equilibrium conditions are reached and no current flows.

In this example the concentrations given are those of the simple cations.   Calculations become more complicated in cases where secondary equilibria exist between the cations and complex ions, such as $FeCl_4^-$ and $Ce(SO_4)_{\frac{3}{2}}$.   (See Sec. 6-3.)

Example 2   What is the potential of the half-cell represented by the following equilibrium equation: $Cr_2O_7^=(0.30\ M) + 14H^+(2.0\ M) + 6e \rightleftharpoons 2Cr^{3+}(0.20\ M) + 7H_2O$?

Solution

$$E = E^0 + \frac{0.0591}{n} \log \frac{[Cr_2O_7^=][H^+]^{14}}{[Cr^{3+}]^2}$$

$$= +1.33 + \frac{0.0591}{6} \log \frac{(0.30)(2.0)^{14}}{(0.20)^2}$$

$$= +1.38 \text{ volts} \qquad Ans.$$

Example 3 What is the emf of the following cell?

$$Zn|Zn^{++}(1.0 \times 10^{-6}\ M)\|Cu^{++}(0.010\ M)|Cu$$

Solution

$$E_1 = E^0_{Zn} + \frac{0.0591}{n} \log [Zn^{++}]$$

$$= -0.763 + \frac{0.0591}{2} \log (1.0 \times 10^{-6})$$

$$= -0.94$$

$$E_2 = E^0_{Cu} + \frac{0.0591}{n} \log [Cu^{++}]$$

$$= +0.337 + \frac{0.0591}{2} \log (0.010)$$

$$= +0.28$$

$$E = E_1 - E_2 = -0.94 - 0.28 = -1.22$$

$$\text{emf} = 1.22 \text{ volts} \qquad Ans.$$

Example 4 Calculate the emf of the following cell:

$$Cu|Cu^{++}(2.0\ M)\|Cu^{++}(0.010\ M)|Cu$$

This type of cell, made up of the same half-cell components but with ions at two different concentrations, is known as a *concentration cell*.

Solution

$$E_1 = +0.337 + \frac{0.0591}{2} \log 2.0$$

$$E_2 = +0.337 + \frac{0.0591}{2} \log 0.010$$

$$E = E_1 - E_2 = 0.068 \text{ volt} \qquad Ans.$$

6-8   Calculation of the Extent to Which a Redox Reaction Takes Place

All reversible reactions proceed in one direction or the other until equilibrium conditions are reached, at which point the two rates of reaction are equal.

During the progress of a redox reaction in a cell, the concentrations of the reacting substances are steadily decreasing and those of the products are increasing. The voltage of the cell decreases steadily until equilibrium is reached, at which point no current flows. At this point of equilibrium the potentials of the two half-cells making up the cell are therefore equal. In order to calculate the extent to which a redox reaction takes place, it is only necessary to express the reaction as two half-cell reactions and to express an equality between the two electrode potentials.

Example 1   When excess metallic aluminum is added to a solution 0.30 M in cupric ions, what is the theoretical concentration of Cu^{++} after equilibrium is reached ($2\underline{Al} + 3Cu^{++} \rightleftharpoons 2Al^{3+} + 3\underline{Cu}$)?

Solution   Experiment shows that the reduction of cupric ions is practically complete.

$$[Al^{3+}] = 0.20\ M \qquad \text{3 moles of } Cu^{++} \text{ give 2 moles of } Al^{3+}$$

$$[Cu^{++}] = xM$$

$$-1.67 + \frac{0.0591}{3} \log 0.20 = +0.337 \mid \frac{0.0591}{2} \log x$$

$$\log x = -68.5$$

$$x = 1 \times 10^{-69} \text{ mole} \qquad Ans.$$

Example 2   A solution is prepared so as to be initially 0.060 M in Fe^{++}, 0.10 M in $Cr_2O_7^=$, and 2.0 M in H^+. After equilibrium is reached, what would be the theoretical concentration of the Fe^{++} remaining ($6Fe^{++} + Cr_2O_7^= + 14H^+ \rightleftharpoons 6Fe^{3+} + 2Cr^{3+} + 7H_2O$)?

Solution   Experiment shows that the oxidation of ferrous ions is practically complete. Since, according to the equation, 0.060 mole of Fe^{++} would react with 0.010 mole of $Cr_2O_7^=$ and 0.14 mole of H^+, the last two are initially present in excess, and the concentration of Fe^{++} is the limiting factor. At equilibrium, $[Fe^{3+}] = 0.060$; $[Fe^{++}] = x$; $[Cr^{3+}] = 0.020$; $[Cr_2O_7^=] = 0.10 - 0.010 = 0.090$; $[H^+] = 2.0 - 0.14 = 1.86$. The two half-cell equilibria are

$$6Fe^{3+}(0.060\ M) + 6e \rightleftharpoons 6Fe^{++}(x\ M)$$

$$Cr_2O_7^=(0.090\ M) + 14H^+(1.86\ M) + 6e \rightleftharpoons 2Cr^{3+}(0.020\ M) + 7H_2O$$

$$+0.771 + \frac{0.0591}{6} \log \frac{[Fe^{3+}]^6}{[Fe^{++}]^6} = +1.33 + \frac{0.0591}{6} \log \frac{[Cr_2O_7^=][H^+]^{14}}{[Cr^{3+}]^2}$$

$$+0.771 + 0.0591 \log \frac{0.060}{x} = +1.33 + \frac{0.0591}{6} \log \frac{(0.090)(1.86)^{14}}{(0.020)^2}$$

$$x = 2 \times 10^{-12}\ M \qquad Ans.$$

6-9   Calculation of an Equilibrium Constant from Electrode Potentials

A mass-action constant (Sec. 5-8) applies to a reaction under conditions of equilibrium.   At this point the electrode potentials of the half-cell equilibria are equal and the overall potential is zero.   It is true then that the equilibrium constant K is equal to the Q ratio in the Nernst equation (Sec. 6-7).   Therefore,

$$E = E_1^0 - E_2^0 = \frac{0.0591}{n} \log K$$

This gives a practical method of calculating equilibrium constants from cell measurements.   The method can even be used to obtain equilibrium constants for reactions other than redox ones.   Thus, the solubility product of silver chloride can be calculated as follows:

(1)	$AgCl(s) + e \rightleftharpoons Ag(s) + Cl^-$	$E_1^0 = +0.222$
(2)	$Ag^+ + e \rightleftharpoons Ag(s)$	$E_2^0 = +0.799$
(1) − (2)	$AgCl(s) \rightleftharpoons Ag^+ + Cl^-$	$E = E_1^0 - E_2^0 = -0.578$

$$-0.578 = 0.0591 \log [Ag^+][Cl^-]$$

$[Ag^+][Cl^-] = $ soly. product (K) of AgCl

$$= \text{antilog } \frac{-0.578}{0.0591}$$

$$= 3.0 \times 10^{-10}$$

Example 1   Calculate the numerical value of the equilibrium constant of the reaction $2Fe^{++} + I_2 \rightleftharpoons 2Fe^{3+} + 2I^-$ (which at moderate concentrations proceeds only very slightly from left to right as written).

Solution

(1)	$I_2 + 2e \rightleftharpoons 2I^-$
(2)	$2Fe^{3+} + 2e \rightleftharpoons 2Fe^{++}$
(1) − (2)	$2Fe^{++} + I_2 \rightleftharpoons 2Fe^{3+} + 2I^-$

$\dfrac{[Fe^{3+}]^2[I^-]^2}{[Fe^{++}]^2[I_2]} = K$ mass-action const.

$E_1 = E_2$ at equilibrium

$$+0.771 + \frac{0.0591}{2} \log \frac{[Fe^{3+}]^2}{[Fe^{++}]^2} = +0.535 + \frac{0.0591}{2} \log \frac{[I_2]}{[I^-]^2}$$

$$\frac{0.0591}{2} \log \frac{[Fe^{3+}]^2[I^-]^2}{[Fe^{++}][I_2]} = -0.236$$

$$\frac{0.0591}{2} \log K = -0.236$$

$$K = 1.1 \times 10^{-8}   \textit{Ans.}$$

PROBLEMS

(See Table 13, Appendix, for the necessary standard potentials.   Temperatures are 25°C.)

*6-1.   Calculate the potentials of the following half-cells:
(a) $Hg^{++}(0.0010) + 2e \rightleftharpoons Hg(s)$
(b) $Co^{++}(0.24 \ M) + 2e \rightleftharpoons Co(s)$
(c) $PbO_2(s) + 4H^+(0.010 \ M) + 2e \rightleftharpoons Pb^{++}(0.050 \ M) + 2H_2O$
(d) $O_2(2 \ atm) + 2H^+(1.5 \ M) + 2e \rightleftharpoons H_2O_2(0.0020 \ M)$

*6-2.   Balance the following equation, and express it as the difference between two half-cell reactions: $PbO_2(s) + Br^- + H^+ \longrightarrow Pb^{++} + Br_2 + H_2O$.

*6-3.   Write the equation showing the net reaction indicated by each of the following pairs of half-cell reactions.   From the respective electrode potentials, show in which direction each reaction will go, assuming all ion concns. to be 1 M.
(a) $Ag^+ + e \rightleftharpoons Ag(s)$, $Cu^{++} + 2e \rightleftharpoons Cu(s)$;   (b) $O_2 + 2H^+ + 2e \rightleftharpoons H_2O_2$, $MnO_2(s) + 4H^+ + 2e \rightleftharpoons Mn^{++} + 2H_2O$.

*6-4.   Write complete, balanced equations for the half-cell reactions indicated by the following changes taking place in the presence of acid: (a) $\underline{Sb} \longrightarrow SbO^+$; (b) $HNO_2 \longrightarrow NO_3^-$; (c) $\underline{As} \longrightarrow HAsO_2$; (d) $BiO^+ \longrightarrow Bi_2O_4(s)$; (e) $Br \longrightarrow BrO_3^-$.

*6-5.   Write complete, balanced equations for the half-cell reactions indicated by the following changes taking place in the presence of alkali: (a) $\underline{Zn} \longrightarrow ZnO_2^=$; (b) $HCHO \longrightarrow HCO_2^-$; (c) $HSnO_2^- \longrightarrow Sn(OH)_6^=$; (d) $\overline{PH}_3 \longrightarrow \underline{P}$; (e) $\underline{Ag} \longrightarrow Ag_2O$.

*6-6.   (a) What is the emf of the following concn. cell?

$Ag|Ag^+(0.40 \ M)||Ag^+(0.0010 \ M)|Ag$

(b) In what direction is the flow of electrons in the wire connecting the electrodes as written?

*6-7.   (a) What emf can be obtained from the following cell?

$Zn|Zn^{++}(0.010 \ M)||Ag^+(0.30 \ M)|Ag$

(b) In what direction is the flow of electrons through the wire connecting the electrodes?   (c) Write an equation for the reaction at each electrode and for the net reaction.   (d) What would the initial concn. of Ag^+ have to be for no current to flow?

*6-8.   Calculate the emf obtainable from each of the following cells.   In each case, indicate the direction of the flow of electrons in the wire connecting the electrodes, and write an equation for the net reaction.

(a) $Cd|Cd^{++}(1.0 \ M)||Cu^{++}(1.0 \ M)|Cu$
(b) $Hg|Hg^{++}(0.10 \ M)||Hg^{++}(0.0071 \ M)|Hg$

(c) $Pt\begin{vmatrix} Fe^{++}(0.10 \ M) \\ Fe^{3+}(0.30 \ M) \end{vmatrix}\begin{Vmatrix} Cr^{3+}(0.010 \ M) \\ Cr_2O_7^=(0.20 \ M) \\ H^+(1.0 \ M) \end{Vmatrix}Pt$

(d)   Pt $\left|\begin{array}{l} \text{Mn}^{++}(0.10\ M) \\ \text{MnO}_4^-(0.060\ M) \\ \text{H}^+(0.20\ M) \end{array}\right| \left|\begin{array}{l} \text{Sn}^{++}(0.050\ M) \\ \text{Sn}^{4+}(0.020\ M) \end{array}\right|$ Pt

(e)   Ag $|$ AgCl, Cl$^-$(1.0 M) $\left|\begin{array}{l} \text{Fe}^{++}(0.10\ M) \\ \text{Fe}^{3+}(0.20\ M) \end{array}\right|$ Pt

*6-9.   What must be the value of x for the following reaction to be at equilibrium?

$$\underline{\text{Cu}} + 2\text{Ag}^+(x\ M) \rightleftharpoons \text{Cu}^{++}(0.10\ M) + 2\underline{\text{Ag}}$$

*6-10.   The standard potential between elementary arsenic and the arsenite ion (AsO$_2^-$) in alkaline soln. is -0.68 volt.   Calculate the potential of this system when the concns. of arsenite and of hydroxyl ions are each 0.10 M.

*6-11.   By how many volts would the potential between iodate (IO$_3^-$) and periodate (H$_3$IO$_6^=$) in alkaline soln. differ from the standard potential if the concns. of the iodate, periodate, and hydroxyl ions are each 0.20 M?

*6-12.   Given the standard half-cell potentials Cr^{3+} + 3e $\rightleftharpoons$ $\underline{\text{Cr}}$ (-0.74); Cr^{++} + 2e $\rightleftharpoons$ $\underline{\text{Cr}}$ (-0.86).   Find the standard potential of Cr^{3+} + e $\rightleftharpoons$ Cr^{++}.

*6-13.   (a) From the standard electrode potentials Hg$_2^{++}$ + 2e $\rightleftharpoons$ 2$\underline{\text{Hg}}$ $(+0.79)$ and 2Hg^{++} + 2e $\rightleftharpoons$ Hg$_2^{++}$ $(+0.92)$, calculate the equilibrium const. for the reaction $\underline{\text{Hg}}$ + Hg^{++} $\rightleftharpoons$ Hg$_2^{++}$.   (b) Derive the standard electrode potential of Hg^{++} + 2e $\rightleftharpoons$ $\underline{\text{Hg}}$.

*6-14.   Write balanced equations for the following indicated half-cell reactions taking place in the presence of acid: $\underline{\text{MnO}_2}$—Mn^{++} $(+1.23)$; MnO$_4^-$—MnO$_4^=$ $(+0.56)$; MnO$_4^=$—MnO$_2$ $(+2.26)$.   From the indicated standard potentials, find the standard potential of MnO$_4^-$ + 8H$^+$ + 5e $\rightleftharpoons$ Mn^{++} + 4H$_2$O.

*6-15.   Write balanced equations for the half-cell reactions (in the presence of acid) between the following pairs of substances, and from the corresponding E^0 values given, calculate the standard potential of the last pair: HClO—$\frac{1}{2}$Cl$_2$ $(+1.62)$; ClO$_3^-$—HClO$_2$ $(+1.21)$; HClO$_2$—HClO $(+1.63)$; ClO$_3^-$—$\frac{1}{2}$Cl$_2$.

*6-16.   Given the following electrode reactions and the corresponding standard potentials: PbCl$_2$(s) + 2e $\rightleftharpoons$ Pb(s) + 2Cl$^-$ (-0.27);   Pb^{++} + 2e $\rightleftharpoons$ Pb(s) (-0.13).   Calculate the soly. product of PbCl$_2$.

*6-17.   When excess metallic Zn is added to a soln. 0.010 M in Ag$^+$, what is the theoretical concn. of Ag$^+$ after equilibrium is reached?   The reaction is practically complete as follows: $\underline{\text{Zn}}$ + 2Ag$^+$ $\longrightarrow$ Zn^{++} + 2$\underline{\text{Ag}}$.

*6-18.   Equal vols. of a soln. 0.10 M in Fe^{++} and a soln. 0.30 M in Ce^{4+} are mixed.   The reaction is practically complete (Fe^{++} + Ce^{4+} $\longrightarrow$ Fe^{3+} + Ce^{3+}).   After equilibrium has been attained, what is the resulting concn. of Fe^{++}?

*6-19.   Calculate the approx. equilibrium const. for each of the following:

(a) $\underline{\text{Zn}}$ + Cu^{++} $\rightleftharpoons$ Zn^{++} + $\underline{\text{Cu}}$
(b)   Fe^{3+} + $\underline{\text{Ag}}$ $\rightleftharpoons$ Fe^{++} + Ag$^+$
(c)   2Ce^{3+} + I$_2$ $\rightleftharpoons$ 2Ce^{4+} + 2I$^-$

(d) $6Fe^{++} + Cr_2O_7^= + 14H^+ \rightleftharpoons 6Fe^{3+} + 2Cr^{3+} + 7H_2O$

(e) $2Fe^{3+} + 2Br^- \rightleftharpoons 2Fe^{++} + Br_2$

6-20.   Write complete and balanced equations for the half-cell reactions indicated by the following changes taking place in acid soln.: (a) $\underline{P} \longrightarrow H_3PO_4$; (b) $\underline{MnO_2} \longrightarrow MnO_4^-$; (c) $U^{4+} \longrightarrow UO_2^{++}$; (d) $SbO^+ \longrightarrow \underline{Sb_2O_5}$; (e) $Cl_2 \longrightarrow HClO_2$; (f) $S_2O_3^= \longrightarrow H_2SO_3$.

6-21.   Write complete and balanced equations for the half-cell reactions indicated by the following changes taking place in alkaline soln.: (a) $\underline{P} \longrightarrow PO_3^-$; (b) $Pb^{++} \longrightarrow \underline{PbO_2}$; (c) $SO_3^= \longrightarrow SO_4^=$; (d) $CrO_2^- \longrightarrow CrO_4^=$; (e) $N_2O_4 \longrightarrow NO_3^-$; (f) $\underline{Ag_2O} \longrightarrow \underline{AgO}$.

6-22.   Calculate the potentials of the following half-cells:

(a) $Ag^+(0.010\ M) + e \rightleftharpoons \underline{Ag}$

(b) $Co^{++}(0.063\ M) + 2e \rightleftharpoons \underline{Co}$

(c) $MnO_4^-(0.020\ M) + 8H^+(0.10\ M) + 5e \rightleftharpoons Mn^{++}(0.030\ M) + 4H_2O$

(d) $Cr_2O_7^=(0.020\ M) + 14H^+(0.030\ M) + 6e \rightleftharpoons 2Cr^{3+}(0.010\ M) + 7H_2O$

6-23.   Balance the following equations, and express each as the difference between two half-cell reactions: (a) $\underline{Fe} + H^+ \longrightarrow Fe^{++} + H_2$; (b) $Fe^{++} + MnO_4^- + H^+ \longrightarrow Fe^{3+} + Mn^{++} + H_2O$; (c) $\underline{Fe} + NO_3^- + H^+ \longrightarrow Fe^{3+} + NO + H_2O$; (d) $Cl_2 + H_2O \longrightarrow HOCl + H^+ + Cl^-$; (e) $\underline{PbS} + H_2O_2 \longrightarrow \underline{PbSO_4} + H_2O$.

6-24.   Balance the following equations, and express each as the difference between two half-cell reactions: (a) $Fe^{++} + H_2O_2 + H^+ \longrightarrow Fe^{3+} + H_2O$; (b) $MnO_4^- + H_2O_2 + H^+ \longrightarrow Mn^{++} + O_2 + H_2O$; (c) $Cr^{3+} + MnO_4^- + H_2O \longrightarrow Cr_2O_7^= + Mn^{++} + H^+$; (d) $I_2 + H_2O_2 \longrightarrow H^+ + IO_3^- + H_2O$; (e) $H_2SO_3 + H_2S \longrightarrow \underline{S} + H_2O$.

6-25.   Write the following as balanced ionic equations, and express each as the difference between two half-cell reactions: (a) $SnSO_4 + K_2Cr_2O_7 + H_2SO_4 \longrightarrow Sn(SO_4)_2 + K_2SO_4 + Cr_2(SO_4)_3 + H_2O$; (b) $\underline{As} + HNO_3 + H_2O \longrightarrow H_3AsO_4 + NO$; (c) $Br_2 + NH_4OH \longrightarrow NH_4Br + N_2 + H_2O$; (d) $KI + KIO_3 + HCl \longrightarrow I_2 + H_2O + KCl$.

6-26.   Write an equation showing the net reaction indicated by each of the following pairs of half-cell reactions.   Show from the respective electrode potentials in which direction each reaction should go, assuming all ion concns. to be 1 M. (a) $Hg^{++} + 2e \rightleftharpoons \underline{Hg}(s)$, $Zn^{++} + 2e \rightleftharpoons \underline{Zn}(s)$; (b) $O_2 + 2H^+ + 2e \rightleftharpoons H_2O_2$, $Fe^{3+} + e \rightleftharpoons Fe^{++}$; (c) $\underline{PbO_2}(s) + 4H^+ + 2e \rightleftharpoons Pb^{++} + 2H_2O$, $Cl_2 + 2e \rightleftharpoons 2Cl^-$; (d) $Cl_2 + 2e \rightleftharpoons 2Cl^-$, $Br_2 + 2e \rightleftharpoons 2Br^-$.

6-27.   Solve the preceding problem with respect to the following half-cell reactions: (a) $Sn^{4+} + 2e \rightleftharpoons Sn^{++}$, $I_2 + 2e \rightleftharpoons 2I^-$; (b) $Cr_2O_7^= + 14H^+ + 6e \rightleftharpoons 2Cr^{3+} + 7H_2O$, $Fe(CN)_6^{3-} + e \rightleftharpoons Fe(CN)_6^{4-}$; (c) $\underline{MnO_2}(s) + 4H^+ + 2e \rightleftharpoons Mn^{++} + 2H_2O$, $Fe^{3+} + e \rightleftharpoons Fe^{++}$; (d) $Ag^+ + e \rightleftharpoons \underline{Ag}(s)$, $NO_3^- + 4H^+ + 3e \rightleftharpoons NO + 2H_2O$.

6-28.   The following reactions take place at ordinary concns. as written:

$V^{++} + TiO^{++} + 2H^+ \longrightarrow V^{3+} + Ti^{3+} + H_2O$

$\underline{Bi} + 3Fe^{3+} + H_2O \longrightarrow BiO^+ + 3Fe^{++} + 2H^+$

$$\underline{Zn} + 2Cr^{3+} \longrightarrow Zn^{++} + 2Cr^{++}$$
$$6Br^- + Cr_2O_7^= + 14H^+ \longrightarrow 3Br_2 + 2Cr^{3+} + 7H_2O$$
$$3Ti^{3+} + BiO^+ + 2H_2O \longrightarrow 3TiO^{++} + \underline{Bi} + 4H^+$$
$$2Fe^{++} + NO_3^- + 3H^+ \longrightarrow 2Fe^{3+} + HNO_2 + H_2O$$
$$\underline{Mg} + Zn^{++} \longrightarrow Mg^{++} + \underline{Zn}$$
$$Cr^{++} + V^{3+} \longrightarrow Cr^{3+} + V^{++}$$
$$HNO_2 + Br_2 + H_2O \longrightarrow NO_3^- + 2Br^- + 3H^+$$

Convert each of these reactions into two half-cell reactions, placing the reduced form on the right and the oxidized form and electrons on the left. Rearrange the half-cell reactions in tabular form in such a manner that the strongest oxidizing agent is at the top left and the strongest reducing agent is at the bottom right. From the tabulation, predict which of the following do not react at ordinary concns., and write balanced ionic equations for those that do: (a) $Zn^{++} + V^{++}$; (b) $Fe^{++} + TiO^{++}$; (c) $Cr^{++} + NO_3^- + H^+$; (d) $\underline{Bi} + Br_2$; (e) $Cr_2O_7^= + TiO^{++} + H^+$.

6-29. Which of the following reactions should take place as indicated when ion concns. are 1 M? (a) $2Cl^- + I_2 \longrightarrow Cl_2 + 2I^-$; (b) $2Fe(CN)_6^{3-} + H_2O_2 \longrightarrow 2Fe(CN)_6^{4-} + O_2 + 2H^+$; (c) $2Fe^{++} + PbO_2 + 4H^+ \longrightarrow 2Fe^{3+} + Pb^{++} + 2H_2O$; (d) $2\underline{Bi} + 2H^+ + 2H_2O \longrightarrow 2BiO^+ + 3H_2$; (e) $10Cr^{3+} + 6MnO_4^- + 11H_2O \longrightarrow 5Cr_2O_7^= + 6Mn^{++} + 22H^+$.

6-30. The standard potential between elementary rhenium and the perrhenate ion (ReO_4^-) in alkaline soln. is -0.81 volt. Calculate the potential of this system when the concns. of perrhenate and of hydroxyl ions are each 0.10 M.

6-31. By how many volts would the potential between hypoiodite (IO^-) and iodate (IO_3^-) in alkaline soln. differ from the standard potential if the concns. of the hypoiodite, iodate, and hydroxyl ions are each 0.30 M?

6-32. Calculate the emf of each of the following cells. In each case indicate the direction of the passage of electrons in the wire connecting the electrodes, and write an equation for the net reaction.

(a) $Ag\,|\,Ag^+(1.0\ M)\,\|\,Cd^{++}(1.0\ M)\,|\,Cd$

(b) $Cu\,|\,Cu^{++}(0.010\ M)\,\|\,Cu^{++}(0.090\ M)\,|\,Cu$

(c) $Pt\begin{vmatrix} Cr^{3+}(0.050\ M) \\ Cr_2O_7^=(0.10\ M) \\ H^+(2.0\ M) \end{vmatrix}\begin{Vmatrix} Fe^{++}(0.090\ M) \\ Fe^{3+}(0.015\ M) \end{Vmatrix}Pt$

(d) $Pt\begin{vmatrix} Sn^{++}(0.020\ M) \\ Sn^{4+}(0.080\ M) \end{vmatrix}\begin{Vmatrix} Mn^{++}(0.050\ M) \\ MnO_4^-(0.10\ M) \\ H^+(0.40\ M) \end{Vmatrix}Pt$

(e) $Pt\begin{vmatrix} Fe^{++}(0.25\ M) \\ Fe^{3+}(0.050\ M) \end{vmatrix}\begin{Vmatrix} \underline{AgCl},\ Cl^-(0.10\ M) \end{Vmatrix}Ag$

6-33. Given the following hypothetical half-cell reactions and their corresponding standard potentials: $AO^{++} + 2H^+ + 2e \rightleftharpoons A^{++} + H_2O$ ($E_1^0 = B$); $AO_4^- + 6H^+ + 3e \rightleftharpoons AO^{++} + 3H_2O$ ($E_2^0 = C$). Express in terms of B and C the standard potential of $AO_4^- + 8H^+ + 5e \rightleftharpoons A^{++} + 4H_2O$.

6-34. Write balanced equations for the half-cell reactions (in the presence of acid) between the following pairs of substances, and calculate the standard potential of the last one:

$$NO_3^- - HNO_2 \ (E^0 = +0.94); \ N_2O_4 - HNO_2 \ (E^0 = +1.07); \ NO_3^- - N_2O_4$$

6-35. Write balanced equations for the following indicated half-cell reactions pertaining to the element rhenium: $\underline{Re}$—ReO_4^-; $\underline{ReO_2}$—ReO_4^-; $\underline{Re}$—ReO_2. The standard potentials for the first two of these are $+0.365$ and $+0.510$ volt, respectively. Find the standard potential of the third reaction.

6-36. The soly. product of PbI_2 is 1.0×10^{-8}. From this value and the necessary data given in the potential table in the Appendix, calculate the standard potential of the half-cell reaction $\underline{Pb} + 2I^- = \underline{PbI_2} + 2e$.

6-37. What must be the value of x in order for the following reaction to be at equilibrium: $\underline{Zn} + 2Ag^+(x \ M) \rightleftharpoons Zn^{++}(1.0 \times 10^{-3} \ M) + 2\underline{Ag}$?

6-38. When excess metallic Al is added to a soln. $0.10 \ M$ in Cu^{++}, what is the theoretical concn. of Cu^{++} after equilibrium is reached? The reaction is practically complete as follows: $2\underline{Al} + 3Cu^{++} \longrightarrow 2Al^{3+} + 3\underline{Cu}$.

6-39. Equal vols. of a soln. $0.40 \ M$ in Fe^{++} and a soln. $0.10 \ M$ in Ce^{4+} are mixed. After the reaction is practically complete ($Fe^{++} + Ce^{4+} \longrightarrow Fe^{3+} + Ce^{3+}$) and equilibrium has been attained, what is the resulting concn. of Ce^{4+}?

6-40. Calculate the equilibrium const. for each of the following:

(a) $Cu^{++} + 2\underline{Ag} \rightleftharpoons \underline{Cu} + 2Ag^+$
(b) $3Cu^{++} + 2\underline{Al} \rightleftharpoons 3\underline{Cu} + 2Al^{3+}$
(c) $Fe^{++} + Ce^{4+} \rightleftharpoons Fe^{3+} + Ce^{3+}$
(d) $2Br^- + I_2 \rightleftharpoons Br_2 + 2I^-$
(e) $10I^- + 2MnO_4^- + 16H^+ \rightleftharpoons 5I_2 + 2Mn^{++} + 8H_2O$

TWO
Gravimetric Analysis

The Chemical Balance

7-1 Sensitivity of the Chemical Balance

The determination of the weight of a body is a fundamental measurement of analytical chemistry and is made with an equal-arm balance of high degree of precision. An equal-arm balance consists essentially of a rigid beam supported horizontally at its center on a knife-edge and so constructed that the center of gravity of the swinging portion is below the point of support.

The *sensitivity* of a balance is the tangent of the angle α through which the equilibrium position of the beam (or pointer) is displaced by a small excess load w on the balance pan:

$$\text{Sensitivity} = \frac{\tan \alpha}{w}$$

With a small excess load (usually 1 mg) the angle is so small that for practical purposes the sensitivity can be defined as the number of scale divisions through which the equilibrium position of the pointer of the balance is displaced by an excess load of 1 mg.

The sensitivity varies directly with the length l of the arm, inversely with the weight W of the beam, and inversely with the distance d between the center of gravity of the swinging portion and the point of support. That is,

$$\frac{\tan \alpha}{w} = \frac{l}{Wd}$$

The sensitivity of a balance decreases slightly with increasing load.

7-2   Methods of Weighing

Most modern analytical balances are provided with a magnetic damping device which cuts down the oscillations of the beam and causes the pointer to come quickly to rest at the zero point on the scale.   Such a balance is also often provided with a notched beam on which a cylindrical rider can be placed to give the reading of the nearest 0.1 g.   A gold chain is suspended from the beam, and the end of the chain is fastened to a sliding device which moves along a graduated scale which serves to extend the reading to the nearest 0.1 mg.

Undamped balances using weights from 50 g down to 10 mg in value and having a graduated beam bearing a wire rider are still in use in some instructional laboratories.   Their operation is comparatively slow, but with weights of high quality they are often more accurate than the more elaborate types of balance.

In most analytical work with an undamped balance, it is sufficiently accurate to make weighings by the *method of short swings.*   The pointer of the balance is allowed to swing only one or two scale divisions to the right or left of the zero point of the scale, and the reading of the weights is taken when the extreme positions of the pointer to the right and left of the zero point are equal.   The balance is, of course, previously adjusted so that with no load on the pans the extreme positions of the pointer are likewise equal.

Some analysts, however, favor the *method of long swings.*   The equilibrium position of the pointer is first determined by allowing the beam of the empty balance to swing so that the pointer passes over six to eight divisions on the scale.   Extreme positions of the pointer in an odd number of consecutive swings are recorded; for example, three readings are taken to the right of the zero point of the scale and two readings are taken to the left of the zero point.   The two sets of readings are averaged, and the equilibrium position of the pointer is taken as the algebraic mean of the two values.   The weight of an object can then be determined by placing it on the left-hand pan and (1) adjusting the weights and rider, or weights and chain, so that the equilibrium position is the same as that obtained with the empty balance, or (2) calculating the weight from the sensitivity of the balance and the equilibrium position corresponding to an approximate weighing of the object.   For example, suppose the equilibrium position of the pointer under zero load is +0.4 as determined above.   Suppose that, when an object is balanced with 20.1260 g, the equilibrium position is found to be +1.6 and the sensitivity of the balance under a 20-g load is 4.0 (i.e., a 1-mg increment shifts the equilibrium position by 4.0 scale divisions); then the necessary shift of 1.2 divisions to the left to bring the equilibrium position to +0.4 is accomplished by increasing the weight on the right-hand side of the balance by 1.2/4.0 = 0.3 mg. The weight of the object is, therefore, 20.1263 g.

7-3   Conversion of Weight in Air to Weight in Vacuo

Archimedes' principle states that any substance immersed in a fluid weighs less by an amount equal to the weight of fluid displaced. Consequently, a substance weighed in the ordinary manner is buoyed up to a slight extent by the surrounding air, and for accurate determinations, especially those involving the weighing of objects of large volume, a correction for this buoyant effect must be applied. Since the usual method of weighing consists in balancing the substance to be weighed against standard weights, the surrounding air likewise exerts a buoyant effect upon the weights. If the volume occupied by the weights used is equal to the volume occupied by the substance, the buoyant effects will be equal and the weight of the substance in vacuo will be the same as its weight in air. If the volume occupied by the substance is greater than the volume occupied by the weights, the substance will weigh more in vacuo than in air; and if the weights have the greater volume, the substance will weigh less in vacuo than in air. In any case, the difference between the weight in air and the weight in vacuo will be equal to the difference between the weight of the air displaced by the substance and the weight of the air displaced by the weights used. The weight in vacuo W^0 can be expressed by the equation

$$W^0 = W + (V - V')a$$

where W = weight of substance in air
$\quad\quad V$ = volume occupied by substance
$\quad\quad V'$ = volume occupied by weights used
$\quad\quad a$ = weight of unit volume of air

Although the value of a varies slightly with the temperature and barometric pressure, the approximate value of 0.0012 g for the weight of 1 ml of air can be used except in cases where great accuracy is required or where the atmospheric conditions are highly abnormal. Also, since the volume occupied by the substance and the volume occupied by the weights are usually unknown, the formula is better written by expressing the volumes in terms of weight and density ($V = W/d$).

The value following the plus sign in the above formula is small compared with the value W to which it is added. Therefore, the terms in the correction value need be expressed to only two significant figures and the computation can be performed with sufficient accuracy with a slide rule. The simplified formula can be written as

$$W^0 = W + \left(\frac{W}{d} - \frac{W}{d'}\right)0.0012$$

where d is the density (in grams per milliliter) of the substance weighed and d' is the density of the weights used.

The densities of a few common substances are given in Table 1.

Table 1   Densities of a few common substances
(In grams per milliliter)

Aluminum	2.7	Mercury	13.6
Brass	8.4	Nickel	8.7
Brass (balance wts.)	8.0	Platinum	21.4
Copper	8.9	Porcelain	2.4
Glass	2.6	Quartz	2.7
Gold	19.3	Silver	10.5
Lead	11.3	Steel	7.8

Example 1   A platinum crucible weighs 25.6142 g in air against brass analytical weights.   What is its weight in vacuo?

Solution

Density of platinum $= 21.4 = d$
Density of brass wts. $= 8.0 = d'$
Wt. of 1 ml of air $= 0.0012$ g $= a$

Substituting in the above formula,

$$W^0 = 25.6142 + \left(\frac{25.6142}{21.4} - \frac{25.6142}{8.0}\right)0.0012$$

$$= 25.6142 + \left(\frac{26}{21} - \frac{26}{8.0}\right)0.0012$$

$$= 25.6142 - 0.0024$$

$$= 25.6118 \text{ g} \qquad Ans.$$

7-4   Calibration of Weights

In an ordinary quantitative chemical analysis, if the same set of weights is used throughout, it is immaterial whether or not the masses of the weights are exactly as marked as long as they are in correct *relative* proportion.   The mass of the 5-g weight should be exactly one-half that of the 10-g weight, and the others should be similarly in proportion.   In order to establish this relationship and to determine what correction factors must be applied to the individual weights of a given set, the weights must be calibrated.

There are several ways of calibrating weights.   One of the simplest is to assume temporarily that one of the smaller weights, say the 10-mg weight, is correct and to determine the value of the other weights in relation to it. In order to allow for the possible fact that the arms of the balance may be slightly unequal in length, weighings should be made by the *method of substitution* in which weights are compared by balancing them in pairs against appropriate tares.

The relative mass of the other 10-mg weight (which can be marked 10′) in the set is determined by comparing with the 10-mg weight; the relative mass of the 20-mg weight is similarly determined by balancing against the combined 10- and 10′-mg weights. This process is continued up through the entire set of weights, the combined values of the smaller weights being used to establish the values of the larger weights. In this way values similar to those listed in the second column of Table 2 are

Table 2   Typical calibration corrections

Face value of weight, g	True value, based on 0.010-g standard	Fractional part of 10-g standard	Necessary correction, mg
0.010 (initial standard)	0.0100	0.0101	−0.1
0.010	0.0101	0.0101	0
0.020	0.0199	0.0202	−0.3
0.050	0.0506	0.0506	0
0.100	0.1012	0.1011	+0.1
0.100	0.1014	0.1015	−0.1
0.200	0.2023	0.2023	0
0.500	0.5056	0.5056	0
1	1.0110	1.0113	−0.3
2	2.0225	2.0226	−0.1
2	2.0228	2.0226	+0.2
5	5.0562	5.0564	−0.2
10 (final standard)	10.1128	10.1128	0
10′	10.1130	10.1128	+0.2
20	20.2262	20.2256	+0.6
50	50.5635	50.5640	−0.5

obtained. Because of the small standard taken, it will usually be found that the larger weights have larger correction factors. It is therefore convenient to convert the values to a larger standard, say one of the 10-g weights of the set (or an auxiliary 10-g weight from a set checked by the Bureau of Standards, which has been included in the above series of weighings). In the case cited in the table, the new 10-g standard has a value of 10.1128 g (relative to the original small standard). The 5-g weight should have a value of exactly one-half of this, or 5.0564 g. Actually its value is 5.0562 g; hence it is 0.0002 g too light. Therefore 0.2 mg must be *subtracted* from a weighing in which its face value is used.

In weighing a given object, instead of applying a correction for each weight used, it is less tedious to construct a table showing cumulative corrections. By means of such a table, the total correction is found from the sum of the face values of the weights on the pan. In this case it is necessary when weighing an object to adopt the convention of using the smallest number of weights possible, to use an "unprimed" weight (for example, 0.100 g) in preference to a "primed" weight (for example, 0.100′ g), and to construct the table accordingly. In the table given, a total weight of 0.18 g would show a net correction of −0.3 mg, which is the algebraic sum of the individual corrections of the weights having the face values 100, 50, 20, and 10 mg (that is, +0.1 + 0.0 − 0.3 − 0.1 = −0.3).

PROBLEMS

*7-1. A crucible weighing approx. 10 g is being weighed. The pointer of the empty balance has an equilibrium position at +0.2 on the scale, and the sensitivity of the balance under a 10-g load is known to be 3.6 divisions. With the rider at 4.8 (mg) on the beam, the equilibrium point of the balance is found to be at +2.7 on the scale. To what point on the beam should the rider be moved to make the correct final reading?

*7-2. When the pointer of an undamped balance (having a 10-g load on each pan) is set in motion, it swings on the scale as follows: right to +7.6, left to −6.4, right to +7.0, left to   5.8, right to +6.2. With an additional 1-mg weight on the right-hand pan, the pointer swings as follows: right to 1.0, left to −8.2, right to +0.4, left to −7.6, right to −0.3. What is the sensitivity (in scale divisions) of the balance under a 10-g load?

*7-3. The balance of Prob. 7-2 is used to weigh a certain crucible but is first adjusted so that the equilibrium position of the pointer is at zero when the balance is empty. With the crucible on the left-hand pan, with weights totaling to 10.12 g on the right-hand pan, and with the rider at 3.0 mg on the right-hand beam, the equilibrium position of the pointer is found to be at −1.7 on the scale division. What is the wt. of the crucible to the nearest 0.1 mg?

*7-4. Find the wt. in vacuo of a piece of gold that weighs 35.0000 g in air against brass wts.

*7-5. A substance weighing 12.3456 g in air has a vol. of 2 ml and a density equal to three times that of the wts. used. What does it weigh in vacuo?

*7-6. A quartz crucible weighing 16.0053 g in vacuo would weigh how many g in air against brass wts.?

*7-7.   A sample of brass weighs 12.8150 g in air against platinum wts.   What is its wt. in vacuo?

*7-8.   (*a*) If a piece of gold in vacuo weighs 35 times as much as a 1-g brass wt. in vacuo, what would the brass wt. weigh in air against gold wts.?   (*b*) What would the piece of gold weigh in air against brass wts.?

*7-9.   In calibrating a given set of wts., the 10-mg wt. is temporarily taken as a standard.   On this basis, the 2-g wt. is found to be 2.0169 g and a 10-g wt. (certi- fied by the Bureau of Standards to be correct to within 0.05 mg) is found to be 10.0856 g.   What correction should be applied for the 2-g wt. in any weighing in which its face value is taken as its true wt.?

7-10.   A wt. of 1 mg on the right-hand pan of a certain balance displaces the equi- librium position of the pointer by 6.0 mm.   The pointer is 24.6 cm long.   (*a*) What is the tangent of the angle through which the pointer has moved?   (*b*) If the beam weighs 32.0 g and is 16.0 cm long, what is the distance between the middle knife- edge and the center of gravity of the moving parts?

7-11.   When the pointer of an undamped balance (having a 20-g load on each pan) is set in motion, it swings on the scale as follows: right to $+6.2$, left to -6.1, right to $+5.7$, left to -5.5, right to $+5.3$.   With an additional 1-mg wt. on the right-hand pan, the pointer swings as follows: right to $+3.1$, left to -9.2, right to $+2.6$, left to -8.7, right to $+2.2$.   What is the sensitivity (in scale divisions) of the balance under a 20-g load?

7-12.   The balance mentioned in the preceding problem is adjusted so that the equilibrium position of the pointer of the empty balance is at zero and is used to weigh a certain crucible.   With the crucible on the left-hand pan, with wts. adding to 19.87 g on the right-hand pan, and with the rider at 8.0 mg on the right-hand beam, the equilibrium position of the pointer is found to be at $+1.2$ on the scale division.   What is the wt. of the crucible to the nearest 0.1 mg?

7-13.   (*a*) What would be the wt. of a piece of gold in vacuo if in air against brass wts. it weighs 14.2963 g?   (*b*) In vacuo, a quartz dish weighs 22.9632 g.   Calcu- late the wt. in air against brass wts.

7-14.   In determining an at. wt., a final product which has a density of 6.32 is weighed in air against gold wts.   What percentage error would be made by failing to convert this wt. (10.0583 g) to the wt. in vacuo?

7-15.   Find the wts. in vacuo of two crucibles, one of gold and one of aluminum, each weighing 15.0000 g in air against brass wts.   What would the gold crucible weigh in air against aluminum wts.?

7-16.   (*a*) What is the density of a solid that weighs approx. 20 g in air against brass wts. and the wt. of which increases by exactly 0.01% in vacuo?   (*b*) What is the density of a similar substance the wt. of which decreases by 0.01% in vacuo?

7-17.   From the correction values given in Table 2, construct a table of cumulative corrections for weighings ranging from 0.01 to 0.99 g, and construct another table of cumulative corrections for weighings ranging from 1 to 99 g.   (*Hint:* To save space, use a tabulation similar to that used in logarithm tables.)

7-18.   (*a*) Assuming that the 20-g wt. in a given set has a value of 20.2364 g in relation to the 10-mg wt. as a standard, what should be the value of a 500-mg wt. to have a zero correction if the 20-g wt. is taken as the final standard and assumed to be 20.000 g?   (*b*) If the 500-mg wt. actually has a value of 0.5063 on the basis of the smaller standard, what correction should be applied for this wt. in any weighing in which its face value is taken as its true wt.?

8 Calculations of Gravimetric Analysis

8-1 Law of Definite Proportions Applied to Calculations of Gravimetric Analysis

Gravimetric analysis is based on the law of definite proportions, which states that in any pure compound the proportions by weight of the constituent elements are always the same, and on the law of constancy of composition, which states that masses of the elements taking part in a given chemical change exhibit a definite and invariable ratio to each other. It consists in determining the proportionate amount of an element, radical, or compound present in a sample by eliminating all interfering substances and converting the desired constituent or component into a weighable compound of definite, known composition. Having then determined the weight of this isolated compound, the weight of the desired component present in the sample can be calculated (see also Chap. 3).

Example 1 A sample of impure sodium chloride is dissolved in water, and the chloride is precipitated with silver nitrate ($Cl^- + Ag^+ \longrightarrow \underline{AgCl}$) furnishing 1.000 g of silver chloride. What is the weight of chlorine in the original sample?

Solution Since silver chloride contains silver and chlorine in the respective ratio of their atomic weights, or in the ratio of 107.87:35.45, in every 143.32 (107.87 + 35.45) g of silver chloride there is 35.45 g of chlorine. In 1.000 g of silver chloride there is

$$1.000 \times \frac{Cl}{AgCl} = 1.000 \times \frac{35.45}{143.32} = 0.2474 \text{ g Cl} \qquad Ans.$$

Example 2 The iron in a sample of $FeCO_3$ containing inert impurities is converted by solution, oxidation, precipitation, and ignition into Fe_2O_3 weighing 1.0000 g.   What is the weight of iron expressed as $FeCO_3$, as Fe, and as FeO in the original sample?

Solution   The reactions can be expressed by the following equations:

$$FeCO_3 + 2H^+ \longrightarrow Fe^{++} + CO_2 + H_2O$$
$$Fe^{++} + \tfrac{1}{2}Br_2 \longrightarrow Fe^{3+} + Br^-$$
$$Fe^{3+} + 3NH_4OH \longrightarrow Fe(OH)_3 + 3NH^+$$
$$2Fe(OH)_3 \longrightarrow Fe_2O_3 + 3H_2O$$

but for purposes of calculations all the intermediate steps can be omitted and the fundamental change expressed by the hypothetical equation

$$2\underline{FeCO_3} + O \longrightarrow \underline{Fe_2O_3} + 2CO_2$$

In general, it is unnecessary to determine the weights of intermediate products in a reaction that takes place in steps, and for purposes of calculation only the initial and final substances need be considered.

Since 2 moles (231.72 g) of $FeCO_3$ will furnish 1 mole (159.70 g) of Fe_2O_3, 1.0000 g of Fe_2O_3 will be obtained from

$$1.0000 \times \frac{2FeCO_3}{Fe_2O_3} = 1.0000 \times \frac{231.70}{159.69} = 1.4510 \text{ g } FeCO_3$$

Since each mole of $FeCO_2$ contains 1 g-at. wt. (55.85 g) of Fe and represents the equivalent of 1 mole (71.85 g) of $FeO(FeCO_3 \longrightarrow FeO + CO_2)$, the corresponding weights of Fe and FeO would be

$$1.0000 \times \frac{2Fe}{Fe_2O_3} = 1.0000 \times \frac{2 \times 55.85}{159.69} = 0.6994 \text{ g Fe} \qquad Ans.$$

$$1.0000 \times \frac{2FeO}{Fe_2O_3} = 1.0000 \times \frac{2 \times 71.85}{159.69} = 0.8998 \text{ g FeO} \qquad Ans.$$

Example 3   What weight of Fe_3O_4 will furnish 0.5430 g of Fe_2O_3?

Solution   Whatever equations may be written to represent the conversion of the Fe_3O_4 to the Fe_2O_3, it will be found that from every 2 moles of Fe_3O_4 there are obtained 3 moles of Fe_2O_3, and the hypothetical equation can be written

$$2\underline{Fe_3O_4} + O \longrightarrow 3\underline{Fe_2O_3}$$

Hence,

$$0.5430 \times \frac{2Fe_3O_4}{3Fe_2O_3} = 0.5430 \times \frac{463.1}{479.1} = 0.5249 \text{ g } Fe_3O_4 \qquad Ans.$$

8-2   Gravimetric Factors

A gravimetric factor (or *chemical factor*) can be defined as the weight of desired substance equivalent to a unit weight of given substance. Thus, in the above three examples, the numbers obtained from the ratios $Cl:AgCl$, $2FeCO_3:Fe_2O_3$, $2Fe:Fe_2O_3$, $2FeO:Fe_2O_3$, and $2Fe_3O_4:3Fe_2O_3$ are gravimetric factors, since they represent the respective weights of Cl, $FeCO_3$, Fe, FeO, and Fe_3O_4 equivalent to one unit weight of $AgCl$ or of Fe_2O_3 as the case may be.

A weight of one substance is said to be *equivalent* to that of another substance when the two will mutually enter into direct or indirect reaction in exact respective proportion to those weights. In the example cited above, 231.70 g of $FeCO_3$ produces 159.69 g of Fe_2O_3. Hence, 231.70 g of $FeCO_3$ is equivalent to 159.69 g of Fe_2O_3. The equivalent weights of elements and compounds may be expressed by mutual proportions as in the case just given, or they may be referred to a common standard for which purpose the atomic weight of hydrogen (1.008) is usually taken (see Sec. 4-7).

Note that in expressing a gravimetric factor the atomic or molecular weight of the substance *sought* is placed in the numerator, the atomic or molecular weight of the substance *weighed* is placed in the denominator, and the coefficients are adjusted *in accordance with the reactions involved*. When the principal element or radical desired occurs in both numerator and denominator, usually the number of atomic weights of this element or radical will be the same in both numerator and denominator, although there are instances when this is not true. For example, in the reaction

$$2CuCl \longrightarrow CuCl_2 + Cu$$

the weight of free copper liberated from 1 g of cuprous chloride is $1.000 \times (Cu/2CuCl) = 0.3209$ g, and 0.3209 is the gravimetric factor in this case.

That the principal element does not always occur in both numerator and denominator is shown in the determination of bromine by precipitation as silver bromide and conversion to silver chloride with a current of chlorine.

$$2AgBr + Cl_2 \longrightarrow 2AgCl + Br_2$$

Here the weight of bromine represented by 1 g of silver chloride is

$$\frac{Br_2}{2AgCl} = \frac{2 \times 79.91}{2 \times 143.32} = 0.5576 \text{ g}$$

8-3   Calculation of Percentages

Since the gravimetric factor represents the weight of desired element or compound equivalent to one unit weight of the element or compound weighed, from any weight of the latter the weight of the former can be calculated.   The percentage of that substance present in the sample can be found by dividing by the weight of the sample and multiplying by 100.

Example 1   If 2.000 g of impure sodium chloride is dissolved in water and, with an excess of silver nitrate, 4.6280 g of silver chloride is precipitated, what is the percentage of chlorine in the sample?

Solution   The gravimetric factor of Cl in AgCl is 0.2474, indicating that 1.000 g of AgCl contains 0.2474 g of Cl.   In 4.6280 g of AgCl there is therefore 4.6280 × 0.2474 = 1.145 g of Cl.   Since this amount represents the chlorine present in 2.000 g of the material, the percentage weight of chlorine must be

$$\frac{1.145}{2.000} \times 100 = 57.25\% \qquad Ans.$$

Example 2   A 0.5000-g sample of impure magnetite (Fe_3O_4) is converted by chemical reactions to Fe_2O_3, weighing 0.4110 g.   What is the percentage of Fe_3O_4 in the magnetite?

Solution   The gravimetric factor in this case is $2Fe_3O_4/3Fe_2O_3 = 0.9666$, which represents the weight of Fe_3O_4 equivalent to 1.000 g of Fe_2O_3. The weight of Fe_3O_4 equivalent to 0.4110 g of Fe_2O_3 must be 0.4110 × 0.9666 = 0.3973 g, and the percentage of Fe_3O_4 in the sample must be

$$\frac{0.3973}{0.5000} \times 100 = 79.46\% \qquad Ans.$$

PROBLEMS

*8-1.   Calculate the gravimetric factors for converting (*a*) $BaSO_4$ to Ba, (*b*) Nb_2O_5 to Nb, (*c*) $Mg_2P_2O_7$ to MgO, (*d*) $KClO_4$ to K_2O, (*e*) Fe_3O_4 to Fe_2O_3.

*8-2.   Calculate the gravimetric factors of the following:

	Weighed	*Sought*
(*a*)	$(NH_4)_2PtCl_6$	NH_3
(*b*)	MoS_3	MoO_3
(*c*)	U_3O_8	U
(*d*)	B_2O_3	$Na_2B_4O_7 \cdot 10H_2O$
(*e*)	$(NH_4)_3PO_4 \cdot 12MoO_3$	P_2O_5

*8-3.   What is the wt. of S in 5.672 g of $BaSO_4$?

*8-4.   How many g of $Na_2SO_4 \cdot 10H_2O$ are equiv. to the Na in the NaCl required to ppt. AgCl from 2.000 g of $AgNO_3$?

*8-5.   A sample of ferrous ammonium sulfate contg. inert material weighs 0.5013 g and furnishes 0.0968 g of Fe_2O_3.   What is the percentage of $FeSO_4 \cdot (NH_4)_2SO_4 \cdot 6H_2O$ in the sample?

*8-6.   A sample of limestone weighing 1.2456 g furnishes 0.0228 g of Fe_2O_3, 1.3101 g of $CaSO_4$, and 0.0551 g of $Mg_2P_2O_7$.   Find the percentage of (a) Fe, (b) CaO, (c) MgO in the limestone.   (d) What wt. of CO_2 could be in combination with the CaO?

*8-7.   What wt. of pyrite contg. 36.40% S must have been taken for analysis in order to give a ppt. of $BaSO_4$ weighing 1.0206 g?

*8-8.   (a) What is the percentage composition of a brass contg. only Cu, Pb, and Zn if a sample weighing 0.5000 g furnishes 0.0023 g of $PbSO_4$ and 0.4108 g of $ZnNH_4PO_4$?   (b) What wt. of $Zn_2P_2O_7$ could be obtained by igniting the $ZnNH_4PO_4$?

*8-9.   If a sample of a salt of the theoretical formula $Mn(NO_3)_2 \cdot 6H_2O$ (f. wt. = 287.04) has lost some of its water of crystallization to the extent that on analysis 0.1020 g of $Mn_2P_2O_7$ (f. wt. = 283.82) was obtained from a 0.2000-g sample, what percentage of the theoretical water of crystallization is shown to have been lost?

*8-10.   The N in a 0.5000-g sample of organic material is converted to NH_4HSO_4 by digestion with concd. H_2SO_4.   If the NH_4^+ ions are pptd. as $(NH_4)_2PtCl_6$ and the ppt. is ignited to Pt, what is the percentage of N in the sample if the Pt weighs 0.1756 g?

*8-11.   A sample of pyrite, FeS_2, contains only inert impurities and weighs 0.5080 g.   After the sample has been decomposed and dissolved, a ppt. of 1.561 g of $BaSO_4$ is subsequently obtained.   (a) Calculate the percentage of S in the sample.   (b) If the Fe in the soln. had been pptd. as $Fe(OH)_3$ and ignited to Fe_2O_3, what wt. of ignited ppt. would have been obtained?

*8-12.   A sample of alum, $K_2SO_4 \cdot Al_2(SO_4)_3 \cdot 24H_2O$, contg. only inert impurities weighs 1.421 g.   It gives a ppt. of $Al(OH)_3$ which ignites to 0.1410 g of Al_2O_3.   What is the percentage (a) of S and (b) of impurities in the sample?

8-13.   Calculate the gravimetric factors for converting (a) Al_2O_3 to Al, (b) AgCl to $KClO_4$, (c) $Cu_3(AsO_3)_2 \cdot 2As_2O_3 \cdot Cu(C_2H_3O_2)_2$ (mol. wt. = 1,016) to As_2O_3, (d) $KClO_4$ to K_2O, (e) $(NH_4)_2PtCl_6$ to NH_3.

8-14.   Calculate the gravimetric factors of the following:

	Weighed	Sought
(a)	$Mg_2P_2O_7$	P
(b)	K_2PtCl_6	KNO_3
(c)	Mn_3O_4	Mn_2O_3
(d)	$Cu_2(SCN)_2$	HSCN
(e)	KBF_4	$Na_2B_4O_7 \cdot 10H_2O$

8-15.   What wt. of AgBr could be obtained from 4.7527 g of $Ag_2Cr_2O_7$?

8-16.   How many lb of phosphorus are contained in 1.000 ton of $Ca_3(PO_4)_2$?

8-17.   An ammonium salt is converted to $(NH_4)_2PtCl_6$ and the latter ignited until only the Pt remains in the crucible.   If the residue weighs 0.1000 g, what wt. of NH_3 was present in the original salt?

8-18.   What wt. of H_2O could be obtained by strongly igniting 2.000 g of datolite, $CaB(OH)SiO_4$ (f. wt. = 160.0)?

8-19.   Find the percentage composition of the following in terms of the oxides of the metallic elements: (a) $FeSO_4 \cdot 7H_2O$, (b) $K_2SO_4 \cdot Al_2(SO_4)_3 \cdot 24H_2O$, (c) $3Ca_3(PO_4)_2 \cdot CaCO_3$ (f. wt. = 1030.7).

8-20.   An alloy is of the following composition: Cu, 65.40%; Pb, 0.24%; Fe, 0.56%; Zn, 33.80%.   A sample weighing 0.8060 g is dissolved in HNO_3 and electrolyzed. Cu is deposited on the cathode; PbO_2 is deposited on the anode.   When NH_4OH is added to the residual soln., $Fe(OH)_3$ is pptd. and the ppt. is ignited to Fe_2O_3.   The Zn in the filtrate is pptd. as $ZnNH_4PO_4$, and the ppt. is ignited to $Zn_2P_2O_7$.   What wts. of deposits and ignited ppts. were obtained?

8-21.   How many g of KNO_3 are equiv. to the K in that wt. of K_3PO_4 contg. the same amt. of combined P_2O_5 that is contained in 1.100 g of $Ca_3(PO_4)_2$?

8-22.   The Sb in a sample of an alloy weighing 0.2500 g is converted to Sb_2O_5, and this substance is ignited to Sb_2O_4.   (a) If the latter weighs 0.1305 g, what is the percentage of Sb in the alloy?   (b) What was the loss in wt. caused by the ignition?

8-23.   A sample of Pb_3O_4 contg. only inert matter weighs 0.1753 g and, after dissolving, subsequently yields 0.2121 g of $PbSO_4$.   What is the purity of the sample expressed (a) in terms of percentage of Pb, (b) in terms of percentage of Pb_3O_4?

8-24.   A sample of $FeSO_4 \cdot (NH_4)_2SO_4 \cdot 6H_2O$ contg. only inert impurities weighs 1.658 g.   After the Fe has been dissolved, oxidized, and pptd., the $Fe(OH)_3$ ignites to 0.3174 g of Fe_2O_3.   Calculate the percentage of S and the percentage of impurities in the sample.

8-4   Calculation of Atomic Weights

Determinations of atomic-weight values have been chiefly revisions of those already established, in order for their accuracy to be consistent with improved apparatus and methods.   In such cases, the formulas of the compounds involved are well established and the required calculations are thereby made every simple.   The experimental procedure usually followed is to prepare from the element a known compound of high degree of purity.   This compound is weighed, and the percentages of its constituents are determined gravimetrically.   The mathematical computations involved are exactly similar to those of an ordinary gravimetric analysis, except that the atomic weight of the desired element is the only unknown factor.

Example 1   Carefully purified sodium chloride weighing 2.56823 g furnished 6.2971 g of silver chloride. Assuming the atomic weights of chlorine and silver were taken as 35.457 and 107.880, respectively, calculate the atomic weight of sodium.

Solution

$$\text{Wt. of NaCl} = \text{wt. of AgCl} \times \frac{\text{NaCl}}{\text{AgCl}}$$

$$2.56823 = 6.2971 \times \frac{\text{NaCl}}{\text{AgCl}}$$

$$2.56823 = 6.2971 \times \frac{\text{Na} + 35.457}{107.880 + 35.457}$$

Solving,

$$\text{Na} = 23.002 \qquad Ans.$$

PROBLEMS

*8-25.   If Ag_3PO_4 was found by careful analysis to contain 77.300% Ag and the at. wt. of Ag was taken as 107.88, what was the calculated at. wt. of P?

*8-26.   From an average of 13 experiments, Baxter found the ratio of the wt. of AgBr to that of an equiv. amt. of AgCl to be 1.310171. If the at. wt. of Ag was taken as 107.880 and that of Cl as 35.457, what was the calculated at. wt. of Br?

*8-27.   In determining the at. wt. of Mn, Berzelius, in 1828, obtained 0.7225 g of Mn_2O_3 from 0.5075 g of Mn. Von Hauer, in 1857, obtained 13.719 g of Mn_3O_4 from 12.7608 g of MnO. In 1906, Baxter and Hines obtained an average of 11.43300 g of AgBr from 6.53738 g of $MnBr_2$. What were the three values as determined? (Br = 79.916; Ag = 107.880.)

*8-28.   In determining the at. wt. of As, Baxter and Coffin converted several samples of Ag_3AsO_4 to AgCl and found the average value for the ratio $3AgCl : Ag_3AsO_4$ to be 0.929550. (*a*) Using the ratio Ag : AgCl as found by Richards and Wells to be 0.752632, calculate the percentage of Ag in Ag_3AsO_4. (*b*) Taking the at. wt. of Ag as 107.880, calculate to five figures the at. wt. of As.

8-29.   In determining the at. wt. of Al, Richards and Krepelka prepared pure samples of $AlBr_3$ and determined the wt. of Ag required to ppt. the Br^-. Results of four runs were as follows:

Sample	Wt. $AlBr_3$	Wt. Ag
1	5.03798	6.11324
2	5.40576	6.55955
3	3.41815	4.14786
4	1.96012	2.40285

If the at. wt. of Ag was taken as 107.880 and that of Br as 79.916, what was the mean value obtained for the at. wt. of Al?

8-30.   The ratio of the wt. of $SiCl_4$ to the wt. of an equiv. amt. of Ag has been found to be 0.393802 ± 0.000008. Assuming that $Cl = 35.453$ and $Ag = 107.870$, calculate the at. wt. of Si.

8-31.   Classen and Strauch determined the wts. of Bi_2O_3 obtainable from several samples of bismuth triphenyl. In one such detn., 5.34160 g of $Bi(C_6H_5)_3$ gave 2.82761 g of Bi_2O_3. Calculate from these figures the at. wt. of Bi. ($C = 12.011$; $H = 1.0080$.)

8-32.   From the ratios $NaNO_3 : NaCl = 1.45422$, $AgCl : Ag = 1.328668$, and $NaCl : Ag = 0.541854$ and assuming that $N = 14.007$, set up algebraic equations which, if solved simultaneously, would give the at. wts. of Ag, Na, and Cl.

8.5   Calculations Involving a Factor Weight Sample

It is sometimes desirable in industrial work, where large numbers of samples of similar material are analyzed, to regulate the weight of sample so that the weight of the final product obtained multiplied by a simple factor will exactly equal the percentage of the desired constituent. This makes it possible to have the sample weighed out directly against a tare, perhaps by someone inexperienced in exact weighing, and at the same time to eliminate both the tedious calculations necessary for each analysis and the possibility of mathematical errors.

The calculation of a desired constituent in a chemical analysis involving a direct gravimetric determination is carried out by means of the following formula:

$$\frac{\text{Grams of product} \times \text{gravimetric factor}}{\text{Grams of sample}} \times 100 = \%$$

Since for a specific determination the gravimetric factor is a constant, the expression contains only three variable factors, viz., the weight of product, the weight of sample, and the percentage of desired constituent. If any two are known, the third can be calculated, or since the expression involves only multiplication and division, if the numerical *ratio* between the weight of product and the weight of sample or between the weight of product and the percentage of desired constituent is known, the remaining term can be determined. Thus, if the weight of product is numerically equal to the percentage of desired constituent, these values cancel and the weight of sample becomes equal to 100 times the gravimetric factor. If the weight of product is numerically equal to the weight of sample, these values cancel and the percentage of desired constituent becomes equal to 100 times the gravimetric factor. Other ratios can be inserted in the expression, and the calculation made in a similar way.

Example 1   The gravimetric factor of a certain analysis is 0.3427.   It is desired to regulate the weight of sample taken so that (*a*) each centigram of the precipitate obtained will represent 1% of the desired constituent, (*b*) the percentage will be twice the number of centigrams of precipitate. What weight of sample should be taken in each case?

Solution

(*a*) The relation between the weight of precipitate and the percentage of constituent is such that 0.01 g $\approx$ 1%.   Hence,

$$\frac{0.01 \times 0.3427}{x} \times 100 = 1$$

$$x = 0.3427 \text{ g} \qquad Ans.$$

(*b*) $\dfrac{0.01 \times 0.3427}{x} \times 100 = 2$

$$x = 0.1714 \text{ g} \qquad Ans.$$

PROBLEMS

*8-33.   What wt. of cast iron should be taken for analysis so that the wt. of ignited SiO_2 in cg will be equal to one-third of the percentage of Si in the cast iron?

*8-34.   Find the wt. of limestone to be taken so that the no. of cg of CaO obtained and the percentage of Ca in the sample will be in the respective ratio of 7:5.

8-35.   What wt. of dolomite should be taken for analysis so that in the detn. of Mg the no. of cg of $Mg_2P_2O_7$ obtained will be twice the percentage of Mg in the mineral?

8-36.   What wt. of magnetite (impure Fe_3O_4) should be taken for analysis so that after decomposition of the sample, pptn. of the Fe as $Fe(OH)_3$, and ignition to Fe_2O_3, (*a*) the no. of cg of Fe_2O_3 obtained will be equal to the percentage of Fe_3O_4 in the sample, (*b*) the no. of mg of Fe_2O_3 obtained will be five times the percentage of Fe_3O_4, (*c*) the percentage of total Fe in the sample and the no. of cg of Fe_2O_3 obtained will be in the ratio of 3:2?

8-6   Calculation of the Volume of a Reagent
Required for a Given Reaction

The volume of a solution required to carry out a given reaction can be calculated if the concentration of the solution is known.   If the concentration is expressed in terms of normality, the calculation is best made by the methods of volumetric analysis, i.e., in terms of milliequivalents (see Sec. 4-7); if the concentration is expressed as grams of solute per unit volume of solution or in terms of specific gravity and percentage composition, the calculation is usually most easily made by the use of the gravimetric factor.

Example 1   How many milliliters of barium chloride solution containing 90.0 g of $BaCl_2 \cdot 2H_2O$ per liter are required to precipitate the sulfate as $BaSO_4$ from 10.0 g of pure $Na_2SO_4 \cdot 10H_2O$?

Solution   Since 1 mole of Ba^{++} reacts with 1 mole of $SO_4^=$ (Ba^{++} + $SO_4^= \longrightarrow BaSO_4$), 1 mole of $BaCl_2 \cdot 2H_2O$ (244 g) reacts with 1 mole of $Na_2SO_4 \cdot 10H_2O$ (322 g).   The simple ratio of molecular weights therefore serves as the gravimetric factor for making the necessary conversion of weights; thus

$$10.0 \times \frac{BaCl_2 \cdot 2H_2O}{Na_2SO_4 \cdot 10H_2O} = 10.0 \times \frac{244}{322} = 7.58 \text{ g } BaCl_2 \cdot 2H_2O$$

Since each milliliter of reagent contains 0.0900 g of $BaCl_2 \cdot 2H_2O$, the volume of solution required is

$$\frac{7.58}{0.0900} = 84.2 \text{ ml} \qquad Ans.$$

When the concentration of the required reagent is expressed in terms of the percentage by weight of the solute, the specific gravity of the solution must also be known in order to determine the volume required.   As stated in Sec. 4-4, there is no exact mathematical relationship between these two factors, but tables are given in all standard chemical handbooks showing this relationship for solutions of common substances experimentally determined at many different concentrations. Consequently, when a problem includes only one of these factors, tables must be consulted in order to determine the other.   In the Appendix, specific gravity–percentage tables are given for a few common acids and bases.   These tables apply to weighings in vacuo at definite temperatures, but since three-significant-figure accuracy is all that is needed in most calculations involving specific gravity of solutions, it is usually not necessary to make corrections for temperature and buoyancy differences.

Example 2   How many milliliters of ammonia water of specific gravity 0.950 (containing 12.74% of NH_3 by weight) are required to precipitate the iron from 0.800 g of pure ferrous ammonium sulfate, $FeSO_4 \cdot (NH_4)_2SO_4 \cdot 6H_2O$, after oxidation of the iron to the ferric state?

Solution   Since three molecules of ammonia are required to precipitate one atom of ferric iron

$$Fe^{3+} + 3NH_3 + 3H_2O \longrightarrow Fe(OH)_3 + 3NH_4^+$$

it follows that the weight of NH_3 necessary to precipitate the iron from 0.800 g of ferrous ammonium sulfate is

$$0.800 \times \frac{3NH_3}{FeSO_4 \cdot (NH_4)_2SO_4 \cdot 6H_2O} = 0.800 \times \frac{51.09}{392.1} = 0.1042 \text{ g } NH_3$$

Since the ammonia water has a specific gravity of 0.950 and contains 12.74% of NH_3 by weight, 1 ml of the solution weighs 0.950 g of which 12.74% by weight is NH_3 and 87.26% by weight is H_2O. The actual weight of NH_3 in 1 ml of solution is therefore $0.950 \times 0.1274 = 0.121$ g. Since 0.1042 g of NH_3 is required to precipitate the iron and since each milliliter of the solution contains 0.121 g of NH_3, it follows that the volume of solution required is

$$\frac{0.1042}{0.121} = 0.861 \text{ ml} \qquad Ans.$$

As explained in Sec. 8-1, in calculations of this type the computations should not be carried through unnecessary steps. For purposes of calculation a knowledge of any intermediate steps that may take place is usually important only in establishing the proper coefficients to be used in the gravimetric factor. With problems of this type, time will be saved if the final multiplications and divisions are not made until all the factors are combined and expressed as a whole. In the above example the only essential factors are

$$\frac{0.800 \times 51.09}{392.1 \times 0.950 \times 0.1274} = 0.861 \text{ ml} \qquad Ans.$$

A very similar type of problem is one in which it is required to calculate the volume of a solution of given percentage composition required to react with a certain volume of another solution of given percentage composition. By computing the weight of reacting component in the given volume of the latter solution, the problem becomes exactly like the one discussed above.

Example 3   How many milliliters of sulfuric acid (sp. gr. 1.135, 18.96% H_2SO_4 by weight) are required to neutralize 75.0 ml of ammonium hydroxide (sp. gr. 0.960, containing 9.91% NH_3 by weight)?

Solution   In 75.0 ml of the ammonia solution there are

$$75.0 \times 0.960 \times 0.0991 \text{ g } NH_3$$

The required weight of H_2SO_4 for this NH_3 is

$$75.0 \times 0.960 \times 0.0991 \times \frac{H_2SO_4}{2NH_3} = 75.0 \times 0.960 \times 0.0991 \times \frac{98.08}{34.06} \text{ g}$$

Since each milliliter of the acid contains 1.135×0.1896 g of H_2SO_4, the volume of acid required is

$$\frac{75.0 \times 0.960 \times 0.0991 \times 98.08}{1.135 \times 0.1896 \times 34.06} = 95.5 \text{ ml} \qquad Ans.$$

8-7   Calculation of the Concentration of a Reagent Mixture

This type of problem is frequently encountered by the chemical engineer and industrial chemist.   It involves fairly concentrated solutions and, as stated in the preceding section, since the percentage composition of such a solution does not bear a direct mathematical relationship to its specific gravity, appropriate tables (see Appendix) must be used in order to find one from the other.   For this reason, too, the required amounts of solutions should be calculated on the basis of weight rather than on the basis of volume.   Standard conditions of temperature are assumed in the following examples and problems.   A precision of three significant figures is adequate.

Example 1   What weight of water must be added to 100 ml of sulfuric acid containing 26.0% by weight of H_2SO_4 in order for the resulting solution to contain 12.3% by weight of H_2SO_4?

Solution   The original solution is of specific gravity 1.19 (Table 8, Appendix) and therefore weighs 119 g.   It contains $119 \times 0.260 = 30.9$ g of pure H_2SO_4.   The desired solution contains 12.3% H_2SO_4.   Let x = number of grams of water added.

$$\frac{\text{Wt. of } H_2SO_4}{\text{Wt. of soln.}} \times 100 = \%$$

$$\frac{30.9}{119 + x} \times 100 = 12.3$$

$$x = 132 \text{ g} \qquad Ans.$$

Example 2   What are the percentage-by-weight composition and the specific gravity of a reagent made by mixing equal volumes of water, HNO_3 (sp. gr. 1.40), and HNO_3 (49.1% HNO_3 by weight)?

Solution   Assume 1.00 ml of each liquid to be used.

1.00 ml H_2O = 1.00 g.

1.00 ml HNO_3 (sp. gr. 1.40) weighs 1.40 g and contains $1.40 \times 0.653 = 0.914$ g of HNO_3 (Table 8, Appendix).

1.00 ml HNO_3 (49.1%) weighs 1.31 g (Table 8) and contains $1.31 \times 0.491 = 0.643$ g of HNO_3.

The mixture therefore weighs $1.00 + 1.40 + 1.31 = 3.71$ g and contains $0.914 + 0.643 = 1.56$ g of HNO_3.

Percentage by wt. of HNO_3 = 1.56/3.71 = 42.0%   *Ans.*

Sp. gr. (Table 8) = 1.26   *Ans.*

Example 3   Given two solutions of hydrochloric acid.   Solution A is of specific gravity 1.160; solution B is of specific gravity 1.060.   In what proportion by weight should these be mixed in order to obtain a solution containing 20.0% HCl by weight?

Solution

  Soln. A contains 31.5% by weight of HCl (Table 8, Appendix).

  Soln. B contains 12.2% by weight of HCl.

  Assume 100 g of A to be used.

  Let x = no. of g of B required.

$$\frac{\text{Wt. of HCl}}{\text{Wt. of soln.}} \times 100 = \% \text{ HCl}$$

$$\frac{(100 \times 0.315) + (x \times 0.122)}{100 + x} \times 100 = 20.0$$

$$x = 147 \text{ g}$$

Ratio: $\dfrac{A}{B} = \dfrac{100}{147}$ *Ans.*

A somewhat more complicated problem arises when a chemical reaction takes place between components of the mixed solutions. A common example of this occurs in the preparation of oleum mixtures. Oleum (fuming sulfuric acid) consists of free SO_3 dissolved in 100% H_2SO_4. If an oleum is mixed with ordinary concentrated sulfuric acid (i.e., containing a little water), some of the free SO_3 of the oleum unites with the free H_2O in the sulfuric acid and forms $H_2SO_4(SO_3 + H_2O \longrightarrow H_2SO_4)$.

Example 4   What relative weights of sulfuric acid (containing 97.8% H_2SO_4 and 2.2% H_2O) and oleum (containing 30.0% SO_3 and 70.0% H_2SO_4) must be mixed in order to prepare an oleum containing 12.0% free SO_3?

Solution   Assume 100 g of the 97.8% H_2SO_4 are taken. Let x = number of grams of 30.0% oleum needed. One hundred grams of the 97.8% H_2SO_4 would unite with

$$2.2 \times \frac{SO_3}{H_2O} = 9.80 \text{ g } SO_3$$

  Free SO_3 remaining = $(0.30x - 9.80)$ g

  Wt. of mixt. = $100 + x$

$$\% \text{ free } SO_3 = \frac{0.30x - 9.80}{100 + x} = 0.12$$

$$x = 121 \text{ g}$$

$$\text{Ratio} = \tfrac{100}{121}$$

$$= \text{approx.} \begin{cases} 45\% \text{ sulfuric acid} \\ 55\% \text{ oleum} \end{cases} \quad Ans.$$

   Figure 2 shows a nomograph which has been constructed for solving this last type of problem.   It is typical of nomographs in general (see
Sec. 1-10).
   To solve the above problem by means of the nomograph, first locate
on scale X the percentage of H_2SO_4 in the concentrated sulfuric acid
($= 97.8$).   Then locate on scale C the percentage of SO_3 in the desired
oleum ($= 12.0$).   Connect these two points by means of a straight line,
and extend the line to the A axis.   On scale X_1 again locate the percentage of H_2SO_4 in the concentrated sulfuric acid ($= 97.8$), and on scale C_1
locate the percentage of SO_3 in the original oleum ($= 30.0$).   Connect
these two points by means of a straight line, and extend the line to the
B axis.   Now connect the points on the A and B axes by means of a
straight line.   The point where this line intersects the inclined scale

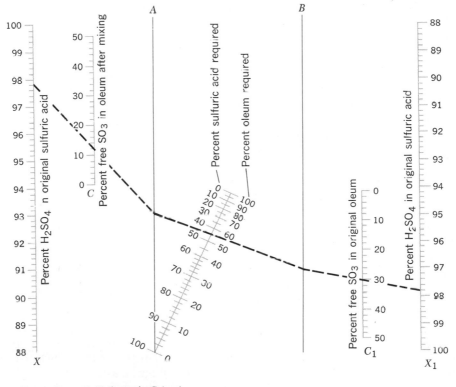

Key: Connect X through C to A
       Connect X_1 through C_1 to B
       Connect A to B through the inclined scale
       Answer is at point of contact with inclined scale

**Fig. 2   Nomograph for calculating the relative amounts by weight of concentrated sulfuric acid
and oleum required to prepare an oleum of desired composition.** (*From an article by C. S. Davis
in Chem. & Met. Eng., vol. 43, no. 3, p. 150, 1936; by permission.*)

shows the relative percentages by weight of the two original solutions required for mixing ($= 45\%$ sulfuric acid, 55% oleum).

PROBLEMS

*8-37. (*a*) What vol. of ammonium oxalate soln. contg. 35.1 g of $(NH_4)_2C_2O_4 \cdot H_2O$ per liter is required to ppt. the Ca as CaC_2O_4 from 0.124 g of $3Ca_3(PO_4)_2 \cdot CaCl_2$? (*b*) What vol. of "magnesia mixture" contg. 1.00 f. wt. of $MgCl_2$ per liter is required to ppt. the phosphate as $MgNH_4PO_4$ from the filtrate from the Ca detn.?

*8-38. (*a*) How many ml of a soln. contg. 20.00 g of $AgNO_3$ per 100 ml are required to ppt. all the Cl as AgCl from a soln. contg. 2.012 g of dissolved $BaCl_2 \cdot 2H_2O$? (*b*) How many ml of H_2SO_4 (sp. gr. 1.105) are required to ppt. the Ba as $BaSO_4$ from the same soln.?

*8-39. In the pptn. of As as $MgNH_4AsO_4$ from a soln. of 0.4000 g of As_2O_3 that has been oxidized to H_3AsO_4, it is desired to add sufficient reagent contg. 64.00 g of $MgCl_2$ per liter to ppt. the As and also have 200 mg of Mg remaining in soln. What vol. is required?

*8-40. Chloride samples are to be prepared for student analysis by using NaCl, KCl, and NH_4Cl, alone or mixed in various proportions. What min. vol. of a 5.00% $AgNO_3$ soln. (sp. gr. 1.041) must be added to a sample weighing 0.300 g in order to ensure complete pptn. in every possible case?

*8-41. How many ml of aq. NH_3 (sp. gr. 0.900) are required to ppt. the Fe as $Fe(OH)_3$ from 5.00 g of $Fe_2(SO_4)_3 \cdot 9H_2O$?

*8-42. Calculate the vol. of HCl soln. (sp. gr. 1.050) required to neutralize (*a*) 48.6 ml of a soln. of KOH contg. 12.0% KOH by wt., (*b*) a soln. contg. 10.0 g of impure KOH (96.6% KOH, 2.2% K_2CO_3, 1.2% H_2O), (*c*) 2.00 g of $Ba(OH)_2 \cdot 8H_2O$.

*8-43. The following are added to water: 1.60 g of Na_2CO_3, 2.21 ml of H_2SO_4 soln. (sp. gr. 1.700), and 16.0 ml of KOH soln. (56.0 g of solid per liter). This soln. is to be brought to the neutral point. The solns. available are HCl (sp. gr. 1.141) and NH_4OH (sp. gr. 0.930). What vol. of which soln. is required?

*8-44. It is desired to add a sufficient vol. of H_2SO_4 (sp. gr. 1.835) to liberate from excess NaCl that amt. of HCl gas which when absorbed in H_2O will furnish 250 ml of soln. of sp. gr. 1.040. Calculate the vol. necessary.

*8-45. A soln. is prepared by dissolving 2.20 g of $FeSO_4 \cdot (NH_4)_2SO_4 \cdot 6H_2O$ in H_2O contg. 15.0 ml of H_2SO_4 (sp. gr. 1.135). The Fe is oxidized by Br_2 to the ferric state, and the excess Br_2 boiled out. What total vol. of NH_4OH contg. 12.74% NH_3 by wt. is required to neutralize the acid and just ppt. all the Fe as $Fe(OH)_3$?

*8-46. For student analysis a sample of iron and sulfate is prepared by thoroughly mixing $FeSO_4 \cdot 7H_2O$ and $FeSO_4 \cdot (NH_4)_2SO_4 \cdot 6H_2O$ in the respective proportion by wt. of 5 to 8. A 1.300-g sample is dissolved in water contg. 5.00 ml of 6.00 N HCl and the iron is oxidized with Br_2 ($2Fe^{++} + Br_2 \longrightarrow 2Fe^{3+} + 2Br^-$). (*a*) Calculate the total vol. of NH_3 soln. (sp. gr. 0.960, contg. 9.91% NH_3 by wt.)

theoretically required to neutralize the acid, ppt. all the iron as $Fe(OH)_3$, and leave an excess of 7.00 meq. of alkali in the soln. (b) Calculate the wt. of the ignited iron ppt. and (c) that of the $BaSO_4$ subsequently obtained in the analysis.

*8-47. (a) What is the percentage-by-wt. composition of a soln. made by mixing H_2SO_4 soln. (sp. gr. 1.205) and H_2O in the respective ratio by vol. of 2:1? (b) What is the sp. gr. of the mixt.?

*8-48. Given two solns. of H_2SO_4. Soln. A has a specific gravity of 1.140; soln. B contains 48.0% of combined SO_3 ($H_2SO_4 = SO_3 + H_2O$). In what proportion by wt. and by vol. should these solns. be mixed in order to obtain a soln. contg. 34.0% H_2SO_4 by wt.?

*8-49. How many g of H_2O should be added to 200 ml of NaOH soln. (sp. gr. 1.320) in order for the specific gravity of the resulting soln. to be 1.157?

*8-50. Equal vols. of NH_4OH (sp. gr. 0.960) and NH_4OH (sp. gr. 0.900) are mixed. (a) What is the percentage of NH_3 in the resulting soln.? (b) What would be the percentage of NH_3 in the resulting soln. if equal wts. of the initial solns. were mixed?

*8-51. An oleum weighing 10.0 g and consisting of 36.0% free SO_3 and 64.0% H_2SO_4 is to be diluted by adding acid contg. 97.0% H_2SO_4 and 3.0% H_2O. It is desired to obtain an oleum contg. 18.0% SO_3 and 82.0% H_2SO_4. Calculate the wt. of the acid to be added, and verify the answer by means of the nomograph given in the text.

*8-52. (a) If 140 g of oleum contg. 40.0% free SO_3 and 60.0% H_2SO_4 is mixed with 60.0 g of an acid contg. 99.0% H_2SO_4 and 1.0% H_2O, what is the percentage of free SO_3 in the resulting soln.? (b) Show how this result can be obtained from the nomograph given in the text.

8-53. (a) How many ml of a soln. contg. 21.05 g of $BaCl_2 \cdot 2H_2O$ per liter are required to ppt. all the sulfate as $BaSO_4$ from a soln. contg. 1.500 g of $Fe_2(SO_4)_3 \cdot 9H_2O$? (b) How many ml of NaOH soln. (sp. gr. 1.200) are required to ppt. all the Fe as $Fe(OH)_3$ from the same soln.?

8-54. A sample of $MgCO_3$ contaminated with SiO_2 weighs 0.500 g and loses 0.1002 g on ignition to MgO. The MgO is dissolved in HCl, and then NH_4OH is added. (a) What vol. of soln. contg. 90.0 g of $Na_2HPO_4 \cdot 12H_2O$ per liter would be required to convert the Mg^{++} to a ppt. of $MgNH_4PO_4 \cdot 6H_2O$? (b) What loss in wt. would this ppt. undergo on being ignited to $Mg_2P_2O_7$?

8-55. How many ml of a chromate soln. contg. 26.30 g of K_2CrO_4 per liter should be taken in order to yield 0.6033 g of Cr_2O_3 after appropriate chemical treatment?

8-56. The As in a sample of As_2S_3 weighing 0.500 g is oxidized to H_3AsO_4 and is pptd. as $MgNH_4AsO_4$ with a soln. of "magnesia mixt." ($MgCl_2 + NH_4Cl$). If 12.6 ml of the mixt. is theoretically required, how many g of $MgCl_2$ per liter does the soln. contain?

8-57. How many g of AgCl will be formed by the addition of an excess of $AgNO_3$ to 10.00 ml of HCl soln. contg. 31.52% HCl by wt.?

8-58. What vol. of H_2SO_4 soln. of sp. gr. 1.800 is required to ppt. all the Ba as $BaSO_4$ from 1.242 g of $BaCl_2 \cdot 2H_2O$?

8-59. How many ml of NH_3 soln. (sp. gr. 0.940) will neutralize 40.00 ml of a soln. contg. 33.00% H_2SO_4 by wt.?

8-60. According to the following equation, what vol. of HNO_3 (sp. gr. 1.050) is required to oxidize the Fe in 1.000 g of $FeSO_4 \cdot 7H_2O$? [$6FeSO_4 + 2HNO_3 + 3H_2SO_4 \longrightarrow 3Fe_2(SO_4)_3 + 2NO + 4H_2O$.]

8-61. How many ml of NH_3 soln. (sp. gr. 0.960) will be required to ppt. the Al as $Al(OH)_3$ from a soln. contg. 50.0 g of $KAl(SO_4)_2 \cdot 12H_2O$ and 100 ml of HCl soln. contg. 23.82% HCl by wt.?

8-62. Alum, $KAl(SO_4)_2 12H_2O$, weighing 0.6000 g is dissolved in H_2O and 1.00 ml of HCl soln. (sp. gr. 1.120) is added. If it takes a total of 0.742 ml of NH_4OH to neutralize the acid and ppt. all the Al as $Al(OH)_3$, find the sp. gr. and percentage-by-wt. composition of the NH_4OH.

8-63. To a suspension of 0.310 g of $Al(OH)_3$ in water is added 13.0 ml of NH_3 soln. (sp. gr. 0.900). How many ml of H_2SO_4 (sp. gr. 1.18) must be added to the mixt. in order theoretically to bring the $Al(OH)_3$ into soln.?

8-64. What is the sp. gr. of a soln. of HNO_3 if, when mixed with an equal wt. of a soln. of HNO_3 contg. 47.5% by wt. of HNO_3, the resulting soln. has the same sp. gr. as that of a soln. of HCl contg. 35.4% HCl by wt.?

8-65. In what proportion by wt. should one mix an oleum contg. 20.0% free SO_3 and 80.0% H_2SO_4 and a soln. contg. 96.0% H_2SO_4 and 4.0% H_2O in order for the resulting liquid to be 100.0% hydrogen sulfate? Solve by numerical calculation, and verify from the nomograph given in the text.

8-66. What is the percentage by wt. of NH_3 in a soln. made by mixing the following liquids in the respective vol. ratio of 3:2:1: (*a*) NH_4OH (sp. gr. 0.900), (*b*) NH_4OH (contg. 11.6% NH_3 by wt.), (*c*) H_2O?

8-67. In what ratio by vol. must H_2O and NH_4OH (sp. gr. 0.900) be mixed in order for the resulting soln. to contain 12.75% NH_3?

8-8   Indirect Gravimetric Methods

The simplest type of indirect analysis is one in which two pure chemical substances are isolated and weighed together. Then, either by further chemical action on the substances or by analysis of a new sample of the material, additional data are derived by which one of the components is determined. The other component is then found by difference.

Example 1   In the analysis of a 2.00-g sample of limestone, the weight of combined oxides of iron and aluminum ($Fe_2O_3 + Al_2O_3$) is found to be

0.0812 g.   By volumetric methods, the percentage in the limestone of total iron calculated as FeO is found to be 1.50.   What is the percentage of Al_2O_3 in the sample?

Solution

$$\text{Wt. of FeO} = 2.00 \times \frac{1.50}{100} = 0.0300 \text{ g}$$

$$\text{Wt. of Fe}_2\text{O}_3 = 0.0300 \times \frac{\text{Fe}_2\text{O}_3}{2\text{FeO}} = 0.0333 \text{ g}$$

$$\text{Wt. of Al}_2\text{O}_3 = 0.0812 - 0.0333 = 0.0479 \text{ g}$$

$$\% \text{ Al}_2\text{O}_3 = \frac{0.0479}{2.00} \times 100 = 2.40 \qquad Ans.$$

The J. Lawrence Smith method for determining sodium and potassium in a silicate is an example of an indirect analysis of this type.   By this method the sample is decomposed and the alkalies are isolated and weighed as combined chlorides.   These are dissolved, and the potassium alone is precipitated from water-alcohol solution as K_2PtCl_6 (or as $KClO_4$) and weighed as such.   The K_2PtCl_6 can also be ignited and weighed as $2KCl + Pt$ or (after washing) as metallic platinum.

Example 2   In the analysis of a sample of feldspar weighing 0.4150 g, a mixture of KCl + NaCl is obtained weighing 0.0715 g.   From these chlorides, 0.1548 g of K_2PtCl_6 is obtained.   Calculate the percentage of Na_2O in the feldspar.

Solution   Let

x = wt. of NaCl in combined chlorides

Then

$$0.0715 - x = \text{wt. of KCl}$$

$$(0.0715 - x) \times \frac{\text{K}_2\text{PtCl}_6}{2\text{KCl}} = 0.1548$$

Solving,

$$x = 0.0240 \text{ g}$$

$$\frac{0.0240 \times (\text{Na}_2\text{O}/2\text{NaCl})}{0.4150} \times 100 = 3.07\% \text{ Na}_2\text{O} \qquad Ans.$$

A second general type of indirect analysis is that in which two chemical substances are isolated and weighed together.   Then another measure of the two substances is obtained either by converting them to different compounds and again finding the combined weights or by determining the amount of reagent required to effect such conversion. In this way, by the use of algebraic symbols to represent the unknown quantities, two independent equations can be formulated, and from them the values of the unknowns can be determined. This type of problem can be extended to any number of unknown quantities, provided sufficient data are given to allow the formulation of as many independent algebraic equations as there are unknowns.

Results of analyses of this type are usually less precise than results of analyses in which a single component is determined by a direct method. In solving simultaneous algebraic equations, there is often a decrease in the number of significant figures that may properly be retained. For example, in solving the following simultaneous equations,

$$
\begin{array}{r}
0.2395x + 0.2689y = 1.937 \\
0.2067x + 0.2689y = 1.222 \\
\hline
0.0328x \qquad\quad\ = 0.715 \\
x = 2.18
\end{array}
$$

there is a decrease from four- to three-significant-figure precision.

Example 3   In the analysis of a 0.5000-gram sample of feldspar, a mixture of the chlorides of sodium and potassium is obtained which weighs 0.1180 g. Subsequent treatment with $AgNO_3$ furnishes 0.2451 g of AgCl. What is the percentage of Na_2O and of K_2O in the sample?

Solution   Let

$$x = \text{wt. of KCl}$$

$$y = \text{wt. of NaCl}$$

$$x + y = 0.1180 \tag{1}$$

No. of g of AgCl obtainable from x g of KCl $= x\left(\dfrac{AgCl}{KCl}\right)$

$$= 1.922x$$

No. of g of AgCl obtainable from y g of NaCl $= y\left(\dfrac{AgCl}{NaCl}\right)$

$$= 2.452y$$

Therefore,

$$1.922x + 2.452y = 0.2451 \tag{2}$$

Solving (1) and (2) simultaneously,

$$x = 0.0834 \text{ g of KCl}$$

$$y = 0.0346 \text{ g of NaCl}$$

$$\left.\begin{array}{l} \% \ K_2O = \left(\dfrac{K_2O}{2KCl}\right)\dfrac{0.0834 \times 100}{0.500} = 10.5 \\[4mm] \% \ Na_2O = \left(\dfrac{Na_2O}{2NaCl}\right)\dfrac{0.0346 \times 100}{0.500} = 3.67 \end{array}\right\} \quad Ans.$$

PROBLEMS

*8-68. A mixt. of Fe_2O_3 and Al_2O_3 weighs 0.7100 g. On ignition in H_2 only the Fe_2O_3 is affected and is reduced to metallic Fe. The mixt. then weighs 0.6318 g. What is the percentage of Al in the original mixt.?

*8-69. A silicate weighing 0.6000 g yields a mixt. of NaCl and KCl weighing 0.1800 g. In this residue the KCl is converted to K_2PtCl_6 and the latter weighs 0.2700 g. Find the percentage of K_2O and of Na_2O in the silicate.

*8-70. In the analysis of a sample of feldspar weighing 0.7500 g there is obtained 0.2200 g of NaCl + KCl. These are dissolved in water + alcohol and treated with H_2PtCl_6. The ppt. of K_2PtCl_6 is ignited in H_2 and after washing with H_2O yields 0.0950 g of metallic Pt. (*a*) Calculate the percentage of Na_2O and of K_2O in the feldspar. (*b*) What wt. of $KClO_4$ would have been obtained if $HClO_4$ had been used as the pptg. agent?

*8-71. A mixt. of AgCl and AgBr is found to contain 66.35% Ag. What is the percentage of Br?

*8-72. A sample of carbonate rock weighing 1.250 g yields a ppt. of the hydrated oxides of Fe and Al. These are filtered off and ignited. The resulting $Fe_2O_3 \times Al_2O_3$ is found to weigh 0.1175 g. On a separate sample of the rock a volumetric method shows 3.22% Fe. Calculate the percentage of Al in the rock.

*8-73. An alloy weighing 0.2500 g gives with HNO_3 a residue of the hydrated oxides of Sn and Sb. On ignition these yield 0.1260 g of $SnO_2 + Sb_2O_4$. This mixt. is brought into soln. and by a volumetric method is found to contain 32.56% Sn. Calculate the percentage of Sb in the original mixt.

*8-74. A mixt. of AgCl and AgBr weighs 0.5267 g. On treating with Cl_2, the AgBr is converted to AgCl, and the total wt. of AgCl becomes 0.4269 g. What is the wt. of Br in the original mixt.?

*8-75. A mixt. of CaO and BaO weighs 0.6411 g and yields 1.1201 g of mixed anhydrous sulfates. Find the percentage of Ba and of Ca in the original mixt.

*8-76. A sample of silicate weighing 0.6000 g yields 0.1803 g of NaCl + KCl. When these chlorides are dissolved and treated with $AgNO_3$, the resulting ppt. of AgCl is found to weigh 0.3904 g. Calculate the percentage of Na_2O and of K_2O in the silicate.

*8-77. From a sample of feldspar a mixt. of KCl and NaCl is obtained that weighs 0.1506 g and contains 55.00% Cl. What wt. of K_2PtCl_6 could be obtained from the KCl?

*8-78.   A mixt. of $BaCl_2 \cdot 2H_2O$ and LiCl weighs 0.6000 g and with $AgNO_3$ yields 1.440 g of AgCl.   Calculate the percentage of Ba in the original mixt.

*8-79.   A mixt. of NaCl and NaI weighs 0.4000 g and yields a ppt. of AgCl + AgI that weighs 0.8981 g.   Find the percentage of I present in the original mixt.

*8-80.   What percentage of $MgCO_3$ is present with $BaCO_3$ if the mixt. has the same percentage of CO_2 as does $CaCO_3$?

8-81.   A sample contg. only $CaCO_3$ + $MgCO_3$ is ignited to CaO + MgO.   The sample weighs 1.0045 g; the product weighs 0.5184 g.   Calculate the percentage of Ca and of Mg in the sample and in the product.

8-82.   The wt. of a certain mixt. of BaO and CaO is found to be exactly one-half that of the $BaSO_4$ + $CaSO_4$ formed from it by the action of H_2SO_4.   What is the percentage of BaO in the original mixt.?

8-83.   Fe and Al are pptd. from a sample of a mineral weighing 0.9505 g, and the combined oxides Al_2O_3 + Fe_2O_3 are found to weigh 0.1083 g.   By a volumetric method this oxide mixt. is found to contain 10.50% Fe.   What is the percentage of Al in the mineral?

8-84.   An alloy weighing 0.5180 g yields a residue of the hydrated oxides of Sn and Sb which on ignition produces 0.1661 g of SnO_2 + Sb_2O_4.   By a titration method a separate sample of the alloy shows the presence of 10.12% Sb.   Calculate the percentage of Sn in the alloy.

8-85.   A silicate rock weighing 0.7410 g is analyzed by the J. L. Smith method, and a mixt. of NaCl + KCl weighing 0.2172 g is obtained.   These chlorides are dissolved in a mixt. of alcohol and water and treated with $HClO_4$.   The ppt. of $KClO_4$ weighs 0.3330 g.   What is the percentage of Na_2O in the rock?   If the K had been pptd. as K_2PtCl_6 and the ppt. converted to metallic Pt, what wt. of Pt would have been obtained?

8-86.   How many g of $BaCO_3$ must be added to 2.40 g of $MgCO_3$ so that the mixt. will contain the same percentage of CO_2 as $CaCO_3$ does?

8-87.   A mixt. of NaBr, NaI, and $NaNO_3$ weighs 0.6500 g.   With $AgNO_3$ a ppt. of the two halides is obtained and is found to weigh 0.9390 g.   When heated in a current of Cl_2, the ppt. is converted entirely to AgCl weighing 0.6566 g.   What is the percentage of $NaNO_3$ in the original sample?

8-88.   A ppt. of AgCl + AgBr weighs 0.8132 g.   On heating in a current of Cl_2, the AgBr is converted to AgCl and the mixt. loses 0.1450 g in wt.   What is the percentage of Cl in the original ppt.?

8-89.   A mixt. of NH_4Cl and KCl weighs 0.5000 g.   With chloroplatinic acid a ppt. of $(NH_4)_2PtCl_6$ + K_2PtCl_6 is obtained.   When the ppt. is ignited $[(NH_4)_2PtCl_6 \longrightarrow$ Pt; $K_2PtCl_6 \longrightarrow 2KCl + Pt)]$, the residual mixt. weighs 1.0400 g.   What is the percentage of NH_3 in the mixt.?   If the ignited ppt. were washed with H_2O and re-ignited, what would be the wt. of the residue?

8-90. A mixt. of AgCl and AgBr contains Cl and Br in the proportion by wt. of Cl:Br = 1:2. (*a*) What is the percentage of Ag in the mixt.? (*b*) If 1.000 g of the sample were heated in a current of Cl_2, thereby converting the AgBr to AgCl, what would be the wt. of the resulting substance?

8-91. A sample consisting of NaCl + NaBr + NaI + inert matter weighs 1.5000 g and is dissolved in H_2O, and the soln. is divided into two equal portions. One portion gives a ppt. of PdI_2 weighing 0.1103 g. The other portion gives a ppt. of AgCl + AgBr + AgI weighing 1.2312 g, and when these salts are heated in a current of Cl_2, they are all converted to AgCl weighing 1.0500 g. What are the percentages of NaCl, NaBr, and NaI in the original sample?

8-92. A mixt. of AgCl and AgI on being heated in a current of Cl_2 is converted entirely to AgCl, and there is found to be a 6.00% loss in wt. What is the percentage of Cl in the original mixt.?

Calculations from Reported Percentages

9-1 Calculations Involving the Elimination or Introduction of a Constituent

It is occasionally necessary to eliminate from or introduce into a report of an analysis one or more constituents and calculate the results to a new basis. Thus, a mineral may contain hygroscopic water which is not an integral part of the molecular structure. After complete analysis, it may be desirable to calculate the results to a dry basis as being more representative of the mineral under normal conditions. On the other hand, a material may contain a very large amount of water, and because of the difficulty of proper sampling, a small sample may be taken for the determination of the water while the bulk of the material is dried, sampled, and analyzed. It may then be desirable to convert the results thus obtained to the basis of the original wet sample. This applies equally well to constituents other than water, and, in any case, the method by which these calculations are made is based upon the fact that the constituents other than the ones eliminated or introduced are all changed in the same proportion and the total percentage remains the same.

Example 1   A sample of lime gave the following analysis:[1]

$$
\begin{aligned}
CaO &= 90.15\% \\
MgO &= 6.14\% \\
Fe_2O_3 + Al_2O_3 &= 1.03\% \\
SiO_2 &= 0.55\% \\
H_2O + CO_2 \text{ (by loss on ignition)} &= \underline{2.16\%} \\
& 100.03\%
\end{aligned}
$$

[1] It is usually difficult to tell in what proportions the positive and negative constituents are actually combined in a mineral. For that reason it is advantageous and customary to report the analysis of the mineral in terms of the constituent oxides.

What is the percentage composition of the ignited sample on the assumption that the volatile constituents are completely expelled?

Solution   In the sample as given, total percentage of all constituents is 100.03.   The slight variation from the theoretical 100% is due to experimental errors in the analysis.   The total percentage of nonvolatile constituents is $100.03 - 2.16 = 97.87$.   Ignition of the sample would therefore increase the percentage of each of the nonvolatile constituents in the ratio of 100.03:97.87, and the percentage composition of the ignited sample would be

$$CaO = 90.15 \times \frac{100.03}{97.87} = 92.14\%$$

$$MgO = 6.14 \times \frac{100.03}{97.87} = 6.28\%$$

$$Fe_2O_3 + Al_2O_3 = 1.03 \times \frac{100.03}{97.87} = 1.05\%$$

$$SiO_2 = 0.55 \times \frac{100.03}{97.87} = 0.56\%$$

$$\overline{100.03\%}$$

Ans.

Example 2   If the original sample of lime mentioned in the preceding problem were heated only sufficiently to reduce the volatile constituents from 2.16% to 0.50%, what would be the percentage composition of the product?

Solution   In the original sample, total percentage of nonvolatile constituents is $100.03 - 2.16 = 97.87$.   In the ignited sample, the total percentage of residual constituents would be $100.03 - 0.50 = 99.53$. The loss of volatile matter would therefore have caused the percentage of the various constituents to increase in the ratio of 99.53:97.87. Hence, the percentage composition would be

$$CaO = 90.15 \times \frac{99.53}{97.87} = 91.68\%$$

$$MgO = 6.14 \times \frac{99.53}{97.87} = 6.24\%$$

$$Fe_2O_3 + Al_2O_3 = 1.03 \times \frac{99.53}{97.87} = 1.05\%$$

$$SiO_2 = 0.55 \times \frac{99.53}{97.87} = 0.56\%$$

$$\text{Volatile matter} = \underline{0.50\%}$$
$$\overline{100.03\%}$$

Ans.

9-2 Cases Where Simultaneous Volatization and Oxidation on Reduction Occur

Occasionally a material on ignition not only may lose volatile constituents but may also undergo changes due to oxidation or reduction effects.   In such cases the percentages of the constituents after ignition can best be calculated by assuming that oxidation or reduction occurs first and loss of volatile material afterward.   In other words, it is easiest to solve the problem in two separate steps.

Example 1   A mineral analyzes as follows:

$$
\begin{aligned}
CaO &= 45.18\% \\
MgO &= 8.10\% \\
FeO &= 4.00\% \\
SiO_2 &= 6.02\% \\
CO_2 &= 34.67\% \\
H_2O &= \underline{2.03\%} \\
&\;100.00\%
\end{aligned}
$$

After heating in oxygen, the ignited material shows the presence of no water and 3.30% CO_2.   The iron is all oxidized to the ferric state. Calculate the percentage of CaO and of Fe_2O_3 in the ignited material.

Solution   Assume first that 100 g of the original mineral is taken and that the only change is that of oxidation of FeO to Fe_2O_3.   Here 4.00 g of FeO would form 4.00 $\times$ $Fe_2O_3/2FeO$ = 4.44 g of Fe_2O_3 and the resulting material would gain in weight by 0.44 g owing to this change alone. The material now weighs 100.44 g and the percentages of the constituents (other than Fe_2O_3) are decreased in the ratio of 100:100.44.   The percentages are now

$$
\begin{aligned}
CaO &= 45.18 \times 100/100.44 = 44.98\% \\
MgO &= 8.10 \times 100/100.44 = 8.07\% \\
Fe_2O_3 &= 4.44 \times 100/100.44 = 4.42\% \\
SiO_2 &= 6.02 \times 100/100.44 = 5.99\% \\
CO_2 &= 34.67 \times 100/100.44 = 34.52\% \\
H_2O &= 2.03 \times 100/100.44 = \underline{2.02\%} \\
&\;100.00\%
\end{aligned}
$$

Assume now that the second change takes place, namely, that all the H_2O is lost and that the CO_2 in the ignited material is brought down to 3.30% owing to loss of most of the CO_2.   The calculation then becomes similar to that of the preceding example:

$$
CaO = 44.98 \times \frac{100.00 - 3.30}{100.00 - (34.52 + 2.02)}
$$

$$
= 68.54\% \qquad Ans.
$$

$$Fe_2O_3 = 4.42 \times \frac{100.00 - 3.30}{100.00 - (34.52 + 2.02)}$$

$$= 6.74\% \quad Ans.$$

PROBLEMS

*9-1. A sample of ore with a moisture content of 8.27% is found to contain 36.47% Cu. What would be the percentage of Cu in a dry sample?

*9-2. A sample of coal as taken from the mine contains 8.32% ash. An air-dried sample contains 10.03% ash and 0.53% moisture. Find the percentage of moisture in the original sample.

*9-3. A powder consisting of a mixt. of $BaCl_2 \cdot 2H_2O$ and SiO_2 contains 20.50% Cl. What would be the percentage of Ba in the material after all the H_2O is expelled by ignition?

*9-4. A sample of lime gives the following analysis: CaO, 75.12%; MgO, 15.81%; SiO_2, 2.13%; Fe_2O_3, 1.60%; CO_2, 2.16%; H_2O, 3.14%; total, 99.96%. What is the percentage of each oxide after superficial heating in which the CO_2 content is reduced to 1.08% and the H_2O content to 1.00%?

*9-5. Lime is to be made by the ignition of a sample of dolomite. The composition of the dolomite is as follows: 96.46% $CaCO_3$ + $MgCO_3$, 10.23% combined MgO, 2.21% SiO_2, 1.33% H_2O. Analysis of the lime shows no H_2O and 1.37% CO_2. Calculate the percentages of CaO, MgO, and SiO_2 in the lime.

*9-6. The oil in a sample of paint is extracted, and the residual pigment is found to be 66.66% of the original wt. Analysis of the pigment shows the following composition: ZnO, 24.9%; lithopone ($BaSO_4$ + ZnS), 51.6%; $BaCrO_4$, 23.5%. Calculate the percentage composition of the original paint.

*9-7. An iron ore is analyzed by two chemists. Chemist A reports: H_2O, 1.62%; Fe, 43.92%. Chemist B reports: H_2O, 0.96%; Fe, 44.36%. What is the difference between the two percentages of Fe after calculating to a dry-sample basis?

*9-8. A cargo of wet coal is properly sampled, and the loss in wt. at 105°C is found to be 10.60%. This dried sample is used for the analysis of other constituents, and the following results are obtained: volatile combustible matter (VCM), 21.60%; coke, 60.04%; ash, 18.36%. The air-dried coal has a moisture content of 1.35% and costs A dollars/ton at the mine. (*a*) What is the percentage of ash in the air-dried sample? (*b*) Neglecting all factors except water content, calculate in terms of A the value of the wet coal.

*9-9. The moisture content of a sample of pure $Al_2(SO_4)_3 \cdot 18H_2O$ is reduced from the theoretical to 7.36%. (*a*) What are the percentages of combined Al_2O_3, combined SO_3, and H_2O in this partly dried material? (*b*) Considering only the loss in H_2O content, if the original salt costs A cents/lb, what (in terms of A) should be the cost of the dried material?

*9-10. In the paper industry "air-dry" paper pulp is considered as contg. 10.00% H_2O. A sample of wet pulp weighs 737.1 g and when heated to "bone dryness" weighs 373.6 g. What is the percentage of air-dry pulp in the original sample?

*9-11. Igniting MnO_2 in air converts it quantitatively to Mn_3O_4. A sample of pyrolusite is of the following composition: MnO_2, 80.0%; SiO_2 and other inert constituents, 15.0%; H_2O, 5.0%. The sample is ignited in air to const. wt. What is the percentage of Mn in the ignited sample?

*9-12. A salt mixt. is found to contain 60.10% UO_3 [essentially as $(NH_4)_2U_2O_7$]. It is also found that 10.00% of the mixt. is combined and uncombined volatile matter (essentially NH_3 and H_2O) and 29.90% is nonvolatile inert matter. What is the percentage of the element U in the material after ignition if the volatile matter is all lost and the U is converted to U_3O_8?

9-13. A sample of a mineral containing H_2O as its only volatile constituent contains 26.40% SiO_2 and 8.86% H_2O. (a) What would be the percentage of SiO_2 in the material after heating sufficiently to drive off all the H_2O, assuming that no chemical changes occur? (b) What would be the percentage of SiO_2 if the ignited material still showed the presence of 1.10% H_2O?

9-14. A powder consisting of a mixt. of $CuSO_4 \cdot 5H_2O$ and SiO_2 contains 18.10% Cu. What would be the percentage of combined S in the material after the H_2O is driven off by ignition?

9-15. A salt mixt. consisting of 98.00% $FeSO_4 \cdot 7H_2O$ and 2.00% inert nonvolatile matter is to be used for its iron content in a certain chemical process. On storage, some of the water of crystallization is lost and an increase of 2% in the price of the mixt. is necessary to take into account the resulting increase in the percentage of Fe. Calculate the percentage of H_2O in the mixt. after storage.

9-16. A sample of dolomite analyzes as follows: SiO_2, 0.31%; Al_2O_3, 0.07%; Fe_2O_3, 0.09%; MgO, 21.54%; CaO, 30.52%; CO_2, 47.55%. The dolomite is ignited, and the ignited material shows the presence of 0.80% CO_2. What wt. of $Mg_2P_2O_7$ could be obtained from 0.5000 g of the ignited material?

9-17. A shipment of meat scrap is sold with the specification that it will contain a min. of 55.00% protein and a max. of 10.00% fat when calculated on a dry basis. The analyst for the sender reports 53.20% protein, 9.59% fat, and 3.60% H_2O. The material takes on moisture during shipment, and the analyst for the receiver reports 50.91% protein, 9.31% fat, and 7.50% H_2O. (a) Do either or both of the analyses show conformity of the material to specifications? (b) On the dry basis, what is the percentage variation between the protein values and between the two fat values as reported?

9-18. A sample of limestone analyzes as follows: $CaCO_3$, 86.98%; $MgCO_3$, 3.18%; Fe_2O_3, 3.10%; Al_2O_3, 0.87%; SiO_2, 5.66%; H_2O, 0.30%; total, 100.09%. Analysis of the ignited material shows no H_2O and only 1.30% CO_2. What is the percentage of Fe in the ignited material?

9-19. A sample of pyrolusite analyzes as follows: MnO_2, 69.80%; SiO_2 and other inert constituents, 26.12%; CO_2, 1.96%; H_2O, 2.15%. On ignition in air, all the H_2O and CO_2 are lost and the MnO_2 is converted to Mn_3O_4. Find the percentage of Mn in the ignited material.

9-20. A carbonate rock analyzes as follows: CaO, 43.18%; MgO, 8.82%; FeO, 3.10%; Fe_2O_3, 1.90%; SiO_2, 7.30%; CO_2, 33.69%; H_2O, 2.00%. A portion of this rock is ignited, and a sample of the ignited material shows 2.00% CO_2 and no H_2O. It also shows that the ferrous iron has been completely oxidized. Calculate the percentage of total Fe_2O_3 and of CaO in the ignited material.

9-3 Calculation of Molecular Formulas from Chemical Analyses

Given a compound of unknown composition, a chemical analysis will determine the proportion in which the constituents of the compound exist. The results of such an analysis can then be used to calculate the empirical formula of the compound. Thus, the analysis of a certain salt gives the following results: Zn, 47.96%; Cl, 52.04%. Dividing the percentage of each constituent by its atomic weight gives the number of gram atoms of that constituent in 100 g of the compound. In 100 g of the above salt there are present $47.96/65.38 = 0.7335$ g atom of zinc and $52.04/35.46 = 1.468$ g atoms of chlorine. These numbers are seen to be in the approximate ratio of 1:2. The empirical formula of the salt is therefore $ZnCl_2$, although, as far as the above analysis is concerned, the actual formula might be Zn_2Cl_4, Zn_3Cl_6, or any other whole multiple of the empirical formula. In general, the determination of the molecular weight of a compound is necessary in order to determine which multiple of the empirical formula will give the actual formula. The usual methods of establishing molecular weights by means of vapor density, freezing-point lowering, boiling-point raising, and other physicochemical phenomena should already be familiar to the student, but the following will serve as a brief review.

Equal volumes of gases under identical conditions of temperature and pressure contain the same number of molecules (Avogadro). Therefore the molecular weights of gases are proportional to their densities. Since under standard conditions of temperature and pressure (0°C, 760 mm) a gram-molecular weight of a gas (for example, 32 g of O_2, 28.014 g of N_2) occupies 22.4 liters, an experimental method of determining the molecular weight of a gas is to measure its density under known conditions of temperature and pressure and calculate the weight of 22.4 liters of it under standard conditions (see Sec. 31-3). The molecular weight of a solid or liquid can also be determined in this way if the substance can be converted to a gas without decomposition or change in degree of molecular association.

A soluble substance lowers the freezing point and raises the boiling point of a definite weight of a solvent in proportion to the number of molecules or ions of solute present. In the case of a nonionized solute, 1 gram-molecular weight of the solute dissolved in 1,000 g of water raises the boiling point of the water by 0.52°C (i.e., to 100.52°C) and lowers the freezing point of the water by 1.86°C (i.e., to −1.86°C). In general, for aqueous solutions of nonionized solutes,

$$\frac{\text{Grams of solute}}{\text{Mol. wt. of solute}} \times \frac{1{,}000}{\text{grams of water}} \times \begin{cases} 0.52 = \text{raising of boiling point} \\ 1.86 = \text{lowering of freezing point} \end{cases}$$

Ionized solutes change the boiling point or freezing point of a solvent to a greater degree owing to the greater number of particles present. Thus, NaCl at ordinary concentrations depresses the freezing point of water and raises the boiling point by about twice as much as calculated from the above formula, owing to ionization into Na^+ and Cl^- ions. Similarly, $CaCl_2$ and Na_2SO_4 give an effect about three times as great as that of a solute that is not ionized.

Solutes dissolved in solvents other than water show analogous behavior in that the changes in freezing point and boiling point brought about by a mole of solute in 1,000 g of solvent are fixed values (but, of course, different from those values given when water is used as the solvent).

The determination of the molecular weight of a soluble substance can therefore be made by preparing a solution of a known weight of it in a known weight of solvent and finding the temperature at which the solution freezes or boils.

Example 1   A certain organic compound is found by analysis to contain 40.00% carbon, 6.71% hydrogen, and the rest oxygen. When converted to a gas, it has a density 2.81 times that of oxygen at the same temperature and pressure. What is the formula of the compound?

Solution

Mol. wt. of compd. $= 2.81 \times 32 = 90$ approx.

In 1 mole ($= 90$ g) of compound there are

$$\frac{90 \times 0.4000}{12.01} = 3.00 \text{ g atoms C}$$

$$\frac{90 \times 0.0671}{1.008} = 6.00 \text{ g atoms H}$$

$$\frac{90 \times 0.5329}{16.00} = 3.00 \text{ g atoms O}$$

Formula of compd. is $C_3H_6O_3$.   *Ans.*

Example 2   Butandione is a yellow liquid which is found on analysis to contain 55.80% carbon, 7.03% hydrogen, and 37.17% oxygen.   It is soluble in H_2O, and the solution does not conduct electricity.   A water solution containing 10.0 g of the compound in 100 g of H_2O freezes at $-2.16°C$.   What is the formula of butandione?

Solution

$$\frac{10.0}{\text{Mol. wt.}} \times \frac{1,000}{100} \times 1.86 = 2.16$$

Solving,

Mol. wt. = 86.1

In 1 mole (= 86.1 g) of compound there are

$$\frac{86.1 \times 0.5580}{12.01} = 4.00 \text{ g atoms C}$$

$$\frac{86.1 \times 0.0703}{1.008} = 6.00 \text{ g atoms H}$$

$$\frac{86.1 \times 0.3717}{16.00} = 2.00 \text{ g atoms O}$$

Formula of compd. is $C_4H_6O_2$.   *Ans.*

9-4   Calculation of the Empirical Formula of a Mineral

The calculation of molecular formulas plays an important part in the analysis of natural minerals.   A careful analysis furnishes a means of establishing the empirical formula of a mineral of high degree of purity, although its actual formula is usually impossible to determine by ordinary physicochemical methods, since minerals cannot be vaporized or dissolved unchanged.   The method of calculation is similar to that of the preceding examples, except that the constituents of a mineral are usually expressed in terms of their oxides.   If the percentage of each constituent is divided by its molecular weight, the number of moles (gram-molecular weights) of that constituent in 100 g of the mineral is obtained.   From the ratios of the number of moles of the various constituents thus obtained, the formula of the mineral can be determined. It should be remembered, however, that analytical methods are subject to errors.   It can hardly be expected, therefore, that the number of moles of the various constituents as determined analytically will be exactly in the ratio of small whole numbers, although in the actual molecule (except in cases involving isomorphism, discussed below) the molar ratios are small whole numbers.   In a few cases, some judgment must be exercised in order to determine from the analysis the true molar ratios of the constituents in the molecule.   A slide rule will be found to be almost indispensable for this purpose, since, with two settings of the rule, all possible ratios are visible.

Example 1   The analysis of a certain mineral gives the following results:

$$Al_2O_3 = 38.07\%$$
$$K_2O = 17.70\%$$
$$CaO = 10.46\%$$
$$\underline{SiO_2 = 33.70\%}$$
$$99.93\%$$

What is the empirical formula of the mineral?

Solution   In 100 g of the mineral there are present

$$\frac{38.07}{Al_2O_3} = \frac{38.07}{102.0} = 0.3732 \text{ mole } Al_2O_3$$

$$\frac{17.70}{K_2O} = \frac{17.70}{94.20} = 0.1879 \text{ mole } K_2O$$

$$\frac{10.46}{CaO} = \frac{10.46}{56.08} = 0.1865 \text{ mole of CaO}$$

$$\frac{33.70}{SiO_2} = \frac{33.70}{60.08} = 0.5609 \text{ mole } SiO_2$$

It is seen that the moles of these constituents are near enough in the ratio of $2:1:1:3$ to be within the limits of experimental error.   The molecule is therefore made up of $2Al_2O_3 \cdot K_2O \cdot CaO \cdot 3SiO_2$ and can be written $K_2CaAl_4Si_3O_{14}$.   *Ans.*

9-5   Calculation of the Formula of a Mineral Exhibiting Isomorphic Replacement

Complications arise in the calculation of formulas in the cases of minerals exhibiting isomorphic replacement, i.e., the partial replacement of one constituent by one or more other constituents having the same general properties.   It therefore happens that, owing to different degrees of replacement, samples of the same kind of mineral obtained from different localities often give on analysis numerical results which apparently bear little resemblance to one another.

As a general rule, a constituent can be replaced only by another of the same type and valence.   Thus, Fe_2O_3 is often partially or wholly replaced by Al_2O_3, and vice versa.   CaO can be replaced by MgO, MnO, FeO, etc.   Exceptions are sometimes met with, but for purposes of calculation, this assumption can usually be made.   Since the isomorphic replacement occurs in no definite proportion, it follows that the molar amounts of the constituents in such minerals do not necessarily bear any

simple relation to one another.   On the other hand, if constituent B partially replaces constituent A, since the valences are the same, the *sum* of
the molar amounts of A and B would be the same as the molar amount
of A if it had not been replaced.   Consequently, when the molar quantities of the constituents of a mineral in themselves bear no simple ratio
to one another, the quantities of constituents of the same type should be
combined in an effort to obtain *sums* that do exist in ratios of simple
whole numbers.

Example 1   A certain mineral gives the following analysis:

$$Al_2O_3 = 20.69\%$$
$$Fe_2O_3 = 7.03\%$$
$$CaO = 27.71\%$$
$$\underline{SiO_2 = 44.55\%}$$
$$99.98\%$$

What is the empirical formula?

Solution   The number of moles of each constituent in 100 g of the
mineral is found to be

$$\left.\begin{array}{l}\dfrac{20.69}{Al_2O_3} = 0.2028 \text{ mole } Al_2O_3 \\[2em] \dfrac{7.03}{Fe_2O_3} = 0.0440 \text{ mole } Fe_2O_3 \end{array}\right\} = 0.2468 \text{ mole}$$

$$\dfrac{27.71}{CaO} = 0.4941 \text{ mole CaO}$$

$$\dfrac{44.55}{SiO_2} = 0.7414 \text{ mole } SiO_2$$

Only when the molar quantities of the first two constituents are
combined are all the above numerical results found to be in simple ratio
to one another, these being approximately as $1:2:3$.   This shows
isomorphic replacement between Fe_2O_3 and Al_2O_3, and the formula of
the mineral can therefore be written

$$(Al,Fe)_2O_3 \cdot 2CaO \cdot 3SiO_2$$

or

$$Ca_2(Al,Fe)_2Si_3O_{11} \qquad Ans.$$

PROBLEMS

*9-21.   From the following percentage composition of ethylamine, calculate its
empirical formula: $C = 53.28\%$; $H = 15.65\%$; $N = 31.07\%$.

*9-22.   Calculate the empirical formula of the compd. having the following composition: Ca = 23.57%; H = 2.37%; P = 36.43%; O = 37.63%.

*9-23.   Calculate the empirical formula of an organic compd. of the following composition: C = 68.85%; H = 4.95%; O = 26.20%.

9-24.   Show that the following analysis of diethylhydrazine agrees well with the formula $(C_2H_5)_2:N\cdot NH_2$; C = 54.50%; H = 13.74%; N = 31.80%; total = 100.04%.

*9-25.   Find the mol. formula of a compd. that has a mol. wt. of approx. 90 and has the following composition: C = 26.68%; H = 2.24%; O = 71.08%.

*9-26.   A certain compd. of C and O has an approx. mol. wt. of 290 and by analysis is found to contain almost exactly 50% by wt. of each constituent. What is the mol. formula of the compd.?

*9-27.   (a) What is the mol. wt. of a compd. if 0.0850 g of it dissolved in 10.0 g of H_2O gives a soln. which does not conduct electricity and which freezes at $-0.465°C$?   (b) What is the mol. formula of the substance if it contains 5.93% H and 94.07% O?

*9-28.   A certain organic compd. which is not ionized in soln. contains 48.64% C, 43.19% O, and the rest H. A soln. of 7.408 g of the solid in 100 g of H_2O boils at 100.52°C. What is the mol. formula of the compd.?

*9-29.   A certain gaseous compd. is found by analysis to consist of 87.42% N and 12.58% H, and it is found that its density is essentially the same as that of O_2 at the same temp. and pressure. What is the mol. formula of the compd.?

*9-30.   A certain organic compd. contains approx. 60.0% C, 5.0% H, and 35.0% N. A soln. of 20.0 g of the compd. in 300 g of H_2O does not conduct electricity and freezes at $-1.55°C$. What is the mol. formula of the compd.?

*9-31.   A certain compd. which is not ionized in soln. contains only C, H, and O. Combustion in O_2 of a sample weighing 1.200 g yields 1.759 g of CO_2 and 0.720 g of H_2O. A soln. of 8.10 g of the substance in 150 g of H_2O boils at 100.156°C. (a) What is the mol. formula of the compd.?   (b) At what temp. will the above soln. freeze?

*9-32.   At a certain temp. and pressure 250 ml of a certain gas consisting of 90.28% Si and 9.72% H has a wt. approx. the same as that of 555 ml of N_2 at the same temp. and pressure. What is the mol. formula of the gas?

*9-33.   When 0.500 g of a certain hydrocarbon is burned in O_2, 0.2816 g of H_2O and 1.717 g of CO_2 are formed. When a certain wt. of this compd. is vaporized, it is found to have a vol. almost exactly one-quarter that of the same wt. of O_2 under the same conditions of temp. and pressure. What is the mol. formula of the compd.?

*9-34.   What is the mol. formula of indigo if its mol. wt. is approx. 260 and its percentage composition is as follows: C = 73.28%; H = 3.84%; O = 12.20%; N = 10.68%?

*9-35.   The analysis of a certain mineral gave the following results: $H_2O = 4.35\%$; $CaO = 27.18\%$; $Al_2O_3 = 24.80\%$; $SiO_2 = 43.70\%$.   Find the empirical formula of the mineral.

9-36.   The composition of the mineral vivianite is as follows: $P_2O_5 = 28.3\%$; $FeO = 43.0\%$; $H_2O = 28.7\%$.   Determine the molar ratios, and show that they conform to the formula $Fe_3P_2O_8 \cdot 8H_2O$.

*9-37.   What is the empirical formula of a certain silicate if its composition is as follows: $K_2O = 21.53\%$; $Al_2O_3 = 23.36\%$; $SiO_2 = 55.06\%$?

*9-38.   A certain compd. contains only the constituents CaO, Na_2O, and SO_3. The percentages of these constituents are in the respective approx. ratio of $9.05:10.0:25.8$.   What is the empirical formula of the compd.?

*9-39.   What is the empirical formula of a simple basic cupric carbonate that contains 57.48% Cu and 8.15% H_2O?

*9-40.   The mineral bismutite is a basic carbonate of Bi, and the analysis of a certain specimen indicates the following composition: $CO_2 = 6.36\%$; $Bi_2O_3 = 89.74\%$; $H_2O = 3.90\%$.   Calculate the empirical formula.

*9-41.   What is the empirical formula of a silicate that gives the following analysis: $CaO = 24.72\%$; $MgO = 11.93\%$; $FeO = 10.39\%$; $SiO_2 = 53.01\%$?

*9-42.   A silicate gives the following analysis: $H_2O = 17.22\%$; $CaO = 8.22\%$; $Na_2O = 0.76\%$; $Al_2O_3 = 16.25\%$; $SiO_2 = 57.48\%$.   If two-thirds of the H_2O exists as water of crystallization, what is the empirical formula?

*9-43.   Determine the empirical formula of a mineral from the following analysis: $MnO = 46.36\%$; $CaO = 6.94\%$; $SiO_2 = 46.75\%$.

*9-44.   The analysis of samples of microcline and albite is given below.   Show that these minerals are of the same type, and give the general empirical formula. Assume that the percentages of SiO_2 and Al_2O_3 are the most reliable.

Microcline	Albite
$Na_2O = 1.51\%$	$Na_2O = 10.10\%$
$K_2O = 14.76\%$	$K_2O = 1.80\%$
$Al_2O_3 = 18.45\%$	$CaO = 0.38\%$
$SiO_2 = 65.27\%$	$Al_2O_3 = 19.30\%$
$\overline{99.99\%}$	$SiO_2 = 68.37\%$
	$\overline{99.95\%}$

*9-45.   Calculate the empirical formula of axinite from the following analysis: $H_2O = 1.58\%$; $CaO = 19.63\%$; $FeO = 9.54\%$; $MnO = 3.01\%$; $Al_2O_3 = 17.92\%$; $B_2O_3 = 6.12\%$; $SiO_2 = 42.23\%$; total $= 100.03\%$.

*9-46.   Calculate the empirical formula of the mineral biotite from the following analysis: $H_2O = 1.10\%$; $FeO = 9.60\%$; $Al_2O_3 = 22.35\%$; $K_2O = 14.84\%$; $MgO = 12.38\%$; $SiO_2 = 39.66\%$; total $= 99.93\%$.

9-47.   What is the empirical formula of a compd. of the following composition: $K = 38.69\%$; $H = 0.50\%$; $As = 37.06\%$; $O = 23.75\%$?

9-48.   Analysis of an organic compd. gave the following results: $C = 60.87\%$; $H = 4.38\%$; $O = 34.75\%$.   Calculate the empirical formula of the compd.

9-49.   An organic acid is found to have a mol. wt. of approx. 160 and to have the following composition: $C = 57.84\%$; $H = 3.64\%$; O (by difference) $= 38.52\%$. What is the mol. formula of the acid?

9-50.   Calculate the empirical formula of the compd. of the following composition: $Sb = 49.88\%$; $O = 6.55\%$; $Cl = 43.57\%$.

9-51.   Metaformaldehyde contains 40.00% C, 6.71% H, and 53.29% O.   A soln. of 10.01 g of the compd. in 250 g of H_2O freezes at $-0.827°C$ and does not conduct electricity.   What is the mol. formula of metaformaldehyde?

9-52.   Glycol is not ionized in aq. soln.   It has a mol. wt. of approx. 62 and contains 38.70% C, 9.74% H, and 51.56% O.   (*a*) What is its mol. formula?   (*b*) What would be the freezing point and what would be the boiling point (at 1 atm) of an aq. soln. prepared by dissolving 50 g of glycol in 500 ml of H_2O?

9-53.   A certain derivative of benzene contains only C, H, and N and is not ionized in aq. soln.   Analysis of the compd. shows 58.51% C and 7.37% H.   A soln. of 30.0 g of the compd. in 150 g of H_2O freezes at $-3.02°C$.   What is the mol. formula of the compd.?

9-54.   A certain hydrocarbon contains 79.89% C and has a density approx. 1.07 times that of N_2 at the same temp. and pressure.   What is the mol. formula of the hydrocarbon?

9-55.   A sample of a certain compd. of C, H, and O weighs 2.000 g and on combustion in O_2 yields 2.837 g of CO_2 and 1.742 g of H_2O.   A soln. of 2.150 g of the compd. in 50.0 g of H_2O is nonconducting and freezes at $-1.288°C$.   (*a*) What is the mol. formula of the compd.?   (*b*) At what temp. would the above soln. boil?

9-56.   Under standard conditions a liter of a certain gaseous compd. of B and H weighs 2.38 g.   When 1.00 g of this compd. is heated, it is completely decomposed into B and H_2, and the latter has a vol. of 2.10 liters under standard conditions. Find the mol. formula of the boron hydride.

9-57.   A certain gas is composed of 46.16% C and 53.84% N.   Its density is approx. 1.80 times that of air at the same temp. and pressure.   What is the mol. formula of the compd.?   (Air is essentially 80% N_2 and 20% O_2.)

9-58.   Calculate the formula of a compd. of C, H, N, and O from the following data: Approx. mol. wt. $= 140$.   Decomposition of a sample weighing 0.2000 g gives 32.43 ml of N_2 when measured dry and under standard conditions.   The same wt. of sample on combustion in O_2 yields 0.3823 g of CO_2 and 0.0783 g of H_2O.

9-59.   What is the empirical formula of a mineral contg. in combination 3.38% H_2O, 19.14% Al_2O_3, 21.06% CaO, and 56.42% SiO_2?

9-60.   Zircon is a silicate of Zr(IV) contg. 32.78% SiO_2.   What is its empirical formula?

9-61.   Analysis of a certain tungstate gives the following values: $WO_3 = 76.51\%$; $FeO = 9.56\%$; $MnO = 13.98\%$.   Find the empirical formula.

9-62.   Calamine is a basic zinc silicate of the following composition: $ZnO = 67.57\%$; $H_2O = 7.48\%$; $SiO_2 = 24.95\%$.   Calculate its empirical formula.

9-63.   A silicate of the following composition is found to have 85% of its H_2O in the form of water of crystallization: $H_2O = 7.70\%$; $K_2O = 28.21\%$; $CaO = 20.39\%$; $SiO_2 = 43.70\%$.   What is the empirical formula?

9-64.   A sample of a certain H-K-Mg-Al silicate weighing 1.2000 g yields the following products: 0.0518 g of H_2O, 0.3984 g of $KClO_4$, 0.9600 g of $Mg_2P_2O_7$, and 0.1466 g of Al_2O_3.   What is the empirical formula of the mineral?

9-65.   From the following data obtained from the analysis of a Na-K-Al silicate calculate the percentage composition of the sample, and determine the empirical formula of the mineral, omitting the Ca from the formula: Sample taken $= 1.3670$ g; silica obtained $= 0.9014$ g; Al_2O_3 obtained $= 0.2549$ g; CaO obtained $= 0.0110$ g; KCl + NaCl obtained $= 0.3374$ g; K_2PtCl_6 obtained $= 0.6806$ g.

9-66.   Find the empirical formula of a silicate of the following composition: $H_2O = 0.83\%$; $K_2O = 1.69\%$; $Na_2O = 4.98\%$; $MnO = 18.00\%$; $FeO = 2.53\%$; $Al_2O_3 = 5.66\%$; $Fe_2O_3 = 14.21\%$; $SiO_2 = 52.10\%$.

THREE

Volumetric Analysis

Calibration of Measuring Instruments

10-1 Measuring Instruments in Volumetric Analysis

The principle of volumetric analysis differs from that of gravimetric analysis in that, instead of isolating and weighing a product of a reaction directly or indirectly involving the desired substance, the volume of a reagent required to bring about a direct or indirect reaction with that substance is measured. From the volume of the reagent and its concentration, the weight of the substance is calculated.

Since volumetric analysis makes use of exact volume relationships, it is essential first to adopt a definite standard for a unit volume and then to calibrate all measuring instruments to conform to that standard. The measuring instruments most often used are burets, pipets, and measuring flasks, and the experimental methods of calibrating them can be found in any standard reference book on quantitative analysis.

10-2 Calculation of True Volume

A *liter* is the volume occupied by one kilogram of water at the temperature of its maximum density (approximately 4°C). A *milliliter* (ml) is 1/1,000 liter. A *cubic centimeter* (cc) is the volume occupied by a cube one centimeter on a side. One liter contains 1000.027 . . . cc. In calibrating a vessel, since the cubical content of the vessel holding the water to be weighed varies with the temperature, it is evident that the temperature of the container must be included in the specifications. Instead of taking the corresponding temperature of 4°C, the temperature of 20°C has been accepted as the *normal temperature* by the Bureau of Standards in Washington, D.C.

To contain a *true liter* then, a flask must be so marked

that at 20°C its capacity will be equal to the volume of water which at 4°C weighs 1 kg in vacuo.   From the density of water at different temperatures (Table 6, Appendix), the coefficient of cubical expansion of glass (0.000026), and the relationship existing between the weight of a substance in air and the weight in vacuo (Sec. 7-3), it is possible to calculate the amount of water to be weighed into a container in order for it to occupy a true liter at any given temperature.

Example 1   How much water at 25°C should be weighed in air with brass weights so that when placed in a flask at the same temperature and under normal barometric pressure it will occupy 1 true liter at 20°C?

Solution

Density of water at 25°C = 0.99707 (Table 6).

At 4°C and in vacuo, 1,000 g of water occupies 1 true liter.

At 25°C and in vacuo, 1,000 × 0.99707 g of water occupies 1 true liter.

At 25°C and in air, the weight of water is found by substituting in the formula

$$W^0 = W + \left(\frac{W}{d} - \frac{W}{d'}\right)a$$

and solving for W (see Sec. 7-3).

Thus,

$$997.07 = W + \left(\frac{W}{0.99707} - \frac{W}{8.0}\right)0.0012$$

Since the term to the right of the plus sign is required to only two significant figures, it is sufficiently accurate to write

$$997.07 = W + \left(\frac{1,000}{1.0} - \frac{1,000}{8.0}\right)0.0012$$

whence

$$W = 996.02 \text{ g}$$

Theoretically, to contain a true liter, the flask must be at 20°C and yet contain this weight of water at 25°C.   Actually, the temperature of the flask is also 25°C.   It has therefore expanded, the cubical content is greater, and the true-liter volume is also greater.   The coefficient of cubical expansion of glass is 0.000026, and the increase in volume from 20 to 25°C is 1,000 × 0.000026(25 − 20) = 0.13 ml.   This volume is represented by 0.13 × 0.99707 = 0.13 g of water.   The required weight of water is therefore

996.02 + 0.13 = 996.15 g   *Ans.*

A general formula can now be written for calculating the weight of water required for a true liter.

$$W = \frac{1,000 \times d}{1 + \frac{a}{d} - \frac{a}{d'}} + [1,000 \times d \times c(t - 20)]$$

where W = weight of water required for 1 true liter, g

t = temperature of water and flask, °C

d = density of water at $t°$

a = weight of 1 ml of air under given conditions, g

d' = density of balance weights

c = coefficient of cubical expansion of container

(The values of these last three terms are usually 0.0012, 8.0, and 0.000026, respectively.)

The correction for the expansion or contraction of the container is in each case small compared with the quantity to which it is added. Consequently, only an approximate value containing two or three significant figures need be used. Indeed, in the case of instruments of 50-ml content or less and for small differences in temperature, this correction can ordinarily be neglected.

By using the third column of Table 6, calculations like the above can be simplified. This column gives the weight of 1 ml of water at a given temperature when the weighing is made in air against brass weights and the water is in a glass container. In other words, corrections for expansion of glass and for conversion to vacuo are incorporated in the values given. It is seen, for example, that the answer to the above problem is found directly by multiplying by 1,000 the weight of 1 ml of water at 25°C under the conditions specified.

0.99615 × 1,000 = 996.15 g   *Ans.*

PROBLEMS

*10-1. Calculate the no. of g of water at 18°C and 760 mm pressure that should be weighed into a tared flask against brass wts. in order that the flask can be marked to contain 250.00 ml.

*10-2. A flask that has been accurately marked to contain a true liter is filled to the mark with water at 15°C, and the temp. of the water is allowed to rise to 25°C. If the neck of the flask has an inner diameter of 15.0 mm, how many ml above the mark does the water now stand?

*10-3. (*a*) In calibrating a flask to contain 500.00 ml, if the water is weighed in air at 26°C against brass wts., what percentage error would be introduced in the wt. of water necessary if the expansion of glass were neglected?   (*b*) What wt. of water should be taken?

*10-4.   What is the true vol. of a flask that contains 746.24 g of water at 30°C when weighed in air against brass wts.?

*10-5.   A flask is accurately marked to contain a true liter, and the inner diameter of the neck of the flask is 16.0 mm.   If 996.00 g of water is weighed out in air against brass wts. at 20°C and placed in the flask at that temp., how far above or below the true-liter mark does the meniscus of the water stand?

10-6.   To calibrate a flask to contain a true liter at 20°C, how many g of water at 31°C and 760 mm pressure should be weighed into the flask in air against brass wts.?

10-7.   (*a*) In calibrating a flask to contain $\frac{1}{2}$ true liter using water at 30°C, what percentage error would be introduced by neglecting the expansion of glass in the calculation of the wt. of water required?   (*b*) What wt. of water should be taken?

10-8.   What is the true vol. of a flask that contains 398.70 g of water at 26°C when weighed in air against brass wts.?

10-9.   A pipet is marked to contain 100 ml according to the true-liter standard. It is filled with water at 12°C.   How much would the water weigh in air under normal barometric pressure against gold wts.?

10-10.   The inner diameter of the neck of a flask is 14 mm, and the flask contains 498.00 g of water at 28°C weighed in air against brass wts.   How far above or below the meniscus of the water should a mark be placed in order to represent a vol. of 500.00 ml according to the true-liter standard?

10-11.   A 50-ml buret is calibrated by weighing in air (against brass wts.) the water delivered between 10-ml intervals in the graduations.   Calculate from the following data the true vol. of soln. that the buret will deliver between each 10-ml interval, calculate the true total vol. delivered between the 0- and the 50-ml mark, and make a graph showing the correction that must be applied to the buret reading to obtain the true vol. in any titration where the buret is initially filled to the zero mark (temp. of the water = 25°C).

Graduation intervals, ml	Weight of water obtained, g
0.03 – 10.07	10.04
10.07 – 19.93	9.84
19.93 – 29.97	10.07
29.97 – 40.03	10.06
40.03 – 49.96	9.94

If this buret is used in a titration and the initial and final readings are 0.11 and 46.38, respectively, what vol. of soln. has actually been delivered?

 **Neutralization
Methods
(Acidimetry and
Alkalimetry)**

11-1   Divisions of Volumetric Analysis

It is customary to divide the reactions of volumetric analysis
into four groups, viz.,

1. Neutralization methods (acidimetry and alkalimetry)
2. Oxidation and reduction ("redox") methods
3. Precipitation methods
4. Complex-formation methods

In Secs. 4-7 and 4-8 the principles underlying the use of
equivalents, milliequivalents, and normal solutions were taken
up in a general way.   In this and succeeding chapters these
principles are reviewed, developed, and applied to the above
four types of volumetric analysis.

11-2   Equivalent Weights in Neutralization Methods

The fundamental reaction of acidimetry and alkalimetry is as
follows:

$$H^+ + OH^- \longrightarrow H_2O$$

i.e., the neutralization of an acid by a base or the neutralization of a base by an acid.

The gram-equivalent weight of a substance acting as an
acid is that weight of it which is equivalent in total neutralizing
power to one gram atom (1.008 g) of hydrogen as hydrogen
ions.   The gram-equivalent weight of a substance acting as a
base is that weight of it which will neutralize one gram atom
of hydrogen ions (or is equivalent in total neutralizing power
to 17.008 g of hydroxyl ions).

A normal solution of an acid or base contains one gram-
equivalent weight of the acid or base in one liter of solution or

one gram-milliequivalent weight in one milliliter of solution (see also Sec. 4-7).

When hydrochloric acid reacts as an acid, the gram-molecular weight (36.46 g) of hydrogen chloride furnishes for the neutralization of any base 1 g atom (1.008 g) of reacting hydrogen. According to the definition, the value 36.46 g constitutes the gram-equivalent weight of hydrogen chloride, and a liter of solution containing this amount is a normal solution of the acid. In this case, the normal solution and the molar solution are identical. On the other hand, the amount of hydrogen sulfate required to furnish in reaction one gram-atomic weight of hydrogen is only one-half the gram-molecular weight, or $H_2SO_4/2 = 49.04$ g, and a normal solution of sulfuric acid contains 49.04 g of hydrogen sulfate per liter of solution. A molar solution of sulfuric acid is therefore 2 N and contains 2 g equiv. wts./liter or 2 g meq. wts./ml.

Acetic acid, $HC_2H_3O_2$, contains four hydrogen atoms in its molecule, but when the compound acts as an acid, only one of these hydrogens is involved in active reaction; thus

$$HC_2H_3O_2 + OH^- \longrightarrow C_2H_3O_2^- + H_2O$$

Consequently, $HC_2H_3O_2/1 = 60.05$ g of acetic acid constitutes the gram-equivalent weight, and the normal solution contains this weight of acid in a liter, or 0.06005 g of acetic acid per ml.

Sodium hydroxide is neutralized as follows:

$$(Na^+)OH^- + H^+ \longrightarrow H_2O \ (\mid Na^+)$$

NaOH/1, or 40.00 g, of sodium hydroxide constitutes 1 g equiv. wt. of the alkali, because that amount will furnish 17.008 g of hydroxyl ions in a neutralization process and will therefore just react with 1 g atom (1.008 g) of hydrogen ions. Therefore, a weight of 40.00 g of sodium hydroxide in a liter of solution represents the normal solution. When calcium oxide is used as a base, each gram molecule reacts with 2 g atoms of hydrogen; thus

$$CaO + 2H^+ \longrightarrow Ca^{++} + H_2O$$

or $CaO/2 = 28.04$ g of calcium oxide is needed to involve in reaction 1 g atom of hydrogen. Therefore, 28.04 g of calcium oxide constitutes the gram-equivalent weight in this case.

In general, if the equation representing the neutralization of a basic substance X with an acid is

$$aX + bH^+ \longrightarrow products$$

and if the equation representing the neutralization of an acidic substance with a base is

$$aX + bOH^- \longrightarrow \text{products}$$

the milliequivalent weight of X in either case is

$$\frac{a \times \text{f. wt. of X}}{b \times 1{,}000}$$

Total neutralizing power should not be confused with degree of ionization. Equal volumes of normal solutions of hydrochloric acid and acetic acid have the same total neutralizing power, but the acids have very different degrees of ionization. In other words, equivalent weight is based on neutralizing power and not on relative "strength" or degree of ionization.

PROBLEMS

*11-1.   What is the g equiv. wt. of each of the following acids, assuming complete neutralization unless otherwise specified: (*a*) $KHSO_4$, (*b*) H_2SeO_4, (*c*) N_2O_5, (*d*) B_2O_3 (reacting with NaOH to form $H_2BO_3^-$), (*e*) As_2O_5 (reacting with base to form $HAsO_4^=$), (*f*) CrO_3?

*11-2.   What is the meq. wt. of each of the following bases, assuming complete neutralization in each case: (*a*) ZnO, (*b*) $Ba(OH)_2 \cdot 8H_2O$, (*c*) $Pb_2(OH)_2CO_3$, (*d*) NH_3, (*e*) Tl_2O?

*11-3.   (*a*) What is the g meq. wt. of K_2CO_3 in the reaction $K_2CO_3 + HCl \longrightarrow$ $KHCO_3 + KCl$?   (*b*) What is the g equiv. wt. of H_3PO_4 in the reaction $H_3PO_4 +$ $2NaOH \longrightarrow Na_2HPO_4 + 2H_2O$?   (*c*) What is the equiv. wt. of Al_2O_3 in the reaction $Al_2O_3 \cdot xH_2O + 3H_2SO_4 \longrightarrow Al_2(SO_4)_3 + (3 + x)H_2O$?

*11-4.   How many g of oxalic acid, $H_2C_2O_4 \cdot 2H_2O$, are required to make (*a*) a liter of molar soln., (*b*) 400.0 ml of 0.5000 N soln.?   What wt. of CaO is necessary for the preparation of (*c*) 500.0 ml of 0.01000 M $Ca(OH)_2$, (*d*) 30.63 ml of $N/100$ $Ca(OH)_2$?

*11-5.   Formic acid, HCOOH, is a monobasic acid that is 3.2% ionized in 0.20 N soln.   What wt. of the pure acid should be dissolved in 250.0 ml in order to prepare a 0.2000 N soln.?

*11-6.   What is the normality as acids and bases of the following solns.: (*a*) sulfurous acid contg. 6.32 g of SO_2 per liter, (*b*) ammonium hydroxide contg. 17.5 g of NH_3 in 480 ml, (*c*) 0.1000 M potassium tetroxalate, $KHC_2O_4 \cdot H_2C_2O_4 \cdot 2H_2O$, assuming replacement of all available hydrogens?

*11-7.   A soln. of H_2SO_4 has a sp. gr. of 1.100 and contains 15.71% H_2SO_4 by wt. (*a*) What is the normality of the soln.?   (*b*) How many g equiv. wts. of combined SO_3 are present in 750 ml of the soln.?

11-8.   Assuming complete neutralization in each case, express the equiv. wts. of the following substances when acting as acids and bases: (*a*) Li_2O, (*b*) N_2O_3, (*c*) Fe_2O_3, (*d*) C_6H_5COOH (benzoic acid), (*e*) $KHC_4H_4O_6$ (potassium bitartrate), (*f*) Tl_2CO_3.

11-9.   What is the g meq. wt. of P_2O_5 in a neutralization process in which the final products are $HPO_4^=$ ions?

11-10.   Chloracetic acid, $CH_2Cl \cdot COOH$ (mol. wt. = 94.50), is a monobasic acid with an ionization const. of 1.6×10^{-3}.   How many g of the acid should be dissolved in 300.0 ml in order to prepare a 0.5000 N soln.?

11-11.   How many g of potassium tetroxalate $(KHC_2O_4 \cdot H_2C_2O_4 \cdot 2H_2O)$ must be dissolved in water and diluted to 780 ml to make a 0.05100 N soln. for use as an acid?

11-12.   (*a*) What is the normality of a soln. of H_2SO_4 that has a sp. gr. of 1.839? (*b*) If 75.0 ml of HCl soln. contg. 20.01% hydrogen chloride by wt. is diluted to 900 ml, what is the normality of the resulting acid (see tables in Appendix)?

11-13.   A 0.0500 N soln. of barium hydroxide is to be prepared from $Ba(OH)_2 \cdot 8H_2O$ crystals that have lost part of their water of crystallization.   How can the soln. be made if no standardized reagents are available?   State specifically the treatment given and the wt. and vol. used.   (*Hint:* An ignition is involved.)

11-3   Normality of a Solution Made by Mixing Similar Components

When several similar components are mixed and dissolved in water, the normality of the resulting solution is determined by calculating the total number of equivalent weights present in a liter of solution.

Example 1   If 3.00 g of solid KOH and 5.00 g of solid NaOH are mixed, dissolved in water, and the solution made up to 1,500 ml, what is the normality of the solution as a base?

Solution   The number of equivalent weights (see footnote, Sec. 4-7) of KOH in 1,500 ml is $\dfrac{3.00}{KOH} = \dfrac{3.00}{56.10}$.   In 1 liter there is $\dfrac{3.00}{56.10} \times \dfrac{1,000}{1,500} =$ 0.0356 equiv. wt. of KOH.   In a liter of the solution there is also $\dfrac{5.00}{40.00} \times$ $\dfrac{1,000}{1,500} = 0.0833$ equiv. wt. of NaOH.   A total of $0.0356 + 0.0833 =$ 0.1189 equiv. wt. of base in a liter makes the solution 0.1189 N as a base.   *Ans.*

PROBLEMS

11-14.   What is the normality of an alkali soln. made by dissolving 6.73 g of NaOH (99.5% NaOH, 0.5% H_2O) and 9.42 g of $Ba(OH)_2 \cdot 8H_2O$ in water and diluting to 850 ml?

11-15.   If 50.00 ml of H_2SO_4 soln. (sp. gr. 1.420) and 50.00 ml of H_2SO_4 soln. (contg. 95.60% hydrogen sulfate by wt.) are mixed and diluted to 1,500 ml, what is the normality of soln. as an acid?

*11-16.   If a sample of solid NaOH is contaminated with 2.00% Na_2CO_3 and 6.00% H_2O, and if 40.0 g is dissolved in water and diluted to a liter, what is the normality of the resulting soln. as a base?   Assume complete neutralization.

*11-17.   If 50.00 g of a solid dibasic acid (mol. wt. 126.0) is mixed with 25.00 g of a solid monobasic acid (mol. wt. 122.0) and the mixt. is dissolved and diluted to 2,500 ml, what is the normality of the soln. as an acid?   Assume comple e neutralization.

11-18.   If 46.32 g of KOH and 4.63 g of $Na_2CO_3 \cdot 10H_2O$ are dissolved in water and the soln. diluted to 1 liter, how many g meq. wts. of total alkali are present in each ml?   Assume complete neutralization.

11-19.   What would be the approx. normality of an acid soln. made by mixing the following amts. of H_2SO_4 solns.: (*a*) 160 ml of 0.3050 N soln., (*b*) 300 ml of 0.4163 M soln., (*c*) 250 ml of soln. of sp. gr. 1.120?

11-4   Volume-normality-milliequivalent Relationship

A normal solution contains one gram equivalent of solute per liter of solution, or one gram-milliequivalent weight per milliliter of solution.   It follows that the product of the number of milliliters of a given solution and the normality of the solution gives the number of gram milliequivalents of solute present, or

$$ml \times N = \text{number of gram milliequivalents}$$

where ml $=$ volume, ml
$\qquad N =$ normality
This simple relationship is the basis of most calculations involving simple volume relationships between solutions and is illustrated in the following sections.

11-5   Adjusting a Solution to a Desired Normality

A solution with a given normality is sometimes found to be too concentrated or too dilute for the purpose for which it is to be used.   In order to decrease its concentration, water is usually added, and in order to increase its concentration, a solution is added which contains the solute in greater concentration than the one given.   The amounts required in each case can be determined by simple calculation.

Example 1   To what volume must 750.0 ml of 2.400 N solution be diluted in order to make it 1.760 N?

Solution

> Before diluting, no. of g meq. $= 750.0 \times 2.400 = 1,800$.
>
> After diluting to x ml, these would be 1,800 g meq. in x ml.

$$\frac{1,800}{x} = \text{normality} = 1.760$$

Solving,

$$x = 1,023 \text{ ml} \qquad Ans.$$

Example 2   How much 0.600 N base must be added to 750 ml of a 0.200 N base in order for the solution to be 0.300 N?

Solution   Let

$x =$ no. of ml of 0.600 N base added

Total vol. after dilution $= 750 + x$

Total no. of g meq. present $= (750 \times 0.200) + (0.600x)$

Resulting normality (no. of g meq./ml) $= 0.300$

$$\frac{(750 \times 0.200) + 0.600x}{750 + x} = 0.300$$

$$x = 250 \text{ ml} \qquad Ans.$$

PROBLEMS

*11-20.   A certain soln. contains 0.0109 g of Na_2CO_3 per ml.   To what vol. should 100.0 ml of the soln. be diluted to make it 0.0100 N?

*11-21.   What vols. of 6.00 N and 3.00 N acid should be mixed in order to pre pare a liter of 5.00 N acid?

*11-22.   A soln. of H_2SO_4 is standardized gravimetrically, and it is found that 25.00 ml will ppt. 0.3059 g of $BaSO_4$.   To what vol. should a liter of the acid be di luted in order to make it 0.1000 N?

*11-23.   A soln. of NaOH is 0.537 N, and a liter of it is available.   How many ml of 1.00 N NaOH soln. should be added in order to make the resulting soln. 0.600 N?

*11-24.   (*a*) What vol. of H_2O should be added to 760 ml of 0.2500 M Ba(OH)$_2$ soln. in order to prepare a soln. that is 0.1000 N?   (*b*) How many g of Ba(OH)$_2 \cdot 8H_2O$ should be dissolved and diluted to 400 ml in order to prepare a soln. that is 0.08333 N?   (*c*) How many moles per liter and how many g equiv. wts. per liter does this last soln. contain?

*11 25.   A 10-ml pipetful of H_2SO_4 (sp. gr. 1.80, contg. the equiv. of 80.0% SO_3 by wt.) is diluted to 500 ml.   (*a*) What is the normality of the soln. as an acid? (*b*) How many ml of 4.00 M H$_3$PO$_4$ should be added to this soln. so that the result ing mixt. will be 1.00 N as an acid in reactions where neutralization to Na_2SO_4 and Na_2HPO_4 takes place?

*11-26.   What vol. of 0.206 N KOH should be added to 150 ml of 0.132 N KOH in order for the resulting soln. to have the same basic strength as a soln. that con tains 15.5 g of Ba(OH)$_2$ per liter?

11-27.   What vols. of 0.500 N and 0.100 N HCl must be mixed to give 2.00 liters of 0.200 N acid?

11-28.   How many ml of H_2O should be added to a liter of 0.167 N H_2SO_4 in order to make it 0.100 N?

11-29.   (*a*) If 10.0 ml of H_2SO_4 (sp. gr. 1.50, contg. 48.7% of combined SO_3 by wt.) is diluted to 400 ml, what is the normality of the soln. as an acid?   (*b*) What vol. of 6.00 M H_2SO_4 should be added to this in order to make the resulting mixt. 1.00 N as an acid?

11-30.   (*a*) If 10.0 ml of Na_2CO_3 soln. (sp. gr. 1.080, contg. 8.00% Na_2CO_3 by wt.) is diluted to 50.0 ml, what is the normality of the resulting soln. as a base? (*b*) What vol. of 4.00 M K_2CO_3 soln. should be added to this soln. in order to prepare a soln. that is 1.00 N?

11-31.   A 500-ml graduated flask contains 150 ml of 0.200 N H_2SO_4.   By adding a more concd. H_2SO_4, the soln. is brought up to the mark and after mixing is found to be 0.300 N.   What was the normality of the acid that was added?

11-32.   A chemist desires to prepare approx. 14 liters of 0.5000 N NaOH. (*a*) What wt. of solid NaOH is required?   After preparing 14.00 liters of the soln., the analyst withdraws 100 ml, and by standardization finds it to be 0.4805 N. (*b*) What vol. of 6.00 N NaOH should be added to the remaining 13.90 liters to bring it to 0.5000 N?   After adding approx. this amt. and mixing the soln., the analyst again withdraws 100 ml and finds it to be 0.5010 N.   (*c*) How much H_2O should be added to the residual soln. to bring it to 0.5000 N?

11-6   Volume and Normality Relationships between Reacting Solutions

Since a gram milliequivalent weight of an acid will just neutralize a gram milliequivalent weight of a base and since the number of milliequivalents in each case is found by multiplying the number of milliliters of solution by its normality, we have the following simple relationship between two reacting solutions:

$$ml_A \times N_A = ml_B \times N_B$$

A solution can therefore be standardized by determining what volume of it will exactly react with a definite volume of another solution the normality of which is already known.   The normalities of the two solutions will then be in inverse ratio to the respective volumes used.   Thus 50 ml of any 0.5 N acid will neutralize 50 ml of any 0.5 N base, or 100 ml of 0.25 N base, since the solutions contain the same number of equivalent weights of reacting substance (that is, 25 g meq.).   To neutralize 60 ml of 0.5 N alkali solution (30 meq.), 15 ml of 2 N acid (30 meq.) will be required regardless of the chemical composition of the acid or alkali used.   The chemical compositions of the reacting substances are taken into account in preparing their standard solutions.

Example 1   What is the normality of a solution of H_2SO_4 if 27.80 ml is required to neutralize a 25-ml pipetful of $0.4820\ N$ alkali?

Solution

$$27.80 \times x = 25.00 \times 0.4820$$
$$x = 0.4334\ N \qquad Ans.$$

PROBLEMS

*11-33.   How many ml of $0.1421\ N$ KOH soln. are required to neutralize 13.72 ml of $0.06860\ M\ H_2SO_4$?

*11-34.   Subtract 34.37 ml of $0.1972\ N$ HCl from 42.00 ml of $0.2000\ N$ HCl by converting both values to the equiv. vols. of $1.000\ N$ acid.   Express the answer in terms of (*a*) no. of ml of $1.000\ N$ HCl, (*b*) no. of meq. of HCl, (*c*) no. of ml of $0.5000\ N\ H_2SO_4$.

*11-35.   If 13.12 ml of $0.1078\ N$ KOH is required to neutralize 10.00 ml of dil. acetic acid, what is the normality of the acid?

*11-36.   To a liter of H_2O are added 31.21 ml of $0.1000\ N$ HCl, 98.53 ml of $0.5000\ N\ H_2SO_4$, and 50.00 ml of $1.002\ N$ KOH.   (*a*) Is the resulting soln. acid or alkaline?   (*b*) How many ml of $0.333\ N$ acid or alkali should be added to make it neutral?

*11-37.   If 50.00 ml of $1.087\ N$ HCl is added to 28.00 ml of a soln. of a solid alkaline substance, the latter is more than neutralized and 10.00 ml of $0.1021\ N$ NaOH is required to bring the soln. to the neutral point.   (*a*) How many meq. did the soln. of solid alkali contain, and (*b*) what was its normality?

11-38.   How many ml of $0.1096\ N$ NaOH are equiv. to 26.42 ml of $0.05360\ M$ H_2SO_4?

11-39.   If 50.00 ml of a soln. of H_2SO_4 contg. 0.1000 millimole of combined SO_3 per ml is mixed with 75.00 ml of a soln. of KOH contg. the equiv. of 0.1100 milli-mole of K_2O per ml, what vol. of $0.1000\ N$ HCl would be required to neutralize the resulting soln.?

11-40.   How many ml of $0.3000\ N\ H_2SO_4$ are required to (*a*) neutralize 30.0 ml of $0.5000\ N$ KOH, (*b*) neutralize 300 ml of $0.0500\ N$ Ba(OH)$_2$, (*c*) neutralize 20.0 ml of a soln. contg. 10.02 g of KHCO$_3$ per 100 ml, (*d*) give a ppt. of BaSO$_4$ weighing 0.4320 g?

11-41.   It is found that 1.000 ml of a soln. of NaOH is equiv. to 1.012 ml of $0.4767\ N$ HCl.   If 100.0 ml of the NaOH is diluted to 500.0 ml with the idea of preparing a soln. that is $0.1000\ N$, how much too large or too small is the vol. of the diluted soln.?

11-7 Determination of the Normality of a Solution

A solution can be standardized (i.e., its normality can be determined) in a variety of ways. In a few specific cases, it is possible to prepare a standard solution by accurately weighing the solute, dissolving, and diluting to a definite volume. This method is applicable only to solutions of such substances as can be weighed accurately and the composition and purity of which are definitely known.

In some cases, it is possible to determine the normality of a given solution by gravimetric methods, i.e., by taking a definite volume of solution and precipitating the principal constituent in the form of a weighable compound of known composition. From the weight of this compound the weight of the solute in the volume of solution taken is calculated. This gives a direct measure of the normality. For example, if a certain volume of hydrochloric acid is treated with an excess of silver nitrate, the weight of the precipitated silver chloride is a measure of the weight of hydrogen chloride in a liter of the acid. Since a liter of normal hydrochloric acid contains 36.46 g of HCl, the normality of the solution is found by direct proportion.

A solution is most often standardized, however, by determining the exact volume of it required to react with a known weight of substance of known purity (usually, but not necessarily, 100% pure). One liter of a normal solution of an acid, for example, contains 1 g equiv. wt. of that acid and therefore must just neutralize 1 g equiv. wt. of any base, or 1 ml (a more convenient unit for ordinary experimental work) of the acid will neutralize 1 g meq. wt. of any base. One milliliter of normal acid will just neutralize 1 meq. wt. in grams of any base. For example, it will neutralize $Na_2CO_3/2,000 = 0.05300$ g of pure sodium carbonate, $K_2CO_3/2,000 = 0.06910$ g of pure potassium carbonate, or $NaOH/1,000 = 0.04000$ g of pure sodium hydroxide. If 1.000 ml of an acid solution were found to neutralize 0.1060 g (that is, 2 g meq.) of pure Na_2CO_3, the acid would be 2.000 N. If 1.000 ml of an acid solution were found to neutralize 0.02000 g ($\frac{1}{2}$ g meq.) of pure NaOH, the acid would be 0.5000 N. The same reasoning holds true for the standardization of alkali solutions against acids and, as seen later, for the standardization of solutions of oxidizing, reducing, and precipitating agents. In calculating the normality of a solution standardized in this way, the number of grams of pure standardizing agent divided by its milliequivalent weight gives the number of gram milliequivalents present. This must be the same as the number of gram milliequivalents of substance in the solution used. Since this equals the number of milliliters times the normality,

$$\text{ml}_s \times N_s = \frac{\text{grams}_x}{\text{meq. wt.}_x}$$

or

$$N_s = \frac{grams_x}{ml_s \times meq.\ wt._x}$$

where meq. wt.$_x$ is the milliequivalent weight (in grams) of pure substance x which is titrated with solution s.

Example 1   A sample of pure oxalic acid ($H_2C_2O_4 \cdot 2H_2O$) weighs 0.2000 g and requires 30.12 ml of KOH solution for complete neutralization. What is the normality of the KOH solution?

Solution   The milliequivalent weight of oxalic acid is

$$\frac{H_2C_2O_4 \cdot 2H_2O}{2,000} = 0.06303$$

No. of meq. of oxalic acid present = 0.2000/0.06303

No. of meq. of KOH required = 30.23 $\times$ N

$$30.12 \times N = \frac{0.2000}{0.06303}$$

$$N = 0.1053 \qquad Ans.$$

11-8   Conversion of Data to Milliequivalents

In general, the student will usually find that the most satisfactory initial step in solving problems in analytical chemistry is to convert amounts of reacting substances to the corresponding number of gram milliequivalents of these substances.   Since the number of milliequivalents of reacting substances are the same, such problems resolve themselves into the simplest types of algebraic equations.   The following three formulas are of general applicability.

1. Solution s of given normality:

$ml_s \times N_s$ = no. of meq. of solute

2. Solution s of given specific gravity and percentage composition:

$$\frac{ml_s \times sp.\ gr._s \times \dfrac{\%\ x\ in\ soln.}{100}}{meq.\ wt._x} = no.\ of\ meq.\ of\ solute$$

3. Solid x:

$$\frac{grams_x}{meq.\ wt._x} = no.\ of\ meq.\ of\ solid$$

where meq. wt.$_x$ is the gram milliequivalent weight of solid or solute.

Even in gravimetric analysis, the gravimetric factor (Sec. 8-2) expresses nothing more than a ratio between two equivalent or milliequivalent weights.   For example, the gravimetric factor $2Na/Na_2O$ represents the weight of sodium *equivalent* to a unit weight of sodium oxide.   It is identical to the fraction $\dfrac{Na/1,000}{Na_2O/2,000}$, which is the ratio of the milliequivalent weights of the two substances.

PROBLEMS

*11-42.   A soln. of HCl is of such concn. that 45.62 ml is equiv. to 1.600 g of Na_2CO_3.   Calculate (*a*) the no. of g equiv. wts. of Na_2CO_3 neutralized by 1.000 liter of the acid, (*b*) the no. of g meq. wts. neutralized by 1.000 ml of the acid, (*c*) the normality of the acid.

*11-43.   What is the normality of a soln. of HCl if 20.00 ml is required to neutralize the NH_3 that can be liberated from 4.000 millimoles of $(NH_4)_2SO_4$?

*11-44.   How many ml of 3.100 N NaOH will be neutralized by (*a*) 105.0 ml of H_2SO_4 (sp. gr. 1.050), (*b*) 10.50 g of SO_3?

*11-45.   Three millimoles of thiourea, $CS(NH_2)_2$, are digested with concd. H_2SO_4, and the N thereby converted to NH_4HSO_4.   Excess NaOH is added, and the liberated NH_3 is caught in 25.00 ml of H_2SO_4 (1.000 ml $\approx$ 2.000 ml NaOH $\approx$ 0.03152 g $H_2C_2O_4 \cdot 2H_2O$).   The excess acid then requires 20.00 ml of KOH soln.   How many ml of P_2O_5 would each ml of the KOH be equiv. to in the neutralization of H_3PO_4 to the point of forming $HPO_4^=$?

*11-46.   A 10-ml pipetful of dil. H_2SO_4 was standardized gravimetrically by pptn. with $BaCl_2$.   What was the normality of the acid if the pptd. $BaSO_4$ was found to weigh 0.2762 g?

*11-47.   A sample of pure sodium oxalate weighing 0.1050 g is ignited ($Na_2C_2O_4 \longrightarrow Na_2CO_3 + CO$) and the resulting product requires 15.00 ml of a soln. of H_2SO_4 for complete neutralization.   (*a*) What is the normality of the acid?   (*b*) If during the ignition 5% of the carbonate had been further decomposed to oxide ($Na_2CO_3 \longrightarrow Na_2O + CO_2$) and this fact was unknown to the analyst, what would have been the calculated value for the normality of the acid?

*11-48.   When $CaCO_3$ is used as a standard for a strong acid, it is necessary to dissolve it in an excess of the acid and back-titrate with NaOH soln.   In such a standardization a water suspension of 1.000 g of $CaCO_3$ was used.   A vol. of 49.85 ml of HCl was added from a buret, and after warming the soln. to remove any dissolved CO_2, the soln. required 6.32 ml of NaOH to reach an end point.   If a separate 50-ml pipetful of the HCl required 48.95 ml of the NaOH for neutralization, what was the normality of the HCl and of the NaOH?

*11-49.   A soln. is prepared by dissolving 0.4200 g of HgO in an aq. soln. of KI, forming $HgI_4^=$.   Write a balanced equation for the reaction.   The resulting soln. is titrated with H_2SO_4, and 20.15 ml of the acid is used, but it is found necessary to titrate back with 2.40 ml of a soln. of NaOH of which each ml contains the equiv. of 0.150 millimole of Na_2O.   Find the normality of the H_2SO_4.

*11-50.   A sample of pure $CaCO_3$ weighs 1.000 g and requires 40.10 ml of a soln. of HCl for neutralization.   (a) What is the normality of the acid?   (b) What vol. of H_2SO_4 of the same normality would be required for the same wt. of $CaCO_3$?   (c) What vol. of KOH soln. of which 20.00 ml will neutralize 1.420 g of $KHC_2O_4 \cdot H_2O$ would be neutralized by 50.32 ml of the acid?

*11-51.   In standardizing a base against 0.1200 g of sulfamic acid, NH_2SO_3H, 38.92 ml of the base is added before it is realized that the end point has been over-stepped.   By introducing 0.0050 g of solid $H_2C_2O_4 \cdot 2H_2O$ into the soln., it is found that an additional 0.58 ml of the base is required for neutralization.   What is the normality of the base?

*11-52.   A soln. of H_2SO_4 was standardized against a solid sample contg. 91.90% $CaCO_3$ and no other basic substance.   The solid weighing 0.7242 g was suspended in H_2O and titrated by adding 29.97 ml of the acid and then neutralizing the excess acid with 10.27 ml of NaOH soln.   If 1.000 ml of the H_2SO_4 is equiv. to 1.024 ml of the NaOH, what is the normality of each soln.?

*11-53.   A sample of potassium acid phthalate, $KHC_8H_4O_4$, monobasic, weighing 4.070 g is titrated with NaOH soln. and back-titrated with HCl.   NaOH required = 46.40 ml; HCl required = 5.35 ml.   If each ml of the HCl is equiv. to 0.01600 g of Na_2O, what vol. of H_2O or of 6.00 N NaOH must be added to 500 ml of the above NaOH to bring it to 0.5000 N?

*11-54.   A sample of CaO has been exposed to dry air and has absorbed sufficient CO_2 to form a small amt. of $CaCO_3$.   A 1.000-g sample of the resulting mixt. has the same total neutralizing power as 34.88 meq. of pure Na_2CO_3.   Calculate the percentage of free CaO in the sample and the percentage of absorbed CO_2.

11-55.   Given the following data: 10.0 ml NaOH $\Rightarrow$ 0.0930 g $H_2C_2O_4 \cdot 2H_2O$; 1.00 ml NaOH $\Rightarrow$ 0.850 ml HCl.   What is the normality of the HCl soln.?

11-56.   What is the normality of a soln. of (a) HCl, (b) H_2SO_4, if 40.0 ml is required to neutralize 0.500 g of pearl ash contg. 95.0% total alkali calculated as K_2CO_3?

11-57.   Three millimoles of urea, $CO(NH_2)_2$, is digested with concd. H_2SO_4, and the N thereby converted to NH_4HSO_4.   Excess NaOH is added, and the liberated NH_3 is caught in a 25-ml pipetful of 0.5200 N H_2SO_4.   (a) How many ml of NaOH soln. (1.000 ml $\Rightarrow$ 0.01640 g $H_2C_2O_4 \cdot 2H_2O$) are required to neutralize the excess acid?   (b) How many millimoles of hydrated Al_2O_3 is each ml of the standard H_2SO_4 capable of reacting with to form $Al_2(SO_4)_3$?

11-58.   A soln. is prepared by dissolving 19.264 g of $KHC_2O_4 \cdot H_2C_2O_4 \cdot 2H_2O$ in H_2O and diluting to 900 ml.   If 50.00 ml of this soln. is neutralized by 35.00 ml of a KOH soln., (a) what is the normality of each soln. and (b) how many g of sulfamic acid, NH_2SO_3H, will each ml of the KOH neutralize?

11-59.   Given: 1.000 ml NaOH $\Rightarrow$ 0.0302 g $H_2C_2O_4 \cdot 2H_2O$, 1.000 ml HCl $\Rightarrow$ 0.1123 g $BaCO_3$.   (a) What is the value of each ml of the HCl in terms of ml of NaOH?   (b) How much solid NaOH must be added to 800 ml of the NaOH soln. so that when diluted to 1 liter it will be 0.5000 N?   (c) What vol. of H_2O must be added to 1,000 ml of the HCl to make it 0.5000 N?   (d) What is the value of each ml of the original NaOH in terms of g of benzoic acid, C_6H_5COOH?

11-60.   What is the normality of a soln. of KOH if 20.60 ml is required to neutralize (a) 32.35 ml of H_2SO_4 (sp. gr. 1.160), (b) 1.000 g of P_2O_5 to the point of forming $HPO_4^=$?

11-61.   An aq. soln. of $HgI_4^=$ is made by dissolving 0.6000 g of HgO in H_2O contg. excess KI.   Write an equation for the reaction.   To the soln. is added a 50-ml pipetful of HCl.   The soln. now requires 11.80 ml of 0.1118 N NaOH for neutralization.   (a) What is the normality of the HCl, and (b) how many millimoles of Na_2O is each ml of the NaOH equiv. to?

11-62.   Given: 1.000 ml NaOH $\approx$ 1.342 ml HCl; 1.000 ml HCl $\approx$ 0.02250 g $CaCO_3$.   (a) What vol. of H_2O must be added to 1,100 ml of the NaOH soln. to make it 0.5000 N?   (b) What vol. of HCl (sp. gr. 1.190) must be added to 1,100 ml of the HCl to make it 0.5000 N?

11-63.   Find the normality of a soln. of NaOH from the following data: Wt. of potassium biphthalate = 4.119 g; NaOH used = 42.18 ml; HCl used = 3.10 ml; 1.000 ml HCl $\approx$ 0.02577 g K_2O.   What vol. of 2.000 N NaOH or of H_2O should be added to 750 ml of the NaOH in order to bring it to 0.5000 N?

11-9   Calculation of Percentage Purity from Titration Values

Just as the normality of a solution can be found from the volume required to react with a definite weight of substance of known purity, the percentage purity of a substance can be determined from the volume of a solution of known normality required to react with a definite weight of the substance.   For example, 1 ml of normal alkali solution will neutralize 1 meq. wt. in grams of any acid.   If an acid is titrated with normal alkali, and exactly 2 ml of the latter is required, it follows that 2 g meq. wts. of the acid must be present.   If 2 ml of 2 N alkali is required, then 4 g meq. wts. of the acid must be present.   In other words, the number of milliliters multiplied by the normality of the solution will give the number of milliequivalents of substance reacted upon.   The number of gram milliequivalents thus found multiplied by the milliequivalent weight of the substance reacted upon will give the number of grams of that substance. If the percentage is desired, all that is necessary is to divide this weight by the weight of sample taken and multiply by 100.

    In general, therefore, if a substance x requires a certain number of milliliters of a solution s of normality N and if meq. wt.$_x$ is the milliequivalent weight of the substance,

$$ml_s \times N_s \times \text{meq. wt.}_x = \text{grams}_x$$

and

$$\frac{ml_s \times N_s \times \text{meq. wt.}_x}{\text{Wt. of sample}} \times 100 = \text{percent}_x$$

Example 1   A sample of soda ash (impure Na_2CO_3) is titrated with 0.5000 N H_2SO_4. If the sample weighs 1.100 g and requires 35.00 ml of the acid for complete neutralization, what is the percentage of Na_2CO_3 in the ash, assuming no other active component to be present?

Solution   One milliliter of normal acid will neutralize 1 g meq. wt. of any base.   Thirty-five milliliters of 0.5000 N acid will neutralize 35.00 $\times$ 0.5000 = 17.50 g meq. wt. of any base.   Since the milliequivalent weight of Na_2CO_3 is $Na_2CO_3/2,000$ = 0.05300, 35.00 ml of the 0.5000 N H_2SO_4 will react with

$$35.00 \times 0.5000 \times 0.05300 = 0.9275 \text{ g } Na_2CO_3$$

As this weight is contained in a sample weighing 1.100 g, the percentage of Na_2CO_3 in the sample is

$$\frac{0.9275}{1.100} \times 100 = 84.32\% \qquad Ans.$$

It is important to remember that the normality of a solution expresses the number of gram milliequivalents of the solute in each milliliter of solution.   Consequently, if the normality of a solution is known, the value of a definite volume of it in terms of other elements, compounds, or radicals can be found directly, even though the solution may not be capable of reacting directly with these elements, compounds, or radicals.   Thus, the weight of hydrogen chloride in 10.00 ml of 0.1000 N hydrochloric acid is

$$10.00 \times 0.1000 \times \frac{HCl}{1,000} = 0.03647 \text{ g}$$

The weight of silver chloride precipitated by adding an excess of silver nitrate to 10.00 ml of 0.1000 N hydrochloric acid is

$$10.00 \times 0.1000 \times \frac{AgCl}{1,000} = 0.1433 \text{ g}$$

The weight of silver sulfate equivalent to the silver in the silver chloride precipitated by adding an excess of silver nitrate to 10.00 ml of 0.1000 N hydrochloric acid is

$$10.00 \times 0.1000 \times \frac{Ag_2SO_4}{2,000} = 0.1559 \text{ g}$$

The weight of barium in the barium sulfate obtained by adding an excess of barium chloride to the silver sulfate above is

$$10.00 \times 0.1000 \times \frac{Ba}{2,000} = 0.06867 \text{ g}$$

In other words, as in the case of gravimetric computations, it is not necessary to calculate the weights of the intermediate products of a reaction. From the milliequivalent weight of the substance required, the weight of that substance can be determined directly.

Example 2   Given the same conditions as in Example 1, what would be the percentage of CO_2 in the soda ash?

Solution

$$35.00 \times 0.5000 = 17.50 \text{ g meq. } CO_2$$

$$17.50 \times \frac{CO_2}{2,000} = 0.3850 \text{ g } CO_2$$

$$\frac{0.3850}{1.100} \times 100 = 35.00\% \ CO_2 \qquad Ans.$$

Example 3   A 0.3000-g sample of impure magnesium oxide is titrated with HCl of which 3.000 ml $\approx$ 0.04503 g $CaCO_3$. The end point is overstepped on the addition of 48.00 ml of the acid, and the solution becomes neutral on the further addition of 2.40 ml of 0.4000 N NaOH. What is the percentage of MgO in the sample?

Solution

$$1 \text{ ml HCl} \approx \frac{0.04503}{3.000} \approx 0.01501 \text{ g } CaCO_3$$

$$\text{Normality of HCl} = \frac{0.01501}{CaCO_3/2,000} = 0.3000$$

$$48.00 \times 0.3000 = 14.40 \text{ meq. HCl}$$

$$2.40 \times 0.4000 = \ 0.96 \text{ meq. NaOH}$$

$$14.40 - 0.96 \ \ = 13.44 = \text{net meq.}$$

$$\frac{13.44 \times MgO/2,000}{0.3000} \times 100 = 90.32\% \ MgO \qquad Ans.$$

11-10   Indirect Volumetric Methods

Instead of titrating a substance directly with a standard solution, it is frequently more feasible to allow the substance to react with a measured amount of a given reagent and then to titrate that part of the reagent left over from the reaction. This is an indirect method and is characterized by the fact that, other factors being fixed, a greater degree of purity of the sample corresponds to a smaller buret reading [Fig. 3(I)].

In acidimetry and alkalimetry an outstanding example of an indirect method is the *Kjeldahl method* for determining nitrogen in organic material. The sample is digested with concentrated H_2SO_4 in the presence of a catalyst and the nitrogen in the material thus converted to ammonium bisulfate. The resulting solution is made alkaline with NaOH, and the

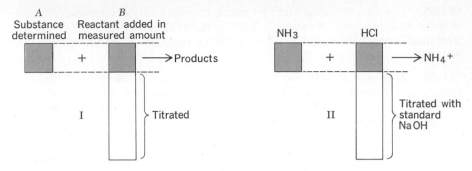

Fig. 3   Indirect volumetric determination. (I) General method. (II) Determination of NH_3.

liberated ammonia gas distilled (through a condenser) into a measured volume of standard acid ($NH_3 + H^+ \longrightarrow NH_4^+$). The acid remaining in the receiving flask after all the NH_3 has been liberated is then titrated with standard NaOH solution [Fig. 3(II)].

Calculation of an indirect volumetric method is usually best made by determining the total number of milliequivalents of reagent added and subtracting the number of milliequivalents used in the titration. This difference is the number of milliequivalents of desired substance.

Example 1   A sample of meat scrap weighing 2.000 g is digested with concentrated H_2SO_4 and a catalyst. The resulting solution is made alkaline with NaOH, and the liberated ammonia distilled into 50.00 ml of 0.0700 N H_2SO_4. The excess acid then requires 30.10 ml of 0.6520 N NaOH for neutralization. What is the percentage of nitrogen in the meat?

Solution

> No. of meq. of H_2SO_4 = 50.00 × 0.0700 = 33.50
>
> No. of meq. of NaOH = 30.10 × 0.6520 = 19.62
>
> Net no. of meq. = 33.50 − 19.62 = 13.88

The value 13.88 represents the number of milliequivalents of H_2SO_4 that have reacted with the NH_3. Since in the above process $NH_3 + H^+ \longrightarrow NH_4^+$, the milliequivalent weight of NH_3 is $NH_3/1,000$ and that of nitrogen is $N/1,000$.

$$\frac{13.88 \times N/1,000}{2.000} \times 100 = 9.72\% \qquad Ans.$$

PROBLEMS

*11-64.   Calculate the percentage of CO_2 in a sample of calcite (essentially $CaCO_3$) from the following titration data: Wt. of sample = 1.000 g; total vol. of 0.5000 N HCl = 35.00 ml; total vol. of 0.1000 N NaOH = 17.50 ml.

*11-65.   From the following data find the percentage purity of a sample of cream of tartar, $KHC_4H_4O_6$: Wt. of sample $= 2.527$ g; NaOH soln. used $= 25.87$ ml; H_2SO_4 soln. used for back titration $= 1.27$ ml; 1.000 ml $H_2SO_4 \backsimeq 1.120$ ml NaOH; 1.000 ml $H_2SO_4 \backsimeq 0.02940$ g $CaCO_3$.

*11-66.   A sample of pearl ash (technical grade of K_2CO_3) weighing 2.000 g is titrated with HCl and requires 25.00 ml.   What is the alkaline strength of the ash in terms of percentage of K_2O if 20.00 ml of the HCl will just neutralize the NH_3 that can be liberated from 4.000 millimoles of $(NH_4)_2HPO_4$?

*11-67.   Given four 10.00-ml portions of 0.1000 N HCl.   (a) How many g of Na_2CO_3 will be neutralized by one portion?   (b) How many g of K_2O are combined in that wt. of KOH which is neutralized by another portion of the acid?   (c) Excess $CaCO_3$ is treated with a third portion of the acid.   Find the wt. of $CaCO_3$ decomposed, the wt. of CO_2 liberated, and the wt. of $CaCl_2$ formed.   (d) Calculate the wt. of $KHC_2O_4 \cdot H_2C_2O_4 \cdot 2H_2O$ equiv. in neutralizing power to a fourth portion of the acid.

*11-68.   A sample of an ammonium salt weighing 1.009 g is heated with KOH, and the liberated NH_3 is caught in 50.00 ml of 0.5127 N acid.   The excess acid then requires 1.37 ml of 0.5272 N alkali for titration.   Find the purity of the ammonium salt in terms of the percentage of N present.

*11-69.   On ignition, rochelle salt, $KNaC_4H_4O_6 \cdot 4H_2O$, is converted to $KNaCO_3$.   A sample of the original salt weighs 0.9546 g, and the ignition product is titrated with H_2SO_4.   From the following data find the percentage purity of the sample: H_2SO_4 used $= 41.72$ ml; 10.27 ml $H_2SO_4 \backsimeq 10.35$ ml NaOH; the NaOH is 0.1297 N; NaOH used for back titration $= 1.91$ ml.

*11-70.   When a direct current is passed through a soln. of NaCl, using metallic Hg as a cathode, a compd. having the formula $NaHg_2$ is formed as an amalgam in the Hg.   It is used as a powerful reducing agent.   A sample of the material weighing 5.00 g is added to water, and after the evolution of H_2 ceases, the resulting soln. requires 40.75 ml of 0.1067 N HCl for titration.   (a) Write an equation for the action of the amalgam, and (b) calculate the percentage of Na in the sample.

*11-71.   If all the N in 10.00 millimoles of urea, $CO(NH_2)_2$, is converted to NH_4HSO_4, and if with excess NaOH the NH_3 is evolved and caught in 50.00 ml of HCl (1.000 ml $\backsimeq 0.03000$ g $CaCO_3$), what vol. of NaOH (1.000 ml $\backsimeq 0.3465$ g $H_2C_2O_4 \cdot 2H_2O$) would be required to complete the titration?

*11-72.   The percentage of protein in meat products is determined by multiplying the percentage of N as determined by the Kjeldahl method by the arbitrary factor 6.25.   A sample of processed meat scrap weighing 2.000 g is digested with concd. H_2SO_4 and Hg (catalyst) until the N present has been converted to NH_4HSO_4.   This is treated with excess NaOH, and the liberated NH_3 is caught in a 50-ml pipetful of H_2SO_4 (1.000 ml $\backsimeq 0.01860$ g Na_2O).   The excess acid requires 28.80 ml of NaOH (1.000 ml $\backsimeq 0.1266$ g potassium acid phthalate, $KHC_8H_4O_4$).   Calculate the percentage of protein in the meat scrap.

*11-73.   A sample of milk weighing 5.00 g is digested with concd. H_2SO_4 plus catalyst, and the nitrogen of the protein is converted to NH_4HSO_4.   Excess NaOH is added, and the liberated NH_3 is caught in 25.0 ml of dil. H_2SO_4. The excess acid then requires 28.2 ml of NaOH of which 31.0 ml is equiv. to 25.8 ml of the dil. H_2SO_4.

The acid and base are standardized by evolving the NH_3 from 1.00 g of pure NH_4Cl, passing it into 25.0 ml of the above dil. H_2SO_4, and titrating the excess acid with the above NaOH. It is found that 11.3 ml of the NaOH is required.

The arbitrary factor for converting N to protein in milk and milk products is 6.38. Calculate the percentage of protein in the above sample of milk.

*11-74. When an aq. soln. of a nitrate is treated with NaOH + metallic Al, the nitrate is reduced as indicated by the equation $3NO_3^- + 8\underline{Al} + 5OH^- + 2H_2O \longrightarrow 8AlO_2^- + 3NH_3$. If in the analysis of a certain sample of Chile saltpeter (natural-occurring $NaNO_3$) the liberated NH_3 is caught in A ml of H_2SO_4 (1.000 ml $\backsimeq$ B milli-moles of K_2O) and the excess acid then requires C ml of NaOH (1.000 ml $\backsimeq$ D mil-limoles of $KHC_2O_4 \cdot H_2C_2O_4 \cdot 2H_2O$) for neutralization, how many g of $NaNO_3$ (f. wt. = 85.01) are shown to be present?

11-75. From the following data, find the percentage purity of a sample of $KHSO_4$: Sample = 1.2118 g; 1.000 ml HCl $\backsimeq$ 1.206 ml NaOH; 1.000 ml HCl $\backsimeq$ 0.02198 g Na_2CO_3; HCl used = 1.53 ml; NaOH used = 26.28 ml.

11-76. A sample of rochelle salt, $KNaC_4H_4O_6 \cdot 4H_2O$, contg. only inert matter is ignited to $KNaCO_3$, and the product is titrated with H_2SO_4. From the following data, calculate the percentage purity of the sample: Wt. of sample = 0.9500 g; H_2SO_4 used = 43.65 ml; NaOH used for back titration = 1.72 ml; 1.000 ml H_2SO_4 $\backsimeq$ 1.064 ml NaOH; the NaOH contains the equiv. of 4.090 g of Na_2O per liter.

11-77. A sample of milk of magnesia [suspension of $Mg(OH)_2$] weighing 5.000 g is titrated with standard HNO_3 and requires 40.10 ml. What is the percentage of MgO in the sample if 20.11 ml of the HNO_3 will just neutralize the NH_3 that can be liberated from 5.000 millimoles of $(NH_4)_3AsO_4 \cdot 5H_2O$?

11-78. The saponification no. of a fat or oil is defined as the no. of mg of solid KOH required to saponify 1.000 g of the fat or oil. To a sample of butter weighing 2.010 g is added 25.00 ml of 0.4900 N KOH soln. After saponification is complete, 8.13 ml of 0.5000 N HCl is found to be required to neutralize the excess ~~acid~~. What is the saponification no. of the butter?   *base*

11-79. Samples of oxalic acid mixed with inert matter are given out for student analysis to determine by acidimetric titration the acid strength in terms of percent-age of $H_2C_2O_4 \cdot 2H_2O$. However, a sample of pure potassium acid tartrate, $KHC_4H_4O_6$, is included among the samples. What percentage of $H_2C_2O_4 \cdot 2H_2O$ would the student report in this case?

11-80. The N in 0.500 g of pure urea, $CO(NH_2)_2$, is determined by the Kjeldahl method. The evolved NH_3 is caught in 150 ml of 0.1200 N H_2SO_4. How many ml of NaOH soln. would be required for the excess acid if 1.000 ml of the NaOH is equiv. to 0.00700 g of hydrated oxalic acid?

11-81. A sample of vinegar weighing 10.52 g is titrated with NaOH. The end point is overstepped, and the soln. is titrated back with HCl. From the following data, calculate the acidity of the vinegar in terms of percentage of acetic acid,

CH_3COOH: NaOH used = 19.03 ml; HCl used = 1.50 ml; 1.000 ml HCl $\backsimeq$ 0.02500 g Na_2CO_3; 1.000 ml NaOH $\backsimeq$ 0.06050 g benzoic acid (C_6H_5COOH).

11-82.   The arbitrary factor 6.25 is used by agricultural chemists to convert percentages of N in meat products to percentages of protein.   A processed pork-scrap product is sold under a guarantee of a min. of 70.00% protein.   A sample weighing 1.000 g is digested with H_2SO_4 and a catalyst, and the N is converted to NH_4HSO_4. When treated with excess NaOH, the NH_3 is liberated and caught in 25.00 ml of H_2SO_4 (1.000 ml $\backsimeq$ 0.05415 g HgO).   What is the max. vol. of 0.5110 N NaOH required to titrate the excess acid if the sample conforms to the guarantee?

11-11   Problems in Which the Volume of Titrating Solution Bears a Given Relationship to the Percentage

In commercial laboratories where many similar titrations are made each day, it is often convenient to simplify computations by taking each time for analysis a weight of sample such that the volume of standard solution used will bear some simple relation to the percentage of desired constituent.   The advantages derived from such a procedure are the same as those discussed in Sec. 8-5, and the computations involved are similar in principle.   In the volumetric problem, it is also possible to fix the weight of sample and determine the normality of the titrating solution which must be used to fulfill a similar condition, although this type of problem is less often encountered in practice.   It is easier in practical work to vary a sample weight than it is to vary a solution concentration.   In either case, the required weight of sample or normality of solution is best found by directly applying the formula previously derived; viz.,

$$\frac{ml_s \times N_s \times meq.\ wt._x}{Wt.\ of\ sample} \times 100 = percent_x$$

In this type of problem, it will always be found that, of the five factors involved, two will be known and a ratio will be given between two others, thus making possible the determination of the fifth factor.

Example 1   What weight of soda ash should be taken for analysis such that the percentage of Na_2O present can be found by multiplying by 2 the number of milliliters of 0.2000 N acid solution used in the titration?

Solution

$$\frac{ml_s \times N_s \times meq.\ wt._x}{Wt.\ of\ sample} \times 100 = percent_x$$

In the problem given, N_s and meq. wt.$_x$ are known.   A relation also exists between the ml and the percent whereby

$$ml \times 2 = \%$$

Substituting in the general equation,

$$\frac{ml_s \times 0.2000 \times Na_2O/2,000}{x} \times 100 = ml \times 2$$

$$\frac{0.2000 \times 62.00/2,000}{x} \times 100 = 2$$

$$x = 0.3100 \text{ g} \qquad Ans.$$

PROBLEMS

*11-83.   In the analysis of oxalic acid using a sample weighing 1.000 g, what must be the normality of the alkali used for titration so that the buret reading will equal one-half the percentage of $H_2C_2O_4 \cdot 2H_2O$?

*11-84.   A sample of a certain acid weighed 0.8250 g and was titrated with 0.2000 N alkali.   After the purity of the sample was calculated in terms of the percentage of constituent A, it was found that the percentage obtained was just equal to the equiv. wt. of A as an acid.   What vol. of titrating soln. was used?

*11-85.   A sample of limestone is titrated for its value as a neutralizing agent.   A sample weighing 1.000 g is taken.   What must be the normality of the titrating acid so that every 10 ml will represent $4\frac{1}{2}$% of the neutralizing value expressed in terms of percentage of CaO?

*11-86.   Samples of pickling soln. are to be analyzed volumetrically for acidity, and results are to be expressed in terms of ml of H_2SO_4 (sp. gr. 1.84, contg. 95.60% H_2SO_4 by wt.).   The sp. gr. of the pickling soln. is 1.270, and a 25-ml pipetful is taken for analysis.   What must be the normality of the standard alkali to satisfy the following conditions: (a) Each ml used represents the equiv. of 0.100 ml of the H_2SO_4 of specified concn in the 25-ml portion; (b) the percentage of pure hydrogen sulfate is one-tenth of the buret reading?

*11-87.   What wt. of soda ash must be taken for analysis so that by using 0.5000 N HCl for titrating, (a) the buret reading will equal the percentage of Na_2O, (b) three times the buret reading will equal the percentage of Na_2O, (c) every 3 ml will represent 1% Na_2O, (d) each ml will represent 3% Na_2O, (e) the buret reading and the percentage of Na_2O will be in the respective ratio of 2:3?

11-88.   What wt. of soda ash should be taken for analysis so that when titrated with HCl [1.00 ml $\backsimeq$ 2.00 ml Ba(OH)$_2$ soln. $\backsimeq$ 0.0254 g $KHC_2O_4 \cdot H_2C_2O_4 \cdot 2H_2O$] the buret reading will be three-quarters of the percentage of combined Na_2O in the ash?

11-89.   A sample of nitrogenous organic matter weighing 2.000 g is digested with concd. H_2SO_4 and a catalyst until the N in the sample has been converted to NH_4HSO_4.   When NaOH is added, NH_3 is liberated and is caught in a soln. of H_3BO_3.   It is then titrated directly with HCl, and the H_3BO_3 has no net quantitative effect.   What must be the value of each ml of the HCl in terms of g of Na_2CO_3 if the buret reading is $2\frac{1}{2}$ times the percentage of N in the material?

11-90. A sample of quicklime is to be analyzed for CaO and $CaCO_3$ by titrating with 0.3572 N HCl. It is desired to start with a sample weighing 10.00 g, mix with H_2O, dil., and take fractional portions of such vol. that (*a*) when titrated with the HCl [phenolphthalein indicator, in which case only $Ca(OH)_2$ is neutralized] the no. of ml will represent directly the percentage of free CaO and (*b*) when titrated by adding an excess of the HCl, heating, and titrating back with NaOH of the same normality as the HCl, the net no. of ml of HCl used will represent directly the total percentage of free and combined CaO. What fractional portion should be taken in each case?

11-12 Determination of the Proportion in Which Components Are Present in a Mixture

Problems involving the determination from titration values of the proportion in which components are present in a mixture are identical in principle with the so-called double chloride problems of gravimetric analysis (see Sec.8-8, Example 2), and the same algebraic method of solution can conveniently be used. The same type of analysis can be applied equally well to methods of oxidation and reduction.

As shown in Sec. 8-8, the precision of the result of an analysis of this type is usually less than that of the data given, and there is often a decrease in the number of significant figures that may properly be retained in the numerical answer.

Example 1 If 0.5000 g of a mixture of $CaCO_3$ and $BaCO_3$ requires 30.00 ml of 0.2500 N HCl solution for neutralization, what is the percentage of each component?

Solution   Let

$$x = \text{no. of g of } CaCO_3$$
$$y = \text{no. of g of } BaCO_3$$

Then

$$x + y = 0.5000 \tag{1}$$

$$\text{No. of g meq. of } CaCO_3 \text{ present} = \frac{x}{CaCO_3/2,000} = \frac{x}{0.05004}$$

$$\text{No. of g meq. of } BaCO_3 \text{ present} = \frac{y}{BaCO_3/2,000} = \frac{y}{0.09869}$$

$$\text{No. of g meq. of HCl used} = 30.00 \times 0.2500$$

Therefore

$$\frac{x}{0.05004} + \frac{y}{0.09868} = 30.00 \times 0.2500 \tag{2}$$

Solving Eqs. (1) and (2) simultaneously,

$x = 0.247$

$y = 0.253$

$$CaCO_3 = \frac{0.247}{0.5000} \times 100 = 49.4\%$$

$$BaCO_3 = \frac{0.253}{0.5000} \times 100 = 50.6\%$$

$Ans.$

11-13   Analysis of Fuming Sulfuric Acid

CASE A

An important titration is that involved in the analysis of fuming sulfuric acid (oleum). This substance may be considered to be a solution of sul-fur trioxide, SO_3, in hydrogen sulfate, H_2SO_4, and when no other compo-nent is present, the analysis is made by dissolving a weighed sample in water and titrating with standard alkali.

Example 1   A sample of fuming sulfuric acid weighing 1.000 g when dissolved in water requires 21.41 ml of 1.000 N NaOH solution for neu-tralization. What is the percentage of each component?

Solution

Method 1.   Since fuming sulfuric acid is a mixture of two pure components, the problem can be solved by the method of the preceding section. Let

$x =$ wt. of free SO_3

$y =$ wt. of H_2SO_4

$x + y = 1.000$

$$\frac{x}{SO_3/2,000} + \frac{y}{H_2SO_4/2,000} = 21.41 \times 1.000$$

When the simultaneous equations are solved,

$x = 0.222$ g SO_3 $= 22.2\%$

$y = 0.778$ g H_2SO_4 $= 77.8\%$ $Ans.$

Method 2.   In dissolving the oleum, the SO_3 unites with part of the water to form H_2SO_4. If the total percentage of acid is computed in terms of H_2SO_4, the following result is obtained:

$$\frac{21.41 \times 1.000 \times H_2SO_4/2,000}{1.000} \times 100 = 105.0\%$$

Since, in the original mixture, $SO_3 + H_2SO_4 = 100.00\%$, the difference of 5.0% is caused by the water that has combined with the SO_3.   The SO_3 and H_2O combine mole for mole.

$$5.0 \times \frac{SO_3}{H_2O} = \% \; SO_3$$

$$\left. \begin{array}{l} = 22.2\% \; SO_3 \\ 100.0 - 22.2 = 77.8\% \; H_2SO_4 \end{array} \right\} \quad Ans.$$

CASE B

Fuming sulfuric acid often contains small amounts of SO_2 which with water forms H_2SO_3 and is included in the alkali titration:

$$H_2SO_3 + 2OH^- \longrightarrow SO_3^= + 2H_2O$$

This is when phenolphthalein is used as the indicator.   With methyl orange, the color change takes place at the bisulfite stage:

$$H_2SO_3 + OH^- \longrightarrow HSO_3^- + H_2O$$

In case SO_2 is present, its amount is usually determined in a separate sample by titration with a standard oxidizing agent, and the other components are then computed from the alkali titration values in the usual way, with a correction for the volume of alkali used by the SO_2.

Example 2   A sample of fuming sulfuric acid containing H_2SO_4, SO_3, and SO_2 weighs 1.000 g and is found to require 23.47 ml of 1.000 N alkali for neutralization (phenolphthalein as indicator).   A separate sample shows the presence of 1.50% SO_2.   Find the percentages of "free" SO_3, H_2SO_4, and "combined" SO_3.

Solution

$$\text{Vol. of alkali used by } SO_2 = \frac{0.0150}{1.000 \times SO_2/2{,}000} = 0.47 \text{ ml}$$

Vol. of alkali used for $H_2SO_4 + SO_3 = 23.47 - 0.47 = 23.00$ ml

$\% \; H_2SO_4 + SO_3 = 100.00 - 1.50 = 98.50$

Let

$$x = \text{wt. of } SO_3$$
$$y = \text{wt. of } H_2SO_4$$
$$x + y = 0.9850$$

$$\frac{x}{SO_3/2{,}000} + \frac{y}{H_2SO_4/2{,}000} = 23.00 \times 1.000$$

Solving,

$$x = 0.636 \text{ g } SO_3 \quad = 63.6\%$$
$$y = 0.349 \text{ g } H_2SO_4 = 34.9\%$$ $\Big\}$ Ans.

Combined $SO_3 = 34.9 \times \dfrac{SO_3}{H_2SO_4} \times 28.5\%$ Ans.

PROBLEMS

*11-91.   A mixt. consisting entirely of $Li_2CO_3 + BaCO_3$ weighs 1.000 g and requires 15.00 ml of 1.000 N HCl for neutralization.   Find the percentage of $BaCO_3$ and of combined Li in the sample.

*11-92.   What wt. of $BaCO_3$ must be added to 1.000 g of Li_2CO_3 so that A g of the mixt. will require the same vol. of standard acid for neutralization as would A g of $CaCO_3$?

*11-93.   A sample consisting entirely of $CaCO_3 + SrCO_3$ weighs 0.5000 g and requires 30.00 ml of 0.2726 N H_2SO_4 for neutralization.   (a) What would be the loss in wt. of the original sample on strong ignition?   (b) What wt. of $CaSO_4 + SrSO_4$ is formed by the neutralization?   (c) What is the wt. of $CaCO_3$ in the original sample?

*11-94.   The combined wt. of LiOH, KOH, and $Ba(OH)_2$ in a mixt. is 0.5000 g, and 25.43 ml of 0.5000 N acid is required for neutralization.   The same wt. of sample with CO_2 gives a ppt. of $BaCO_3$ that requires 5.27 ml of the above acid for neutralization.   Find the wts. of LiOH, KOH, and $Ba(OH)_2$ in the original mixt.

*11-95.   A mixt. of pure $BaCO_3$ and pure Na_2CO_3 weighs 1.000 g and has the total neutralizing power of 15.37 meq. of $CaCO_3$.   Calculate the percentage of combined CO_2 in the mixt. and the wt. of Li_2CO_3 that has the same neutralizing power as 1.000 g of the above mixt.

*11-96.   The total acidity of a certain sample of fuming sulfuric acid (contg. no SO_2 or other impurity) is found by titration to be 108.5% when expressed in terms of H_2SO_4.   Find the percentage of free SO_3 in the sample.

*11-97.   A sample of fuming sulfuric acid contg. only SO_3 and H_2SO_4 is titrated, and the total SO_3 (free and combined) is found to be 84.00%.   What is the percentage of H_2SO_4 in the original sample?

*11-98.   A soln. of SO_3 in H_2SO_4 requires 65.10 ml of 0.9000 N alkali for the titration of a sample weighing 2.604 g.   What is the proportion by wt. of free SO_3 to H_2SO_4 in the sample?

*11-99.   A sample of oleum consisting of a soln. of SO_3 and SO_2 in H_2SO is found to contain 2.00% SO_2.   A sample weighing 1.5000 g requires 21.64 ml of 1.5000 N KOH for complete neutralization.   What are the percentages of free SO_3 and H_2SO_4 in the sample?

11-100.   A sample, supposed to be pure $CaCO_3$, is used to standardize a soln. of HCl.   The substance really was a mixt. of $MgCO_3$ and $BaCO_3$, but the standardization was correct in spite of the erroneous assumption.   Find the percentage of combined MgO in the mixt.

11-101.   A sample of P_2O_5 is known to contain H_3PO_4 as its only impurity.   The sample is weighed in a closed container, the container is opened under water ($P_2O_5 + 3H_2O \longrightarrow 2H_3PO_4$), and the soln. is titrated with standard NaOH to form Na_2HPO_4 at the end point.   If A ml of B N NaOH was used for a C-g sample, set up an expression to show how the no. of g free P_2O_5 in the original sample could be determined.   Express all meq. wts.

11-102.   The titration of a sample of fuming sulfuric acid contg. no SO_2 shows the presence of the equiv. of 109.22% H_2SO_4.   Calculate the percentage composition of the sample and the percentage of combined SO_3.

11-103.   A sample of oleum weighing 1.762 g requires 42.80 ml of 0.8905 N NaOH for neutralization.   Calculate the proportion by wt. of free SO_3 to combined SO_3 in the sample.

11-104.   An oleum consists of a mixt. of SO_2, SO_3, and H_2SO_4.   By means of an oxidimetric titration, the amt. of SO_2 in the material is found to be 1.50%.   A sample weighing 1.200 g requires 25.21 meq. of base for complete neutralization of all three components.   What are the percentages of free and combined SO_3 in the sample?

11-105.   A mixt. of pure acetic acid and acetic anhydride is dissolved in H_2O and titrated with NaOH.   The acidity of the sample expressed in terms of CH_3COOH is found to be 114.0%.   What is the composition of the original mixt.?   Acetic anhydride reacts with H_2O to form acetic acid: $(CH_3CO)_2O + H_2O \longrightarrow 2CH_3COOH$.

11-14   Indicators

An indicator is used in volumetric analysis for the purpose of detecting the point at which a reaction is just completed.   The indicators used in acidimetry and alkalimetry are usually organic dyestuffs which are in themselves either weak acids (e.g., phenolphthalein) or weak bases (e.g., methyl orange), and the change in color that they undergo can be attributed to the fact that the arrangement of the atoms in their molecules is somewhat different from the arrangement of the atoms in the molecules of their corresponding salts.

Consider a weak organic acid indicator of the general formula HX. This acid ionizes as follows: HX $\rightleftharpoons$ H$^+$ + X$^-$.   The undissociated molecule HX is, for example, colorless; the ion X$^-$ is colored, usually because of a rearrangement of atoms to form a quinoid structure.   In water solution the ionization of the acid is so slight that the color of the ion is too faint to be seen.   The addition of an alkaline substance to the solution, however, by reacting with the hydrogen ion, displaces the above equilibrium to the right and increases the concentration of the X$^-$ ion to the point where its color becomes visible.   The ionization constant of the above indicator is $\dfrac{[H^+][X^-]}{[HX]} = K$ and is called an *indicator constant*.   If it is assumed that with this type of indicator a titration is stopped when one-half of the un-ionized molecules have been converted by a base to the colored ionic form, then $[HX] = [X^-]$ and the indicator constant is equal to the hydrogen-ion concentration of the solution at the end point.

Similarly, a weak basic indicator of the general formula XOH ionizes as follows: $XOH \rightleftharpoons X^+ + OH^-$, and the ionization constant (= indicator constant) is $\dfrac{[X^+][OH^-]}{[XOH]} = K$. In water solution the color of the XOH molecule predominates, but the addition of acid increases the concentration of the X^+ form and the color changes. If it is assumed that the color change is seen when three-fourths of XOH has been converted to X^+, then the hydroxyl-ion concentration at the end point is equal to $\frac{1}{3}K$.

With a given concentration of indicator, the color change takes place at a point where the hydrogen-ion or the hydroxyl-ion concentration in the solution has attained a definite value that is characteristic of the indicator in question. Thus, a solution containing about 0.001% of phenolphthalein turns from colorless to pink when the hydroxyl-ion concentration has attained the value of about 1×10^{-5} mole/liter, and the corresponding hydrogen-ion concentration has therefore been reduced to about 1×10^{-9} mole/liter (pH $-$ 9). Figure 4 shows the approximate hydrogen-ion and hydroxyl-ion concentrations at which dilute solutions of the common indicators change color. It will be noted that on this chart each color change is spread over a certain range of pH values. Each indicator may be said to have a *pH differential* over which the transition in shade of color is gradual; the analyst might stop a titration anywhere within the range in question.

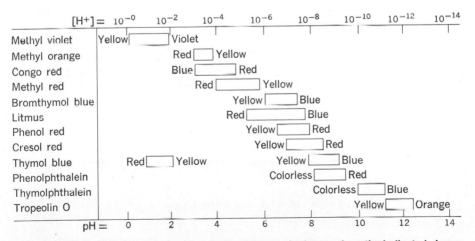

Fig. 4   Hydrogen-ion concentrations and pH values required to produce the indicated change of color in dilute solutions (0.001%) of some of the more common indicators.

11-15   Equivalence Point

The *equivalence point* in any titration is the point where the amount of titrating solution added is chemically equivalent to the amount of substance being titrated; the analyst attempts to make the *end point* (i.e., the point where the indicator changes color) coincide with this.   In an acidimetric or alkalimetric titration the equivalence point is not necessarily the same as the *neutral point* (pH = 7.00 at 25°C).   For example, in the titration of acetic acid with sodium hydroxide, when the latter has been added in an amount equivalent to the former, the acidity of the solution is the same as that resulting from dissolving the corresponding amount of sodium acetate in water.   Such a solution is basic owing to hydrolysis of the salt.   Similarly, in the titration of a weak base with a strong acid, the equivalence point is at a point where the solution is slightly acidic (pH < 7.00).

Other conditions being equal, the correct indicator for a given titration is one in which the color change takes place when the solution has that pH value which exists in a solution obtained by dissolving in the same volume of water the salt formed by the neutralization.   In other words, an indicator should be chosen that will change color at a pH value approximately equal to the pH value at the equivalence point.   Just how that pH value can be calculated is shown in the following section.

11-16   Change in Hydrogen-ion Concentration during Titrations

During an acidimetric or alkalimetric titration, the pH value of the solution changes progressively, and when pH values are plotted (usually as ordinates) against corresponding buret readings (usually as abscissas), a *titration curve* is obtained which is a very valuable aid in determining the proper indicator to use, in establishing the equivalence point in a potentiometric titration (see Chap. 16), and in obtaining information as to the precision of the titration.

Four general types of acidimetric titrations are considered here, and the method of establishing the titration curve in each case is illustrated by calculating the pH values at different points in the titration.   The following symbols will be used:

$$pH = -\log [H^+]$$

$$pOH = -\log [OH^-]$$

$$K_w = \text{ion-product const. of water} = [H^+][OH^-] = 1.00 \times 10^{-14} \qquad \text{at 25°C}$$

$$pK_w = -\log K_w = 14.0 \qquad \text{at 25°C}$$

$$K_a = \text{ionization const. of weak acid being titrated} = [H^+][X^-]/[HX]$$

$$pK_a = -\log K_a$$

$$K_b = \text{ionization const. of weak base being titrated} = [X^+][OH^-]/[XOH]$$

$$pK_b = -\log K_b$$

C = molar concn. at equivalence point of salt formed by neutralization process

CASE A   Strong acid titrated with strong base; strong base titrated with strong acid

Example 1   Twenty milliliters of 0.50 N HCl is diluted with water to 100 ml, and the resulting solution is titrated with 0.50 N NaOH. Calculate the pH value (*a*) at the start, (*b*) when 8.0 ml of the NaOH has been added, (*c*) at the equivalence point (i.e., when 20 ml of the NaOH has been added), (*d*) when 30 ml of the NaOH has been added. Show the general form of the titration curve, and show the form of the curve in the reverse titration of 20 ml of 0.50 N NaOH with 0.50 N HCl.

Solution

(*a*) At the beginning of the titration, $[H^+]$ = 20 × 0.50 = 10 meq./ 100 ml = 0.10 N = 0.10 M. Therefore pH = 1.00.

(*b*) When 8.0 ml of 0.50 N NaOH has been added, the unneutralized HCl is at a concentration of 12 × 0.50 = 6.0 meq./108 ml. $[H^+]$ is therefore 6/108 = 5.56 × 10^{-2} N, and pH = $-\log$ (5.56 × 10^{-2}) = 1.26.

(*c*) At the equivalence point (20 ml NaOH added), the solution contains only sodium chloride dissolved in water, and since there is no appreciable hydrolysis, pH = 7.00.

(*d*) When 30 ml of 0.50 N NaOH has been added, the volume of the solution is 130 ml and 10 × 0.50 = 5.0 meq. of NaOH are in excess. The $[OH^-]$ concentration is therefore 5/130 = 3.84 × 10^{-2} N, pOH = 1.42, and pH = 12.58.

The graph for this titration in which the above buret readings (and others similarly obtained) are plotted against corresponding pH values is shown in Fig. 5, curve *AA*. The curve as it crosses the 20-ml line is represented in the figure as a vertical line. Actually it is not quite vertical but slopes slightly from left to right as it passes upward. It crosses the line at pH 7.00. At the right of the figure are shown the approximate pH values at which four common indicators change color. In titrations of this type, the true equivalence point is at pH 7.00, but near the equivalence point the change in pH is so rapid that almost any indicator that changes color between about pH 3 and 11 should be suitable. In other words, in titrations of strong acids with strong bases, although an indicator changing at pH 7.00 is indicated (e.g., bromthymol blue), the error involved in the use of such indicators as phenolphthalein or methyl orange is negligible, being usually within the error of reading a buret.

The curve representing the titration of 20 ml of 0.50 N NaOH

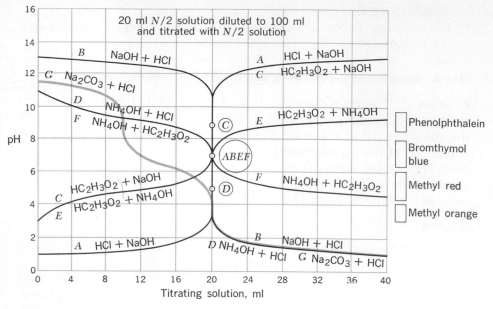

Fig. 5   Acidimetric titration curves.

(diluted to 100 ml) with 0.50 N HCl is shown in curve BB of Fig. 5.   Here each pH value is 14 minus the corresponding value in the titration of the HCl.   Here again there is actually a slight left-to-right slope in the curve as it crosses the 20-ml line (at pH 7.00), and the proper indicator is established as in the preceding case.

CASE B   Weak acid titrated with strong base

Example 2   Twenty milliliters of 0.50 N HC$_2$H$_3$O$_2$ is diluted with water to 100 ml, and the resulting solution is titrated with 0.50 N NaOH.   Calculate the pH value (*a*) at the start, (*b*) when 8.0 ml of the NaOH has been added, (*c*) at the equivalence point (when 20 ml of NaOH has been added), (*d*) when 30 ml of the NaOH has been added.   Show the general form of the titration curve.

Solution

   (*a*) At the beginning of the titration, the pH value can be calculated from the ionization constant of acetic acid, $K_a = 1.86 \times 10^{-5}$; thus

$$HC_2H_3O_2 \rightleftharpoons H^+ + C_2H_3O_2^-$$

$$\frac{[H^+][C_2H_3O_2^-]}{[HC_2H_3O_2]} = K_a = 1.86 \times 10^{-5}$$

$$\frac{x \times x}{0.10 - x} = 1.86 \times 10^{-5}$$

$$x = 1.36 \times 10^{-3} = [H^+]$$

$$pH = - \log [H^+] = 2.87$$

(b) When 8.0 ml of 0.50 N NaOH has been added, an excess of 12.0 ml of 0.50 N (= 6.0 meq.) of acetic acid is still present, but the acid is considerably buffered by the sodium acetate formed during the titration. The acetate-ion concentration (mostly from the salt formed) at this point is 8.0 $\times$ 0.50 = 4.0 meq. The total volume is 180 ml. Since

$$\frac{[H^+][C_2H_3O_2^-]}{[HC_2H_3O_2]} = K_a = 1.86 \times 10^{-5}$$

$$[H^+] = K_a \frac{[HC_2H_3O_2]}{[C_2H_3O_2^-]} = 1.86 \times 10^{-5} \times \frac{6.0/108}{4.0/108}$$

$$= 2.79 \times 10^{-5}$$

$$pH = - \log [H^+] = 4.55$$

(c) At the equivalence point (20 ml NaOH added), the pH value of the solution can be calculated from either of the following formulas (which are general for titrations of this type):

$$pH = -\tfrac{1}{2} \log K_w - \tfrac{1}{2} \log K_a + \tfrac{1}{2} \log C$$

or

$$pH = \tfrac{1}{2}pK_w + \tfrac{1}{2}pK_a + \tfrac{1}{2} \log C$$

These can be derived by considering the numerical equilibrium relationships at the equivalence point in the titration just cited. The salt, sodium acetate, formed at the equivalence point at concentration C, hydrolyzes as follows:

$$C_2H_3O_2^- + H_2O \rightleftharpoons HC_2H_3O_2 + OH^-$$

The mass-action expression for this hydrolysis is

(1) $$\frac{[HC_2H_3O_2][OH^-]}{[C_2H_3O_2^-]} = K$$

but

(2) $$[H^+][OH^-] = K_w$$

and

(3) $$\frac{[H^+][C_2H_3O_2^-]}{[HC_2H_3O_2]} = K_a$$

Dividing (2) by (3) gives (1).   Hence,

$$\frac{[HC_2H_3O_2][OH^-]}{[C_2H_3O_2^-]} = \frac{K_w}{K_a}$$

but, as seen from the above hydrolysis equilibrium,

$$[HC_2H_3O_2] = [OH^-]$$

and, if the extent of hydrolysis is not too great,

$$[C_2H_3O_2^-] \cong C$$

Therefore,

$$[OH^-]^2 = C\frac{K_w}{K_a}$$

$$[OH^-] = \sqrt{C\frac{K_w}{K_a}}$$

$$[H^+] = \frac{K_w}{[OH^-]}$$

$$= \frac{K_w}{\sqrt{C(K_w/K_a)}}$$

$$pH = -[\log K_w - (\tfrac{1}{2}\log C + \tfrac{1}{2}\log K_w - \tfrac{1}{2}\log K_a)]$$
$$= -\tfrac{1}{2}\log K_w - \tfrac{1}{2}\log K_a + \tfrac{1}{2}\log C$$
$$= \tfrac{1}{2}pK_w + \tfrac{1}{2}pK_a + \tfrac{1}{2}\log C$$

In the case at hand, we have $K_w = 1.0 \times 10^{-14}$, $K_a = 1.86 \times 10^{-5}$, and

$$C = \frac{10 \text{ meq. } NaC_2H_3O_2}{120 \text{ ml soln.}} = 0.0833\ N = 0.0833\ M$$

$$pH = \frac{14.0}{2} + \frac{4.73}{2} + \frac{(-1.08)}{2} = 8.83$$

(d) Beyond the equivalence point, excess NaOH is present and the pH values are the same as in the preceding titration of HCl with NaOH. The right-hand arms of the curves therefore coincide.

The titration curve in this case is represented by curve CC in Fig. 5. Point C shows the pH value (8.83) at the equivalence point.   The common indicator that changes color at this point is phenolphthalein and is the indicator suitable for the titration.   As can be seen from the titration graph, the use of an indicator like methyl orange would give erroneous results.

If half-normal bases are used, the titration of acids with ionization constants less than about 10^{-7} is not feasible; if tenth-normal bases are used, the titration of acids with ionization constants less than about 10^{-6} is not feasible.   In either case, the inflection at the equivalence point is not sharp and the change of color of even the most nearly appropriate indicator is gradual and extends over a considerable volume of titrating solution.

The titration of a weak polybasic acid (H_3PO_4) is illustrated in Prob. 11-138.

CASE C   Weak base titrated with strong acid

Example 3   Twenty milliliters of 0.50 N NH_4OH is diluted to 100 ml with water and titrated with 0.50 N HCl.   Calculate the pH value (a) at the start, (b) at the equivalence point.   Show the general form of the titration curve.

Solution

(a) The calculation of the hydroxyl-ion concentration at the start is exactly similar to the calculation of the hydrogen-ion concentration in the acetic acid solution of case B [see Example 2(a) above], except that the ionization constant of NH_4OH ($K_b = 1.75 \times 10^{-5}$) is used.   The corresponding pH value is 11.1.

(b) At the equivalence point, the pH value can be calculated from either of the following formulas (which are general for titrations of this type):

$$pH = -\tfrac{1}{2} \log K_w + \tfrac{1}{2} \log K_b - \tfrac{1}{2} \log C$$

or

$$pH = \tfrac{1}{2}pK_w - \tfrac{1}{2}pK_b - \tfrac{1}{2} \log C$$

These equations are derived from the hydrolysis constant of ammonium chloride by a method analogous to that in case B.

In the case at hand, we have $K_w = 1.0 \times 10^{-14}$, $K_b = 1.75 \times 10^{-5}$, and $C = 0.0833$.

$$pH = \frac{14.0}{2} - \frac{4.76}{2} - \frac{(-1.08)}{2}$$

$$= 5.16$$

This is point D on the titration curve DD.

The common indicator that changes color at approximately this point is methyl red.   As seen from the chart, an indicator like phenolphthalein would give erroneous results.   The change of color would be gradual, and the end point would occur considerably before the true equivalence point.

CASE D   Weak acid titrated with weak base; weak base titrated with weak acid

The titration curves for the neutralization of a weak acid like acetic acid with a weak base like ammonium hydroxide and for the reverse titration are represented by curves EE and FF in Fig. 5. The pH value at the equivalence point can be found from either of the following formulas (which are general for titrations of this type):

$$pH = -\tfrac{1}{2} \log K_w - \tfrac{1}{2} \log K_a + \tfrac{1}{2} \log K_b$$

or

$$pH = \tfrac{1}{2}pK_w + \tfrac{1}{2}pK_a - \tfrac{1}{2}pK_b$$

Such titrations are of no value in general analytical work, for as seen from the figure, there is no sudden inflection of the curve at the equivalence point and no indicator has a sharp enough change in color to indicate the equivalence point with satisfactory precision.

11-17   Calculation of the Degree of Hydrolysis of a Salt

Not only are the above formulas useful for calculating the pH value at the equivalence point in a given titration, but they can be used to calculate the approximate extent of hydrolysis of a salt of a weak acid and a strong base or of a salt of a weak base and a strong acid. For example, in the hydrolysis of sodium acetate ($C_2H_3O_2^- + H_2O \longrightarrow HC_2H_3O_2 + OH^-$), the value of the concentration of OH^- can be found from the pH value calculated from the appropriate formula above; the value of the concentration of acetate is that of the concentration of the salt (C) in the formula. The ratio of $[OH^-]:[C_2H_3O_2^-]$ indicates the degree of hydrolysis of the salt.

Example 1   What is the percentage hydrolysis of a 0.0010 M solution of NH_4Cl ($NH_4^+ + H_2O \longrightarrow NH_4OH + H^+$)?

Solution

$$pH = \tfrac{1}{2}pK_w - \tfrac{1}{2}pK_b - \tfrac{1}{2} \log C$$

where $pK_w = 14$
$$pK_b = - \log K_{NH_4OH} = - \log 1.75 \times 10^{-5}$$
$$C = 0.0010$$

Solving,

$$pH = 6.12$$

$$[H^+] = 10^{-6.12} = 7.6 \times 10^{-7}$$

$$[NH_4^+] = 0.0010$$

$$\text{Extent of hydrolysis} = \frac{[H^+]}{[NH_4^+]} \times 100 = 0.076\% \qquad \textit{Ans.}$$

PROBLEMS

(A temperature of 25°C is assumed in these problems.)

*11-106. (a) What is the pH value of a soln. that has a hydroxyl-ion concn. of 4.2×10^{-8} M? What color would be given to the soln. (b) by methyl orange, (c) by thymol blue?

*11-107. (a) What is the H^+-ion concn. of a soln. that has a pOH value of 8.85? (b) What common indicator would change color at approx. this concn.?

*11-108. In the titration of a weak base like NH_4OH with a strong acid like HCl, what relationship exists between the pH value of the soln. and the ionization const. K_b of the base at that point in the titration which is halfway to the equivalence point?

*11-109. A certain weak monobasic acid is colorless in acid soln. and blue in alkaline soln. and serves as an indicator. Assuming that the blue is seen when two-fifths of the indicator has been converted to ions and that at this point the pOH value of the soln. is 3.6, what is the indicator const.?

*11-110. A certain weak monobasic acid has an ionization const. of 2.0×10^{-4}. If 0.0100 mole is dissolved in H_2O and the soln. diluted to 200 ml and titrated with 0.250 N NaOH, calculate the pH value of the soln. at the following points: (a) the original soln., (b) one-fifth of the way to the equivalence point, (c) at the equivalence point.

*11-111. (a) What is the pH value of a 0.0100 M soln. of KCN? (b) of NH_4Cl? (c) What common indicator is therefore suitable for the titration with HCl of a soln. approx. $N/100$ in NH_4OH?

*11-112. What is the percentage hydrolysis in a 0.0050 M soln. of potassium acetate?

*11-113. What is the percentage hydrolysis in a 0.10 M soln. of Na_2CO_3? (Consider hydrolysis only to HCO_3^-.)

*11-114. (a) What are the pH value, the hydroxyl-ion concn., and the percentage hydrolysis in a 0.10 M soln. of NaCN? (b) What is the pH value of a 0.20 M soln. of ammonium formate?

*11-115. In an aq. soln. of KClO, how many moles per liter of ClO^- are present if the soln. has an OH^--ion concn. of 2.0×10^{-6} M?

*11-116.   A sample of vinegar weighing 6.00 g is diluted with H_2O to 50.0 ml and titrated with 0.505 N NaOH.   After 12.40 ml of the base has been added, it is found necessary to back-titrate to the equivalence point with 2.00 ml of 0.606 N HCl.   (*a*) What is the acidity of the vinegar in terms of percentage of acetic acid?   (*b*) Assuming that this is the only acid present in the vinegar, calculate the pH value of the soln. at the equivalence point at the end of the above titration.   (*c*) Is phenolphthalein shown to be a suitable indicator for this titration?

*11-117.   When a soln. of a certain weak organic base of the formula type ROH is titrated with HCl, the pH value at the point two-thirds of the way to the equivalence point is 8.90.   What is the ionization const. of the base?

*11-118.   In 0.100 M soln., an acid of the formula HX (in which X represents an organic radical) is 1.00% ionized.   What is the pH value of a 0.0100 M soln. of the salt NaX?

*11-119.   If 400 ml of a soln. contg. NH_4OH is titrated with 0.250 N HCl, 40.0 ml of the acid is required to reach the equivalence point.   (*a*) What is the pH value of the soln. at the start of the titration, halfway to the equivalence point, and at the equivalence point?   (*b*) What indicator is shown to be suitable?

*11-120.   Formic acid, HCOOH, is a monobasic acid that is 4.6% ionized in 0.100 M soln.   (*a*) Calculate the ionization const. of HCOOH.   (*b*) If 50.0 ml of 0.100 N HCOOH is diluted to 250 ml and titrated with 0.200 N NaOH, what would be the pH value at the equivalence point?   (*c*) What indicator is shown to be suitable?

11-121.   (*a*) What is the pOH value of a soln. the H^+-ion concn. of which is 9.0 $\times$ 10^{-10} M?   (*b*) What common indicator would change color at approx. this concn.?

11-122.   (*a*) What is the hydroxyl-ion concn. of a soln. that has a pH value of 6.30?   (*b*) What color is given to the soln. by congo red?   By cresol red?

11-123.   Derive the formula pH $= \frac{1}{2}pK_w - \frac{1}{2}pK_b - \frac{1}{2}\log C$, which represents the pH value at the equivalence point in the titration of a weak base with a strong acid.

11-124.   A certain weak monoacidic organic base serves as an indicator.   Assuming that the color change is seen when one-third of the indicator has been converted to ions and that at that point the pH value of the soln. is 4.8, what is the indicator const.?

11-125.   In the titration of a soln. of a certain monoacidic base with HCl, with methyl red as the indicator, the appearance of a shade of pink in the soln. is taken as the end point.   On the assumption that the concn. of the resulting salt soln. is 0.100 N and that the indicator used is best suited for this titration, what is the approx. ionization const. of the base?

11-126.   What is the OH^- concn. of a 0.100 M soln. of ammonium cyanide?

11-127.   In 0.200 M soln., a base of the formula XOH (in which X represents an organic radical) is 0.500% ionized.   What is the pH value of a 0.0500 M soln. of the salt XCl?

11-128.   Benzoic acid, C_6H_5COOH, is a monobasic acid with an ionization const. of 6.6×10^{-5}. A sample of the pure acid weighing 0.610 g is dissolved in 500 ml of water and titrated with 0.500 N NaOH. (a) Calculate the pH value of the soln. at the start of the titration, halfway to the equivalence point, and at the equivalence point. (b) What indicator is shown to be suitable for this titration? (c) Sketch the titration curve.

11-129.   What is the percentage hydrolysis in a 0.0500 M soln. of $NaNO_2$?

11-130.   By how many times is the percentage hydrolysis of NH_4NO_3 increased when its 0.10 M soln. is diluted tenfold?

11-131.   What is the pH value of a soln. 0.10 M in $KHCO_3$? (See Sec. 5-14.)

11-132.   How many g of each of the following substances must be dissolved in 100 ml in order for the resulting soln. to have a pH value of 9.0: (a) NH_3, (b) NaOH, (c) KNO_2?

11-133.   What is the percentage hydrolysis in 0.10 M soln. of Na_3PO_4 (PO_4^{3-} + $H_2O \rightleftharpoons HPO_4^- + OH^-$)?

11-134.   In the titration of a weak monobasic acid with a strong base, what is the relationship between the pH value of the soln. and the ionization const. of the acid K_a at that point in the titration which is two-thirds of the way to the equivalence point?

11-135.   A certain organic amine is a weak monoacidic base like NH_4OH. Its ionization const. is 1.0×10^{-4}. (a) If 100 ml of a 0.020 M soln. is titrated with 0.020 N HCl, what is the hydroxyl-ion concn. at the equivalence point? (b) Which of the following four indicators would be best suited for the titration: methyl orange, phenolphthalein, methyl red, bromthymol blue? (c) Carefully sketch the titration curve (pH against ml), and show from it why the other three indicators would not be as satisfactory. (d) Show clearly the positions of pH 4, 7, and 10 on the graph.

11-136.   Propionic acid is a monobasic acid with an ionization const. of 1.6×10^{-5}. If 0.100 mole of the pure acid is dissolved in 100 ml and titrated with 4.00 N NaOH, calculate the pH value (a) of the original soln., (b) of the soln. when the acid is two-thirds neutralized, (c) at the equivalence point.

11-137.   When a soln. of a certain weak organic monobasic acid is titrated with NaOH, the equivalence point is found to be the point where 40.0 ml of NaOH has been added. If at the point where 16.0 ml of NaOH has been added the pH value of the soln. is 6.20, what is the ionization const. of the organic acid?

11-138.   In the titration of a certain soln. of H_3PO_4 with 0.300 N NaOH, the pH values corresponding to the added vols. of NaOH were found experimentally to be the following: 0.01 ml = 1.71; 4.0 ml = 1.81; 8.0 ml = 1.99; 10.0 ml = 2.13; 11.0 ml = 2.30; 11.5 ml = 2.51; 12.0 ml = 3.50; 12.5 ml = 4.59; 13.0 ml = 4.81; 14.0 ml = 5.01; 16.0 ml = 5.22, 18.0 ml = 5.53; 20.0 ml = 6.04; 22.0 ml = 6.80; 23.0 ml = 7.35; 24.0 ml = 8.55; 25.0 ml = 9.76; 26.0 ml = 10.15; 28.0 ml = 10.46; 32.0 ml = 10.75; 36.0 ml = 10.85; 40.0 ml = 10.95; 44.0 ml = 11.04.

Sketch the titration curve from the above data and calculate from the first inflection the number of g of H_3PO_4 present in the original soln. From the curve, determine the *difference* between the pH values (*a*) at 1.0 ml before the first equivalence point and 1.0 ml beyond the first equivalence point, (*b*) at 1.0 ml before the second equivalence point and 1.0 ml beyond the second equivalence point, (*c*) at 1.0 ml before the theoretical third equivalence point and 1.0 ml beyond the theoretical third equivalence point. (*d*) Explain why these three values are different. (*e*) From Fig. 4, determine what indicator would be suitable for the first inflection point and the second inflection point, and explain why no indicator is suitable for the theoretical third step in the titration.

11-18   Titration of Sodium Carbonate

In Fig. 5, curve GG represents the titration of a solution of sodium carbonate with a half-normal solution of hydrochloric acid. It will be noted that there are two points of inflection. The first is at about pH = 9 and corresponds to the completion of the reaction

$$CO_3^= + H^+ \longrightarrow HCO_3^-$$

The second is at about pH = 4 and corresponds to the completion of the reaction

$$HCO_3^- + H^+ \longrightarrow CO_2 + H_2O$$

Phenolphthalein should therefore indicate the conversion of sodium carbonate to bicarbonate, and methyl orange should change color only when complete neutralization has taken place. Use is made of this principle in titrations of certain mixtures of substances as illustrated in the following section.

11-19   Analyses Involving the Use of Two Indicators

The fact that certain indicators change color at different stages of a neutralization is sometimes made use of in volumetric work to determine the proportions of the components of certain mixtures by the employment of two end points in a single titration. This may be brought about by means of two indicators, and the volumes of titrating solution required for the respective end points give a direct measure of the amounts of substances present. Only the two common indicators, methyl orange and phenolphthalein, will be considered.

Assume a solution to contain only sodium hydroxide and inert impurities. The weight of NaOH present can be found by direct titration with a standard solution of any strong acid and with either methyl orange or phenolphthalein as the indicator. In either case, the color change will take place only when the alkali is completely neutralized, and the volume of standard acid used in the titration is a direct measure of the weight of NaOH present.

If a solution contains only sodium carbonate and inert impurities and is titrated with standard acid, with methyl orange as the indicator, the color change takes place only when the Na_2CO_3 has been completely neutralized

$$CO_3^= + H^+ \longrightarrow HCO_3^-$$
$$HCO_3^- + H^+ \longrightarrow H_2O + CO_2$$

The volume of acid required is a measure of the total alkaline strength of the sample and of the actual weight of Na_2CO_3 present. In calculating, the equivalent weight of the Na_2CO_3 would be taken as one-half of the molecular weight. On the other hand, if phenolphthalein were used as the indicator and the titration were carried out in the cold, the color change from pink to colorless would occur when the carbonate had been changed to bicarbonate.

$$CO_3^= + H^+ \longrightarrow HCO_3^-$$

The volume of standard acid required to titrate sodium carbonate to an end point with methyl orange as the indicator is twice that required if phenolphthalein is used as the indicator, since twice the number of hydrogen-ion equivalents is involved. The equivalent weight of sodium carbonate is $Na_2CO_3/1$, and the calculated weight of Na_2CO_3 present is the same in the two cases. It is important to note that if, with phenolphthalein as the indicator, an excess of standard acid is added to the carbonate solution and *the carbon dioxide is expelled by boiling,* the sodium carbonate will be completely neutralized. Neutralization of the excess acid with standard alkali will give a *net* volume of acid which will be the same as that used with methyl orange as the indicator.

If a solution contains sodium bicarbonate and inactive impurities, the $NaHCO_3$ may be titrated with standard acid, with methyl orange as the indicator, or in boiling solution with phenolphthalein, in the latter case by adding excess acid and titrating back with alkali.

$$HCO_3^- + H^+ \longrightarrow H_2O + CO_2$$

The equivalent weight of $NaHCO_3$ in either case is identical to the molecular weight. As stated above, a cold solution of pure sodium bicarbonate gives no color with phenolphthalein and therefore cannot be titrated with phenolphthalein as the indicator.

There now remains the question of possible mixtures of the three alkalies just discussed. Altogether, there are the following theoretical possibilities:

(*a*)   NaOH
(*b*) Na_2CO_3
(*c*) $NaHCO_3$

(d)   NaOH + Na$_2$CO$_3$
(e)   Na$_2$CO$_3$ + NaHCO$_3$
(f)   NaOH + NaHCO$_3$
(g)   NaOH + Na$_2$CO$_3$ + NaHCO$_3$

Inert impurities may be present in each case.   The components of the last two mixtures, however, cannot coexist in solution, for sodium hydroxide and sodium bicarbonate interact mole for mole to form the normal carbonate:

$$OH^- + HCO_3^- \longrightarrow CO_3^= + H_2O$$

Strictly speaking, these last two mixtures can exist when in the *perfectly dry* form, although this condition would be difficult to realize in practice. When they are treated with water or even in the presence of superficial moisture, the reaction takes place, forming the carbonate and leaving a possible excess of hydroxide or bicarbonate as the case may be.

The mixtures ordinarily encountered in practice are therefore those of (d) and (e), viz., sodium hydroxide with sodium carbonate and sodium carbonate with sodium bicarbonate.   With two end points used, it is possible to determine the proportions of the components of either of these mixtures even when inactive impurities are present.

Example 1   Mixture of Hydroxide and Carbonate   A 1.200-g sample of a mixture of NaOH and Na$_2$CO$_3$ containing inert impurities is dissolved and titrated cold with 0.5000 N HCl.   With phenolphthalein as indicator, the solution turns colorless after the addition of 30.00 ml of the acid. Methyl orange is then added, and 5.00 ml more of the acid is required before this indicator changes color.   What is the percentage of NaOH and of Na$_2$CO$_3$ in the sample?

Solution   If the acid is added slowly, the stronger base (NaOH) is neutralized first, as follows:

$$OH^- + H^+ \longrightarrow H_2O$$

After this reaction is complete, the carbonate is converted to bicarbonate:

$$CO_3^= + H^+ \longrightarrow HCO_3^-$$

At this point, the phenolphthalein changes from pink to colorless and a total of 30.00 ml of acid has been added.   Then the bicarbonate formed is neutralized by 5.00 ml more of acid:

$$HCO_3^- + H^+ \longrightarrow H_2O + CO_2$$

Since each mole of Na$_2$CO$_3$ reacts with 1 mole of HCl to give 1 mole of NaHCO$_3$ and this, in turn, is neutralized by 1 mole of HCl, it follows that the volume of acid required to convert the Na_2CO_3 into $NaHCO_3$ is the same as the volume required to neutralize the $NaHCO_3$, viz., 5.00 ml.

Therefore, the volume of acid necessary to neutralize completely the Na_2CO_3 is 10.00 ml. Since the total volume added was 35.00 ml, it is evident that $35.00 - 10.00 = 25.00$ ml was necessary to neutralize the NaOH. Hence,

$$\left.\begin{array}{c} \dfrac{25.00 \times 0.5000 \times \dfrac{NaOH}{1,000}}{1.200} \times 100 = 41.67\% \text{ NaOH} \\[4mm] \dfrac{10.00 \times 0.5000 \times \dfrac{Na_2CO_3}{2,000}}{1.200} \times 100 = 22.08\% \text{ } Na_2CO_3 \end{array}\right\} \quad Ans.$$

These volume relationships are shown diagrammatically in Fig. 6.

Example 2   Mixture of Carbonate and Bicarbonate   A 1.200-g sample of an impure mixture of Na_2CO_3 and $NaHCO_3$ containing only inert impurities is dissolved and titrated cold with 0.5000 N HCl. With phenolphthalein as indicator, the solution turns colorless after the addition of 15.00 ml of the acid. Methyl orange is then added, and 22.00 ml more of the acid is required to change the color of this indicator. What is the percentage of Na_2CO_3 and of $NaHCO_3$ in the sample?

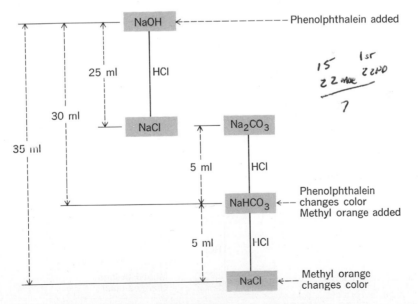

Fig. 6   Titration of NaOH + Na₂CO₃ mixture.

Solution   When the acid is added slowly, the Na_2CO_3 is converted to $NaHCO_3$.   At this point, the phenolphthalein changes color, and 15.00 ml of HCl has been added.   As in Example 1, the same volume of HCl as was used for the conversion of the Na_2CO_3 to $NaHCO_3$ would be required to convert this $NaHCO_3$ formed from the Na_2CO_3 to NaCl, H_2O, and CO_2. It follows that $15.00 + 15.00 = 30.00$ ml of acid was required to neutralize completely the Na_2CO_3 present in the sample.   The total volume being $15.00 + 22.00 = 37.00$ ml, it is evident that $37.00 - 30.00 = 7.00$ ml of HCl was required to neutralize the $NaHCO_3$ present in the original sample.   Hence,

$$\left. \begin{array}{l} \dfrac{30.00 \times 0.5000 \times \dfrac{Na_2CO_3}{2{,}000}}{1.200} \times 100 = 66.25\% \ Na_2CO_3 \\[4ex] \dfrac{7.00 \times 0.5000 \times \dfrac{NaHCO_3}{1{,}000}}{1.200} \times 100 = 24.50\% \ NaHCO_3 \end{array} \right\} \quad Ans.$$

These volume relationships are shown diagrammatically in Fig. 7.

11-20   Relation of Titration Volumes to Composition of Sample

In an analysis of the type discussed in Sec. 11-19, it is not always true that the analyst is previously aware of the exact composition of the

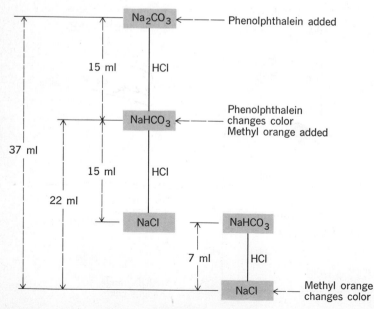

Fig. 7   **Titration of Na_2CO_3 + $NaHCO_3$ mixture.**

sample. He may not know whether the sample contains hydroxide, carbonate, bicarbonate, or possible combinations of these components. By means of a simple titration, however, and the use of a double end point, the composition of the alkali can be determined so far as these negative radicals are concerned.

In this connection, let A represent the volume of standard acid required to titrate the cold solution to a change of color of phenolphthalein, and let B represent the *additional* volume of the acid to continue the titration to a change of color of methyl orange. The following relationships exist:

Active ions present	Volume for first end point	Additional volume for second end point
OH^-	A	0
HCO_3^-	0	B
$CO_3^=$	A	B = A
$CO_3^= + OH^-$	A	B < A
$CO_3^= + HCO_3^-$	A	B > A

PROBLEMS

*11-139. A sample of material contains for its active components NaOH, Na_2CO_3, $NaHCO_3$, or compatible mixts. of these. Two samples, each weighing 1.000 g, are dissolved in H_2O. To one sample phenolphthalein is added and the soln. is titrated cold with 1.038 N acid, of which 17.96 ml is required. The other sample is titrated cold, with methyl orange as indicator, and 21.17 ml of the same acid is required. What alkalies are present, and what is the percentage of each in the original sample?

*11-140. From the following data, find the percentages of Na_2CO_3 and $NaHCO_3$ in a mixt. in which they are the only alkaline components: Sample = 1.272 g. Vol. of 0.2400 N HCl required for phenolphthalein end point = 26.92 ml. After the addition of 52.21 ml more of the HCl and boiling out the CO_2, the vol. of 0.1200 N NaOH required to give a pink color to the soln. = 4.00 ml. Show the general appearance of the titration curve.

*11-141. A chemist received different mixts. for analysis with the statement that they contained NaOH, $NaHCO_3$, Na_2CO_3, or compatible mixts. of these substances, together with inert material. From the data given, identify the respective materials, and calculate the percentage of each component. 1.000-g samples and 0.2500 N HCl were used in all cases.

Sample 1. With phenolphthalein as an indicator, 24.32 ml was used. A duplicate sample required 48.64 ml with methyl orange as an indicator.

Sample 2. The addition of phenolphthalein caused no color change. With methyl orange, 38.47 ml of the acid was required.

Sample 3. To cause a color change in the cold with phenolphthalein, 15.29 ml

$$NaOH + CO_2 \rightarrow NaCO_3$$

of the acid was necessary, and an additional 33.19 ml was required for complete neutralization.

Sample 4.   The sample was titrated with acid until the pink of phenolphthalein disappeared; this process required 39.96 ml.   On adding an excess of the acid, boiling, and titrating back with alkali, it was found that the alkali was exactly equivalent to the excess acid added.

*11-142.   A sample is known to contain NaOH, NaHCO$_3$, or Na$_2$CO$_3$ or compatible mixtures of these, together with inert matter.   A 1.200-g sample requires 42.20 ml of 0.5000 N HCl, with methyl orange as indicator.   The same wt. of sample requires 36.30 ml of the acid with phenolphthalein indicator.   Calculate the percentage of inert matter in the sample.

*11-143.   In a certain industrial process a gas mixt. is passed through a "scrubber" soln., which is approx. 2% in NaOH, in order to remove CO$_2$ from the gas.   Samples of the scrubber soln. are taken at intervals and titrated with standard HCl to determine the extent to which the NaOH has been used up.   At a certain point in the process a 25.0-ml portion of the partially spent caustic soln. requires 30.0 ml of 0.300 N HCl for titration to a phenolphthalein end point.   Another 25.0-ml portion of the same soln. requires 48.0 ml for titration to a methyl orange end point.   Calculate the percentage of the original NaOH which has been converted to Na$_2$CO$_3$ in the scrubber.

*11-144.   Pure dry NaOH and pure dry NaHCO$_3$ are mixed in the respective proportion by wt. of 2:1, and the mixt. is dissolved in H$_2$O.   Calculate to three significant figures the ratio of the vol. of standard acid required with phenolphthalein as an indicator to the additional vol. required with methyl orange.

*11-145.   A mixt. that contains KOH and K$_2$CO$_3$ weighs a g and, in the cold solution with phenolphthalein, requires b ml of c N acid.   After methyl orange is added, d ml of the acid is required.   Calculate the percentage of KOH and of K$_2$CO$_3$. Reduce to simplest terms.

*11-146.   Solve the preceding problem with respect to a mixt. of Na$_2$CO$_3$ and NaHCO$_3$.   Reduce to simplest terms.

*11-147.   A certain soln. contains 38.00 g of NaOH and 2.00 g of Na$_2$CO$_3$ per liter. It is to be used as a standard base in the titration of an acid.   (*a*) What is the normality of the soln. if it is completely neutralized in the titration?   (*b*) What would be its effective normality if it is used in a titration in the cold with phenolphthalein as the indicator?

11-148.   Analysis of a mixt. consisting of NaOH + Na$_2$CO$_3$ + inert matter gives the following data: Sample = 10.00 g.   Its aq. soln. is diluted to 250 ml and two separate 25.00-ml portions are titrated.   With one portion, an end point with phenolphthalein is obtained in cold soln. with 44.52 ml of 0.5000 N HCl.   The other portion requires 46.53 ml of the acid for an end point with methyl orange. Calculate the percentage composition of the original sample.

11-149.   A mixt. contg. Na$_2$CO$_3$, NaOH, and inert matter weighs 0.7500 g.   When the aq. soln. is titrated cold with 0.5000 N HCl, the color of phenolphthalein disappears when 21.00 ml of the acid has been added. Methyl orange is then added, and 5.00 ml more of the acid is required to give a red color to the soln. Find the percentage composition of the sample, and show the general appearance of the titration curve.

11-150. A sample is known to contain NaOH, $NaHCO_3$, Na_2CO_3, or compatible mixtures of these, together with inert material. With methyl orange indicator, a 1.100-g sample requires 31.40 ml of HCl (1.000 ml $\approx$ 0.01400 g CaO). With phenolphthalein indicator, the same wt. of sample requires 13.30 ml of the acid. What is the percentage of inert material in the sample? Show the general appearance of the titration curve.

11-151. A powder gives an alkaline reaction in aq. soln., and the alkalinity is due either to K_2CO_3 + KOH or to K_2CO_3 + $KHCO_3$. Find the percentage of each alkaline component from the following data: When phenolphthalein is the indicator (in a cold soln.), 1.500 g of the powder reacts with 26.27 ml of 0.3333 N HCl. When methyl orange is the indicator, the same wt. of sample requires 59.17 ml of the acid.

11-152. A soln. of alkali is prepared from NaOH which is contaminated with Na_2CO_3. With phenolphthalein in the cold soln., 36.42 ml of the alkali is required to neutralize 50.00 ml of 0.5280 N H_2SO_4. With methyl orange indicator, 35.60 ml of the alkali is required for the same amt. of acid. How many g of NaOH and of Na_2CO_3 are contained in each ml of the alkali soln.?

11-21 Analysis of Phosphate Mixtures

Phosphoric acid ionizes in three steps. The ionization constant for the first hydrogen is 1.1×10^{-2}; for the second, 2.0×10^{-7}; and for the third, 3.6×10^{-13}. In the titration of phosphoric acid with an alkali like NaOH, the replacement of the first hydrogen results in the formation of NaH_2PO_4 (H_3PO_4 + OH^- $\longrightarrow$ $H_2PO_4^-$ + H_2O). At approximately this point, methyl orange changes color. The replacement of the second hydrogen results in the formation of Na_2HPO_4 ($H_2PO_4^-$ + OH^- $\longrightarrow$ $HPO_4^=$ + H_2O). At approximately this point, phenolphthalein changes color. The reverse titration of Na_3PO_4 with a strong acid like HCl results first in the formation of $HPO_4^=$, at which point phenolphthalein changes color, and then in the formation of $H_2PO_4^-$, at which point methyl orange changes color. A titration of this sort is represented in Fig. 8.

Only adjacent substances shown on the diagram can exist together in solution. Other combinations interact. As in the case of the carbonate titrations of the preceding section, it is possible to analyze certain mixtures of phosphates by means of titrations involving the use of two indicators. Actually, the titrations should be carried out on fairly concentrated solutions and at a temperature of about 55°C.

Example 1 A sample, which is known to contain Na_3PO_4, NaH_2PO_4,

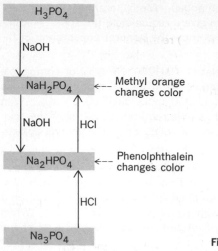

Fig. 8   Titration of phosphate mixture.

Na_2HPO_4, or compatible mixtures of these, together with inert impurity, weighs 2.00 g. When this sample is titrated with 0.500 N HCl, using methyl orange, 32.0 ml of the acid is required. The same weight of sample when titrated with 0.500 N HCl, using phenolphthalein, requires 12.0 ml of the acid. What is the percentage composition of the sample?

Solution.   From simple inspection of the diagram and consideration of the two volumes involved, it is evident that both Na_3PO_4 and Na_2HPO_4 are present. A volume of 12.0 ml must have been required to convert the Na_3PO_4 to Na_2HPO_4, and, since 12.0 ml more would be required to convert the Na_2HPO_4 *formed* to NaH_2PO_4, a volume of 32.0 − (2 × 12.0) = 8.0 ml is required to convert the *original* Na_2HPO_4 to NaH_2PO_4.

$$\left. \begin{array}{l} \dfrac{12.0 \times 0.500 \times \dfrac{Na_3PO_4}{1{,}000}}{2.00} \times 100 = 49.2\% \ Na_3PO_4 \\[4ex] \dfrac{8.0 \times 0.500 \times \dfrac{Na_2HPO_4}{1{,}000}}{2.00} \times 100 = 28.4\% \ Na_2HPO_4 \end{array} \right\} \quad \textit{Ans.}$$

PROBLEMS

*11-153.   A sample that contains $Na_3PO_4 \cdot 12H_2O$, $Na_2HPO_4 \cdot 12H_2O$, $NaH_2PO_4 \cdot H_2O$, or compatible combinations of these weighs 3.00 g. When it is titrated with 0.500 N HCl, 14.00 ml is required if methyl orange indicator is used. A similar sample requires 5.00 ml of 0.600 N NaOH if phenolphthalein indicator is used. Find the percentage composition of the sample.

*11-154.   A certain soln. is known to contain a noninteracting combination of two of the following substances: HCl, Na_2HPO_4, NaH_2PO_4, H_3PO_4, NaOH.   Titration of a sample with 0.500 N NaOH (using phenolphthalein) requires 27.0 ml of the NaOH. With methyl orange indicator, the same wt. of sample requires 17.2 ml of the NaOH.   How many g of which components are present in the sample taken?

*11-155.   A certain soln. is known to contain HCl + H_3PO_4, H_3PO_4 + NaH_2PO_4, or the three compounds existing alone.   A sample is titrated with NaOH, requiring A ml with methyl orange indicator, but the same wt. of sample requires B ml of the NaOH with phenolphthalein indicator.   (a) What mathematical relationship would exist between A and B to indicate the first combination?   (b) What relationship would exist between A and B to indicate the second combination?   (c) What relationship would indicate the presence of H_3PO_4 alone?

11-156.   A soln. known to contain H_3PO_4, Na_2HPO_4, NaH_2PO_4, or compatible mixtures of these weighs 1.10 g.   When it is titrated with 0.520 N NaOH, 27.0 ml is required to change the color of phenolphthalein but only 10.0 ml to change the color of methyl orange.   What is the percentage composition of the soln.?

11-157.   A certain soln. is known to contain a compatible combination of two of the following substances: HCl, Na_2HPO_4, NaH_2PO_4, H_3PO_4, NaOH, Na_3PO_4.   Titration of a sample with 0.510 N HCl, using methyl orange, requires 28.1 ml of the acid.   With the same wt. of sample and phenolphthalein indicator, 17.1 ml of the HCl is required.   What components are present, and how many g of each are in the sample taken?

11-158.   A series of solns. is known to contain H_3PO_4, NaH_2PO_4, Na_2HPO_4, alone or mixed in varying compatible combinations.   In each case, the titration is made with 1.000 N NaOH to a pink color with phenolphthalein and the soln. is then back-titrated with 1.000 N HCl to a pink color with methyl orange.   In each of the following four cases, determine which components are present and the no. of millimoles of each: (a) initial titration 48.36 ml, back titration 33.72 ml; (b) initial titration 37.33 ml, back titration 39.42; (c) initial titration 24.36 ml, back titration 24.36 ml; (d) initial titration 36.24 ml, back titration 18.12 ml.

 **Redox Methods (Oxidimetry and Reductimetry)**

12-1 Fundamental Principles

This phase of volumetric analysis has to do with the titration of an oxidizing agent with a standard solution of a reducing agent or the titration of a reducing agent with a standard solution of an oxidizing agent. This type of determination embraces the greater part of volumetric analysis, for the number of substances capable of oxidation or reduction is comparatively large.

Oxidation is the increase in the positive direction of the electrical valence or oxidation number of an element or radical; reduction is the decrease in electrical valence or oxidation number of an element or radical. Oxidation and reduction must evidently take place simultaneously, for in any reaction of this type the oxidizing agent is always reduced and the reducing agent is always oxidized and to the same degree. The methods of expressing concentration and the definitions given in Chap. 4 hold true for solutions of oxidizing and reducing agents. Therefore, the relationships existing between these agents are the same as those existing between acids and bases. However, it is necessary in the case of concentrations of solutions expressed in terms of normality to consider the hydrogen equivalent from a different point of view.

12-2 Equivalent Weights of Oxidizing and Reducing Agents

As in acidimetry and alkalimetry, the concentration of a solution of an oxidizing or reducing agent is best expressed in terms of its relation to the normal solution, and the gram atom of hydrogen is taken as the ultimate unit. We must, however, consider the unit from the point of view of oxidation and reduction; thus

$$H^+ + e \rightleftharpoons H^0$$

The hydrogen ion is an oxidizing agent and is capable of being reduced to hydrogen gas (for example, $\underline{Zn} + 2H^+ \longrightarrow Zn^{++} + H_2$). Free hydrogen is a reducing agent and is capable of being oxidized to hydrogen ion (for example, $2Fe^{3+} + H_2 \longrightarrow 2Fe^{++} + 2H^+$).

The conversion of one atom of hydrogen to the ion, or vice versa, involves a change of 1 in oxidation number and a transfer of one electron. To find the equivalent weight of an oxidizing or reducing agent, we must, therefore, take that fraction of its formula weight so that in the oxidation or reduction process there will be involved the equivalent of a transfer of one electron. This will be accomplished (1) by dividing the formula weight of the substance by the total change in oxidation number involved in the oxidation-reduction process or (2) by dividing the formula weight of the substance by the number of electrons transferred per formula weight of substance. The gram-equivalent weight of an oxidizing agent is the equivalent weight in grams and is equivalent in oxidizing power to 1.008 g of hydrogen as hydrogen ion. It is likewise equivalent in oxidizing power to 8.000 g of oxygen. The gram equivalent weight of a reducing agent is equivalent in reducing power to 1.008 g of elementary hydrogen gas. As seen later, a substance may have two different equivalent weights, depending on whether it is used as an acid or as an oxidizing or reducing agent. As in acidimetry, a normal solution of an oxidizing or reducing agent contains one gram equivalent weight of substance per liter of solution, or one gram milliequivalent per milliliter. Hence, as in acidimetry,

$$ml_s \times N_s = \text{no. of g meq.}$$

and

$$ml_s \times N_s \times \text{meq. wt.}_x = \text{grams}_x$$

Example 1 How many grams of the following reducing substances constitute the gram equivalent weight in each case: (a) $FeSO_4 \cdot 7H_2O$, (b) $SnCl_2$, (c) $H_2C_2O_4 \cdot 2H_2O$ (oxalic acid), (d) $KHC_2O_4 \cdot H_2O$ (potassium binoxalate), (e) $KHC_2O_4 \cdot H_2C_2O_4 \cdot 2H_2O$ (potassium tetroxalate), (f) H_2S (oxidized to S), (g) H_2S (oxidized to H_2SO_4), (h) $Na_2S_2O_3 \cdot 5H_2O$ (oxidized to $Na_2S_4O_6$), (i) H_2O_2?

Solution

(a) $FeSO_4 \cdot 7H_2O$. In solution, this gives ferrous ions which can be oxidized to ferric ions.

$$Fe^{++} \longrightarrow Fe^{3+} + e$$

for example,

$$2Fe^{++} + Br_2 \longrightarrow 2Fe^{3+} + 2Br^-$$

Each ferrous ion changes in oxidation number by 1 unit and hence is equivalent in reducing power to the hydrogen unit. The molecular weight of $FeSO_4 \cdot 7H_2O$ is therefore the equivalent weight as a reducing agent and, expressed in grams, is equivalent in reducing power to 1.008 g of hydrogen.

$$\frac{FeSO_4 \cdot 7H_2O}{1} = 278.0 \text{ g} \qquad Ans.$$

(b) $SnCl_2$. In solution, this gives stannous ions which can be oxidized to stannic ions: $Sn^{++} \longrightarrow Sn^{4+} + 2e$. The change in oxidation number is 2. The gram molecular weight of $SnCl_2$ is, therefore, equivalent in reducing power to 2 g atoms of hydrogen, or one-half the molecular weight represents the equivalent weight.

$$\frac{SnCl_2}{2} = 94.80 \text{ g} \qquad Ans.$$

(c) $H_2C_2O_4 \cdot 2H_2O$. In solution, this gives oxalate ions, $C_2O_4^=$, which can be oxidized to CO_2 gas.

$$C_2O_4^= \longrightarrow 2CO_2 + 2e$$

for example,

$$5C_2O_4^= + 2MnO_4^- + 16H^+ \longrightarrow 10CO_2 + 2Mn^{++} + 8H_2O$$

The oxidation number of carbon in the oxalate radical is $+3$. The oxidation number of carbon in CO_2 is $+4$. Each carbon changes by 1 unit in oxidation number, but since there are two carbon atoms in the oxalate radical, the change for the oxalate radical is 2. The radical is, therefore, equivalent in reducing power to two hydrogen atoms.

$$\frac{H_2C_2O_4 \cdot 2H_2O}{2} = 63.03 \text{ g} \qquad Ans.$$

(d) $KHC_2O_4 \cdot H_2O$. Here again, each molecule of the dissolved salt gives an oxalate ion which is oxidized to CO_2 as in the preceding case.

$$\frac{KHC_2O_4 \cdot H_2O}{2} = 73.07 \text{ g} \qquad Ans.$$

It should be noted that the equivalent weight of this salt *as an acid* is the molecular weight, or 146.14. Hence, a solution of potassium binoxalate which is $0.1 \text{ } N$ as an acid is $0.2 \text{ } N$ as a reducing agent.

(e) $KHC_2O_4 \cdot H_2C_2O_4 \cdot 2H_2O$. Since each molecule of this salt in solution gives two oxalate ions which are oxidized as above to CO_2, the equivalent weight of potassium tetroxalate as a reducing agent is

$$\frac{KHC_2O_4 \cdot H_2C_2O_4 \cdot 2H_2O}{4} = 63.55 \text{ g} \qquad Ans.$$

When this salt is reacting as an acid, its equivalent weight is one-third of the molecular weight, or 84.73. A given solution of potassium tetroxalate has four-thirds the normality as a reducing agent that it has as an acid.

(f) H_2S. When this substance is oxidized to free sulfur, the change in oxidation number of sulfur is 2.

$$\frac{H_2S}{2} = 17.04 \text{ g} \qquad Ans.$$

(g) H_2S. When this substance is oxidized to sulfate, the change in oxidation number of sulfur is from -2 to $+6$.

$$\frac{H_2S}{8} = 4.260 \text{ g} \qquad Ans.$$

(h) $Na_2S_2O_3 \cdot 5H_2O$. In aqueous solution, this salt gives thiosulfate ions which can be oxidized to tetrathionate ions.

$$2S_2O_3^= \longrightarrow S_4O_6^= + 2e$$

for example,

$$2S_2O_3^= + I_2 \longrightarrow S_4O_6^= + 2I^-$$

In the thiosulfate radical, the *average* oxidation number of sulfur is $+2$; in tetrathionate, the *average* oxidation number of sulfur is $+2\frac{1}{2}$. The average change for each sulfur is $\frac{1}{2}$, but since in thiosulfate there are two sulfurs, the total change in oxidation number is 1.

$$\frac{Na_2S_2O_3 \cdot 5H_2O}{1} = 248.2 \text{ g} \qquad Ans.$$

(i) H_2O_2. When hydrogen peroxide acts as a reducing agent, it is oxidized to free oxygen; for example,

$$5H_2O_2 + 2MnO_4^- + 6H^+ \longrightarrow 5O_2 + 2Mn^{++} + 8H_2O$$

Average change in oxidation number of each oxygen atom in the hydrogen peroxide molecule is from -1 to 0. Total change for the molecule is 2.

$$\frac{H_2O_2}{2} = 17.01 \text{ g} \qquad Ans.$$

Example 2   How many grams of the following oxidizing substances constitute the gram milliequivalent weight in each case: (a) $K_3Fe(CN)_6$, (b) $KMnO_4$, (c) $K_2Cr_2O_7$, (d) I_2, (e) $KBrO_3$ (reduced to bromide), (f) H_2O_2?

Solution

(a) $K_3Fe(CN)_6$.   In solution, this salt gives ferricyanide ions which are capable of being reduced to ferrocyanide ions.

$$Fe(CN)_6^{3-} + e \longrightarrow Fe(CN)_6^{4-}$$

The change in oxidation number of the iron is from $+3$ to $+2$.

$$\frac{K_3Fe(CN)_6}{1,000} = 0.3293 \text{ g} \qquad Ans.$$

(b) $KMnO_4$.   When reduced *in the presence of acid,* permanganate ions form manganous ions.

$$MnO_4^- + 8H^+ + 5e \longrightarrow Mn^{++} + 4H_2O$$

for example,

$$MnO_4^- + 5Fe^{++} + 8H^+ \longrightarrow Mn^{++} + 5Fe^{3+} + 4H_2O$$

Change in oxidation number of manganese is from $+7$ to $+2$.

$$\frac{KMnO_4}{5,000} = 0.03161 \text{ g} \qquad Ans.$$

In alkaline solution, permanganate is reduced to MnO_2 with a change in oxidation number of 3 (from $+7$ to $+4$).

$$MnO_4^- + 2H_2O + 3e \longrightarrow \underline{MnO_2} + 4OH^-$$

Here the equivalent weight is *one-third* of the molecular weight.

(c) $K_2Cr_2O_7$.   Dichromate ions are ordinarily reduced to chromic ions.

$$Cr_2O_7^= + 14H^+ + 6e \longrightarrow 2Cr^{3+} + 7H_2O$$

for example,

$$Cr_2O_7^= + 6Fe^{++} + 14H^+ \longrightarrow 2Cr^{3+} + 6Fe^{3+} + 7H_2O$$

The change in oxidation number of each chromium atom is from $+6$ to $+3$, or the change of the dichromate ion (since it contains two chromium atoms) is 6.

$$\frac{K_2Cr_2O_7}{6,000} = 0.04903 \text{ g} \qquad Ans.$$

(d) I_2.   Iodine is reduced to iodide.

$$I_2 + 2e \longrightarrow 2I^-$$

There is 1 unit change in oxidation number for each iodine atom or 2 unit changes for the molecule.

$$\frac{I_2}{2,000} = 0.1269 \text{ g} \qquad Ans.$$

(e) $KBrO_3$. Bromate reduced to bromide involves a change in oxidation number of the bromine from $+5$ to -1, or a change of 6 units.

$$BrO_3^- + 6H^+ + 6e \longrightarrow Br^- + 3H_2O$$

$$\frac{KBrO_3}{6,000} = 0.02784 \text{ g} \qquad Ans.$$

(f) H_2O_2. As an oxidizing agent, hydrogen peroxide is reduced to water.

$$H_2O_2 + 2H^+ + 2e \longrightarrow 2H_2O$$

Average change of each oxygen is from -1 to -2. Total change for the molecule is 2.

$$\frac{H_2O_2}{2,000} = 0.01701 \text{ g} \qquad Ans.$$

12-3   Calculations of Redox Processes

Since the concentration of solutions in redox titrations, like those in acidimetry and alkalimetry, is based on the hydrogen equivalent, the general methods of calculation are identical. Thus, 1 liter of a normal solution of an oxidizing agent will exactly oxidize 1 liter of a normal solution of a reducing agent or 2 liters of a half-normal solution.

In titrating a reducing agent with a solution of oxidizing agent or an oxidizing agent with a solution of reducing agent, reasoning similar to that described in Secs. 11-7, 11-8, and 11-9 will evolve the same general formulas as were there derived, namely,

$$ml_s \times N_s \times meq. \text{ wt.}_r = grams_x$$

and

$$\frac{ml_s \times N_s \times meq. \text{ wt.}_x}{\text{Wt. of sample}} \times 100 = percent_x$$

PROBLEMS

*12-1. What fraction of the f. wt. of each of the following compds. represents the equiv. wt. in a redox process in which the product formed is as indicated: (a) $Ce(SO_4)_2 \cdot 2(NH_4)_2SO_4 \cdot 2H_2O$ ($\to Ce^{3+}$), (b) As_2O_5 ($\to As^{3+}$), (c) KIO_3 ($\to ICl_2^-$), (d) Na_2SeO_4 ($\to SeO_3^=$), (e) $VOSO_4$ ($\to VO_3^-$), (f) Mo_2O_3 ($\to H_2MoO_4$).

CHEEK

*12-2.   A ferrous soln. contains 1.176 g of $FeSO_4 \cdot (NH_4)_2SO_4 \cdot 6H_2O$ in 30.00 ml; a dichromate soln. contains 0.2940 g of $K_2Cr_2O_7$ in 20.00 ml.   Find (a) the normality of the ferrous soln. as a reducing agent, (b) the normality of the dichromate soln. as an oxidizing agent, (c) the vol. of the dichromate equiv. to 1.000 ml of the ferrous soln.

*12-3.   A soln. of HNO_3 is 3.00 N as an acid.   What vol. of H_2O must be added to 50 ml of the acid to make it 3.00 N as an oxidizing agent?   (Assume reduction of HNO_3 to NO.)

*12-4.   What is the normality as a reducing agent of a soln. contg. 10.00 g of $K_4Fe(CN)_6 \cdot 3H_2O$ in 500 ml?

*12-5.   From the following data, calculate the normality ratio of the HNO_3 as an oxidizing agent to the tetroxalate soln. as a reducing agent (assuming reduction of HNO_3 to NO): 1.000 ml $HNO_3 \backsimeq 1.246$ ml NaOH; 1.000 ml $KHC_2O_4 \cdot H_2C_2O_4 \cdot 2H_2O \backsimeq$ 1.743 ml NaOH; 1.000 ml NaOH $\backsimeq 0.06000$ millimole $H_2C_2O_4 \cdot 2H_2O$.

*12-6.   To oxidize the Fe in 1.00 g of $FeSO_4 \cdot (NH_4)_2SO_4 \cdot 6H_2O$ requires 5.00 ml of HNO_3 ($3Fe^{++} + NO_3^- + 4H^+ \longrightarrow 3Fe^{3+} + NO + H_2O$).   How much H_2O must be added to 500 ml of this acid to make the concn. as an acid 0.100 N?

*12-7.   A certain vol. of a soln. of $KHC_2O_4 \cdot H_2O$ is oxidized in the presence of acid by an equal vol. of 0.01000 M $KMnO_4$.   How many ml of 0.01000 M $Ba(OH)_2$ soln. would be neutralized by 20.00 ml of the binoxalate?

*12-8.   A method of standardizing $KMnO_4$ soln. against a standard soln. of NaOH consists of dissolving a small (unweighed) amt. of oxalic acid (or acid oxalate) in H_2O and, with phenolphthalein indicator, titrating with the standard NaOH.   The resulting soln. is then acidified with H_2SO_4 and titrated with the $KMnO_4$.   If $KHC_2O_4 \cdot H_2O$ were used as the intermediate compd. and the titrations required 10.58 ml of 0.2280 N NaOH and 38.10 ml of $KMnO_4$, find the normality of the $KMnO_4$ as an oxidizing agent.

*12-9.   Solid $KHC_2O_4 \cdot H_2C_2O_4 \cdot 2H_2O$ and $Na_2C_2O_4$ are to be mixed in such proportion that the normality of a soln. of the mixt. as a reducing agent will be 2.150 times the normality as an acid.   What proportion by wt. should be used?

*12-10.   Find the normality as an acid and as a reducing agent of a soln. made by dissolving a mixt. of 20.00 g of $H_2C_2O_4 \cdot 2H_2O$, 10.00 g of KHC_2O_4, and 15.00 g of $KHC_2O_4 \cdot H_2C_2O_4 \cdot 2H_2O$ in H_2O and diluting to 1 liter.

*12-11.   In the reaction expressed by the equation $13Pb_3O_4(s) + 2Mn_3O_4(s) + 72H^+ \longrightarrow 6MnO_4^- + 39Pb^{++} + 36H_2O$, (a) what is the numerical value of the equiv. wt. of Pb_3O_4 as an oxidizing agent, (b) the meq. wt. of Mn_3O_4 as a reducing agent, and (c) the vol. of 0.1500 N $FeSO_4$ soln. required to titrate the permanganate formed from 0.2000 millimole of Mn_3O_4?

12-12.   What fraction of the f. wt. of each of the following compds. represents the meq. wt. in a redox process in which the product formed is as indicated: (a) P_2O_3 ($\rightarrow H_3PO_4$), (b) H_2SeO_3 ($\rightarrow$ Se), (c) $U(SO_4)_2$ ($\rightarrow UO_2^{++}$), (d) $Fe_2(SO_4)_3 \cdot 9H_2O$ ($\rightarrow Fe^{++}$), (e) $KH(IO_3)_2$ ($\rightarrow I^-$), (f) Mn_3O_4 ($\rightarrow Mn^{++}$)?

12-13.   In the titration of $K_2Cr_2O_7$ with a reducing agent to the formation of Cr^{3+} ions, what is the equiv. wt. expressed in terms of (*a*) Cr_2O_3, (*b*) Cr?

12-14.   What vol. of HCl soln. is theoretically required to dissolve 1.000 g of Fe out of contact with air ($Fe + 2H^+ \longrightarrow Fe^{++} + H_2$) if 3.00 ml of the acid will neutralize that vol. of KOH soln. which will react with 6.00 ml of a soln. of KHC_2O_4 that is 2.00 N as a reducing agent?

12-15.   When 25.00 ml of HCl soln. is treated with excess $AgNO_3$, 0.5465 g of AgCl is obtained.   If 24.36 ml of the HCl neutralizes 27.22 of NaOH soln. and 26.24 ml of the NaOH neutralizes 30.17 ml of a soln. of $KHC_2O_4 \cdot H_2C_2O_4 \cdot 2H_2O$, what vol. of H_2O must be added to a liter of the oxalate soln. to make it 0.02500 N as a reducing agent?

12-16.   If a certain vol. of $KHC_2O_4 \cdot H_2C_2O_4 \cdot 2H_2O$ soln. would be neutralized by an equal vol. of 0.01000 M Na_2CO_3 soln., how many ml of 0.02000 M $K_2Cr_2O_7$ would be required to oxidize 25.00 ml of the tetroxalate soln.?

12-17.   Equal wts. of $Na_2C_2O_4$, $KHC_2O_4 \cdot H_2O$, and $KHC_2O_4 \cdot H_2C_2O_4 \cdot 2H_2O$ are mixed and dissolved in H_2O.   What is the ratio of the normality of the soln. as an acid to its normality as a reducing agent?

12-18.   A soln. is prepared by dissolving in H_2O 0.500 millimole of $KMnO_4$ and 0.500 millimole of $K_2Cr_2O_7$ and diluting to 100 ml.   What is the normality of the soln. as an oxidizing agent in the presence of acid?

12-4   Permanganate Process

Potassium permanganate is extensively used as an oxidimetric standard. It serves as its own indicator.   A normal solution contains one-fifth the gram molecular weight per liter (see Sec. 12-2, Example 2) if used in the presence of acid.   A standard solution of potassium permanganate is used in three ways:

1. It is used in the presence of acid in the direct titration of a large number of oxidizable cations and anions.   Among them are the following:

Substance	Oxidized to	
Fe^{++}	Fe^{3+}	1
Sn^{++}	Sn^{4+}	2
VO^{++}	VO_3^-	1
$C_2O_4^=$	CO_2	2
NO_2^-	NO_3^-	2
$SO_3^=$	$SO_4^=$	2
H_2O_2	O_2	2
Mo^{3+}	$MoO_4^=$	3
Ti^{3+}	TiO^{++}	1
U^{4+}	UO_2^{++}	2
As^{3+}	AsO_4^{3-}	2

2. It is used in the presence of acid in the indirect titration of a large number of reducible substances. In each case a measured amount of a reducing agent (e.g., a ferrous salt or an oxalate) is added, and after reduction is complete, the excess reducing agent is titrated with standard permanganate (cf. Sec. 11-10). Among the many substances that can be determined in this way are the following:

Substance	Reduced to
MnO_4^-	Mn^{++}
$Cr_2O_7^=$	Cr^{3+}
MnO_2, Mn_3O_4	Mn^{++}
PbO_2, Pb_2O_3, Pb_3O_4	Pb^{++}
Ce^{4+}	Ce^{3+}

3. It is used in neutral or alkaline solution in the titration of a few substances. In these cases the permanganate is reduced to MnO_2, which precipitates. The permanganate, therefore, has an oxidizing power only three-fifths of what it has when used in the presence of acid (see Sec. 12-2). This fact must be made use of in the calculations of such analyses (see Example 6, below).

Substance	Oxidized to
Mn^{++}	MnO_2
HCOOH (formic acid)	CO_2

Example 1 What is the normality of a solution of potassium permanganate if 40.00 ml will oxidize that weight of potassium tetroxalate, $KHC_2O_4 \cdot H_2C_2O_4 \cdot 2H_2O$, which requires 30.00 ml of 0.5000 N sodium hydroxide solution for its neutralization, and what is the value of 1.000 ml of the $KMnO_4$ in terms of grams of As_2O_3 in the titration of As^{3+} to H_3AsO_4 in the presence of acid?

Solution   The weight in grams of tetroxalate that requires 30.00 ml of 0.5000 N NaOH for neutralization is

$$30.00 \times 0.5000 \times \frac{KHC_2O_4 \cdot H_2C_2O_4 \cdot 2H_2O}{3,000}$$

The weight of potassium tetroxalate oxidized by 40.00 ml of $x\ N$ $KMnO_4$ is

$$40.00 \times x \times \frac{KHC_2O_4 \cdot H_2C_2O_4 \cdot 2H_2O}{4,000}$$

Since these two expressions are equal to each other, the equality can be expressed by an equation in which the molecular weights of the potassium tetroxalate cancel and

$$x = 0.5000 \; N \qquad Ans.$$

In As_2O_3 the oxidation number of each arsenic changes by 2 units; therefore,

$$1.000 \times 0.5000 \times \frac{As_2O_3}{4,000} = 0.02473 \; g \qquad Ans.$$

Example 2   What is the percentage of iron in a sample of iron ore weighing 0.7100 g if, after solution and reduction of the iron with amalgamated zinc, 48.06 ml of $KMnO_4$ (1.000 ml $\backsimeq$ 0.006700 g $Na_2C_2O_4$) is required to oxidize the iron?   How many grams of $KMnO_4$ are contained in each milliliter of the solution?

Solution

$$\text{Normality of the } KMnO_4 = \frac{0.006700}{\dfrac{Na_2C_2O_4}{2,000}} = 0.1000$$

$$\frac{48.06 \times 0.1000 \times \dfrac{Fe}{1,000}}{0.7100} \times 100 = 37.80\% \; Fe \qquad Ans.$$

Each ml of normal $KMnO_4$ contains $KMnO_4/5,000 = 0.03161$ g.

Each ml of this $KMnO_4$ contains $0.03161 \times 0.1000 = 0.003161$ g.   *Ans.*

Example 3   How many grams of H_2O_2 are contained in a solution that requires for titration 14.05 ml of $KMnO_4$ of which 1.000 ml $\backsimeq$ 0.008378 g Fe (i.e., will oxidize that amount of iron from the divalent to the trivalent state)?   How many grams and how many milliliters of oxygen measured dry and under standard conditions are evolved during the titration?

Solution

$$\text{Normality } KMnO_4 = \frac{0.008378}{Fe/1,000} = 0.1500$$

$$\text{Wt. } H_2O_2 = 14.05 \times 0.1500 \times \frac{H_2O_2}{2,000} = 0.03583 \; g \qquad Ans.$$

Each mole of H_2O_2 corresponds to a mole of O_2 evolved [see Sec. 12-2, Example 1(*i*)].   Therefore,

Wt. O_2 evolved $= 14.05 \times 0.1500 \times \dfrac{O_2}{2,000} = 0.03372$ g   *Ans.*

Each mole of O_2 occupies 22,400 ml.   Therefore,

Vol. O_2 evolved $= 14.05 \times 0.1500 \times \dfrac{22,400}{2,000} = 23.60$ ml   *Ans.*

Example 4   What is the percentage of MnO_2 in a pyrolusite ore if a sample weighing 0.4000 g is treated with 0.6000 g of pure $H_2C_2O_4 \cdot 2H_2O$ and dilute H_2SO_4 and after reduction has taken place ($\underline{MnO_2} + H_2C_2O_4 + 2H^+ \longrightarrow Mn^{++} + 2CO_2 + 2H_2O$), the excess oxalic acid requires 26.26 ml of 0.1000 N $KMnO_4$ for titration?   If pure As_2O_3 were used instead of oxalic acid, how many grams would be required in order for the other numerical data to remain the same?

Solution

Meq. of $H_2C_2O_4 \cdot 2H_2O$ used $= \dfrac{0.6000}{H_2C_2O_4 \cdot 2H_2O/2,000} = 9.526$

Meq. of $KMnO_4$ used $= 26.26 \times 0.1000 = 2.626$

Net meq. $= 9.526 - 2.626 = 6.900$

$\dfrac{6.900 \times MnO_2/2,000}{0.4000} \times 100 = 74.99\%$ MnO_2 *Ans.*

Meq. of As_2O_3 required $= 9.526$

$9.526 \times \dfrac{As_2O_3}{4,000} = 0.4711$ g As_2O_3 *Ans.*

Example 5   What is the milliequivalent weight of Pb_3O_4 and of Pb in the calculation of the analysis of red lead (impure Pb_3O_4) by a method similar to that of the preceding example ($\underline{Pb_3O_4} + H_2C_2O_4 + 3SO_4^= + 6H^+ \longrightarrow 3\underline{PbSO_4} + 2CO_2 + 4H_2O$)?

Solution   The oxidation number of Pb changes from an average of $2\frac{2}{3}$ (in Pb_3O_4) to 2 (in $PbSO_4$).   Each Pb therefore changes by an average of $\frac{2}{3}$ unit, and there is a 2-unit change for 3Pb.   Hence,

Meq. wt. $Pb_3O_4 = \dfrac{Pb_3O_4}{2,000} = 0.3428$ *Ans.*

Meq. wt. Pb $= \dfrac{3Pb}{2,000} = 0.3108$ *Ans.*

Example 6   A steel containing 0.90% Mn is analyzed by the three standard methods below, in each case with a 2.50-g sample, 0.0833 N $KMnO_4$, and 0.100 N $FeSO_4$ solutions.   Calculate in each case the volume of $KMnO_4$ required.

Solution

Bismuthate Method.   The Mn is oxidized to $KMnO_4$, and after reduction with 25.0 ml of the standard $FeSO_4$ ($MnO_4^- + 5Fe^{++} + 8H^+ \longrightarrow Mn^{++} + 5Fe^{3+} + 4H_2O$) the excess ferrous iron is titrated with the standard $KMnO_4$.

Let x = ml of $KMnO_4$ used in the titration.

$$\text{Meq. of } FeSO_4 \text{ used} = 25.0 \times 0.100 = 2.50$$

$$\text{Meq. of } KMnO_4 \text{ used} = x \times 0.0833$$

$$\text{Net meq.} = 2.50 - 0.0833x$$

$$\frac{(2.50 - 0.0833x) \times Mn/5{,}000}{2.50} \times 100 = 0.90$$

$$x = 5.42 \text{ ml} \qquad Ans.$$

Chlorate (Williams) Method.   The Mn is oxidized with $KClO_3$ to MnO_2, which is filtered and dissolved in 25.0 ml of the standard $FeSO_4$ ($MnO_2 + 2Fe^{++} + 4H^+ \longrightarrow Mn^{++} + 2Fe^{3+} + 2H_2O$). The excess $FeSO_4$ is titrated with the standard $KMnO_4$.

Let x = no. of ml of $KMnO_4$ used in the titration.

$$\text{Meq. of } FeSO_4 \text{ used} = 25.0 \times 0.100 = 2.50$$

$$\text{Meq. of } KMNO_4 \text{ used} = x \times 0.0833$$

$$\text{Net meq.} = 2.50 - 0.0833x$$

$$\frac{(2.50 - 0.0833x) \times Mn/2{,}000}{2.50} \times 100 = 0.90$$

$$x = 20.2 \text{ ml} \qquad Ans.$$

Volhard Method.   The Mn is titrated directly with $KMnO_4$ in a solution kept neutral with ZnO ($3Mn^{++} + 2MnO_4^- + 2ZnO \longrightarrow 5MnO_2 + 2Zn^{++}$).

Let x = no. of ml of $KMnO_4$ used in the titration.

In this case the normality of the $KMnO_4$ cannot be taken as 0.0833 because it is used in neutral solution where the change in oxidation number of its manganese is 3 instead of 5. In other words, the oxidizing power of $KMnO_4$ in neutral solution is only three-fifths as great as it is in acid solution. In this particular case the normality is $0.0833 \times \frac{3}{5}$. The change in oxidation number of the titrated Mn is 2.

$$\frac{x(0.0833 \times \frac{3}{5}) \times Mn/2{,}000}{2.50} \times 100 = 0.90$$

$$x = 16.4 \text{ ml} \qquad Ans.$$

Example 7   A 1.00-g sample of steel containing 0.90% Mn is analyzed by the persulfate (peroxydisulfate) method whereby the manganese is oxidized to permanganate by ammonium peroxydisulfate and the resulting permanganate is titrated with a standard solution of sodium arsenite. If 7.68 ml of arsenite solution (0.0400 M in Na_3AsO_3) is required and the arsenite is oxidized to arsenate in the titration, to what average oxidation number was the manganese reduced in the titration?

Solution

$$0.0400 \ M \ Na_3AsO_3 = 0.800 \ N$$

Let $x =$ change in oxidation no. of Mn during titration.

$$7.68 \times 0.0800 \times \frac{Mn}{x \times 1,000} = 0.0090$$

Solving,

$$x = 3.75$$

Oxidation no. of Mn in reduced form $= 7 - 3.75 = 3.25$ *Ans.*

Example 8   If 1.000 ml of a solution of $KMnO_4$ is equivalent to 0.1000 millimole of sodium formate (HCO_2Na) in the following titration: $3HCO_2^- + 2MnO_4^- + H_2O \longrightarrow 3CO_2 + 2MnO_2 + 5OH^-$, what is the value of the $KMnO_4$ in terms of grams of CaO in the volumetric method for calcium in which that element is precipitated as $CaC_2O_4 \cdot H_2O$, the precipitate filtered and dissolved in dilute H_2SO_4, and the oxalate titrated with permanganate?

Solution

$$0.1000 \text{ millimole } HCO_2Na = 0.2000 \text{ meq.}$$

(since in the titration the oxidation number of C changes from $+2$ to $+4$)

$$\text{Normality of the } KMnO_4 = 0.2000$$

This normality applies only to the above type of titration in which the oxidation number of Mn in $KMnO_4$ changes by 3 units.   Therefore,

$$\text{Normality of } KMnO_4 \text{ (presence of acid)} = 0.2000 \times \tfrac{5}{3} = 0.3333$$

Each atom of Ca is combined with an equivalent to 1 mole of oxalate.   Since the milliequivalent weight of the oxalate radical is its molecular weight over 2,000, the milliequivalent weight of CaO must be its molecular weight over 2,000.

$$1.000 \times 0.3333 \times \frac{CaO}{2,000} = 0.009347 \text{ g } CaO \quad \textit{Ans.}$$

12-5   Dichromate Process

Potassium dichromate is occasionally used as an oxidimetric standard. With chemical indicators (e.g., diphenylamine sulfonate), the use of dichromate in direct titrations is restricted to the titration of ferrous iron. Oxidizing substances can be determined by the dichromate process, as in the permanganate process, by the addition of a measured excess of a ferrous salt and the titration of the excess with the standard solution. Potassium dichromate titrations have greater applicability in potentiometric titrations where chemical indicators are not necessary.

The normal solution of potassium dichromate contains one-sixth of the gram molecular weight of $K_2Cr_2O_7$ per liter (see Sec. 12-2).

Example 1   What is the percentage of Fe_2O_3 in a sample of limonite ore if the iron from a 0.5000-g sample is reduced and titrated with 35.15 ml of a potassium dichromate solution of which 15.00 ml is equivalent in oxidizing power to 25.00 ml of a potassium permanganate solution which has an "iron value" of 0.004750 g?   (This last expression is a conventional means of signifying that 1.000 ml of the solution will oxidize 0.004750 g of iron *from the divalent to the trivalent state*.)

Solution

$$\text{Normality of KMnO}_4 = \frac{0.004750}{1.000 \times \text{Fe}/1,000} = 0.08505$$

$$\text{Normality of K}_2\text{Cr}_2\text{O}_7 = 0.08505 \times 25.00/15.00 = 0.1418$$

$$\frac{35.15 \times 0.1418 \times \dfrac{Fe_2O_3}{2,000}}{0.5000} \times 100 = 79.60\% \text{ Fe}_2\text{O}_3 \qquad Ans.$$

Example 2   Fusion with Na_2O_2 oxidizes the chromium in a 0.2000-g sample of chromite ore to chromate.   The addition of a 50-ml pipetful of ferrous sulfate solution reduces this in acid solution to chromic ions $(Cr_2O_7^= + 6Fe^{++} + 14H^+ \longrightarrow 2Cr^{3+} + 6Fe^{3+} + 7H_2O)$, and the excess ferrous ions are titrated with 7.59 ml of 0.1000 N $K_2Cr_2O_7$.   Each pipetful of ferrous solution is equivalent to 47.09 ml of the standard $K_2Cr_2O_7$ solution.   What is the percentage of Cr in the sample?   What weight of sample of the chromite ore should be taken so that the number of milliliters of standard 1.000 N $K_2Cr_2O_7$ that are equivalent to the ferrous solution added, minus the number of milliliters of K_2CrO_7 used in the titration, will equal the percentage of Cr_2O_3 in the sample?

Solution   Net $K_2Cr_2O_7$ solution (equivalent to the Cr in the ore) = 47.09 − 7.59 = 39.50 ml.

$$\frac{39.50 \times 0.1000 \times \dfrac{Cr}{3,000}}{0.2000} \times 100 = 34.24\% \text{ Cr} \qquad Ans.$$

The second part of this problem merely states that the net volume of $0.1000\ N\ K_2Cr_2O_7$ (i.e., the number of milliliters equivalent to the Cr in the sample) is equal in value to the percentage of Cr_2O_3.

$$\frac{a \times 0.1000 \times Cr_2O_3/6,000}{x} \times 100 = a$$

$x = 0.2533$ g   *Ans.*

12-6   Ceric Sulfate or Cerate Process

Cerium in the 4-valent state is a very powerful oxidizing agent, the yellow ceric or complex cerate ions[1] being reduced to colorless 3-valent cerous ions.

$$Ce^{4+} + e \longrightarrow Ce^{3+}$$

A solution of ceric sulfate is satisfactory for oxidimetry titrations and has certain advantages over potassium permanganate, particularly with respect to its greater stability and its lesser tendency to oxidize chloride ions. In the titration of reducing substances that in solution are color-less, the yellow color of the excess ceric ions serves as a fairly satisfactory indicator. Titration of ferrous ions can be accomplished with ortho-phenanthroline ("ferroin") as an internal indicator. The potential of the indicator in its two states of oxidation lies between those of ferric-ferrous iron and ceric-cerous cerium.

$$Ce^{4+} + e \rightleftharpoons Ce^{3+} \qquad +1.61 \text{ volts}$$
$$\text{ferroin' (blue)} + e \rightleftharpoons \text{ferroin'' (red)} \qquad +1.06 \text{ volts}$$
$$Fe^{3+} + e \rightleftharpoons Fe^{++} \qquad +0.77 \text{ volt}$$

Ceric sulfate is particularly satisfactory in potentiometric titrations.

Example 1   What weight of limonite should be taken so that after solution in HCl and reduction of the iron, the volume of a standard ceric solution required for titration will be one-half the percentage of Fe_2O_3 in the sample (6.000 ml of the ceric solution $\approx$ 2.000 ml KHC_2O_4 solution $\approx$ 3.000 ml of 0.08000 N NaOH)?

[1] In acid solutions of cerium(IV) salts a considerable part of the element is in the form of complex anions, the extent of complexing varying with the nature and concentration of the acid supplying the anions. In such cases the cerium salts can properly be called *cerates,* and the half-cell potential between Ce(IV) and Ce(III) varies somewhat under these conditions. However, in order to simplify nomenclature and equations, we shall avoid the use of such words as *perchloratocerate ion* and *sulfatoceric acid* and their corresponding formulas and simply use the word *ceric ion,* symbolizing it as Ce^{4+}. Oxidation of ferrous ions and of oxalate in the presence of acid will be represented simply as $Fe^{++} + Ce^{4+} \longrightarrow Fe^{3+} + Ce^{3+}$ and $C_2O_4^{=} + 2Ce^{4+} \longrightarrow 2CO_2 + 2Ce^{3+}$.

In calculations pertaining to potentials, we shall use the value $+1.61$ volts for the standard potential of $Ce^{4+} + e \rightleftharpoons Ce^{3+}$.

Solution

$$\text{Concn. of KHC}_2\text{O}_4 \text{ soln.} = 0.08000 \times \frac{3.000}{2.000}$$

$$= 0.1200 \ N \quad \textit{as an acid}$$

$$= 0.2400 \ N \quad \textit{as a reducing agent}$$

$$\text{Concn. of ceric soln.} = 0.2400 \times \frac{2.000}{6.000} = 0.08000 \ N$$

$$\frac{1 \times 0.08000 \times \text{Fe}_2\text{O}_3/2,000}{x} \times 100 = 2$$

$$x = 0.3194 \ g \quad \textit{Ans.}$$

PROBLEMS

*12-19. A soln. contains 2.608 g of $KMnO_4$ per 750 ml. (*a*) What is its normality as an oxidizing agent, and what is the value of each ml in terms of g of (*b*) $FeSO_4 \cdot (NH_4)_2SO_4 \cdot 6H_2O$, (*c*) As_2O_3, (*d*) KHC_2O_4, (*e*) H_2O_2, (*f*) $U(SO_4)_2$ (oxidized to UO_2^{2+})?

*12-20. Given a soln. of $KMnO_4$ of which 1.000 ml $\backsimeq$ 1.000 ml KHC_2O_4 soln. $\backsimeq$ 1.000 ml NaOH $\backsimeq$ 0.1000 millimole of $KHC_8H_4O_4$ (potassium acid phthalate). (*a*) What is the value of 1.000 ml of it in terms of g of Fe_2O_3? (*b*) How many milli-moles of Mn are present in each ml?

*12-21. How many g of $KMnO_4$ are contained in a liter of soln. if a certain vol. of it will oxidize that wt. of potassium tetroxalate requiring one-half that vol. of 0.2000 *N* NaOH soln. for neutralization?

*12-22. Given: 1.000 ml $KHC_2O_4 \cdot H_2C_2O_4 \cdot 2H_2O \backsimeq$ 0.2000 ml $KMnO_4$; 1.000 ml $KMnO_4 \backsimeq$ 0.1117 g Fe. What is the normality of the tetroxalate soln. when used as an acid?

*12-23. Given two permanganate solns. Soln. A contains 0.01507 g of $KMnO_4$ per ml. Soln. B is of such concn. that 20.00 ml will oxidize 0.01200 g of Fe(II). In what proportion by vol. should the two solns. be mixed in order for the resulting soln. to have the same oxidizing normality in the presence of acid as 0.05555 *M* $K_2Cr_2O_7$ has?

*12-24. (*a*) How many ml of $K_2Cr_2O_7$ soln. contg. 25.00 g of the salt per liter would react with 3.402 g of $FeSO_4 \cdot 7H_2O$ in dil. acid soln.? (*b*) What is the normal-ity of the dichromate soln. as a potassium salt?

*12-25. How many g of $K_2Cr_2O_7$ must be weighed out, dissolved, and diluted to 700 ml to make a soln. which, when used in the titration of Fe in a sample of ore, will be of such strength that four times the no. of ml used with a 0.5000-g sample will represent one-half the percentage of FeO in the sample?

*12-26. How many g of pure Pb_3O_4 (= $PbO_2 \cdot 2PbO$) must be dissolved in a mixt. of 30 ml of 6 *N* H_2SO_4 and 2.000 millimoles of $KHC_2O_4 \cdot H_2C_2O_4 \cdot 2H_2O$ so that 30.00 ml of 0.1000 *N* $KMnO_4$ will be required for the excess oxalate?

*12-27. What wt. of spathic iron ore (impure $FeCO_3$) should be taken for analysis so that the no. of ml of $KMnO_4$ (1.000 ml $\approx$ 0.3000 ml of potassium tetroxalate soln., which is 0.2500 N as an acid) used in titration will be twice the percentage of FeO in the ore?

*12-28. A soln. contains 2.608 g of $KMnO_4$ per 750 ml. (a) What is the molarity of the soln., (b) what is its normality as a K salt, (c) what is its normality as an oxidizing agent in the presence of acid, and (d) how many g of $VOSO_4$ (f. wt. = 163.0) would be oxidized (to HVO_3) by 1.000 ml of it?

*12-29. (a) What is the normality of a soln. of $KMnO_4$ in relation to its use in slightly alkaline soln. (i.e., when reduced to MnO_2) if each ml will oxidize 0.1000 millimole of As_2O_3 in the presence of acid? (b) How many millimoles of $K_4Fe(CN)_6$ will each ml of the permanganate oxidize (to ferricyanide) in the presence of acid?

*12-30. A sample of pyrolusite weighing 0.6000 g is dissolved in a soln. contg. 5.00 ml of 6 N H_2SO_4 and 0.9000 g of $H_2C_2O_4 \cdot 2H_2O$. The excess oxalate then requires 24.00 ml of $KMnO_4$ soln. for titration. If each ml of the $KMnO_4$ will oxidize the Fe(II) in 0.03058 g of $FeSO_4 \cdot 7H_2O$, what is the oxidizing power of the sample in terms of percent MnO_2?

*12-31. (a) What is the percentage of Cr in a sample of chromite if when 0.2000 g of the ore is fused with Na_2O_2, and the acidified extract (contg. all the Cr as dichromate) is treated with 5.000 millimoles of $FeSO_4 \cdot 7H_2O$, the soln. then requires one-sixth of a millimole of $K_2Cr_2O_7$? (b) The dichromate used corresponds to what vol. of $N/20$ soln.?

*12-32. What is the redox normality of a soln. of ceric ammonium sulfate [ammonium hexasulfatocerate, $(NH_4)_4Ce(SO_4)_4 \cdot 2H_2O$] and the value of each ml of it in terms of mg of ferrous ammonium sulfate hexahydrate if each ml of the Ce(IV) soln. will oxidize 0.02000 millimole of As_2O_3 (OsO_4 catalyst)?

*12-33. A 0.5000-g sample of chromite ore is fused with Na_2O_2 and the acidified extract of dichromate is reduced with a soln. contg. 2.780 g of $FeSO_4 \cdot 7H_2O$. The excess Fe(II) ions then require 10.00 ml of $K_2Cr_2O_7$ soln. of which each ml is equivalent in a redox reaction to 0.01597 g of Fe_2O_3. Calculate the percentage of Cr in the ore.

*12-34. A soln. contg. 0.7500 g of $CuSO_4 \cdot 5H_2O$ is made 2 N in HCl and passed through a silver reductor ($Cu^{++} + 3Cl^- + Ag \longrightarrow AgCl + CuCl_2^-$) directly into 25 ml of $M/2$ $Fe_2(SO_4)_3$ ($Fe^{3+} + CuCl_2^- \longrightarrow Fe^{++} + Cu^{++} + 2Cl^-$). The resulting soln. requires 30.00 ml of a Ce(IV) soln. for titration. What is the normality of the ceric soln. as an oxidizing agent?

*12-35. If 0.9000 g of oxalic acid, $H_2C_2O_4 \cdot 2H_2O$, is allowed to react with 0.5000 g of pyrolusite and the excess oxalic acid is titrated with permanganate, (a) what must be the normality of the permanganate in order that one-half the percentage of MnO_2 can be obtained by subtracting the buret reading from the vol. A of the permanganate equiv. to the 0.9000 g of oxalic acid used? (b) What is the value of A?

*12-36.   A sample of steel weighing 2.20 g and contg. 0.620% Mn is dissolved, and the Mn is eventually titrated in neutral soln. with standard $KMnO_4$. ($3Mn^{++} + 2MnO_4^- + 2H_2O \longrightarrow 5MnO_2 + 4H^+$.) If 6.88 ml is required, what is the value of each ml of the $KMnO_4$ in terms of g of (a) $H_2C_2O_4 \cdot 2H_2O$, (b) As_2O_3?

*12-37.   Balance the following equation:

$$K_2Na[Co(NO_2)_6] + MnO_4^- + H^+ \longrightarrow K^+ + Na^+ + Co^{++} + NO_3^- + Mn^{++} + H_2O$$

This represents a volumetric method for determining potassium. Calculate from the molar relationships the value of 1.00 ml of $KMnO_4$ (of which 1.00 ml $\backsimeq$ 0.0080 g Fe_2O_3) in terms of g of K.

*12-38.   Sodium formate, HCO_2Na, can be titrated in neutral soln. according to the equation $3HCO_2^- + 2MnO_4^- + H_2O \longrightarrow 2MnO_2 + 3CO_2 + 5OH^-$. If 10.00 ml of the $KMnO_4$ is equiv. to 0.08161 g of sodium formate by this method, (a) what is the "iron value" of each ml of the $KMnO_4$, (b) what is the value of each ml in terms of no. of millimoles of H_2O_2, (c) what is the value of each ml in terms of g of CaO, and (d) what is the value of each ml in terms of g of Mn by the Volhard method?

*12-39.   Calcium can be pptd. as $CaC_2O_4 \cdot H_2O$, and the ppt. filtered, washed, and dissolved in dil. H_2SO_4. The oxalic acid formed can then be titrated with permanganate. If a 0.1000 N soln. of $KMnO_4$ is used, calculate the value of 1.000 ml in terms of g of (a) Ca, (b) CaO, (c) $CaCO_3$.

*12-40.   If the iron in a 0.1500-g sample of iron ore is reduced and subsequently requires 15.03 ml of permanganate for oxidation, what is the purity of the ore expressed as percentage of (a) Fe, (b) FeO, (c) Fe_2O_3? (4.000 ml $KMnO_4$ $\backsimeq$ 3.000 ml $KHC_2O_4 \cdot H_2C_2O_4$ soln. $\backsimeq$ 3.000 ml NaOH contg. the equiv. of 50.00 millimoles of Na_2O per liter.)

*12-41.   (a) What is the percentage purity of a sample of impure $H_2C_2O_4 \cdot 2H_2O$ if a sample weighing 0.2003 g requires 29.30 ml of permanganate soln. of which 1.000 ml $\backsimeq$ 0.006023 g Fe? (b) During the titration, what vol. of CO_2 (dry, standard conditions) is produced?

*12-42.   To 0.5000 g of pyrolusite is added a certain vol. of $NaAsO_2$ soln. After reaction in the presence of acid is complete, the excess arsenite requires 30.00 ml of 0.1000 N $KMnO_4$ for oxidation. If the pyrolusite is found to contain 86.93% MnO_2, what wt. of dissolved As_2O_3 was contained in the arsenite soln. added?

*12-43.   In the cerimetric titration of Fe the color change of the ferroin indicator is very abrupt. It has been proposed [*Anal. Chem.*, **29**, 1226 (1957)] to use an auxiliary indicator to give a warning signal when 99% of the ferrous ions have been oxidized. The desired auxiliary indicator should begin to be oxidized at this point, but it can be assumed that the optimum color change would occur with an indicator having a standard potential about 0.05 volt above this point in the potential series. Taking the standard potential of ferric-ferrous in the acid medium used as +0.68 volt, what should be the corresponding potential of the auxiliary indicator?

*12-44.   If 100.0 ml of a soln. contg. 10.00 g $K_2Cr_2O_7$ per liter, 5.00 ml of 6 N H_2SO_4, and 75.0 ml of a soln. contg. 80.0 g $FeSO_4 \cdot 7H_2O$ per liter are mixed and the resulting soln. titrated with 0.2121 N $KMnO_4$, (a) what vol. of the $KMnO_4$ is required, (b) how many millimoles of $KMnO_4$ are required?

*12-45. (a) In titrating a 1.000-g sample of H_2O_2 with $KMnO_4$, what must be the normality of the permanganate for the buret reading to represent directly the percentage of H_2O_2? (b) In the titration, each ml of the $KMnO_4$ would produce how many millimoles of O_2 gas?

*12-46. A sample of magnetite (essentially Fe_3O_4) is fused with Na_2O_2, and the material leached with H_2O and acidified. The Fe, now completely in the ferric state, is reduced with zinc and titrated with $KMnO_4$ of such concn. that 2.000 ml $\backsimeq$ 3.000 ml KHC_2O_4 soln. $\backsimeq$ 2.000 ml NaOH $\backsimeq$ 1.000 ml H_2SO_4 $\backsimeq$ 0.008138 g ZnO. Vol. of $KMnO_4$ required = 30.10 ml. (a) What is the normality of the $KMnO_4$, and (b) how many g of Fe_2O_4 are present in the sample of magnetite?

*12-47. Six millimoles of MnO are ignited in air ($6\underline{MnO} + O_2 \longrightarrow 2Mn_3O_4$), and the resulting mixed oxide is dissolved in a soln. contg. 25 ml of 6 N H_2SO_4 and A g of $FeSO_4 \cdot (NH_4)_2SO_4 \cdot 6H_2O$. The Mn is reduced by the ferrous ions completely to the dipositive form. If the excess ferrous ions require 12.00 ml of $KMnO_4$ contg. 0.05000 millimole of $KMnO_4$ per ml, find the numerical value of A.

*12-48. A sample of steel weighs 2.00 g and contains 0.55% Mn. After dissolving in HNO_3, the Mn is oxidized to MnO_4^- with Bi_2O_4 and the excess Bi_2O_4 is filtered off. Excess $FeSO_4 \cdot 7H_2O$ (dissolved in H_2O) is added, and the excess ferrous ions require 20.0 ml of 0.200 N $KMnO_4$. (a) How many g of $FeSO_4 \cdot 7H_2O$ were used? (b) If the reduction had been made with $Na_2C_2O_4$ instead of with the ferrous salt, how many millimoles of the oxalate should be used in order for 20.0 ml of the $KMnO_4$ to be required for the excess oxalate?

*12-49. A sample of chromite contains 30.08% Cr_2O_3. (a) After fusion of a 0.2000-g sample with Na_2O_2 and dissolving in acid, how many g of $FeSO_4 \cdot (NH_4)_2SO_4 \cdot 6H_2O$ should be added so that the excess ferrous ions will require 15.00 ml of 0.6011 N $K_2Cr_2O_7$? (b) How many mg atoms of Cr does each ml of the dichromate contain? (c) If 3.000 ml of this dichromate $\backsimeq$ 2.000 ml of $KHC_2O_4 \cdot H_2C_2O_4 \cdot 2H_2O$ soln. $\backsimeq$ 1.000 ml KOH $\backsimeq$ 3.000 ml H_2SO_4, how many moles of $Fe_2O_3 \cdot xH_2O$ is each ml of the H_2SO_4 theoretically capable of dissolving, and how many meq. as an oxidizing agent would this amt. of $Fe_2O_3 \cdot xH_2O$ represent?

*12-50. A sample of steel weighing 2.00 g is analyzed for Mn by the bismuthate method. If a 25-ml pipetful of 0.120 N $FeSO_4$ was used for the reduction of the oxidized Mn and 22.9 ml of 0.0833 N $KMnO_4$ was used in the titration of the excess ferrous ions, what vol. of the $KMnO_4$ would have been used if the same wt. of sample had been analyzed (a) by the chlorate method (using a 25-ml pipetful of the above $FeSO_4$), (b) by the Volhard method on a $\frac{1}{2}$-aliquot portion of the prepared soln.? (c) What is the percentage of Mn in the steel?

*12-51. A sample of chromite weighing 0.3010 g is fused with Na_2O_2, leached with H_2O, and acidified with H_2SO_4. The resulting soln. of dichromate is treated with a soln. contg. dissolved crystals of $FeSO_4 \cdot (NH_4)_2SO_4 \cdot 6H_2O$, and the excess ferrous ions are titrated with standard dichromate (contg. 5.070 g of $K_2Cr_2O_7$ per liter). If it is known that a maximum of 45.00% of Cr_2O_3 can be present in the ore, what minimum wt. of the ferrous crystals should be used so that not more than a 50-ml buretful of the dichromate would be required?

*12-52. A sample of pure $Na_2C_2O_4$ weighing 0.2500 g is dissolved in dil. H_2SO_4 and requires 40.15 ml of a ceric sulfate soln. for oxidation. (a) What is the normality of the ceric soln. as an oxidizing agent? (b) How many g of $Ce(SO_4)_2 \cdot 2(NH_4)_2SO_4 \cdot 2H_2O$ should be dissolved in 500 ml in order to prepare a soln. of this normality? (c) If a sample of limonite weighing 0.3000 g is dissolved in HCl, the Fe reduced by metallic Ag, and the soln. then requires 25.03 ml of the above ceric soln. to change the color of o-phenanthroline indicator, what is the percentage of Fe_2O_3 in the limonite?

*12-53. A sample of KNO_2 contg. only inert impurities weighs 10.936 g. It is dissolved in water and a $\frac{1}{20}$-aliquot portion is taken for analysis. A vol. of 0.2037 N $KMnO_4$ which would theoretically oxidize this amt. of sample on the basis of 100% purity is run into the flask and acidified. The aliquot portion is added to it with const. swirling, and to the diluted excess permanganate is added 15.00 ml of 0.2137 N $Na_2C_2O_4$. The excess oxalate then requires 4.42 ml of the standard $KMnO_4$ for titration. Calculate the percentage purity of the original sample.

*12-54. A 1.000-g sample of impure $KClO_3$ is dissolved in water and diluted to 1 liter. A 50.00-ml-aliquot portion is acidified, a pipetful of $FeSO_4$ is added, and the soln. heated to convert chlorate to chloride. The soln. then requires 21.48 ml of 0.1232 N $KMnO_4$. If a separate pipetful of the ferrous soln. requires 39.86 ml of the $KMnO_4$, what is the oxidizing power of the sample in terms of percentage of $KClO_3$?

*12-55. A sample of technical grade formic acid (HCOOH + inert matter) weighs 0.1050 g. It is dissolved in water and made slightly alkaline. A 100-ml pipetful of 0.1000 N $KMnO_4$ is added, and the formate ions are oxidized as indicated by the equation $3HCOO^- + 2MnO_4^- + H_2O \longrightarrow 2MnO_2 + 3CO_2 + 5OH^-$. The suspension is acidified with H_2SO_4 and 75.00 ml of 0.1100 N $H_2C_2O_4$ is added. The oxalate reduces and dissolves the pptd. MnO_2 and reduces the excess permanganate ($MnO_2 + C_2O_4^= + 4H^+ \longrightarrow Mn^{++} + 2CO_2 + 2H_2O$; $2MnO_4^- + 5C_2O_4^= + 16H^{++} \longrightarrow 2Mn^{++} + 10CO_2 + 8H_2O$). The excess oxalate is then titrated with 0.1000 N $KMnO_4$, requiring 24.64 ml. Calculate the purity of the sample in terms of percentage of HCOOH.

*12-56. Selenious acid, H_2SeO_3, and tellurous acid, H_2TeO_3, are similar in properties and both are oxidized (to H_2SeO_4 and H_2TeO_4) in a permanganate titration, but only H_2TeO_3 is oxidized in a dichromate titration. If an equimolar mixt. of the two acids requires A ml of $\frac{1}{20}$ M $KMnO_4$ for titration, in terms of A how many ml of $\frac{1}{20}$ M $K_2Cr_2O_7$ would be required for the titration of the same wt. of sample?

12-57. (a) What is the normality of a soln. of $KMnO_4$, and what is the value of each ml in terms of g of Fe if when titrating a 0.1000-g sample of impure KNO_2 (which is oxidized to nitrate) the buret reading is one-half the percentage of N_2O_3 in the sample? (b) How many g atoms of Mn does each liter of the $KMnO_4$ contain?

12-58. (*a*) What must be the value of 1.000 ml of ceric sulfate in terms of g of Fe_2O_3 so that in the titration of a 0.5000-g sample of impure sodium arsenite (arsenite oxidized to arsenate), the percentage of As_2O_3 in the sample will be twice the buret reading? (*b*) What is the molarity of the ceric soln.?

12-59. A stock soln. of $KMnO_4$ is made up and standardized. It is found that each ml is equiv. to 0.01597 g of Fe_2O_3. A 10-ml pipetful of the permanganate is reduced with H_2O_2 in the presence of acid, and the excess H_2O_2 is destroyed by boiling. The resulting soln. is then made neutral, and the manganous ions in the soln. are titrated with more of the original stock $KMnO_4$, the soln. being kept neutral with ZnO (Volhard method). How many ml of $KMnO_4$ would be required in the titration?

12-60. A student standardized a soln. of KOH and one of $KMnO_4$ against the same salt ($KHC_2O_4 \cdot H_2C_2O_4 \cdot 2H_2O$). The normality of the former was found to be 0.09963 as a base and of the latter to be 0.1328 as an oxidizing agent. By coincidence, exactly 50.00 ml of soln. was used in each standardization. Calculate the ratio of the wt. of tetroxalate used in the first case to that used in the second case.

12-61. A powder is composed of oxalic acid, $H_2C_2O_4 \cdot 2H_2O$; potassium binoxalate, $KHC_2O_4 \cdot H_2O$; and an inert impurity. Find the percentage of each component from the following. A sample of the powder weighing 1.200 g reacts with 37.80 ml of 0.2500 N NaOH soln.; 0.4000 g of the powder reacts with 43.10 ml of 0.1250 N $KMnO_4$ soln.

12-62. From the following data, calculate the purity of a sample of chromite ore in terms of the percentage of Cr and of Cr_2O_3. Wt. of sample = 0.2500 g; vol. of $FeSO_4$ soln. used to reduce the dichromate ions after fusion of the sample with Na_2O_2 and acidifying = 53.40 ml; vol. of $K_2Cr_2O_7$ soln. required to titrate the excess ferrous ions = 8.00 ml. The ferrous soln. used has a redox normality exactly four-fifths that of the dichromate used, and 40.00 ml of the latter is required to titrate the iron in the analysis of 0.5000 g of limonite contg. 79.84% Fe_2O_3.

12-63. It requires 15.27 ml of $SnCl_2$ soln. to reduce an amt. of Fe from ferric to ferrous that requires 16.27 ml of $KMnO_4$ for reoxidation. This vol. of the $KMnO_4$ will oxidize that amt. of $KHC_2O_4 \cdot H_2C_2O_4 \cdot 2H_2O$ which is neutralized by 16.24 ml of 0.1072 N NaOH. What is the normality of the $SnCl_2$ soln. as a reducing agent?

12-64. Find the percentage of MnO_2 in a sample of pyrolusite from the following data: Sample = 0.5217 g; 4.470 g of $FeSO_4 \cdot (NH_4)_2SO_4 \cdot 6H_2O$ and 20 ml of dil. H_2SO_4 are added to dissolve the MnO_2; 22.42 ml of $KMnO_4$ are required for the excess Fe(II); 1.000 ml $KMnO_4 \backsimeq 0.007620$ g As_2O_3.

12-65. A sample of pure Mn_3O_4 (= $MnO_2 \cdot 2MnO$) is dissolved in dil. H_2SO_4 contg. a 50-ml pipetful of 0.2016 N $H_2C_2O_4$. The oxalate reduces the Mn completely to the dipositive form, and the excess oxalate requires 10.15 ml of $KMnO_4$ (1.000 ml $\backsimeq$ 0.01000 g Fe) for its oxidation. What wt. of Mn(IV) is in the sample?

12-66. How many g of Cr_2O_3 are present in a sample of chromite ore if when decomposed by fusion with Na_2O_2, acidified with H_2SO_4, and treated with 3.000 millimoles of $KHC_2O_4 \cdot H_2C_2O_4 \cdot 2H_2O_7$ the excess oxalate requires 20.00 ml of $M/50$ $KMnO_4$?

12-67.   In the analysis of uranium ore, the U is brought to the form corresponding to the formula $UOSO_4$ and is then titrated with standard $KMnO_4$ to the form corresponding to the formula UO_2SO_4.   If in this titration each ml of the $KMnO_4$ is equiv. to 1.000 mg of elementary U, what is the value of each ml of the $KMnO_4$ (*a*) in terms of g of As_2O_3, (*b*) in terms of g of CaO in the titration of CaC_2O_4?

12-68.   The qualitative analysis of a certain silicate shows the presence of a large amt. of Ca and only traces of other positive elements.   In the quantitative analysis of a 0.5000-g sample, the SiO_2 is removed and the Ca is pptd. from the filtrate as $CaC_2O_4 \cdot 2H_2O$.   It is found that the no. of ml of 0.1660 N $KMnO_4$ required to oxidize the oxalate is almost exactly equal to the percentage of SiO_2 in the silicate. What is the empirical formula of the mineral (see Sec. 9-4)?

12-69.   A 0.3000-g sample of a powder known to consist only of a mixt. of FeO, Fe_2O_3, and Fe_3O_4 is fused with $KHSO_4$.   The fused material is dissolved, and all the Fe is brought to the divalent state with $SnCl_2$.   The excess Sn(II) is destroyed, and the Fe(II) is titrated with 35.80 ml of 0.1037 N $KMnO_4$.   Another sample weighing 1.000 g is heated with H_2SO_4 + HF in an inert atmosphere to prevent premature oxidation of Fe(II) by the air.   The resulting soln. is diluted and titrated with 25.44 ml of the above $KMnO_4$.

Set up simultaneous algebraic equations which, if solved, would give the percentages of the three components of the original powder.   The equations should show the numerical value of each meq. wt.

12-70.   Heulandite is hydrous acid calcium metasilicate, and analysis shows 14.80% H_2O and 16.78% Al_2O_3.   If the Ca were pptd. as $CaC_2O_4 \cdot 2H_2O$ from a sample weighing 1.000 g, 32.87 ml of 0.1000 N $KMnO_4$ would be required for oxidation.   Three-fifths of the H_2O exists as water of crystallization.   What is the empirical formula of heulandite (see Sec. 9-4)?

12-71.   A sample of an alloy contg. Mn and weighing 4.35 g is dissolved, and the Mn eventually titrated in *neutral* soln. with a standard $KMnO_4$ having an "iron value" of 0.00640 g [that is, 1.000 ml will oxidize that wt. of Fe(II) in acid soln.]. If 13.05 ml is required, what is the percentage of Mn in the alloy?   What is the value of each ml of the $KMnO_4$ in terms of g of sodium formate, HCOONa, in the titration expressed by the equation $3HCOO^- + 2MnO_4^- + H_2O \longrightarrow 3CO_2 + MnO_2 + 5OH^-$?

12-72.   A sample of magnetite is fused with Na_2O_2, and all the Fe in the acid soln. of the fused material is in the tripositive state.   The Fe is determined by reducing to the ferrous state and titrating with 0.3000 N $K_2Cr_2O_7$.   (*a*) If 30.00 ml is required, find the no. of g of Fe_3O_4 in the sample.   (*b*) How many g of Cr are present in each ml of the dichromate soln.?   (*c*) How many mg of CoO_2 is each ml of the dichromate equiv. to as an oxidizing agent?

12-73.   From the following data, find the wt. of iron ore to be taken so that the percentage of Fe_2O_3 present is numerically equal to twice the no. of ml of $K_2Cr_2O_7$ used in the titration.   40.00 ml HCl $\approx$ 2.880 g AgCl; 35.00 ml of the HCl $\approx$ 40.00 ml $KHC_2O_4 \cdot H_2C_2O_4 \cdot 2H_2O$ soln.; 35.00 ml of the tetroxalate $\approx$ 40.00 ml of the $K_2Cr_2O_7$ soln.

12-74.   A soln. of dichromate is prepared by dissolving 4.883 g of $K_2Cr_2O_7$ and diluting to exactly 1 liter; a soln. of ferrous salt is prepared by dissolving 39.46 g of $FeSO_4 \cdot (NH_4)_2SO_4 \cdot 6H_2O$ in dil. acid and diluting to 1 liter.   What vol. of the dichromate soln. must be transferred to the ferrous soln. and thoroughly mixed so that the normality of one soln. as a reducing agent will be the same as the normality of the other soln. as an oxidizing agent?

12-75.   A sample of magnetite consisting of over 90% Fe_3O_4, plus only inert matter, is fused with an oxidizing flux, and the resulting material is leached with water and acidified.   The ferric ions are reduced with Zn and titrated with standard $KMnO_4$.   The end point is overstepped, and the soln. is back-titrated with standard $FeSO_4$ soln.   Make up a problem which incorporates the above information.   Use a wt. of sample and vols. of $KMnO_4$ and $FeSO_4$ that are reasonable for obtaining four-significant-figure precision.   Express the concn. of the $KMnO_4$ in terms of g of As_2O_3 and that of the $FeSO_4$ in terms of g of $K_2Cr_2O_7$.   From the numerical data, calculate the normality of the titrating solutions and the percentage of Fe in the ore.

12-76.   An oxide of Fe weighing 0.1000 g is fused with $KHSO_4$, and the fused mass is dissolved in acid.   The Fe is reduced to ferrous and titrated back with 0.1000 N $K_2Cr_2O_7$.   If 12.96 ml is required, what is the formula of the oxide—FeO, Fe_2O_3, or Fe_3O_4?

12-77.   Two millimoles of pure Pb_3O_4 ($= PbO_2 \cdot 2PbO$) is dissolved in a soln. contg. a mixt. of 25 ml of 6 N H_2SO_4 and A g of $FeSO_4 \cdot (NH_4)_2SO_4 \cdot 6H_2O$, the 4-valent lead being reduced to Pb^{++}.   The excess of ferrous ions requires 12.00 ml of 0.2500 N $KMnO_4$ for oxidation.   (a) What is the value of A?   (b) How many mg atoms of Mn are present in each ml of the $KMnO_4$?   (c) If potassium tetroxalate, $KHC_2O_4 \cdot H_2C_2O_4 \cdot 2H_2O$, had been substituted for the ferrous ammonium sulfate above, how many meq., how many millimoles, and how many g of the oxalate would have been used for the reduction so that the excess oxalate would have required 12.00 ml of 0.2500 N $KMnO_4$?   (d) If lead sesquioxide, Pb_2O_3, were analyzed by a similar method, what would be the meq. wt. of Pb_2O_3?

12-78.   From the following data, calculate the percentage of Fe in a sample of limonite: Sample $= 0.6170$ g; dichromate soln. used $= 47.56$ ml; ferrous soln. used $= 2.85$ ml; 1.000 ml ferrous soln. $\backsim 1.021$ ml dichromate soln.   The dichromate soln. is 0.1130 N.

12-79.   A certain chromite ore contains 24.80% Cr.   A sample weighing 0.2580 g is fused with Na_2O_2, leached with H_2O, and acidified.   The resulting soln. of dichromate is treated with a wt. of $FeSO_4 \cdot 7H_2O$ that happens to be just 50% more than the amt. necessary to reduce the dichromate.   The excess ferrous salt is titrated with dichromate soln. contg. 0.02000 millimole $K_2Cr_2O_7$ per ml.   What vol. is required?

12-80.   A soln. of ceric sulfate is of such normality that 26.73 ml is required to titrate the ferrous iron obtainable from 1.052 g of $FeSO_4 \cdot (NH_4)_2SO_4 \cdot 6H_2O$.   (a) How many g of $Ce(SO_4)_2 \cdot 2(NH_4)_2SO_4 \cdot 2H_2O$ should be dissolved in 750 ml of H_2O and the resulting soln. diluted to a liter in order to prepare a soln. of such concn. that each ml will oxidize in the presence of acid 0.006850 g of $Na_2C_2O_4$? (b) What is the ratio of the normalities of the two solns.?

12-81. (a) What is the normality of a soln. of $KMnO_4$ if each ml will oxidize 0.008377 g of ferrous ions? (b) How many g of Mn does 10.00 ml of such a soln. contain? (c) How many g of Mn would 10.00 ml of this $KMnO_4$ oxidize to MnO_2 by the Volhard method? (d) How many ml of this $KMnO_4$ would be required to titrate 0.1200 millimole of sodium formate HCO_2Na, according to the equation $3HCO_2^- + 2MnO_4^- + H_2O \longrightarrow 2MnO_2 + 3CO_2 + 5OH^-$? (e) How many g of CaO would each ml of the $KMnO_4$ be equiv. to in the volumetric method for calcium? (f) How many g of As_2O_3 would each ml of the $KMnO_4$ be equiv. to in the titration of arsenite to arsenate?

12-82. Find from the following data the percentage of Pb_3O_4 in a sample of red lead that also contains PbO. A sample of the pigment weighing 2.500 g is treated with 50.00 ml of potassium tetroxalate soln. which is 0.1500 N as an acid, and the excess of the latter requires 30.00 ml of $KMnO_4$ of which each ml will oxidize 0.005585 g of ferrous iron.

12-83. A sample of steel weighing 2.50 g is analyzed for Mn by the chlorate method. If a 25-ml pipetful of 0.110 N $FeSO_4$ was used to dissolve the pptd. MnO_2 and 18.4 ml of 0.125 N $KMnO_4$ was required to titrate the excess ferrous ions, what vol. of the $KMnO_4$ would have been required if the same wt. of sample had been analyzed (a) by the bismuthate method (using a 25-ml pipetful of the above $FeSO_4$), (b) by the Volhard method on a $\frac{1}{2}$-aliquot portion of the prepared soln.? (c) What is the percentage of Mn in the steel?

12-84. An oxide of Mn weighing 0.4580 g is treated with dil. H_2SO_4 and 50.00 ml of 0.1000 N $FeSO_4$ soln. After the reduction of the Mn to the dipositive form, the excess ferrous reacts with 30.00 ml of 0.0333 N $KMnO_4$. The sample is which one of the common oxides of Mn?

12-7 Iodimetric Process

The fundamental reaction in this process is that between iodine and sodium thiosulfate, with starch (or sometimes chloroform) as the indicator.

$$I_2 + 2S_2O_3^= \longrightarrow 2I^- + S_4O_6^=$$

Titrations by this process can be divided into two groups, those involving direct titrations with standard iodine and those involving titrations with standard sodium thiosulfate.

Iodine solutions are prepared by dissolving iodine crystals, together with potassium iodide, in water.[1] A normal solution contains $I_2/2 = 126.9$ g of iodine per liter. Standard solutions are used to titrate directly certain reducing agents of which the following are typical:

---

[1] In a solution containing excess iodide ions, iodine exists essentially as triiodide (I_3^- or $I_2 \cdot I^-$) ions. However, in order to simplify equations and for the purpose of making calculations, the iodine can be considered as existing in the simple molecular form of I_2.

Substance	Oxidized to
H_2S	S
$SO_3^=$	$SO_4^=$
$S_2O_3^=$	$S_4O_6^=$
AsO_3^{3-}	AsO_4^{3-}
SbO_3^{3-}	SbO_4^{3-}

Sodium thiosulfate solutions are prepared by dissolving crystals of the salt in water. A normal solution contains $Na_2S_2O_3 \cdot 5H_2O/1 = 248.2$ g of the hydrated salt per liter (see Sec. 12-2). Standard solutions of thiosulfate can be used to titrate almost any oxidizing substance. The titration is made, however, by adding to the solution of oxidizing sub-stance a large excess (roughly measured) of potassium iodide. The oxidizing substance is reduced, liberating *an equivalent amount* of iodine, and the liberated iodine is titrated with thiosulfate. Typical oxidizing agents determined in this way are as follows:

Substance	Equation
$Cr_2O_7^=$	$Cr_2O_7^= + 6I^- + 14H^+ \longrightarrow 2Cr^{3+} + 3I_2 + 7H_2O$
MnO_4^-	$2MnO_4^- + 10I^- + 16H^+ \longrightarrow 2Mn^{++} + 5I_2 + 8H_2O$
BrO_3^-	$BrO_3^- + 6I^- + 6H^+ \longrightarrow Br^- + 3I_2 + 3H_2O$
Cu^{++}	$2Cu^{++} + 4I^- \longrightarrow 2CuI + I_2$
Cl_2	$Cl_2 + 2I^- \longrightarrow 2Cl^- + I_2$
H_2O_2	$H_2O_2 + 2I^- + 2H^+ \longrightarrow I_2 + 2H_2O$

Since an oxidizing agent liberates its own equivalent of iodine, the volume of thiosulfate required for the liberated iodine in any given case is the same as would be required if the thiosulfate were used directly and reduced the substance to the form indicated. In calculations, there-fore, the equivalent weight of the substance titrated can be found in the usual way by dividing the formula weight of the substance by the total change in oxidation number.

In titrations in acid solution, a standard solution of potassium iodate containing an excess of potassium iodide is a convenient substitute for standard iodine. It is a colorless, stable solution, but when it comes in contact with acid, the two ingredients immediately interact and liberate free iodine ($IO_3^- + 5I^- + 6H^+ \longrightarrow 3I_2 + 2H_2O$). In the titration of a substance in acid solution, this standard solution, therefore, behaves as if it were a standard solution of iodine. It is used, for example, in the determination of sulfur in steel. Since the iodate molecule has the oxidizing equivalent of six iodine atoms, a tenth-normal solution contains $KIO_3/60 = 3.567$ g of KIO_3 per liter and can be prepared by dissolving this amount of the pure crystals, together with an excess of potassium iodide, in water and diluting to exactly 1 liter.

Example 1   An excess of potassium iodide is added to a solution of potassium dichromate, and the liberated iodine is titrated with 48.80 ml of 0.1000 N sodium thiosulfate solution.   How many grams of $K_2Cr_2O_7$ did the dichromate solution contain?

Solution   Potassium dichromate liberates an equivalent amount of iodine from an iodide (that is, 6 g atoms = 6 g equiv. of iodine per mole of dichromate):

$$Cr_2O_7^= + 6I^- + 14H^+ \longrightarrow 2Cr^{3+} + 3I_2 + 7H_2O$$

and the liberated iodine is titrated with thiosulfate

$$2S_2O_3^= + I_2 \longrightarrow S_4O_6^= + 2I^-$$

The volume of titrating solution is the same as it would have been if the original solution had been titrated directly to the indicated products.

$$\text{Grams of } K_2Cr_2O_7 = 48.80 \times 0.1000 \times \frac{K_2Cr_2O_7}{6,000} = 0.2393 \qquad \textit{Ans.}$$

Example 2   The sulfur from 4.00 g of steel is evolved as H_2S and titrated with 1.60 ml of 0.05000 N iodine solution.   What is the percentage of S in the steel?   What is the value of 1.000 ml of the iodine in terms of grams of As_2O_3?   How many milliliters of the iodine will be reduced by 40.00 ml of $Na_2S_2O_3$ solution of which 1.000 ml ≈ 0.006354 g Cu? What volume of iodate-iodide solution containing 10.0 millimoles of KIO_3 and 50.0 g of KI per liter would be required to titrate the H_2S from 5.00 g of the above steel?   The equations involved are as follows:

$$H_2S + I_2 \longrightarrow S + 2I^- + 2H^+$$
$$AsO_3^{3-} + 2HCO_3^- + I_2 \longrightarrow AsO_4^{3-} + 2I^- + 2CO_2 + H_2O$$
$$2Cu^{++} + 4I^- \longrightarrow 2CuI + I_2$$
$$IO_3^- + 6I^- + 6H^+ \longrightarrow 3I_2 + I^- + 3H_2O$$

Solution

$$\frac{1.60 \times 0.05000 \times \frac{S}{2,000}}{4.00} \times 100 = 0.0320\% \text{ S} \qquad \textit{Ans.}$$

$$1.000 \times 0.05000 \times \frac{As_2O_3}{4,000} = 0.002473 \text{ g } As_2O_3 \qquad \textit{Ans.}$$

The addition of KI to a Cu(II) solution will cause reduction to Cu(I) and the liberation of an amount of iodine equivalent to the copper present. This iodine can be titrated with thiosulfate, and the normality of the latter found from the amount of Cu present. In the above case,

$$\text{Normality of Na}_2\text{S}_2\text{O}_3\text{soln.} = \frac{0.006354}{1.000 \times \text{Cu}/1{,}000} = 0.1000$$

$$\text{Vol. of } 0.0500 \; N \; \text{I}_2 \text{ soln.} = 40.00 \times \frac{0.1000}{0.05000} = 80.00 \text{ ml} \qquad Ans.$$

$$10.0 \text{ millimoles KIO}_3 = 60.0 \text{ meq.}$$

$$\text{Normality of KIO}_3 = 0.0600$$

$$\frac{x \times 0.0600 \times S/2{,}000}{5.00} \times 100 = 0.0320$$

$$x = 1.67 \text{ ml} \qquad Ans.$$

The reaction $\text{AsO}_3^{3-} + \text{I}_2 + \text{H}_2\text{O} \rightleftharpoons \text{AsO}_4^{3-} + 2\text{I}^- + 2\text{H}^+$ is reversible, for arsenic(III) is oxidized by iodine in neutral solution whereas arsenic(V) is reduced by iodide in the presence of acid with the liberation of free iodine. These reactions can be made use of in the determination of the two forms of arsenic when present in the same solution.

Example 3 A powder consists of $\text{Na}_2\text{HAsO}_3 + \text{As}_2\text{O}_5 + $ inert material. A sample weighing 0.2500 g is dissolved and titrated with standard iodine in a solution kept nearly neutral by excess dissolved NaHCO_3 $(\text{AsO}_3^{3-} + \text{I}_2 + 2\text{HCO}_3^- \longrightarrow \text{AsO}_4^{3-} + 2\text{I}^- + 2\text{CO}_2 + \text{H}_2\text{O})$. The titration requires 15.80 ml of $0.1030 \; N \; \text{I}_2$. HCl and an excess of KI are added $(\text{AsO}_4^{3-} + 2\text{I}^- + 8\text{H}^+ \longrightarrow \text{As}^{3+} + \text{I}_2 + 4\text{H}_2\text{O})$, and the liberated iodine requires 20.70 ml of $0.1300 \; N \; \text{Na}_2\text{S}_2\text{O}_3$. Calculate the percentages of Na_2HAsO_3 and As_2O_5 in the sample.

Solution

$$15.80 \times 0.1030 = 1.627 \text{ meq. As(III)}$$

$$20.70 \times 0.1300 = 2.691 \text{ meq. total As}$$

$$2.691 - 1.627 = 1.064 \text{ meq. As(V)}$$

$$\frac{1.627 \times \dfrac{\text{Na}_2\text{HAsO}_3}{2{,}000}}{0.2500} \times 100 = 55.29\% \text{ Na}_2\text{HAsO}_3$$

$$\frac{1.064 \times \dfrac{\text{As}_2\text{O}_5}{4{,}000}}{0.2500} \times 100 = 24.45\% \text{ As}_2\text{O}_5$$

$Ans.$

PROBLEMS

*12-85.   A soln. contains 15.76 g of I_2 per liter.   What is the value of each ml as an oxidizing agent in terms of g of (a) SO_2, (b) H_2SO_3, (c) $Na_2S_2O_3$, (d) As?

*12-86.   (a) What is the value of 1.000 ml of 0.04000 N thiosulfate soln. in terms of g of Cu? (b) What is the normality of a thiosulfate soln. if 25.00 ml is required to titrate the I_2 liberated from KI by 0.01563 g of Cu^{++}?

*12-87.   If 1.000 ml of a certain soln. of $KMnO_4$ will liberate 0.01750 g of I_2 from excess KI in the presence of acid, what wt. of pyrolusite contg. 89.21% MnO_2 and 10.79% inert matter will oxidize the same wt. of $H_2C_2O_4 \cdot 2H_2O$ as can be oxidized by 37.12 ml of the $KMnO_4$?

*12-88.   What is the value of 1.000 ml of an I_2 soln. in terms of g of As_2O_3 if each ml will oxidize 0.03000 g of anhydrous $Na_2S_2O_3$?

*12-89.   From the following data, find (a) the normality and molarity of the thiosulfate soln. and (b) the value of 1.000 ml in terms of g of $KH(IO_3)_2$: 1.000 ml $K_2Cr_2O_7 \approx 0.005585$ g Fe; 20.00 ml of the dichromate liberates sufficient I_2 from KI to require 32.46 ml $Na_2S_2O_3$ soln. for reduction.

*12-90.   If 35.90 ml of a thiosulfate soln. is required to titrate the I_2 liberated from excess KI by 40.00 ml of $KMnO_4$ (1.000 ml $\approx$ 0.007149 g Fe_2O_3), what is the value of each ml of the thiosulfate soln. in terms of g of $CuSO_4 \cdot 5H_2O$?

*12-91.   A soln. of $Na_2S_2O_3$ is freshly prepared, and 48.00 ml is required to titrate the I_2 liberated from excess KI by 0.3000 g of KIO_3.   (a) What is the normality of the thiosulfate, and what is its value in terms of g of I_2?   (b) On standing, 1.00% of the thiosulfate decomposes according to the equation $S_2O_3^= \longrightarrow SO_3^= + S$. What is now the normality of the soln. as an iodimetric reducing agent, assuming oxidation by I_2 of sulfite to sulfate?

*12-92.   A steel weighing 5.00 g is treated with HCl. H_2S is evolved and is eventually titrated with a soln. contg. 0.0100 mole of KIO_3 and 80 g of KI per liter.   If 3.00 ml is required, what is the percentage of S in the steel?

*12-93.   If 20.00 ml of thiosulfate (1.000 ml $\approx$ 0.03750 g $CuSO_4 \cdot 5H_2O$) is required for a certain wt. of pyrolusite by the Busen iodimetric method, what wt. of $H_2C_2O_4 \cdot 2H_2O$ should be added to a similar sample to require 20.00 ml of 0.1000 N $KMnO_4$ by the commonly used indirect method?   In the Bunsen method MnO_2 is reduced by HCl, the Cl_2 liberated from the latter is passed into KI soln., and the liberated I_2 is titrated with thiosulfate.

*12-94.   (a) Titrating with 0.05000 N I_2, what wt. of stibnite ore should be taken so that the percentage of Sb_2S_3 in the sample will be $1\frac{1}{2}$ times the buret reading? $(SbO_3^{3-} + I_2 + 2HCO_3^- \longrightarrow SbO_4^{3-} + 2I^- + 2CO_2 + H_2O.)$ (b) How many millimoles of $Na_2S_2O_3 \cdot 5H_2O$ is each liter of the above I_2 equiv. to?

*12-95.   A sample consisting of a mixt. of Na_2SO_3 and inert matter weighs 1.468 g and is added to 100.0 ml of 0.1000 N I_2.   The excess I_2 is titrated with 42.40 ml of thiosulfate soln. of which 1.000 ml is equiv. to the I_2 liberated by an oxidizing agent from 0.01574 g of KI. Calculate the percentage of Na_2SO_3 in the sample.

*12-96. A sample of stibnite contg. 70.00% Sb is given to a student for analysis. He titrates the Sb(III) with a soln. of I_2 of which he had previously found 1.000 ml to be equiv. to 0.02500 millimole of As_2O_3. Since standardization, however, the normality of the soln. has changed, owing to volatilization of I_2, and the student reports 70.25% Sb. (*a*) What are the percentage error and the present normality of the I_2 soln., and (*b*) what vol. of 0.2000 N I_2 should be added to a liter of the soln. to bring it back to its original concn.?

*12-97. A sample of impure KI weighing 0.3100 g is dissolved and treated with 1.000 millimole of K_2CrO_4 and 20 ml of 6 N H_2SO_4. The soln. is then boiled to expel the I_2 formed by the reaction. The soln. contg. the excess chromate is cooled and treated with excess KI and the liberated I_2 titrated with 0.1000 N $Na_2S_2O_3$. If 12.00 ml is required, what is the percentage purity of the original KI sample?

*12-98. A stock soln. is made by dissolving 50.0 millimoles of KIO_3 and 100 g of KI in H_2O and diluting to 10.0 liters. A standard steel weighing 5.00 g and contg. 0.0530% S is treated with HCl. The S is liberated as H_2S, which is eventually titrated in the presence of acid with the above stock soln. (*a*) What vol. is required? (*b*) What is the oxidizing normality of the iodate soln.? (*c*) How many g of KI in excess of the theoretical amt. required to form triiodide, I_3^-, ions with the KIO_3 in the presence of acid were used in preparing the stock soln.?

*12-99. Addition of potassium periodate to a soln. of a mercuric salt ppts. mercuric periodate, $Hg_5(IO_6)_2$. This ppt. can be dissolved in a mixt. of KI and HCl. I_2 is thereby liberated and can be titrated with thiosulfate. Balance the following equation which represents the reaction, and from it calculate the value of each ml of the thiosulfate (of which 1.00 ml $\backsimeq$ 0.0500 g $CuSO_4 \cdot 5H_2O$) in terms of g of Hg:

$$Hg_5(IO_6)_2 + I^- + H^+ \longrightarrow HgI_4^= + I_2 + H_2O$$

*12-100. The Cu in a 0.2500-g sample of ore is treated in acid soln. with excess KI, and the liberated I_2 is titrated with 16.50 ml of $Na_2S_2O_3$ (1.000 ml $\backsimeq$ 0.003619 g $KBrO_3$). What is the purity of the ore expressed in terms of percentage of Cu_2S?

*12-101. If the $AsCl_3$ from 50 g of Cu alloy is distilled off, absorbed in dil. alkali, and finally titrated with 20.0 ml of I_2 soln. which is 0.0100 M in I_3^- ions, what is the percentage of As in the alloy?

*12-102. When titrated in neutral soln. with 0.05000 N I_2, a mixt. of As_2O_3, As_2O_5, and inert material requires 20.10 ml. The resulting soln. is then acidified, and excess KI is added. The liberated I_2 requires 29.92 ml of 0.1500 N $Na_2S_2O_3$. Calculate the sum of the wts. of As_2O_3 and As_2O_5 in the sample.

*12-103. A solid mixt. contains only $KMnO_4$ and K_2CrO_4. A sample weighing 0.2400 g, when treated in acid soln. with KI, liberates sufficient I_2 to react with 60.00 ml of 0.1000 N thiosulfate. Find the percentages of Cr and Mn in the mixt.

*12-104.   A sample of pyrolusite is treated with HCl, the liberated Cl_2 passed into KI soln., and the resulting liberated I_2 titrated with thiosulfate soln. contg. 49.64 g of $Na_2S_2O_3 \cdot 5H_2O$ per liter.   If 38.70 ml is required, what vol. of 0.2500 N KMnO$_4$ would be required in an indirect detn. in which a similar sample is reduced with 0.9000 g of $H_2C_2O_4 \cdot 2H_2O$ and the excess oxalic acid is titrated with the permanganate?

*12-105.   Iodate liberates I_2 from excess iodide only in the presence of acid $(IO_3^- + 5I^- + 6H^+ \longrightarrow 3I_2 + 3H_2O)$.   Potassium biiodate $(KIO_3 \cdot HIO_3)$ ionizes in aq. soln. to give $2IO_3^- + K^+ + H^+$.   A sample of pure $KIO_3 \cdot HIO_3$ is dissolved in water, treated with excess KI, and the liberated I_2 titrated with $Na_2S_2O_3$, requiring A ml.   The soln. is now treated with an excess of H_2SO_4.   In terms of A, how many more ml of the $Na_2S_2O_3$ would be required to titrate the additional I_2 which is liberated?

*12-106.   "Sodium bismuthate" is a powerful oxidizing agent, but since it is usually of variable composition, its oxidizing power is best expressed in terms of the equiv. amt. of oxygen ("available" or "active" oxygen).   A half-gram sample of technical grade sodium bismuthate when treated with HCl and excess KI liberates sufficient I_2 to require 29.42 ml of 0.1022 N $Na_2S_2O_3$ for reduction.   (a) Calculate the percentage of available oxygen in the material, and also (b) express the oxidizing power in terms of percentage of $NaBiO_3$.

*12-107.   Calculate the percentage of Cr in a sample of chromite ore from the following data: Wt. of sample $= 0.4000$ g. $FeSO_4$ soln. added $=$ three pipetfuls (approx. 75 ml).   Back titration requires 21.45 ml $K_2Cr_2O_7$.   One pipetful $FeSO_4 \propto$ 28.93 ml $K_2Cr_2O_7$.   The normality of the dichromate is established from the fact that 48.54 ml of 0.1262 M $Na_2S_2O_3$ soln. is required to titrate the I_2 liberated from excess KI in the presence of acid by the action of 46.04 ml of the dichromate.

*12-108.   Ammonium peroxysulfate, $(NH_4)_2S_2O_8$, is used in analytical chemistry as an oxidizing agent.   A sample of the powder contg. only inert impurities weighs 0.3000 g.   It is dissolved in water, acidified, and treated with excess KI.   The liberated I_2 requires 24.42 ml of 0.1023 M $Na_2S_2O_3$ for titration.   (a) Calculate the percentage purity of the sample.   (b) In hot aq. soln. peroxysulfates slowly decompose (to sulfate and O_2).   If the above sample were completely decomposed in this way, what would be the no. of meq. gain or loss in acidity?

*12-109.   "Bleaching powder" is of variable composition, but when treated with water it behaves like a mixt. of $Ca(OCl)_2$ and $CaCl_2$; the $Ca(OCl)_2$ is a powerful oxidizing and bleaching agent.   Its oxidizing power is often expressed in terms of "available (i.e., reactive) chlorine."

A sample weighing 2.500 g is treated with water and brought to a vol. of 500 ml.   A 25-ml pipetful of the mixt. is acidified, treated with excess KI, and the liberated I_2 titrated with $Na_2S_2O_3$ of which 26.10 ml is equiv. in conventional redox reactions to 25.00 ml of 0.02100 M KMnO$_4$.   What is the percentage of "available chlorine" in the sample if 13.40 ml is used in the titration?

12-110.   If a sample consists of 98.00% of the bleaching powder of Prob. 12-109 and 2.00% of pure $KClO_3$, what vol. of thiosulfate of the concn. given would have been required for the titration?

12-111.   What wt. of $FeSO_4 \cdot 7H_2O$ will reduce in the presence of acid that wt. of pyrolusite (with an oxidizing power equiv. to 92.50% MnO_2) which will oxidize the same amt. of $H_2C_2O_4 \cdot 2H_2O$ as 35.00 ml of $KMnO_4$ soln. of which 1.000 ml will liberate 0.01750 g of I_2 from KI + acid?

12-112.   If 1.000 ml of a thiosulfate soln. is equiv. to 0.005642 g of Cu and is also equiv. to 1.500 ml of a certain I_2 soln., find the value of 1.00 ml of the I_2 soln. in terms of g of (a) Sb, (b) As, (c) As_2S_3, (d) Sb_2O_3.

12-113.   Calculate the percentage of Fe in a sample of crude $FeCl_3$ from the following data: Sample $= 1.000$ g; its acid soln. liberates from excess KI sufficient I_2 to require 7.85 ml of a soln. of I_2 for back titration after adding a 50-ml pipetful of thiosulfate soln.   45.00 ml I_2 soln. $\backsimeq$ 45.95 ml thiosulfate; 45.00 ml arsenite soln. $\backsimeq$ 45.20 I_2; 1.000 ml arsenite soln. contains 0.00516 g As_2O_3.

12-114.   (a) What wt. of Cu ore should be taken for analysis so that when the Cu is determined by the regular iodimetric method using 0.05000 N $Na_2S_2O_3$, the buret reading will be two-thirds of the percentage of CuS in the ore?   (b) What is the molarity of the thiosulfate soln.?   (c) What vol. of $KMnO_4$ (1.000 ml $\backsimeq$ 0.0005493 g Mn by the Volhard method) will react with an excess of KI in the presence of acid to liberate sufficient I_2 to require 20.00 ml of the thiosulfate for reduction?

12-115.   A qualitative analysis of the corrosion product of a bronze casting showed the presence of only Cu, H_2O, and CO_2.   A sample weighing 0.0539 g is dissolved in acid and the Cu^{++} detnd. iodimetrically.   A vol. of 9.75 ml of 0.0500 N $Na_2S_2O_3$ is required.   Assuming the corrosion product to be a basic cupric carbonate, give its probable formula.

12-116.   A soln. of hydroxylamine is treated with A ml (an excess) of $Fe_2(SO_4)_3$ [$2NH_2OH + 2Fe_2(SO_4)_3 \longrightarrow 4FeSO_4 + 2H_2SO_4 + N_2O + H_2O$].   The Fe^{++} in the resulting soln. is titrated with B N $KMnO_4$ requiring C ml.

Another soln. of hydroxylamine is treated with HCl and D millimoles (an excess) of $KBrO_3$ ($NH_2OH + HBrO_3 \longrightarrow HNO_3 + HBr + H_2O$).   The addition of KI and acid to the excess bromate liberates sufficient I_2 to require E ml of F N $Na_2S_2O_3$ for titration.

In terms of the appropriate letters, how many g of NH_2OH are shown to be present in each case?

12-117.   What wt. of pyrolusite contg. 75.0% MnO_2 will oxidize the same amt. of oxalic acid as 35.0 ml of a $KMnO_4$ soln. of which 1.00 ml will liberate 0.0175 g of I_2 from an excess of KI?

12-118.   When an aq. suspension of a certain wt. of pure Mn_3O_4 is treated with 0.5500 g of $Na_2C_2O_4$ and 10 ml of 6 N H_2SO_4, the sample dissolves and the resulting soln. requires 30.80 ml of $KMnO_4$ (1.000 ml $\backsimeq$ 0.01050 g Fe_2O_3).   (a) If the same wt. of sample is treated in a distilling flask with concd. HCl and the evolved

Cl_2 is passed into KI soln., how many ml of $Na_2S_2O_3$ (1.000 ml $\approx$ 0.01000 g $KBrO_3$) are required to titrate the liberated I_2?   (b) How many g of total elementary Mn are present in the wt. of Mn_3O_4 taken?

12-119.   If 50.00 ml of a soln. of I_2 is equiv. in oxidizing power to 49.97 ml of a soln. of $K_2Cr_2O_7$ of which 1.000 ml will liberate 0.004263 g of I_2 from excess KI, calculate the normality of each soln. as an oxidizing agent.

12-120.   Pure $K_2Cr_2O_7$ weighing 0.3321 g is boiled with an excess of concd. HCl, and the evolved Cl_2 passed into a soln. of KI.   The liberated I_2 requires 68.21 ml of thiosulfate.   What are the normality and the molarity of the thiosulfate?

12-121.   What must be the normality of a soln. of I_2 so that if a 0.5000-g sample of stibnite is taken for analysis, the no. of ml of the I_2 required to oxidize Sb(III) to Sb(V) will represent directly the percentage of Sb?

12-122.   A powder consists of a mixt. of $Na_3AsO_4 \cdot 12H_2O$, Na_2HAsO_3, and inert material.   It is dissolved and in neutral soln. requires 15.60 ml of 0.08100 N I_2 for titration.   The resulting soln. is acidified and excess KI is added.   The liberated I_2 requires 18.58 ml of 0.1200 M $Na_2S_2O_3$ for reduction.   Calculate the amt. of As(V) and of As(III) in terms of g of $Na_3AsO_4 \cdot 12H_2O$ and g of combined As_2O_3, respectively.

12-123.   If the amt. of Cu in a carbonate ore expressed in terms of percentage of $Cu_2(OH)_2CO_3$ is 53.05, and if 25.72 ml of $Na_2S_2O_3$ soln. is eventually required to titrate the I_2 liberated from excess KI by the Cu^{++} from a 0.5000-g sample, what is the value of each ml of the thiosulfate in terms of g of (a) $KBrO_3$, (b) $KH(IO_3)_2$?

12-124.   The S from a 5.00-g sample of steel is evolved as H_2S and eventually titrated in the presence of acid with standard I_2 soln. (1.00 ml $\approx$ 0.004945 g As_2O_3), of which 1.90 ml is required.   (a) What is the percentage of S in the steel? (b) If a standard $KIO_3 + KI$ soln. had been substituted for the I_2 and a vol. identical with the above had been required, how many g of KIO_3 would have been present in each ml of the soln.? (c) Could the iodate soln. have been standardized against pure As_2O_3 as the I_2 soln. was?   Explain your answer.

12-125.   A soln. contg. $NaHSO_3$ is titrated with standard NaOH (1.000 ml $\approx$ 0.04084 g potassium acid phthalate) to the formation of a pink color with phenol-phthalein.   7.80 ml is required.   The resulting soln. is then titrated with I_2 [1.000 ml $\approx$ 1.000 ml $Na_2S_2O_3 \approx$ 0.01000 millimole $KH(IO_3)_2$] with starch as indicator. How many ml are required?

12-8   Iodate Process

Potassium iodate in the presence of dilute acid is a fairly strong oxidizing agent.   Its behavior is indicated by the half-cell reaction

$$IO_3^- + 6H^+ + 5e = \tfrac{1}{2}I_2 + 3H_2O \qquad E^0 = +1.20 \text{ volts}$$

If the titration of an oxidizable substance is carried out with potassium iodate in a solution greater than 4 N in HCl, a secondary reaction takes place in which the liberated iodine is subsequently acted on by the iodate to form iodine chloride:

$$2I_2 + IO_3^- + 6H^+ + 10Cl^- \longrightarrow 5ICl_2^- + 3H_2O$$

Chloroform (or carbon tetrachloride) serves as the indicator. Free iodine dissolves in chloroform to give a purple color, and iodine chloride dissolves to give a yellow color. The solution being titrated is vigorously agitated with chloroform. The violet color that forms subsequently fades to yellow, and the latter change is taken as the end point.

The following reducing agents can be satisfactorily determined by the iodate process, and the net reaction in each case is indicated by the accompanying equation:

Iodide:	$2I^- + IO_3^- + 6H^+ + 6Cl^- \longrightarrow 3ICl_2^- + 3H_2O$
Iodine:	$2I_2 + IO_3^- + 6H^+ + 10Cl^- \longrightarrow 5ICl_2^- + 3H_2O$
Arsenic:	$2As^{3+} + IO_3^- + 5H_2O + 2Cl^- \longrightarrow ICl_2^- + 2H_3AsO_4 + 4H^+$
Antimony:	$2Sb^{3+} + IO_3^- + 5H_2O + 2Cl^- \longrightarrow ICl_2^- + 2H_3SbO_4 + 4H^+$
Copper:	$2Cu^{++} + H_2SO_3 + 2CNS^- + H_2O \longrightarrow$

$$2CuCNS + SO_4^= + 4H^+$$

$$4CuCNS + 7IO_3^- + 14H^+ + 14Cl^- \longrightarrow$$
$$4Cu^{++} + 7ICl_2^- + 4HCN + 4SO_4^= + 5H_2O$$

Mercury:	$Hg_2^{++} + 2Cl^- \longrightarrow Hg_2Cl_2$
	$2Hg_2Cl_2 + IO_3^- + 6H^+ + 6Cl^- \longrightarrow 4HgCl_2 + ICl_2^- + 3H_2O$
Tin:	$2Sn^{++} + IO_3^- + 6H^+ + 14Cl^- \longrightarrow 2SnCl_6^= + ICl_2^- + 3H_2O$

Example 1   A solution of KIO_3 is 0.100 N, as used in ordinary iodimetric processes (see Sec. 12-7). How many grams of $CuSO_4 \cdot 5H_2O$ must be present in a solution in order to require 10.0 ml of this KIO_3 in a direct titration to the disappearance of a violet color in $CHCl_3$?

Solution   In iodimetric processes $KIO_3 \backsim 3I_2 \backsim 6$ hydrogen equivalents. Since $4 Cu \backsim 7KIO_3$, $4Cu \backsim 42$ hydrogen equivalents.

$$10.0 \times 0.100 \times \frac{4CuSO_4 \cdot 5H_2O}{42,000} = 0.0238 \text{ g} \qquad Ans.$$

12-9   Bromate Process

Potassium bromate, like potassium iodate, is a strong oxidizing agent in the presence of acid. In a titration of a reducing agent in fairly concentrated HCl solution with potassium bromate, the bromate is reduced to bromide, and the next drop of bromate results in the formation of free bromine:

$$5Br^- + BrO_3^- + 6H^+ \longrightarrow 3Br_2 + 3H_2O$$

Any one of a number of organic dyes (e.g., methyl red) serves as an indicator, for the liberated bromine oxidizes the dye to a colorless product.

The oxidizable substance is therefore titrated with a standard solution of potassium bromate to the disappearance of the color of the indicator dye.

Arsenic and antimony are among the constituents that can be satisfactorily determined by the bromate process, and the net reaction in each case is as follows:

$$3As^{3+} + BrO_3^- + 9H_2O \longrightarrow 3H_3AsO_4 + Br^- + 9H^+$$
$$3Sb^{3+} + BrO_3^- + 9H_2O \longrightarrow 3H_3SbO_4 + Br^- + 9H^+$$

In addition, several metal ions can be precipitated by 8-hydroxyquinoline (oxine), which has one replaceable hydrogen. The precipitate can be dissolved in HCl, and the liberated oxine, C_9H_6NOH, titrated with potassium bromate in the presence of potassium bromide. As in the above cases, methyl red or a similar oxidizable dye is used as the indicator. The net equation for the titration is as follows:

$$3C_9H_6NOH + 2BrO_3^- + 4Br^- + 6H^+ \longrightarrow 3C_9H_4NBr_2OH + 6H_2O$$

Ions commonly determined in this way include Al^{3+}, Mg^{++}, Cd^{++}, Co^{++}, Ni^{++}, TiO^{++}, and Zn^{++}. In the case of aluminum, for example, the formula of the precipitate is $Al(C_9H_6NO)_3$, and therefore each atom of aluminum is equivalent to two molecules of potassium bromate or to 12 hydrogen units.

Example 1   What is the value of 1.00 ml of 0.0100 M $KBrO_3$ in terms of grams of Ti in the method whereby the titanium is precipitated as titanyl oxinate, $TiO(C_9H_6NO)_2$, and the oxine in the precipitate is titrated with the bromate in the regular way?

Solution   The 0.0100 M $KBrO_3$ is 0.0600 N (see Sec. 12-7). Each Ti is equivalent to 2 oxines, which in the bromate titration are equivalent to $\frac{4}{3}KBrO_3$ or to $\frac{4}{3} \times 6 = 8$ hydrogen units.

$$1.00 \times 0.0600 \times \frac{Ti}{8,000} = 0.000359 \text{ g}   \text{ \textit{Ans.}}$$

PROBLEMS

*12-126.   A 10.0-ml portion of a soln. contg. I_2 and KI requires 0.83 ml of 0.120 N $Na_2S_2O_3$ to titrate to an end point with starch indicator. Another 10.0-ml portion, after acidification with concd. HCl, requires 10.50 ml of 0.0100 M KIO_3 to titrate to an end point with chloroform indicator. How many g of I_2 and of KI are in the 10.0-ml portion?

*12-127.   A 25.0-ml pipetful of H_2O_2 soln. is diluted to 250 ml, and 25.0 ml of the resulting soln. is treated in alkaline soln. with 50.0 ml of a soln. of Na_3AsO_3 which is 0.100 N as a reducing agent. The H_2O_2 is reduced to H_2O; the As(III) is oxidized to As(V). The remaining As(III) is determined by acidifying the soln. with concd. HCl and titrating with KIO_3 to an end point with $CHCl_3$ indicator. The KIO_3 is 0.150 N when used as an ordinary iodimetric standard, and 20.0 ml is required in the titration. Calculate the no. of g of pure H_2O_2 contained in the original soln.

*12-128. What is the meq. wt. of Mg in the detn. of that element by pptg. with 8-hydroxyquinoline and titrating the oxine liberated from the ppt. by HCl with standard $KBrO_3$ + KBr?

*12-129. If a ppt. of Hg_2Cl_2 requires a vol. of KIO_3 (0.100 N as an ordinary iodimetric standard for thiosulfate) for titration in 4 N HCl soln. ($CHCl_3$ indicator) that is equal to the vol. of 0.1200 M $Na_2S_2O_3$ soln. required to titrate the I_2 liberated from 0.1392 g of $KBrO_3$ by excess KI in the presence of dil. acid, what wt. of Hg is present in the Hg_2Cl_2 titrated?

*12-130. When 10.0 ml of a certain KIO_3 soln. is treated in the presence of dil. acid with excess KI, the amt. of I_2 liberated is found to be the same as that contained in 10.0 ml of a certain standard I_2 soln. If a given wt. of Sb(III) is titrated in neutral soln. with the standard I_2 and the same wt. of Sb(III) is titrated in a soln. 4 N in HCl with the standard KIO_3 soln. ($CHCl_3$ indicator), what is the ratio of the two vols. of titrating soln. used?

*12-131. On long standing, a soln. of KI becomes discolored as a result of the formation of small amts. of free I_2. If a pipetful of the soln. requires A ml of B M $Na_2S_2O_3$ in a conventional iodimetric titration, and a similar vol. of the soln. requires C ml of B M KIO_3 in the conventional iodate titration, what, in terms of the appropriate letters A, B, and C, is the ratio of the wts. of I^- and I_2 in the sample?

*12-132. Vanadium (in soln. as vanadate) can be determined by the iodate method by first adding a measured amt. of iodide to the soln. which is moderately concd. in HCl ($2VO_4^{3-} + 2I^- + 12H^+ \longrightarrow 2VO^{++} + I_2 + 6H_2O$) and then in one operation titrating both the liberated I_2 and the excess iodide with standard KIO_3 (see equations, Sec. 12-8).

If 50.00 ml of 0.05000 M KI and 40.00 ml of 0.02500 M KIO_3 are used in the above analysis, how many g of V are present in the sample?

12-133. (*a*) Write a balanced equation to show the initial step in the titration of CuCNS with KIO_3 in which free I_2 is liberated. (*b*) Assuming this reaction to be complete before the secondary reaction begins, calculate the no. of ml of KIO_3 (0.100 N as ordinarily used in iodimetric processes) that are required per 100 mg of Cu to give the maximum intensity of violet to the $CHCl_3$ indicator.

12-134. Vanadium can be determined by adding a measured amt. of KI to a dil. acid soln. of VO_3^- (forming VO^{++}) and titrating the liberated I_2 plus the excess I^- in the presence of 4 N HCl with standard KIO_3 ($CHCl_3$ indicator). (*a*) Write equations for all reactions involved, and (*b*) find the no. of g of elementary V equiv. to each ml of 0.100 M KIO_3.

12-135. A soln. contains dissolved Na_3AsO_3 and Na_3AsO_4. If 0.100 millimole of $KBrO_3$ is required to oxidize the As(III) and bleach methyl red indicator, and if the total As(V) in the resulting soln. gives with uranyl ions a ppt. of $UO_2NH_4AsO_4 \cdot xH_2O$

which eventually forms 0.400 millimole of U_3O_8, how many g of Na_3AsO_4 are shown to be originally present?

12-136. A ppt. of Hg_2Cl_2 contains 0.1000 g of combined Hg. How many ml of KIO_3 (1.000 ml $\approx$ 0.1000 millimole of $Na_2S_2O_3 \cdot 5H_2O$ in ordinary iodimetric titrations) would be required to titrate a suspension of the Hg_2Cl_2 in a soln. 4 N in HCl ($CHCl_3$ indicator)?

12-137. When 10.0 ml of a certain standard KIO_3 soln. is treated in the presence of dil. acid with excess KI, the amt. of I_2 liberated requires 10.0 ml of a standard soln. of thiosulfate for reduction. A given wt. of Cu^{++} is reduced and pptd. as CuCNS, and the ppt. is titrated with the above KIO_3 soln. The same wt. of Cu^{++} is separately treated with excess KI in the presence of dil. acid, and the liberated I_2 is titrated with the above thiosulfate. What is the ratio of the two vols. of titrating soln. used?

12-138. A certain soln. of KI contains a small amt. of free I_2. A 25-ml pipetful is made 4 N in HCl and with $CHCl_3$ indicator requires 15.80 ml of 0.02500 M KIO_3 to give a violet-to-yellow change in color. Another 25-ml pipetful with starch indicator requires 1.90 ml of 0.02000 N $Na_2S_2O_3$ to destroy the blue color of the soln. Calculate the no. of g of KI and of free I_2 in the soln.

Precipitation
Methods
(Precipitimetry)

13-1   Equivalent Weights in Precipitation Methods

In precipitation (or "saturation") methods a substance is titrated with a standard solution of a precipitating agent. At the completion of the precipitation the precipitating agent reacts with an indicator and a color change takes place. For example, in the *Volhard method* for silver, silver ions are titrated with a standard solution of potassium thiocyanate ($Ag^+ + CNS^- \longrightarrow \underline{AgCNS}$) and the end point is determined by the red color formed when an additional drop of the thiocyanate reacts with ferric alum indicator to form a series of ferric thiocyanate complexes.

Similarly, silver ions and halide ions can be titrated in neutral solution with standard NaCl or standard $AgNO_3$ using certain *adsorption indicators* (e.g., dichlorofluorescein), which form colored compounds on the surface of the particles of precipitate and give a change of color at the equivalence point.

Halide ions can also be titrated with standard silver nitrate with chromate ions as the indicator (*Mohr method*). The formation of red silver chromate is taken as the end point.

In determining the equivalent weight of a constituent being precipitated, 1.008 g of hydrogen ion is again taken as the standard of reference. The equivalent weight is that weight which in precipitation reacts with the equivalent of that amount of hydrogen ion. Here the point of view is that of metathesis rather than that of neutralization or of oxidation and reduction. Knowledge of valence and a simple inspection of the equation usually suffice to determine the correct equivalent weight. In most cases the gram-equivalent weight is found by dividing the formula weight by the net number of charges on the constituent actually taking part in the reaction.

In the reaction between silver nitrate and sodium chloride ($Ag^+ + Cl^- \longrightarrow AgCl$) the equivalent weights of the reacting substances are $AgNO_3/1$ and $NaCl/1$, respectively. In the reaction between barium chloride and sodium sulfate ($Ba^{++} + SO_4^= \longrightarrow BaSO_4$) the equivalent weight in each case is one-half of the molecular weight. The equivalent weight of anhydrous disodium phosphate as a sodium salt is $Na_2HPO_4/2 = 71.02$; and as a phosphate, $Na_2HPO_4/3 = 47.35$.

Reactions in this class may be direct or indirect. That is, the titrating solution may be added in amounts just sufficient to precipitate all the substance to be determined, or in certain cases an excess of the precipitating agent can be added and the excess titrated by means of a precipitating agent. Because of the difficulty of finding suitable indicators to show the completion of the reactions, a great many precipitation reactions cannot be used satisfactorily as a basis for quantitative titrations.

The Volhard method for silver is a direct method and is illustrated in Example 1 below. The Volhard method can also be applied as an indirect process to the determination of chloride, bromide, iodide, cyanide, and thiocyanate. This is illustrated in Example 2.

Example 1   What is the percentage of silver in a coin if a 0.2000-g sample requires 39.60 ml of potassium thiocyanate solution (0.4103 g of KCNS per 100 ml) for the precipitation of the silver?

$$Ag^+ + CNS^- \longrightarrow AgCNS$$

Solution   A liter of the KCNS solution contains 4.103 g of the salt. Its normality is

$$\frac{4.103}{KCNS/1} = \frac{4.103}{97.18} = 0.04222$$

$$\frac{39.60 \times 0.04222 \times \dfrac{Ag}{1,000}}{0.2000} \times 100 = 90.18\% \ Ag \qquad Ans.$$

Example 2   A sample of impure strontium chloride weighs 0.5000 g. After the addition of 50.00 ml of 0.2100 N $AgNO_3$ and filtering out of the precipitated AgCl, the filtrate requires 25.50 ml of 0.2800 N KCNS to titrate the silver. What is the percentage of $SrCl_2$ in the sample?

Solution

Meq. of $AgNO_3$ added $= 50.00 \times 0.2100 = 10.50$

Meq. of KCNS required $= 25.50 \times 0.2800 = 7.14$

Net meq. $= 10.50 - 7.14 = 3.36$

$$\frac{3.36 \times \dfrac{SrCl_2}{2,000}}{0.5000} \times 100 = 53.3\% \; SrCl_2 \qquad \textit{Ans.}$$

Example 3   A sample of feldspar weighing 1.500 g is decomposed, and eventually there is obtained a mixture of KCl and NaCl weighing 0.1801 g.   These chlorides are dissolved in H_2O, a 50-ml pipetful of 0.08333 N $AgNO_3$ is added, and the precipitate is filtered off.   The filtrate requires 16.47 ml of 0.1000 N KCNS, with ferric alum as indicator.   Calculate the percentage of K_2O in the silicate.

Solution   Let

$x =$ no. of g of KCl obtained

Then

$$0.1801 - x = \text{no. of g of NaCl}$$

$$\text{Total meq. of mixed halides} = \frac{x}{KCl/1,000} + \frac{0.1801 - x}{NaCl/1,000}$$

$$\frac{x}{KCl/1,000} + \frac{0.1801 - x}{NaCl/1,000} = (50 \times 0.08333) - (16.47 \times 0.1000)$$

$$x = 0.152 \text{ g KCl}$$

$$\frac{0.152 \times K_2O/2KCl}{1.500} \times 100 = 6.40\% \qquad \textit{Ans.}$$

PROBLEMS

*13-1.   What vol. of 0.1233 N $AgNO_3$ soln. is required to ppt. the Cl from 0.2280 g of $BaCl_2 \cdot 2H_2O$?

*13-2.   (*a*) What vol. of 0.08333 N $BaCl_2$ soln. is required to ppt. all the sulfate from a soln. contg. 0.4770 g of $K_2SO_4 \cdot Al_2(SO_4)_3 \cdot 24H_2O$?   (*b*) What is the molarity of the $BaCl_2$ soln.?

*13-3.   A soln. of Na_3PO_4 that is 0.2000 N as a salt is used to ppt. the Mg as $MgNH_4PO_4$ from a 1.000-g sample of dolomite contg. 14.01% $MgCO_3$.   What vol. is theoretically required?

*13-4.   A soln. of $K_2Cr_2O_7$ that is 0.1121 N as an oxidizing agent is used to ppt. $BaCrO_4$ from 0.5060 g of $BaCl_2 \cdot 2H_2O$.   (*a*) What is the normality of the dichromate soln. as a pptg. agent in this reaction, (*b*) what is its normality as a K salt, and (*c*) what vol. is required?

*13-5.   (*a*) What vol. of $KHC_2O_4 \cdot H_2C_2O_4 \cdot 2H_2O$ soln. that is 0.2000 N as an acid is required to ppt. the Ca as $CaC_2O_4 \cdot 2H_2O$ from 0.4080 g of cement contg. 60.32% CaO?   (*b*) What is the normality of the tetroxalate soln. as a reducing agent in a permanganate process?

*13-6.   A sample of a silver coin weighing 0.5000 g and contg. 90.00% Ag is analyzed by the Volhard method.   What is the least normality that a KCNS soln. may have and not require more than 50.00 ml in the titration?

*13-7.   A certain soln. of $FeCl_3 \cdot 6H_2O$ contains in each ml a wt. of Fe equal to that in 0.300 mg of Fe_2O_3.   How many ml of 0.0500 N $AgNO_3$ would be required to titrate 50.0 ml of the chloride soln. to a red color with K_2CrO_4 indicator?

*13-8.   (a) A sample of pure As weighing 0.1500 g is dissolved in HNO_3 (forming H_3AsO_4).   The resulting soln. is made neutral and then treated with 120.0 ml of 0.06667 N $AgNO_3$, which ppts. all the As as Ag_3AsO_4.   The ppt. is washed and dissolved in acid, and the Ag^+ in the soln. of the ppt. is titrated with 0.1000 N KCNS (with ferric ions as indicator).   How many ml are required?   (b) Under the same numerical conditions, how many ml of the KCNS would have been required if an indirect method had been used (i.e., if the Ag in the acidified filtrate from the arsenate ppt. had been titrated)?

*13-9.   What is the percentage of Br and of inert matter in a 1.600-g sample consisting of a mixt. of $CaBr_2 \cdot 6H_2O$ (f. wt. = 308.0) and inert matter if to an aq. soln. of the sample is added 52.00 ml of 0.2000 N $AgNO_3$ and the excess Ag^+ requires 4.00 ml of 0.1000 N KCNS for the pptn. of AgCNS?

*13-10.   The purity of a soluble iodide is determined by pptg. the I^- with an excess of standard $AgNO_3$ soln. and titrating the excess Ag^+ with KCNS soln.   The $AgNO_3$ soln. is prepared by dissolving 2.122 g of Ag in HNO_3, evaporating to dryness, dissolving the residue in H_2O, and diluting to a liter.   From a buret 60.00 ml of this soln. is added to 100.0 ml of the iodide, and the excess requires 1.03 ml of KCNS soln. of which 1.000 ml will ppt. 0.001247 g of Ag as AgCNS.   Find the wt. of I present as iodide in the 100-ml portion of the soln.

*13-11.   A mixt. of LiCl and BaI_2 weighing 0.6000 g is treated with 45.15 ml of 0.2000 N $AgNO_3$ soln., and the excess Ag^+ is then titrated with 0.1000 N KCNS soln. (ferric alum indicator).   If 25.00 ml is required, what is the percentage of I in the sample?

*13-12.   A sample of feldspar contains 7.58% Na_2O and 9.93% K_2O.   What must be the normality of a soln. of $AgNO_3$ if it takes 22.71 ml of it to ppt. the Cl^- from the combined alkali chlorides obtained from a sample weighing 0.1500 g?

*13-13.   A sample of feldspar weighing 2.000 g yields a mixt. of NaCl and KCl weighing 0.2558 g.   If 35.00 ml of 0.1000 N $AgNO_3$ is added to the dissolved chlorides and the excess Ag^+ requires 0.92 ml of 0.02000 N KCNS soln. for titration, what is the percentage of K in the feldspar?

*13-14.   Potassium cyanide of technical grade is usually contaminated with NaCN as well as with small amts. of chloride and other inert matter.   From the following data, express (a) the total cyanide content of the sample as percentage of KCN and (b) the chloride content as percentage of KCl.   (c) Explain why the sum of these two values can be greater than 100%.

   Sample = 1.000 g.   Vol. of 0.1625 N $AgNO_3$ required to titrate the soln. to a faint permanent turbidity = 46.84 ml.   Additional vol. of the $AgNO_3$ required to continue the titration to a point where a reddish color is obtained with K_2CrO_4 indicator (Mohr method) = 47.83 ml.

*13-15.   A sample of technical grade sodium hyposulfite ($Na_2S_2O_4 \cdot H_2O$) weighing 0.2000 g is treated with an excess of an ammoniacal soln. of $AgNO_3$. In the overall reaction that takes place, hyposulfite ions are oxidized to sulfite and silver ammonio ions are reduced to metallic silver. The pptd. Ag is filtered off and dissolved in HNO_3. This soln. then requires 20.06 ml of 0.1000 N KCNS to give a pink color with ferric alum indicator. Calculate the reducing power of the original sample in terms of percentage of $Na_2S_2O_4 \cdot H_2O$ (f. wt. = 192.12), and write the equation representing the above oxidation of hyposulfite ions.

13-16.   How many ml of 0.2500 N $AgNO_3$ soln. are required to titrate directly the chloride in a soln. contg. 0.5680 g of $BaCl_2 \cdot 2H_2O$?

13-17.   A soln. of $Na_2HPO_4 \cdot 12H_2O$ is 0.1000 N as a sodium salt. What vol. of it is required to ppt. the Ca as $Ca_3(PO_4)_2$ from a soln. contg. 0.5000 g of $Ca(NO_3)_2$?

13-18.   (*a*) How many ml of $K_2Cr_2O_7$ (of which 1.000 ml will oxidize the Fe in 0.1000 millimole of $FeSO_4 \cdot 7H_2O$) will ppt. all the Pb as $PbCrO_4$ from a soln. contg. 0.2510 g of $Pb(NO_3)_2$?   (*b*) What is the normality of the dichromate soln. as a potassium salt?

13-19.   To ppt. the sulfate from a certain wt. of $FeSO_4 \cdot (NH_4)_2SO_4 \cdot 6H_2O$ contaminated only with SiO_2 and H_2O requires a no. of ml of 0.2000 N $BaCl_2$ soln. exactly equal to the percentage of Fe in the sample. What is the wt. of sample?

13-20.   In the analysis of a sample of a silicate weighing 0.8000 g, a mixt. of NaCl and KCl weighing 0.2400 g was obtained. The chlorides were dissolved in H_2O, 50.00 ml of 0.1000 N $AgNO_3$ was added, and the excess Ag^+ was titrated with KCNS soln. (ferric alum indicator). If the titration required 14.46 ml and the KCNS was 0.30% greater in normality than the $AgNO_3$ soln., what was the percentage of K_2O and of Na_2O in the silicate?

13-21.   A sample consisting only of $CaCl_2 \cdot 2H_2O$ and KNO_3 weighs 1.100 g. It is dissolved in water, 50.00 ml of 0.2000 N $AgNO_3$ is added, and the filtrate from the ppt. of AgCl is found to require 0.80 meq. of KCNS for titration. Calculate the percentage of combined K in the sample.

13-22.   A sample of feldspar weighs 0.1500 g and contains 7.73% Na_2O and 9.17% K_2O. What must be the normality of a soln. of $AgNO_3$ if 25.18 ml is required to ppt. the Cl^- from the combined NaCl + KCl obtained from the sample?

13-23.   A mixt. of LiCl and $BaBr_2$ weighing 0.5000 g is treated with 37.60 ml of 0.2000 N $AgNO_3$, and the excess of the latter requires 18.50 ml of 0.1111 N KCNS soln. for titration. Find the percentage of Ba in the mixt.

13-24.   Express in letters the percentage of Na_2O in a silicate contg. Na and K from the following data: Wt. of sample = A g; wt. of NaCl + KCl obtained = B g; wt. of $AgNO_3$ crystals added to ppt. the Cl^- from these chlorides and give an excess = C g; vol. of D N KCNS required to titrate the excess Ag^+ = E ml.

Complex-ion-formation Methods (Compleximetry)

14-1 Equivalent Weights in Compleximetric Methods

Reactions in which complex ions are formed are common in chemistry, particularly in qualitative analysis, and many of them should already be familiar to the student. The following are typical cases:

$$Ag^+ + 2NH_4OH \longrightarrow Ag(NH_3)_2^+ + 2H_2O$$
$$Cd^{++} + 4CN^- \longrightarrow Cd(CN)_4^=$$
$$Sn^{4+} + 6Cl^- \longrightarrow SnCl_6^=$$
$$Hg^{++} + 4I^- \longrightarrow HgI_4^=$$

Unfortunately, because of lack of suitable indicators, few of the many reactions of this class can be used as a basis for a volumetric analysis. Most of those that are in common use are covered by the examples and problems below.

The gram-equivalent weight of a substance involved in a complex-ion-forming reaction is based as usual on 1.008 g of H^+ as the standard of reference. As in all previous cases, if one formula weight of a substance reacts with A hydrogen equivalents, its equivalent weight is its formula weight divided by A. If we consider the hydrogen ion equivalent of NH_4OH, CN^-, Cl^-, and I^- to be one in each case (i.e., as in simple metathetical reactions), then the milliequivalent weights of the metal ions in the above four equations are Ag/2,000, Cd/4,000, Sn/6,000, and Hg/4,000, respectively.

Example 1 Liebig Method How many grams of NaCN are present in a solution that is titrated just to a permanent turbidity with 26.05 ml of $AgNO_3$ solution containing 8.125 g of $AgNO_3$ per liter?

Solution

$$2CN^- + Ag^+ \longrightarrow Ag(CN)_2^-$$

The next drop of $AgNO_3$ gives a permanent precipitate of $Ag[Ag(CN)_2]$, which serves as the indicator for the above reaction.

$$Ag(CN)_2^- + Ag^+ \longrightarrow Ag[Ag(CN)_2] \qquad \text{indicator}$$

$$\text{Normality of } AgNO_3 = \frac{8.125}{169.9} = 0.04782$$

The milliequivalent weight of NaCN in this case is not NaCN/1,000, since *two* cyanide ions react with *one* silver ion in the titration. The milliequivalent weight of NaCN may be considered here to be 2NaCN/1,000. Then,

$$26.05 \times 0.04782 \times \frac{2NaCN}{1,000} = 0.1221 \text{ g NaCN} \qquad \textit{Ans.}$$

Or, from another point of view, if 26.05 ml is necessary to form the complex ion as shown above, then *twice* that amount is necessary to precipitate the cyanide completely:

$$2CN^- + 2Ag^+ \longrightarrow Ag[Ag(CN)_2]$$

Therefore,

$$2 \times 26.05 \times 0.04782 \times \frac{NaCN}{1,000} = 0.1221 \text{ g NaCN} \qquad \textit{Ans.}$$

Example 2   Combined Liebig and Volhard Methods   A solution contains KCN and KCl. It is titrated with 0.1000 N $AgNO_3$ to a faint turbidity, requiring 15.00 ml. Then 32.10 ml more of the $AgNO_3$ is added and the precipitates of $Ag[Ag(CN)_2]$ and AgCl are filtered off. The filtrate requires 7.20 ml of 0.08333 N KCNS to give a red color with ferric indicator. How many grams of KCN and of KCl are present in the original solution?

Solution

$$15.00 \times 0.1000 \times \frac{KCN}{500} = 0.1954 \text{ g KCN} \qquad \textit{Ans.}$$

Total vol. $AgNO_3$ added $= 15.00 + 32.10 = 47.10$ ml

$AgNO_3$ required to ppt. KCN completely as

$$Ag[Ag(CN)_2] = 2 \times 15.00 = 30.00 \text{ ml}$$

$47.10 - 30.00 = 17.10$ ml $AgNO_3$ reacting with KCl and giving excess

$$[(17.10 \times 0.1000) - (7.20 \times 0.08333)] \times \frac{KCl}{1,000} = 0.08276 \text{ g KCl} \qquad \textit{Ans.}$$

Example 3   Volumetric Nickel   How many grams of Ni are contained in an ammoniacal solution that is treated with 49.80 ml of KCN solution (0.007814 g/ml) and the excess KCN titrated with 5.91 ml of 0.1000 N $AgNO_3$, KI being used as an indicator?

Solution   The essential reactions are

$$Ni(NH_3)_6^{++} + 4CN^- + 6H_2O \longrightarrow Ni(CN)_4^= + 6NH_4OH$$
$$2CN^- + Ag^+ \longrightarrow Ag(CN)_2^-$$

Unlike the Liebig method above, the formation of $Ag[Ag(CN)_2]$ cannot be used as an indicator, since this salt is soluble in NH_4OH.   Instead, excess Ag^+ is indicated by the formation of AgI which is insoluble in NH_4OH.

$$\text{Normality of KCN soln.} = \frac{0.007814}{KCN/1,000} = 0.1200$$

$$5.91 \text{ ml AgNO}_3 \simeq 5.91 \times \frac{0.1000}{0.1200} \times 2 = 9.85 \text{ ml KCN soln.}$$

(see Example 1)

Net vol. of KCN = 49.80 − 9.85 = 39.95 ml

$$39.95 \times 0.1200 \times \frac{Ni}{4,000} = 0.07036 \text{ g Ni} \qquad Ans.$$

Example 4   Volumetric Zinc   A volumetric method for zinc consists of titrating it in acid solution with a standard solution of $K_4Fe(CN)_6$.   The reaction takes place in two steps.   The net reaction is indicated by the equation

$$3Zn^{++} + 2Fe(CN)_6^{4-} + 2K^+ \longrightarrow K_2Zn_3[Fe(CN)_6]_2$$

Ferric ions or uranyl ions are used to indicate the completion of the reaction (by forming a highly colored insoluble ferrocyanide).   If 15.5 ml of a solution of $K_4Fe(CN)_6$ that is 0.100 N as a potassium salt is used in a given titration, what weight of zinc is shown to be present?

Solution

1 f. wt. of $K_4Fe(CN)_6$ as a salt = 4 g atoms H^+

Therefore each g atom $Zn^{++} \simeq \frac{8}{3}$ g atoms H^+.

$$15.5 \times 0.100 \times \frac{3Zn}{8,000} = 0.380 \text{ g Zn} \qquad Ans.$$

14-2   Organic Chelating Reagents

The organic chelating reagents are quite different from the complex-forming ions referred to in Sec. 14-1.   The term *chelate* used above refers to a specific type of complex, namely, one that has heterocyclic rings which are formed from a metal ion and at least two functional groups in a single ligand or electron-pair donating molecule. The ligand molecule is then referred to as being multidendate, as opposed to the unidendate ligands, such as ammonia, cyanide, or halide, discussed earlier. Multidendate ligands may have as few as two coordinating functional groups or sites or as many as eight. Two frequently encountered examples of multidendate ligands are "trien" (triethylenetetramine) which is quadridendate and EDTA (ethylenediaminetetraacetic acid or ethylenedinitrilotetraacetic acid) which is sexadendate. Their structural formulas are as follows:

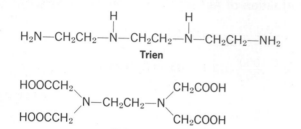

Most of the following discussion will be concerned with EDTA, though many of the generalizations also apply to other organic chelating agents. EDTA has four acidic groups capable of ionization, with $pK_{a_1} = 1.99$, $pK_{a_2} = 2.67$, $pK_{a_3} = 6.16$, and $pK_{a_4} = 10.26$. In order to make notation easier, it has been common practice to refer to EDTA and its four ions as H_4Y, H_3Y^-, $H_2Y^=$, HY^{3-}, and Y^{4-}. The specific form of EDTA used in a titration, therefore, depends on the pH value of the solution, and the overall reaction depends also on the metal ion involved. Several representative reactions are given below:

$$M^{++} + H_2Y^= \rightleftharpoons MY^= + 2H^+$$
$$M^{++} + H_3Y^- \rightleftharpoons MY^= + 3H^+$$
$$M^{3+} + H_2Y^= \rightleftharpoons MY^- + 2H^+$$
$$M^{3+} + H_3Y^- \rightleftharpoons MY^- + 3H^+$$

It is obvious from the above that the stability of a chelate depends on the pH value, since hydrogen ions are also competing for the ligand sites, and on the ion charge.

Titrations with EDTA and many other organic ligands have become very common and of great practical value, because of the stability of the chelates, ease of use, and wide versatility (almost all metals can be analyzed by some type of EDTA titration). Though most metals are analyzed by EDTA using either direct or back-titration procedures, indirect methods are also frequently used. For purposes of end-point determination, certain indicators such as Erichrome Black T, calmagite, and PAN [1-(2-pyridylazo)-2-naphthol] can be used. The Hg–HgY= electrode can be used successfully for the potentiometric titration of most metals which can be titrated with EDTA. Since some of the EDTA complexes are colored, photometric titrations have also been used.

Although specific applications of EDTA titrations are very extensive, the application which has received the most attention has been the titration of water to determine its hardness. Usually the combined Ca^{++} and Mg^{++} are titrated, and Erichrome Black T and calmagite have been used as indicators. The reactions associated with this titration are particularly interesting, as they give an indication of the manner in which EDTA titrations can be adjusted to serve a specific purpose.

Calcium forms a stronger complex with EDTA than does magnesium. Magnesium forms a stronger complex with the weak-acid indicator, Erichrome Black T, than does calcium. The predominant form of the indicator at the pH used for water analysis is $H_2In=$, which is blue in color. The magnesium complex with the indicator, $MgIn^-$, is red.

If a solution containing only calcium ions were to be titrated with EDTA (actually $H_2Y=$) in the presence of Erichrome Black T, no appreciable color change would be observed. In the presence of a small amount of magnesium ions, however, a sharp color change from red to blue will occur at the end point. The detailed changes taking place in this case are indicated in the next paragraph.

Initially, we have Ca^{++}, Mg^{++}, and $HIn=$ to give Ca^{++} and $MgIn^-$ (red). As $H_2Y=$ is added, $CaY=$ forms first and the red $MgIn^-$ remains. As the end point is approached, all the Ca^{++} is chelated as $CaY=$, some $MgY=$ is formed in preference to $MgIn^-$, and the released In^{3-} forms $HIn=$ (blue). At the end point, all the Ca^{++} and Mg^{++} are chelated, the indicator exists solely as $HIn=$, and the solution is blue.

In order to be certain that magnesium is present during the titration, a small quantity of Mg^{++} is usually added to the titrant.

PROBLEMS

*14-1. How many ml of 0.1000 N $AgNO_3$ are required to titrate to a faint permanent turbidity a soln. contg. 10.00 millimoles of KCN?

*14-2. A soln. contg. KCN and KCl requires 20.0 ml of 0.100 N $AgNO_3$ soln. to titrate the KCN by the Liebig method. After the addition of 50.0 ml more of the $AgNO_3$ and filtering, the filtrate requires 16.0 ml of 0.125 N KCNS to give a color with ferric ions. Calculate the no. of millimoles of KCN and of KCl in the original soln.

*14-3.   A sample consists of 80.00% KCN, 15.00% KCl, and 5.00% K_2SO_4.   (a) A 0.5000-g sample would require how many ml of 0.1000 M $AgNO_3$ for titration to a permanent turbidity?   (b) If 80.00 ml more of the $AgNO_3$ is added, how many ml of 0.2000 M KCNS would be required to complete the titration?

*14-4.   A powder contg. KCN, KCNS, and inert material weighs 1.2000 g, and the soln. of it requires 23.81 ml of 0.08333 N $AgNO_3$ to titrate the KCN by the Liebig method.   A 50-ml pipetful of the $AgNO_3$ soln. is then added, and the pptd. Ag[Ag(CN)$_2$] and AgCNS are filtered off.   The filtrate requires 10.12 ml of 0.09090 N KCNS for the excess Ag^+ (ferric alum indicator).   Calculate the percentage of KCN and of KCNS in the powder.

*14-5.   Zinc can be determined by direct titration with standard $K_4Fe(CN)_6$ (see Sec. 14-1, Example 4).   If the $K_4Fe(CN)_6$ is 0.1000 N as a potassium salt, what is the value of each ml of it in terms of g of Zn?   If the $K_4Fe(CN)_6$ were 0.1000 N as a reducing agent (in reactions where it is oxidized to ferricyanide), what would be the value of 1.000 ml of it in terms of g of Zn?

*14-6.   Find the wts. of dissolved KCl, KCN, and KCNS in 500 ml of a soln. that analyzed as follows: 30.0 ml of the soln. when titrated for KCN by the Liebig method reacted with 9.57 ml of the $AgNO_3$ soln. (15.0 g/liter).   Then 75.0 ml more of the $AgNO_3$ soln. was added, and the soln. was filtered.   The filtrate contained enough Ag^+ to react with 9.50 ml of 0.100 N KCNS.   The ppt. was heated with HNO_3 to decompose the Ag[Ag(CN)$_2$] and AgCNS, the H_2SO_4 formed was pptd. with $Ba(NO_3)_2$, and the soln. then reacted with 58.4 ml of 0.100 N KCNS.

*14-7.   A soln. contg. $\frac{1}{2}$ millimole of KCl, $\frac{1}{3}$ millimole of KCN, and $\frac{1}{4}$ millimole of KCNS is titrated with 0.0667 M $AgNO_3$ to a faint turbidity, requiring A ml.   Then enough more of the $AgNO_3$ is added to make a total of 30.00 ml of the $AgNO_3$.   The ppt. is filtered off, and the filtrate requires B ml of 0.100 M KCNS to give a red color with ferric ions.   The ppt. is decomposed with concd. HNO_3, and the soln. is diluted, leaving only AgCl as a residue.   The HNO_3 soln. contg. the Ag^+ from the Ag[Ag(CN)$_2$] and AgCNS is titrated with 0.100 M KCNS, requiring C ml.   What are the values of A, B, and C?

*14-8.   An ore contains 10.11% Ni.   A 0.5000-g sample is decomposed, and the ammoniacal soln. is treated with 60.00 ml of 0.08333 M KCN soln.   A little KI is added as an indicator, and the soln. is titrated with 0.06667 M $AgNO_3$ to a faint turbidity.   What vol. of the $AgNO_3$ is required?

*14-9.   Find the percentage of Ni in an ore if the sample weighs 0.3000 g and after treating the ammoniacal soln. with 20.00 ml of KCN (31.2 g/liter) the vol. of $AgNO_3$ soln. (25.5 g/liter) required to give a turbidity with KI indicator is 14.00 ml.

*14-10.   A standard soln. of EDTA is prepared, and by titration each ml is found to complex with the Mg in 10.0 ml of a soln. contg. 0.300 g of $MgCl_2$ per liter.   A 100-ml pipetful of a certain well water is found to require 8.60 ml of the standard EDTA.   With the knowledge that the conventional method of expressing water hardness is in terms of p.p.m. of $CaCO_3$ regardless of the nature of the cations and anions actually present, what is the hardness of the well water?

*14-11.   A sample consisting of 0.5000 g of $CaCO_3$ and 0.3000 g of $MgCl_2$ was dissolved in HCl, a buffer was added, and the soln. was diluted to 2.000 liters.   It was then titrated with EDTA.   What was the hardness of the water?   (See preceding problem.)

*14-12.   If 50.00 ml of the soln. in Prob. 14-11 was titrated with an EDTA soln. prepared by dissolving 3.720 g of $Na_2H_2Y \cdot 2H_2O$ in 1.000 liter of water, how many ml would be required?

*14-13. Pb^{++} ions form a stronger complex with EDTA than do Mg^{++} ions, but the pH value required for the reaction is so high that the lead would normally ppt. To a 25.00-ml aq. sample is added 50.00 ml of 0.0100 M EDTA.   The pH is adjusted and the excess EDTA is back-titrated with 1.000 $\times$ 10^{-2} M Mg^{++}, requiring 14.7 ml.   Calculate the molar concn. of Pb in the sample.

*14-14.   A 0.5000-g sample contg. traces of zinc is dissolved in 100 ml of acid. Then 25.00 ml of the acid soln. is buffered and requires 10.25 ml of 1.000 $\times$ 10^{-2} M EDTA for titration to a potentiometric end point.   Calculate the percentage by wt. of Zn in the sample.

*14-15.   A titrimetric method for the detn. of zirconium using EDTA and a back-titration procedure has been described by Su [*Anal. Chem.*, **37**, 1067 (1965)].   The zirconium sample weighing 1.7080 g was fused and the zirconium was finally pptd. with mandelic acid.   The ppt. was placed in a beaker to which was added acid and 20.00 ml of EDTA.   The soln. was heated to dissolve the ppt. and form the complex, the pH was adjusted, and the excess EDTA was back-titrated with a standard Zn^{++} soln., requiring 17.85 ml.   Calculate the percentage by wt. of ZrO_2 in the sample.   The concn. of the EDTA soln. was 0.0521 M, the Zn^{++} soln. was 0.0222 M, and xylenol orange was used as the indicator.

*14-16.   As discussed in the text, calcium forms a stronger complex with EDTA than does magnesium.   A soln. contains an unknown amt. of calcium.   To 25.00 ml of this soln. is added a buffer and 20.00 ml of a soln. which is 0.0100 M in $H_2Y=$ and 0.0100 M in Mg^{++}.   The substitution reaction liberates Mg ions which are then back-titrated with 27.24 ml of a 0.02472 M soln. of $H_2Y=$.   Calculate the molar concn. of calcium in the unknown soln.

14-17.   What wt. of KCN is equiv. to 30.00 ml of $AgNO_3$ soln. contg. 15.00 g/liter (*a*) by the Volhard method for cyanide and (*b*) by the Liebig method?

14-18.   A sample contg. KCN weighs 1.000 g and requires 24.00 ml of 0.08333 N $AgNO_3$ soln. to obtain a permanent turbidity.   (*a*) What is the percentage of KCN? (*b*) If the sample also contains 10.00% KCl, what vol. of the $AgNO_3$ soln. would be required to ppt. the cyanide and chloride completely?

14-19.   A soln. contains dissolved KCl, KCNS, and KCN.   It is titrated to a faint turbidity of the Liebig method for cyanide, and 25.00 ml of 0.0880 N $AgNO_3$ is required.   A 100-ml pipetful of the $AgNO_3$ is then added, and the soln. is filtered. The excess Ag^+ in the filtrate requires 50.4 ml of 0.0833 N KCNS soln.   The ppt. of the three Ag salts is boiled with HNO_3, which decomposes the $Ag[Ag(CN)_2]$ and

AgCNS and leaves the AgCl, which is filtered off. The filtrate requires 65.0 ml of the above KCNS soln. for the Ag$^+$. Find the no. of mg of KCN, KCl, and KCNS in the original soln.

14-20. A mixt. consisting entirely of KCNS, KCN, and KCl weighs 0.687 g. In soln. it reacts with 30.0 ml of 0.0500 N AgNO$_3$ in the Liebig titration and with 150 ml more in the Volhard titration. Find the percentage composition of the original mixt.

14-21. What is the percentage of Ni in an ore if the ammoniacal soln. of a 1.00-g sample is treated with 50.0 millimoles of KCN and the excess CN$^-$ requires 50.0 ml of 0.100 M AgNO$_3$ soln. to obtain a turbidity with KI indicator?

14-22. The Ni in a sample of ore weighing 0.9000 g is converted to the NH$_3$ complex, and to the soln. is added 0.25 ml of a soln. contg. 20.00 g of AgNO$_3$ per liter. A little KI is also added to serve as indicator. By adding two 10-ml pipetfuls of KCN soln. (13.00 g KCN per liter), the turbidity due to the AgI is found to have disappeared, but it just reappears on adding 1.50 ml more of the AgNO$_3$. Find the percentage of Ni in the ore.

14-23. If each ml of a soln. of KCN is equiv. to 0.01000 g of Ag by the Liebig method, how many g of Cu are equiv. to each ml of the KCN in the titration represented by the equation 2Cu(NH$_3$)$_4^{++}$ + 7CN$^-$ + H$_2$O $\longrightarrow$ 2Cu(CN)$_3^-$ + CNO$^-$ + 6NH$_3$ + 2NH$_4^+$?

14-24. If hypothetical substance A can be titrated with thiosulfate according to the equation 3A + 5S$_2$O$_3^=$ $\longrightarrow$ complex ion + $\cdots$, express in terms of the f. wt. of A the no. of g of A equiv. to 10.0 ml of a soln. of Na$_2$S$_2$O$_3$ that is (a) 0.100 N as a sodium salt, (b) 0.100 N as an iodimetric reducing agent.

14-25. Solve Prob. 14-10 under the assumption that each ml of the EDTA is equivalent to 0.0100 g of MgSO$_4 \cdot$7H$_2$O, that a 200-ml pipetful of a sample of lake water is taken for analysis, that 4.20 ml of the EDTA is required, and that the water hardness is to be expressed in terms of grains of CaCO$_3$ per gal. Consult an appropriate reference book for the necessary conversion factors.

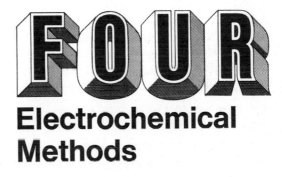

FOUR

Electrochemical Methods

Electrolytic Methods

15-1 Electrolysis

In analytical chemistry the term *electrolysis* is applied to a reaction in which a chemical change is caused to take place by the passage of a current through a solution of an electrolyte. Oxidation (loss of electrons) takes place at the anode; reduction (gain of electrons) takes place at the cathode. Typical electrolytic reactions in analytical chemistry are shown in Table 3.

Table 3   Some electrolysis reactions

		Per faraday		
		Moles of gas	Moles deposit	Equivalents change in H^+
(1)	Cathode: $Cu^{++} + 2e \longrightarrow Cu$	$\frac{1}{4}$	$\frac{1}{2}$	$+1$
(2)	Anode: $H_2O \longrightarrow \frac{1}{2}O_2 + 2H^+ + 2e$			
(3)	Cathode: $2H^+ + 2e \longrightarrow H_2$	$\frac{1}{2} + \frac{1}{4}$	0	0
(4)	Anode: $H_2O \longrightarrow \frac{1}{2}O_2 + 2H^+ + 2e$			
(5)	Cathode: $2H^+ + 2e \longrightarrow H_2$	$\frac{1}{2}$	$\frac{1}{2}$	$+1$
(6)	Anode: $Pb^{++} + 2H_2O \longrightarrow PbO_2 + 4H^+ + 2e$			
(7)	Cathode: $Cu^{++} + 2e \longrightarrow Cu$	0	$\frac{1}{2} + \frac{1}{2}$	$+2$
(8)	Anode: $Pb^{++} + 2H_2O \longrightarrow PbO_2 + 4H^+ + 2e$			
(9)	Cathode: $NO_3^- + 10H^+ + 8e \longrightarrow NH_4^+ + 3H_2O$	$\frac{1}{4}$	0	$-\frac{1}{4}$
(10)	Anode: $4H_2O \longrightarrow 2O_2 + 8H^+ + 8e$			

15-2 Ohm's Law

Ohm's law expresses the numerical relationship among three fundamental electrical quantities, namely, (1) electromotive force E (measured in volts), (2) current strength I (measured in amperes), and (3) resistance R (measured in ohms). The relationship is

$$E = IR$$

15-3   Faraday's Laws

Although electrochemical methods are used in analytical chemistry to effect various separations and to bring about changes in state of oxidation, this and the following sections are devoted primarily to the determination of metals by electrodeposition. An electric current is passed, under suitable conditions, through a solution of the salt of a metal, and the metal itself is gradually deposited, usually in the elementary condition, upon one of the electrodes. The calculation of the amount of metal which will be deposited at the end of a given time is founded on Faraday's laws which may be stated as follows:

1. *The mass of any substance deposited at an electrode is proportional to the quantity of electricity which passes through the solution.*
2. *The amounts of different substances liberated at the electrodes by the passage of the same quantity of electricity are proportional to the equivalent weights of the substances.*

Current strength is expressed in terms of the *ampere*, which is defined as that strength of current which, when passed through a solution of silver nitrate under certain standard conditions, will deposit silver at the rate of 0.001118 g/sec.

Quantities of electricity are expressed in terms of the *coulomb*, which is defined as that quantity of electricity which passes through a conductor in one second when the current is one ampere. That is,

$$Q = It$$

where Q = quantity of electricity, coul
I = current strength, amp
t = time, sec

From Faraday's first law, it follows that the weight of a substance liberated from solution by electrolysis during a given time will be directly proportional to the current strength and under a given amperage will be directly proportional to the time.

Faraday's second law states that the weights of different substances liberated at the electrodes by a given quantity of electricity are proportional to the respective equivalent weights. The equivalent weight of a substance in this case is the atomic or molecular weight divided by the electron change per atom or mole occurring at the electrode. It is found by experiment that 96,500 coul are required to liberate a gram-equivalent weight (equivalent weight in grams) of any substance. Thus, 96,500 coul of electricity are capable of depositing at the cathode

$$\frac{Ag}{1} = 107.87 \text{ g of silver from a solution of a silver salt}$$

$$\frac{Fe}{2} = 27.92 \text{ g of iron from a solution of a ferrous salt}$$

$$\frac{Au}{3} = 65.73 \text{ g of gold from a solution of an auric salt}$$

The value 96,500 coul is therefore a unit of quantity in electrochemical measurements, and in that capacity it is called a *faraday*. One faraday = 96,500 coul = 96,500 amp-sec = 26.81 amp-hr. It is also equivalent to 6.023×10^{23} electrons (Avogadro's number).

The above reactions may be expressed by equations, as follows:

(a) $Ag^+ + e \longrightarrow Ag$
(b) $Fe^{++} + 2e \longrightarrow Fe$
(c) $AuCl_4^- + 3e \longrightarrow Au + 4Cl^-$

where the symbol e represents the electron, or unit of negative electricity. If the equations are considered as representing gram atomic or gram molecular ratios, then the symbol represents the faraday. That is, 1, 2, and 3 faradays are required to deposit a gram atomic weight of metal from a solution of silver salt, ferrous salt, and auric salt, respectively.

Example 1   How many grams of copper will be deposited in 3.00 hr by a current of 4.00 amp, on the assumption that no other reactions take place at the cathode?

Solution

$t = 3.00 \times 3,600 = 10,800 \text{ sec}$

No. of coul = $It = 4.00 \times 10,800 = 43,200$

1 faraday would deposit $\dfrac{Cu^{++}}{2} = 31.8$ g of copper

43,200 coul would deposit $\dfrac{43,200}{96,500} \times 31.8 = 14.2$ g Cu   *Ans.*

Faraday's laws apply to each electrode. The pairs of reactions indicated in Table 3 take place at the two electrodes during the electrolysis of certain combinations of Cu^{++}, Pb^{++}, H^+, and NO_3^-.

In the electrolysis of a solution of copper sulfate, Eqs. (1) and (2), Table 3, apply, and it is seen that the passage of 1 faraday (e.g., a current of 1 amp for 96,500 sec) is capable of causing the deposition of $\frac{1}{2}$ mole of copper ($= 31.8$ g) at the cathode and at the same time will liberate $\frac{1}{4}$ mole of oxygen (= 8.00 g) at the anode. Under standard conditions this volume of oxygen occupies $\frac{22.4}{4} = 5.60$ liters. Also, per faraday, the acidity of the solution increases by 1 g equiv. ($\approx$ 1 mole of HNO_3, $\approx \frac{1}{2}$ mole of H_2SO_4, etc.). In fact, it is possible to prepare a solution suitable for use in acidimetry as a standard by electrolyzing a neutral solution of $CuSO_4$ and determining the acid concentration of the resulting solution from the weight of metallic copper deposited.

Similarly Table 3 shows the quantitative effects resulting from the electrolysis of a dilute sulfuric acid solution [Eqs. (3) and (4)], from the electrolysis of an acid solution of Pb^{++} [Eqs. (5) and (6)], and from the electrolysis of a solution containing both Cu^{++} and Pb^{++} [Eqs. (7) and (8)].

A typical brass is an alloy of about 60% Cu, about 40% Zn, and about 0.5% Pb. If such an alloy is dissolved in nitric acid and the solution electrolyzed, then, theoretically at least, the copper and lead would first deposit simultaneously as indicated by Eqs. (7) and (8). When all the lead has been deposited, the remaining copper would plate out as indicated by Eqs. (1) and (2). Finally water would be decomposed as indicated by Eqs. (3) and (4). Zinc ions would be unaffected since their deposition potential is greater than the potential required for the reduction of hydrogen ions.

Example 2   A neutral solution containing 0.4000 g of copper is electrolyzed until all the copper is plated out, and the electrolysis is continued 7 min longer. The volume of the solution is kept at 100 ml, and the current strength is maintained at an average of 1.20 amp. On the basis of 100% current efficiency (a) how long did it take for the copper to deposit, (b) what total volume of gas was evolved during the entire electrolysis, (c) what was the acidity of the solution at the end of the electrolysis?

Solution

(a) 1 faraday deposits $\frac{Cu}{2} = 31.8$ g Cu

No. of faradays to deposit 0.4000 g Cu $= \frac{0.4000}{31.8} = 0.0126$

Time required $= \frac{0.0126 \times 96,500}{1.20} = 1,013$ sec $= 16.9$ min   *Ans.*

(b) During deposition of Cu, each faraday (i.e., each $\frac{1}{2}$ mole Cu) corresponds to $\frac{1}{4}$ mole O_2.

Moles O_2 evolved $= 0.0126 \times \frac{1}{4} = 0.00315$

After Cu deposited, no. of faradays passed $= \dfrac{7 \times 60 \times 1.20}{96,500} = 0.00522.$

Each faraday evolves $\frac{1}{2}$ mole H_2 and $\frac{1}{4}$ mole O_2

    Moles $H_2 + O_2$ evolved $= 0.00522 \times \frac{3}{4} = 0.00392$
    Total gas evolved $= 0.00315 + 0.00392 = 0.00707$ mole   *Ans.*

    (*c*) During Cu deposition, each faraday corresponds to a gain of 1 g atom of H^+.

    After Cu deposition, acidity does not change.
    Gain in acidity $= 0.0126$ g equiv. of H^+ *Ans.*
    (Resulting solution is $10 \times 0.01258 = 0.1258$ *N* as an acid.)

In the above calculations involving Faraday's second law, it has been assumed that all the current serves for the decomposition of the substance in question; that is, 100% current efficiency has been assumed. In actual analyses, this is usually not the case. Not only will the electrolysis of an acid solution of a copper salt cause the deposition of copper at the cathode, but small amounts of hydrogen will usually be given off at the same electrode before the copper has all plated out unless a properly controlled potential is used for the deposition. In such cases, the *sum* of the weights of the products discharged at each electrode exactly corresponds to the law. That is, in the copper electrolysis, for each faraday of electricity passed, the number of gram equivalent weights of copper deposited added to the number of gram equivalent weights of hydrogen liberated will be unity.

Other effects may complicate electrolysis calculations. For example, when a nitric acid solution of an alloy is electrolyzed, it is usually found that reduction of nitrate ions takes place to some extent at the cathode with the formation of such products as nitrous acid, ammonium ions, nitrogen gas, etc. [see Eqs. (9) and (10) in Table 3].

In problems of electroanalysis in this book, 100% current efficiency is to be assumed unless otherwise specified. In addition, a constant current during the time period of the electrolysis should be assumed.

Other electrical units which are frequently used in electrochemical computations are as follows:

The *ohm R* is the unit of resistance.

The *volt E* is the unit of electromotive force or electrical pressure. Its relation to the ampere and ohm is expressed by Ohm's law:

$$E = IR$$

The *joule J* is the unit of work. It is represented by the energy expended in 1 sec by a current of 1 amp against a resistance of 1 ohm.

$$J = EIt = EQ$$

The *watt* W is the unit of power. It is represented by the work done at the rate of 1 joule/sec.

$$W = EI$$
$$J = Wt$$

15-4   Decomposition Potentials

The electrode potentials existing between metals and their ions and the effect of concentration on these potentials were considered in the discussions of Secs. 6-1, 6-2, and 6-7, and these sections should be reviewed at this point.

The *decomposition potential* of an electrolyte is the lowest emf that must be applied in order to bring about the continuous electrode reaction.

If a nitric or sulfuric acid solution of copper is electrolyzed between platinum electrodes, the copper plates out on the cathode.

$$Cu^{++} + 2e \longrightarrow Cu$$

Water is decomposed at the anode.

$$H_2O \longrightarrow \tfrac{1}{2}O_2 + 2H^+ + 2e$$

As a result, there is produced a voltaic cell of the type

$$Cu|Cu^{++}\|2H^+, \tfrac{1}{2}O_2|Pt$$

This cell exerts a "back emf" which opposes the applied voltage and which can be calculated from the formula

$$E = E_1 - E_2$$
$$= \left(E^0_{Cu^{++},Cu} + \frac{0.0591}{2} \log [Cu^{++}]\right) - \left(E^0_{H_2O,H_2} + \frac{0.0591}{2} \log [H^+]^2 [press. O_2]^{1/2}\right)$$

In order to continue the electrolysis, a voltage at least equal to this must be applied. In addition, enough voltage to overcome the simple ohmic resistance of the solution is necessary, and in cases where polarization effects occur, the emf must be still further increased.

15-5   Polarization and Overpotential

The term *polarization* is used to indicate a condition at an electrode which causes the potential of the corresponding half-cell to differ from the theoretical value as calculated from the Nernst equation for the prevailing concentrations in the solution. It can be attributed to a counter-electromotive force brought about either by the accumulation at the electrode of products of the reaction or by the exhaustion at the electrode of substances necessary for the reaction.   When such conditions exist, in order to cause electrodeposition to take place, it is necessary to apply a voltage somewhat greater than that calculated from the back emf and the ohmic resistance of the solution.   This excess potential is called *overpotential* (or *overvoltage*).

Decomposition potential = back emf + IR + overpotential

The magnitude of overpotential depends on such factors as current density (amperes per square centimeter of electrode surface), concentration, temperature, nature of substance liberated, and character of the electrodes.   Overpotentials are usually negative ($-$) for reductions and positive ($+$) for oxidations.   Overpotentials are relatively low with reversible electrode reactions, such as those occurring when metals are deposited; they are relatively high if the electrode reaction is irreversible, which is frequently the case when a gas is liberated.   The overpotential is particularly large when a gas is liberated at an electrode composed of copper, nickel, zinc, or mercury.

15-6   Electrolytic Separations

If the difference between the decomposition potentials of two metals in solution is sufficiently great, it is usually possible to effect a separation of those metals by electrolytic means.   Thus, if a solution containing silver ions and cupric ions at moderate concentrations is electrolyzed under proper conditions, the silver plates out first, and the plating can be continued until the concentration of the remaining silver ions has been reduced to such a value that the decomposition potential is equal to that of the copper.   Any attempt to plate out the copper would cause simultaneous deposition of the remaining silver, but that amount of silver would be negligibly small.

Example 1   A solution is 0.0010 M in Cu^{++} and contains Ag^+ ions. Neglecting overpotential, what approximate value would the concentration of Ag^+ have to be before silver would deposit simultaneously with the copper in the electrolysis of the solution?   (The anode reaction is the oxidation of water.)

Solution

Standard potentials: Cu^{++}, Cu $+0.337$ volt

Ag^+, Ag $+0.799$ volt

$$+0.337 + \frac{0.0591}{2} \log 0.0010 = +0.799 + \frac{0.0591}{2} \log [Ag^+]$$

Solving,

$$\log [Ag^+] = -9.32$$

$$[Ag^+] = 4.8 \times 10^{-10} \qquad Ans.$$

Many other separations are possible. The separation of metals above hydrogen in the potential series from those below hydrogen is especially easy. In the electrolysis of an acid solution of brass (Cu + Zn), for example, essentially all the copper plates out at the cathode. After that, hydrogen ions are reduced to hydrogen gas, and no zinc ions can be reduced as long as the solution remains acidic.

Under certain conditions, however, zinc (and several other metals relatively low in the potential series) can be electrolyzed from solution. It is necessary to use an alkaline solution in such cases since the decomposition potential of the hydrogen is thereby lowered. The high overpotential for the evolution of hydrogen on the zinc electrode (that results from the plating of the zinc on the original platinum electrode) is a help in this process in that it permits the electrolytic reduction of zinc ions in only moderately alkaline solutions.

Example 2   What must be the pH value of a solution which is 2.0×10^{-4} M in Zn^{++} to allow deposition of the zinc? Assume the hydrogen overpotential on zinc to be 0.30 volt.

Solution

Standard potentials: Zn^{++}, Zn -0.763 volt

                              $H^+, \frac{1}{2}H_2$ 0.000 volt

$$-0.763 + \frac{0.0591}{2} \log (2.0 \times 10^{-4}) = 0.000 + \frac{0.0591}{2} \log [H^+] - 0.30$$

Solving,

$$\log [H^+] = \frac{-0.763 - 0.109 + 0.30}{0.0591} = -9.68$$

$$pH = -\log [H^+] = 9.68 \qquad Ans.$$

15-7   Controlled Potential Electrolysis

The electrolytic separation and analysis of metals having small differences in their standard potentials may sometimes be accomplished under conditions of controlled potential. In this process, a third electrode, acting as an auxiliary reference electrode, is used. The potential at the electrode on which the plating is occurring (the working electrode) may be measured with respect to the auxiliary reference electrode. Using this potential, it is possible to adjust the potential of the working electrode to a predetermined value, either manually or automatically. Controlled potential electrolysis can also be used for specific syntheses or to change the oxidation state of an electroactive compound.

The current flow in a controlled potential electrolysis will start at an initially high level and decrease in a manner indicated by the equations

$$i_t = i_0 10^{-kt}$$

$$i_0 = \frac{nFACD}{\delta}$$

where i_0 = initial current
i_t = current after time t
$k = 0.434\ DA/V\delta$, in min^{-1}, and depends on the electrode area A, the volume of the solution V, the diffusion layer thickness δ, and the diffusion coefficient D

It is frequently difficult to know when a separation is complete. In theory only, the current should fall to zero after all the electroactive species have reacted. For practical applications, the electrolysis is usually continued for a total of 10 half-times [one half-time equals the time required for the initial current (i_0) to decrease to one-half that value] or until the current has decreased to 0.1% of its initial value.

By integrating the current passed in a specific length of time and assuming 100% current efficiency, it is possible to calculate the concentration of an electroactive substance even if it is not deposited and subsequently weighed.

Example 1   Silver is to be separated by controlled potential deposition from a solution containing both copper(II) and silver(I). (*a*) At what value should the potential be set if the copper(II) concentration is $1.00 \times 10^{-3}\ M$? (*b*) How much time would be required to remove 99.9% of the silver from a solution 0.01 M in Ag(I) if $\delta = 1.0 \times 10^{-3}$ cm, $D = 5.0 \times 10^{-5}$ cm^2 sec^{-1}, $V = 200$ ml, and $A = 100$ cm^2?

Solution

$$\text{Cu}^{++} + 2e = \text{Cu}(s) \qquad E^0 = 0.337 \text{ volt}$$
$$\text{Ag}^+ + e = \text{Ag}(s) \qquad E^0 = 0.799 \text{ volt}$$

(*a*) Copper would start to plate out at a cathode potential of

$$E = 0.337 + \frac{0.0591}{2} \log 1.00 \times 10^{-3}$$

$$= 0.248 \text{ volt vs. SHE (standard hydrogen electrode)}$$

Silver deposition may be considered quantitatively complete when

$[Ag^+] = 1.00 \times 10^{-5}$ M; the cathode potential required to accomplish this would be

$$E = 0.799 + \frac{0.059}{1} \log 1.00 \times 10^{-5}$$

$$= 0.503 \text{ volt vs. SHE}$$

The cathode potential should therefore be set between 0.30 and 0.40 volt vs. SHE   *Ans.*

(b) $k = \dfrac{(0.434)(5.0 \times 10^{-5})(60)(100)}{(200)(1.00 \times 10^{-3})}$

$$= 6.52 \times 10^{-1} \text{ min}^{-1}$$

then

$$t_{1/2} = \frac{0.301}{k}$$

$$= 0.462 \text{ min}$$

For complete deposition, 10 half-times, or 4.62 min are required.   *Ans.*

PROBLEMS

(Assume 100% current efficiency unless otherwise specified.)

*15-1.   A 100-watt 110-volt incandescent lamp is connected in series with an electrolytic cell of negligible resistance.   What wt. of Cd could be deposited from soln. by the current in 30 min?

*15-2.   How many min will it take for a current of 0.500 amp to cause the deposition of 500 mg of Ag from KNO_3 soln. on the basis of 80.0% current efficiency?

*15-3.   (a) How many coul are required to deposit 0.1000 g of Co from a soln. of Co(II) salt?   (b) How many amp would be required to deposit that amt. in 20 min 20 sec?   (c) How many g of Pd would be deposited under identical conditions from a Pd(IV) soln.?

*15-4.   With a current at 8.00 volts, how much electrical energy is theoretically required to deposit (a) 0.100 g of Au, (b) 0.100 g of Hg, from solns. contg. these metals in their higher state of oxidation?

*15-5.   Using a rotating electrode, it was found that with a current of 17.0 amp at a potential of 10.0 volts, 0.200 g of Pt could be deposited in 5.00 min from a soln. of K_2PtCl_6.   (a) How much electrical energy was expended per sec?   (b) What quantity of electricity was used?   (c) What was the current efficiency?

*15-6.   What quantity of electricity is required for (a) the electrolytic deposition of 1.196 g of PbO_2, (b) the liberation of 0.800 g of O_2 gas, (c) the liberation of 30.0 ml of Cl_2 (measured dry under standard conditions)?

*15-7.   For how long must a current of 1.00 amp be passed through a dil. soln. of H_2SO_4 in order to liberate a total vol. of 600 ml of gas when measured dry and under standard conditions?

*15-8.   Crystals of $CuSO_4 \cdot 5H_2O$ are dissolved in H_2O, and the soln. is electrolyzed until colorless.   The cathode gains 0.4290 g in wt.   If the soln. is now diluted to 250 ml, (a) what is its molar concn. in H_2SO_4 and (b) what is the acid normality of the soln.?

*15-9.   What would be the net gain or loss in g equivs. of H^+ per faraday in the electrolysis of a soln. of HNO_3 in which 80% of the current goes to the simple decomposition of H_2O and 20% goes to the reaction involving the reduction of nitrate to N_2 at the cathode and the liberation of O_2 at the anode?

*15-10.   An alloy consists of 20.72% Pb and 79.28% Zn.   A sample weighing 1.000 g is dissolved in acid, and the soln. diluted to 1,000 ml.   A 100-ml pipetful is titrated with 0.1000 N NaOH and requires 30.00 ml to neutralize the acid present.   The remaining 900 ml is electrolyzed under 2.00 amp for 5.00 min, with the deposition of Pb as PbO_2.   (a) How many ml of gas (dry standard conditions) are evolved?   (b) If the vol. of the soln. after electrolysis is brought again to 900 ml, what would be the normality of the soln. in acid?

*15-11.   An average current of 0.5000 amp is passed through a dil. acid soln. of an alloy contg. 0.5000 g of Cu, 0.2000 g of Zn, and 0.1000 g of Pb.   Calculate the theoretical total gain in acidity in terms of moles of H_2SO_4 (a) at the end of the PbO_2 deposition at the anode, (b) at the end of the Cu deposition at the cathode, (c) after the current has been continued for 5.00 min longer.   (d) What vol. of gas (dry, standard conditions) has been evolved during the entire process?

*15-12.   A soln. is 0.0010 M in Ag^+ and contains auric ions (Au^{3+}).   Neglecting overpotential effects, at approx. how high a concn. of auric ions would the two metals deposit simultaneously on electrolysis?

*15-13.   What overpotential of hydrogen would allow Ni to be electrolyzed out of a soln. that is 0.010 M in Ni^{++} and 0.10 M in H^+?

*15-14.   A soln. is 0.10 M in Cd^{++} and 0.10 M in H^+.   (a) What is the difference between the potential of Cd^{++}—Cd and that of H^+—$\frac{1}{2}H_2$?   (b) To the soln. are added sufficient NH_3 and NH_4^+ to convert nearly all the Cd^{++} to $Cd(NH_3)_4^{++}$ and to make the soln. 0.10 M in free NH_3 and 0.60 M in NH_4^+.   Assuming the vol. of the soln. to be the same as before, what is the difference between the two potentials?

*15-15.   A 0.020 M aq. soln. of $CdSO_4$ in 1.0 M H_2SO_4 is to be electrolyzed between platinum electrodes.   To overcome the IR drop of the soln., 0.10 volt is required; the overpotential for oxygen evolution on platinum is 0.20 volt.   Assuming that the overpotential and IR drop remain const., calculate the applied potential required for electrolysis (a) initially, (b) after 90.0% deposition, (c) after 99.0% deposition and (d) after 99.9% deposition.   (e) What reaction is occurring at the anode?

*15-16.   For a particular cell, the overpotential for the evolution of hydrogen at a copper electrode is -0.65 volt; the overpotential for the evolution of oxygen from acid soln. on a platinum electrode is 0.40 volt.   If a 0.010 M aq. soln. of $CuSO_4$ at pH $= 1.0$ is to be electroanalyzed in this cell, (a) what potential must be applied to initiate copper deposition?   (b) What potential must be applied after all the copper is deposited in order to electrolyze the water?   (Assume the IR drop is negligible and that the partial pressure of O_2 is 0.20 atm.)

*15-17.   The metals in a mixt. of copper and silver (as nitrates), both at 0.010 M, are to be separated electrolytically from an acid soln. of pH $= 0.8$.   (a) What element will be deposited first?   (b) What applied potential should be selected to ensure max. deposition for the element named in (a) without depositing more than 0.1% of the other element?   (Assume negligible overpotentials and that the anode reaction is the oxidation of water.)

*15-18.   A 5.00×10^{-3} M soln. of zinc nitrate in dil. acid is to be analyzed electrogravimetrically at controlled potential.   Oxygen is produced at the anode assume its overpotential is 0).   (a) Will the pH of the soln. have any effect on the cell potential which must be applied?   If so, in what way?   (b) Assuming the proper buffering of the soln. (if required), calculate the cathode potential to be used to assure 99.9% electrodeposition.   (c) If $k = 1.50 \times 10^{-2}$ min^{-1}, how long would it take to deposit 50.0% of the zinc?

*15-19.   Under certain operating conditions for the analysis of 100-ml aliquots of a zinc soln. by controlled potential electrolysis, k is known to equal 4.0×10^{-1} min^{-1}. For a particular unknown soln., the current after 90 sec is found to be 0.50 amp. Calculate the concn. of zinc in the unknown soln.

15-20.   Assuming that the vol. of a soln. in an electrolytic cell is maintained at 125 ml and that the soln. contains initially 144 meq. of acid, 0.420 g of Cu, 0.200 g of Pb, and 0.260 g of Zn, find the normality in acid (a) after just enough current has passed to deposit all the Pb as PbO_2 and assuming no other reaction takes place at the anode during that time, (b) after all the Cu has deposited, (c) when the current of 1.80 amp has been continued 30 min longer.   (d) Find also the total vol. of gas (dry, standard conditions) evolved during the entire electrolysis.

15-21.   A current of 1.00 amp is passed for 1.00 hr through a satd. soln. of NaCl connected in series with a copper coulometer consisting of Cu electrodes dipping in a soln. of $CuSO_4$.   (a) Write equations for the anode and cathode reactions that take place in the two cells.   (b) Calculate no. of g of Cu deposited on the cathode of the coulometer, (c) no. of liters of Cl_2 gas evolved (dry, standard conditions), (d) no. of ml of 0.100 N HCl required to titrate one-tenth of the cathode portion of the NaCl cell.

15-22.   A copper coulometer, consisting of Cu electrodes dipping in a soln. of $CuSO_4$, is connected in series with a cell contg. a concd. soln. of NaCl.   After a current is passed through the two cells for 50.0 min, it is found that 0.636 g of Cu has been dissolved from the coulometer anode.   (a) What is the average amperage?   (b) How many g of $NaClO_3$ could be produced from the Cl_2 and NaOH formed ($3Cl_2 + 6OH^- \longrightarrow ClO_3^- + 5Cl^- + 3H_2O$)?

15-23.   What wt. of $CuSO_4 \cdot 5H_2O$ should be dissolved in H_2O so that after complete deposition of the Cu by electrolysis, a soln. is obtained that is equiv. to 100 ml of 0.100 N acid?

15-24.   Crystals of $CuSO_4 \cdot 5H_2O$ weighing 1.00 g are dissolved in H_2O, and the soln. electrolyzed at 1.30 amp for 20.0 min.   (*a*) What wt. of Cu is deposited? (*b*) What vol. of gas (dry, standard conditions) is liberated?   (*c*) If the resulting soln. is made up to 100.0 ml with H_2O, what is its normality as an acid?

15-25.   Crystals of $CuSO_4 \cdot 5H_2O$ are dissolved in H_2O, and the soln. electrolyzed with a current of 0.600 amp.   The electrolysis is continued for 5.00 min after all the Cu has been deposited, and it is found that a total vol. of 62.5 ml of gas measured dry at 18°C and 745 mm pressure has been evolved.   (*a*) What wt. of crystals was taken?   (Assume that all the Cu is deposited before H_2 is evolved.) (*b*) How many ml of 0.100 N NaOH will the resulting soln. neutralize?

15-26.   A soln. of brass in HNO_3 contains 1.10 g of Cu and 0.50 g of Zn and is 2.00 N in acid.   It is electrolyzed at 1.50 amp, and the vol. is kept at 100 ml. (*a*) If all the current goes to the deposition of Cu at the cathode, what is the acid normality of the soln. when all the Cu has just deposited?   (*b*) What is the acid normality of the soln. if the current is continued 20.0 min longer and 40.0% of it goes to the reduction of nitrate ions to ammonium ions?   (*c*) How long before the acid would be entirely destroyed?

15-27.   (*a*) Assuming that the electrolysis is discontinued as soon as the Cu has deposited, find the time required, the vol. of gas evolved (dry, standard conditions), and the gain in acidity in terms of millimoles of H^+ when 0.8000 g of brass (Cu + Pb + Zn) in dil. HNO_3 is electrolyzed.   Cathode gains 0.6365 g; anode gains 0.0240 g.   Current = 0.900 amp.   (*b*) Calculate also the percentage composition of the brass.

15-28.   Calculate the minimum concn. of Zn^{++} required for the deposition of Zn on a Zn electrode from a soln. having a pH value of 7.5, assuming the overpotential of hydrogen on zinc to be 0.50 volt.

16 Potentiometric Titrations

16-1 Potentiometric Acidimetric Titrations

In a potentiometric titration the principles discussed in Chap. 6 are applied in a practical way.   Suppose a solution of hydrochloric acid is to be titrated potentiometrically with a standard solution of sodium hydroxide.   Although seldom used in actual practice, a theoretically simple method is to use a hydrogen electrode (consisting of a platinum electrode coated with platinum black over which pure hydrogen gas is allowed to bubble) immersed in the solution.   This is one half-cell. The other half-cell is a calomel cell.   This consists of a tube containing metallic mercury in contact with a solution saturated with mercurous chloride and usually either 1 M with respect to chloride or saturated with potassium chloride.   The two half-cells are connected by means of a capillary tube filled with potassium chloride solution.   The whole cell (assuming 1 M chloride to be used) is expressed as follows:

$$Hg(l)\,|\,Cl^-\,(1\ M),\ \tfrac{1}{2}Hg_2Cl_2(s)\,\|\,H^+\,|\,\tfrac{1}{2}H_2(1\ atm),\ Pt$$

The mercury half-cell expressed here is sometimes referred to as the normal calomel half-cell or normal calomel "electrode." At 25°C its potential is $+0.285$ volt (see Table 13, Appendix). When saturated KCl is used (as is the case with most commercial instruments), the potential is $+0.246$ volt.

$$\tfrac{1}{2}Hg_2Cl_2(s) + e \rightleftharpoons Hg(l) + Cl^-(1\ M)$$

$$E_1^0 = +0.285$$

$$H^+ + e \rightleftharpoons \tfrac{1}{2}H_2(1\ atm)$$

$$E_2 = E_2^0 + \frac{0.0591}{1}\,\log\,\frac{[H^+]}{(\text{press. }H_2)^{1/2}}$$

$$= 0.00 + 0.0591\,\log\,[H^+]$$

$$E = E_1 - E_2 = 0.285 - 0.0591 \log [H^+]$$

$$- \log [H^+] = pH = \frac{E - 0.285}{0.0591}$$

By measurement of the emf of the cell, the pH value of the solution can be determined from this equation. Furthermore, the pH values of the solution can be determined in the same way at successive points in the titration, and these pH values plotted against corresponding buret readings. There is obtained a curve similar to curve AA in Fig. 5, Sec. 11-16. The point of maximum slope of the curve is found (by bisecting the nearly vertical part of the titration curve), and this is the equivalence point in the titration. Since the titration is independent of color indicators, the titration can be as successfully carried out in a dark-colored or turbid solution as in a colorless one. Plotting the results of potentiometric titrations of weak acids like acetic acid and weak bases like ammonia gives curves like CC and DD in Fig. 5, and the pH value at the equivalence point or at any other stage of the titration can be readily found in each case.

Example 1   If, at the equivalence point in the titration of a certain solution of acetic acid, pH = 9.10, what emf would be given by the cell made up of this solution in contact with a hydrogen electrode and a normal calomel half-cell?

Solution

$$pH = \frac{E - 0.285}{0.0591}$$

$$9.10 \times 0.0591 = E - 0.285$$

$$E = 0.823 \text{ volt} \qquad Ans.$$

The essential parts of a simple form of potentiometric titration apparatus of the type discussed above are shown in diagrammatic form in Fig. 9.

16-2   Quinhydrone Electrode

Several substitutes for the cumbersome hydrogen electrode are available. Among these substitutes is the quinhydrone electrode. This consists of a few crystals of quinhydrone added directly to the solution to be titrated. A platinum wire serves as the measuring or indicator electrode, and a calomel cell is used as the other half-cell.

When quinhydrone is added to water, a very small amount dissolves and dissociates into an equimolecular mixture of quinone, $C_6H_4O_2$, and hydroquinone, $C_6H_4O_2H_2$. These two substances are in equilibrium with each other, as shown by the equation

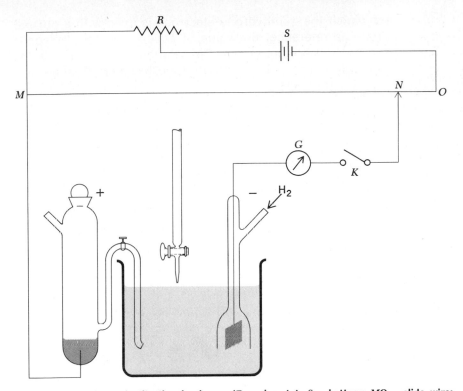

Fig. 9 Potentiometric titration hookup. (R = rheostat; S = battery; MO = slide wire; G = galvanometer; K = key. The position of N on the slide wire is adjusted until no current flows through the galvanometer. The distance MN is then a measure of the voltage.)

$$C_6H_4O_2 + 2H^+ + 2e \rightleftharpoons C_6H_4O_2H_2$$

The potential of this electrode is therefore a function of the hydrogen-ion concentration.

$$E = E^0 + \frac{0.0591}{2} \log \frac{[C_6H_4O_2][H^+]^2}{[C_6H_4O_2H_2]}$$

$$= E^0 + \frac{0.0591}{2} \log [H^+]^2$$

$$= +0.700 + 0.0591 \log [H^+] \qquad \text{at } 25°C$$

Using a normal calomel half-cell as the reference half-cell we have

$$E_1 = +0.700 + 0.0591 \log [H^+] = +0.700 - 0.0591 \text{ pH}$$

$$E_2 = +0.285$$

$$E = E_1 - E_2 = +0.415 + 0.0591 \log [H^+]$$

$$\text{pH} = -\log [H^+] = \frac{0.415 - E}{0.0591}$$

In a titration in which the quinhydrone electrode is used with a normal calomel electrode as reference, the value of E becomes zero at about pH $= 7$. Correct values are not obtained in solutions where pH > 9, for in such alkaline solutions the $1:1$ molarity ratio between quinone and hydroquinone no longer holds.

16-3   Antimony Electrode

Another substitute for the hydrogen gas electrode is the antimony electrode. This consists of metallic antimony coated with antimonous oxide. Although several equilibria are involved, the principal equilibrium can be considered to be the following:

$$\tfrac{1}{2}Sb_2O_3(s) + 3H^+ + 3e \rightleftharpoons Sb(s) + \tfrac{3}{2}H_2O$$

The electrode potential is therefore a function of the hydrogen-ion concentration and has been found to be

$$E = +0.145 + 0.0591 \log [H^+] = +0.145 - 0.0591 \text{ pH}$$

The antimony–antimony oxide electrode is not satisfactory in the presence of any substance that will either oxidize Sb_2O_3 or form complexes with it.

16-4   Glass Electrode

A glass electrode consists of a thin-walled bulb of special glass containing an electrode and a standard reference solution (usually silver–silver chloride and HCl solution). The exact mechanism of this electrode is not entirely understood, but hydrogen ions can apparently move in and out of the surface of the glass, and the glass bulb thus seems to behave like a semipermeable membrane between the reference solution and the solution being tested. Because of the high resistance of the bulb, electronic amplification of the current is necessary.

Owing to variations in composition of the glass used in the glass electrode and the slight changes that occur over long periods of time, a general formula for calculating pH values cannot be given for this type of electrode.

Most modern pH meters use glass electrodes and calomel cells in compact form and are of such construction that pH values and voltages can be read directly from the instrument.

16-5   Nonaqueous Acid-Base Titrations

The acidity or basicity in water of many organic compounds is too weak to permit titration, because water can also act as a weak acid or base. If such compounds are soluble in a nonaqueous solvent, it is frequently possible to titrate them in the same way that a strong acid or base is titrated in water.   The experimental system is usually composed of a glass electrode as the indicator electrode and a calomel or silver–silver chloride electrode as the reference half-cell.   Although many titrants have been used, perchloric acid and (as bases) sodium methoxide, sodium aminoethoxide, and quarternary bases have been most fre-quently employed.

In principle as well as in operation and in the type of data obtained, a nonaqueous titration is similar to a standard acidimetric titration.   It is usually very important to avoid the presence of water, which under these conditions behaves as another solute.   Special precautions must also be taken to make sure that the glass electrode is working properly. The use of the term pH under these conditions is somewhat misleading.

16-6   Potentiometric Redox Titrations

The hookup for the potentiometric titration of a reducing or oxidizing agent is similar to that of an acidimetric titration except that a platinum wire serves as the electrode.   A calomel half-cell is used as the second-ary half-cell.

Suppose a solution of ferrous sulfate is titrated with a standard solution of ceric sulfate ($Fe^{++} + Ce^{4+} \longrightarrow Fe^{3+} + Ce^{3+}$).*   At all times during the titration, there is an equilibrium between ferric and ferrous ions ($Fe^{3+} + e \rightleftharpoons Fe^{++}$) and between ceric and cerous ions ($Ce^{4+} + e \rightleftharpoons Ce^{3+}$).   Before the equivalence point is reached, the more easily calculated redox ratios are those between ferric and ferrous ions; during this part of the titration, the cell can be represented by

$$Pt\,|\,Fe^{3+},\ Fe^{++}\,\|\,Cl^-(1\ M),\ \tfrac{1}{2}Hg_2Cl_2(s)\,|\,Hg(l)$$

$$E = E_1 - E_2$$

$$= \left(+0.771 + \frac{0.0591}{1} \log \frac{[Fe^{3+}]}{[Fe^{++}]}\right) - (+0.285)$$

$$= 0.486 + 0.0591 \log \frac{[Fe^{3+}]}{[Fe^{++}]}$$

Beyond the equivalence point, the more easily calculated ratios are those existing between ceric and cerous ions; during this part of the titration, the cell can be represented by

$$Pt\,|\,Ce^{4+},\ Ce^{3+}\,\|\,Cl\ (1\ M),\ \tfrac{1}{2}Hg_2Cl_2(s)\,|\,Hg(l)$$

---

* The possibility of the formation of complex ions is not considered in this discussion.   See Sec. 6-3.

$$E = E_1 - E_2$$

$$= \left(+1.61 + \frac{0.0591}{1} \log \frac{[Ce^{4+}]}{[Ce^{3+}]}\right) - (+0.285)$$

$$= 1.32 + 0.0591 \log \frac{[Ce^{4+}]}{[Ce^{3+}]}$$

The graph of a typical titration of this type is shown in Fig. 10. When dichromate is used for the titration of iron, the potential obtained beyond the equivalence point depends on the hydrogen-ion concentration of the solution, since in this case the predominating equilibrium is $Cr_2O_7^= + 14H^+ + 6e \rightleftharpoons 2Cr^{3+} + 7H_2O$, and

$$E_1 = +1.36 + \frac{0.0591}{6} \log \frac{[Cr_2O_7^=][H^+]^{14}}{[Cr^{3+}]^2}$$

In all titrations of this kind when the potentials are plotted against volumes of titrating solution added, the equivalence point is found by bisecting the nearly vertical part of the curve.

Potentiometric titrations can, of course, be applied to oxidation

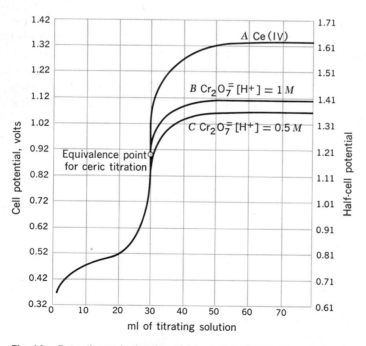

Fig. 10   Potentiometric titration of 30 ml of 0.10 N FeSO$_4$.   Curve A: with 0.10 N Ce(SO$_4$)$_2$.   Curve B: with 0.10 N K$_2$Cr$_2$O$_7$, [H$^+$] = 1 M. Curve C: with 0.10 N K$_2$Cr$_2$O$_7$, [H$^+$] = 0.5 M.   A normal calomel half-cell is used as the reference electrode.

reactions other than the change from ferrous to ferric ions.   The emf at the equivalence point is different for different reactions, but the sudden change in voltage is common to all feasible titrations.

16-7   Half-cell Potentials at the Equivalence Point in Redox Titrations

At any point in a redox titration all constituents are at equilibrium, and hence the potential as calculated from one redox system is the same as that calculated from the other redox system.   At the equivalence point it is also true that a simple stoichiometric relationship exists between the concentrations of the products of the reaction and between the concentrations of the small amounts of reagent and reactant remaining unacted upon.

Consider the simple hypothetical titration of A^{++} with B^{3+} according to the equation $A^{++} + B^{3+} \longrightarrow A^{3+} + B^{++}$, and assume the standard half-cell potential of $A^{3+} + e \rightleftharpoons A^{++}$ to be E_A and that of $B^{3+} + e \rightleftharpoons B^{++}$ to be E_B^0.   Then

$$E = E_A^0 + 0.0591 \log \frac{[A^{3+}]}{[A^{++}]}$$

$$E = E_B^0 + 0.0591 \log \frac{[B^{3+}]}{[B^{++}]}$$

Adding,

$$2E - (E_A^0 + E_B^0) + 0.0591 \log \frac{[A^{3+}][B^{3+}]}{[A^{++}][B^{++}]}$$

But at the equivalence point, $[A^{3+}] = [B^{++}]$ and $[A^{++}] = [B^{3+}]$, and the fractional term becomes unity.   Since $\log 1 = 0$,

$$E = \frac{E_A^0 + E_B^0}{2}$$

The half-cell potential at the equivalence point in a titration of this type is therefore the algebraic mean of the standard half-cell potentials of the two redox systems involved.   A similar situation exists in any titration where a transfer of the same number of electrons occurs in the two redox systems.

In the hypothetical titration of A^{++} with B^{4+} to give A^{4+} and B^{3+} $(A^{++} + 2B^{4+} \longrightarrow A^{4+} + 2B^{3+})$, there is a different setup, for

$$E = E_A^0 + \frac{0.0591}{2} \log \frac{[A^{4+}]}{[A^{++}]}$$

$$E = E_B^0 + 0.0591 \log \frac{[B^{4+}]}{[B^{3+}]}$$

Multiplying the first of these by 2 and adding the second, we obtain

$$3E = 2E_A^0 + E_B^0 + 0.0591 \log \frac{[A^{4+}][B^{4+}]}{[A^{3+}][B^{3+}]}$$

At the equivalence point, $[A^{4+}] = \frac{1}{2}[B^{3+}]$ and $[A^{++}] = \frac{1}{2}[B^{4+}]$, and so again the fractional term becomes unity and its log becomes zero. Therefore

$$E = \frac{2E_A^0 + E_B^0}{3}$$

In general, in the titration of A ions with B ions in cases where E_A^0 applies to $A_{oxid} + ae = A_{red}$, and E_B^0 applies to $B_{oxid} + be = B_{red}$,

$$E = \frac{aE_A^0 + bE_B^0}{a + b}$$

When hydrogen ions or hydroxyl ions are involved in the titration equation, the calculation becomes slightly more complex, as shown in the following example.

Example 1   What is the half-cell potential at the equivalence point in the titration of Fe^{++} with MnO_4^- in the presence of acid if at the equivalence point the pH value of the solution is 2.3?

Solution

$$5Fe^{++} + MnO_4^- + 8H^+ \longrightarrow 5Fe^{3+} + Mn^{++} + 4H_2O$$

$$Fe^{3+} + e \rightleftharpoons Fe^{++} \qquad E_1^0 = +0.771$$

$$MnO_4^- + 8H^+ + 5e \rightleftharpoons Mn^{++} + 4H_2O \qquad E_2^0 = +1.51 \text{ when } [H^+] = 1.0 \ M$$

(1) $E = E_1^0 + 0.0591 \log \dfrac{[Fe^{3+}]}{[Fe^{++}]}$

(2) $E = E_2^0 + \dfrac{0.0591}{5} \log \dfrac{[MnO_4^-][H^+]^8}{[Mn^{++}]}$

Multiplying (2) by 5 and adding (1),

$$6E = E_1^0 + 5E_2^0 + 0.0591 \log \frac{[Fe^{3+}][MnO_4^-][H^+]^8}{[Fe^{++}][Mn^{++}]}$$

but at the equivalence point, $[Fe^{3+}] = 5[Mn^{++}]$ and $[Fe^{++}] = 5[MnO_4^-]$, so

$$E = \frac{E_1^0 + 5E_2^0}{6} + \frac{0.0591}{6} \log [H^+]^8$$

$$= \frac{E_1^0 + 5E_2^0}{6} - \frac{0.0591 \times 8}{6} \times pH$$

$$= \frac{+0.771 + 7.56}{6} - (0.079 \times 2.3)$$

$$= +1.21 \text{ volts} \qquad Ans.$$

Example 2   Thirty milliliters of 0.10 N $FeSO_4$ is diluted to 100 ml and titrated with 0.10 N $Ce(SO_4)_2$. A normal calomel half-cell is used. Calculate the emf of the cell when the following volumes of ceric sulfate have been added: (*a*) 20 ml, (*b*) 30 ml, (*c*) 50 ml.

Solution

(*a*) Since the equivalence point is at the addition of 30 ml of ceric sulfate, when 20 ml has been added, two-thirds of the ferrous ions have been oxidized ($Fe^{++} + Ce^{4+} \longrightarrow Fe^{3+} + Ce^{3+}$). At that point the ratio of the concentration of the ferric ions formed to that of the ferrous ions remaining is 2:1.

$$E_1 = +0.771 + \frac{0.0591}{1} \log \frac{2}{1} = +0.789$$

$$E_2 = +0.285 \qquad \text{calomel half-cell}$$

$$E = E_1 - E_2 = 0.504 \text{ volt} \qquad Ans.$$

(*b*) At the point where 30 ml of ceric sulfate has been added, the equivalence point has been reached. Essentially all the ferrous ions have been converted to ferric ions, and an equivalent amount of cerous ions has been formed. Neglecting the possible formation of complex ions, the half-cell potential at the equivalence point in this case is the algebraic mean of the standard potential of ferric-ferrous and that of ceric-cerous:

$$E_1 = \frac{+0.771 + (+1.61)}{2} = +1.19$$

$$E = (+1.19) - (+0.285) = 0.90 \text{ volt} \qquad Ans.$$

(*c*) When 50 ml of 0.10 N ceric sulfate (-5.0 meq.) has been added, there are 2.0 meq. of ceric ions in the solution (since 3.0 meq. have been reduced to cerous). The ratio of $[Ce^{4+}]:[Ce^{3+}]$ is therefore 2:3.

$$E_1 = +1.61 + \frac{0.0591}{1} \log \frac{2}{3} = +1.60$$

$$E_2 = +0.285 \qquad \text{calomel half-cell}$$

$$E = E_1 - E_2 = 1.32 \text{ volts} \qquad Ans.$$

Example 3   In the titration in Example 2 above, calculate (*a*) the theoretical concentration of ceric ions at the point where 20 ml of ceric sulfate has been added and (*b*) the theoretical concentration of ferrous ions at the point where 50 ml of ceric sulfate has been added.

Solution   At all points in the titration the potential of the ferric-ferrous system is equal to that of the ceric-cerous system, since these four metal ions are all at equilibrium.   Therefore,

$$\left(+1.61 + \frac{0.0591}{1} \log \frac{[Ce^{4+}]}{[Ce^{3+}]}\right) = \left(+0.771 + \frac{0.0591}{1} \log \frac{[Fe^{3+}]}{[Fe^{++}]}\right)$$

(a) At the point where 20 ml of ceric sulfate has been added, the potential of the ferric-ferrous system is $+0.789$ volt [see solution to Example 2(a)].   Since at this point the total volume of the solution is 120 ml, and $20 \times 0.10 = 2.0$ meq. of cerous ions ($= 2.0$ millimoles) have been formed, the cerous-ion concentration is $2.0/120 = 0.0167$ M.

$$\left(+1.61 + 0.0591 \log \frac{[Ce^{4+}]}{0.0167}\right) = +0.789$$

$[Ce^{4+}] = 2.2 \times 10^{-16}\ M$ *Ans.*

(b) At the point where 50 ml of ceric sulfate has been added, the potential of the ceric-cerous system is $+1.60$ volts [see solution to Example 2(c) above].   Since at this point the total volume of the solution is 150 ml, and $30 \times 0.10 = 3.0$ meq. ($= 3.0$ millimoles) of ferric ions have been formed, the ferric-ion concentration is $3.0/150 = 0.020$ M.

$$+1.60 = \left(+0.771 + 0.0591 \log \frac{0.020}{[Fe^{++}]}\right)$$

$[Fe^{++}] = 1.8 \times 10^{-16}\ M$ *Ans.*

16-8   Potentiometric Precipitation Titrations

The potentiometric principle can be applied to certain precipitation titrations.   For example, in the titration of silver ions with halide ions, the concentration of silver ions changes during the progress of the titration. Using a silver electrode and a calomel half-cell, we have the cell

$Ag\,|\,Ag^+\,\|\,Cl^-(1\ M),\ \tfrac{1}{2}Hg_2Cl_2(s)\,|\,Hg(l)$
$E_1 = +0.799 + 0.0591 \log [Ag^+]$
$E_2 = +0.285$ calomel half-cell
$E = E_1 - E_2 = +0.514 + 0.0591 \log [Ag^+]$

The graph of a titration of this type shows an inflection at the equivalence point as in the case of acidimetric titrations and redox titrations.

The reverse titration of a halide with a standard solution of $AgNO_3$ (and with a silver electrode and calomel half-cell) is the same in principle. If 100 ml of 0.025 N KBr solution is titrated with 0.100 N $AgNO_3$, at the start of the titration when a precipitate of AgBr has just begun to form, $[Br^-] = 0.0250\ M$, and since the solubility product of AgBr is 5.0×10^{-13}, $[Ag^+] = \dfrac{5.0 \times 10^{-13}}{0.0250} = 2.00 \times 10^{-11}$.

$$E = [+0.799 + 0.0591 \log (2.00 \times 10^{-11})] - (+0.825)$$
$$= +0.118 \text{ volt}$$

At the equivalence point, $[Ag^+] = \sqrt{5.00 \times 10^{-13}} = 7.07 \times 10^{-7}$.

$$E = [+0.799 + 0.0591 \log (7.07 \times 10^{-7})] - (+0.285)$$
$$= +0.150 \text{ volt}$$

At the point where 30.00 ml of the $AgNO_3$ has been added (that is, 5.00 ml beyond the equivalence point), $[Ag^+] = \dfrac{5.00 \times 0.100}{125} = 4.00 \times 10^{-3}$.

$$E = [+0.799 + 0.0591 \log (4.00 \times 10^{-3})] - (+0.285)$$
$$= +0.372 \text{ volt}$$

By plotting these and other similarly determined points against buret readings, a curve similar in general appearance to one of those shown in Fig. 10 is obtained.

16-9 Specific Ion Electrodes

In recent years a number of electrodes have been developed which are sensitive to specific ions or classes of ions (both cations and anions). The membranes are frequently made from ion-exchange polymers or from a metal or metal compound deposited in an inert medium, such as silicone rubber or paraffin, and usually contain a considerable quantity of the ion under consideration.   Doped rare-earth crystals have also been introduced for the analysis of some ions.   As with glass electrodes, the ion-sensitive electrode is usually composed of an appropriate reference electrode and an internal solution in addition to the membrane.   Though the exact mechanism of their operation is not fully understood, the ion-sensitive electrodes are finding increasing use, particularly where similar ions are known to be absent.   Just as the glass electrode is known to have a "sodium error," the ion-sensitive electrodes are simply more sensitive, by factors of from 50 to 10,000, to a specific ion than to similar ions.

The application of ion-sensitive electrodes differs from that of glass electrodes in that it is more frequently necessary to prepare calibration curves for the direct potentiometric measurement of the ion's activity. In addition, many of the ion-sensitive electrodes are pH-dependent. Generally there is a linear relationship between the voltage and the logarithm of the activity of the ion.   The linear region usually covers from four to six orders of magnitude with the minimum detectable concentration in the region from 10^{-5} to 10^{-9} M, depending on the ion.   Alternatively, just as with a glass electrode, it is possible to use an ion-sensitive electrode as an indicator for the potentiometric titration of a specific ion or class of ions.

PROBLEMS

(Unless otherwise specified, it is assumed in the following problems that the temperature is 25°C and that a calomel half-cell with a potential of +0.285 volt is used.)

*16-1.   A cell containing an alkaline soln. and with hydrogen gas–calomel electrodes has an emf of 0.825 volt. (*a*) What is the pH value, and (*b*) what is the hydroxyl-ion concn. of the soln.?

*16-2.   A certain soln. of acid is 3.60×10^{-3} *M* in H^+ ions. (*a*) What is the pOH value? (*b*) With hydrogen gas–calomel electrodes, what emf could be obtained?

*16-3.   (*a*) With quinhydrone-calomel electrodes, approx. what emf would be obtained with a 0.0500 *N* soln. of acetic acid (ionization const. $= 1.86 \times 10^{-5}$)? (*b*) What emf could be obtained from the same soln. contg. an additional mole of acetate ion per 500 ml?

*16-4.   With quinhydrone-calomel electrodes, a 0.100 *M* soln. of a certain monobasic acid gives an emf of 275 mv. (*a*) What is the approx. ionization const. of the acid? (*b*) What emf would be obtained if an antimony electrode were substituted for the quinhydrone electrode?

*16-5.   What is the OH^--ion concn. of a soln. which with quinhydrone-calomel electrodes gives an emf of zero?

*16-6.   In the titration of a weak base like NH_3 with a strong acid like HCl, using a hydrogen gas electrode and calomel half-cell, what numerical relationship exists between the emf E and the ionization const. K_b of the base at that point in the titration which is halfway to the equivalence point?

*16-7.   If the potentiometric titration of a soln. of Sn^{++} with Ce^{4+} were feasible, what would be the emf of the circuit at the equivalence point? Standard calomel half-cell is used. Assume no complex ions are formed.

*16-8.   Calculate the potential obtainable from the cell made by connecting the half-cell

$$Pt \mid Sn^{4+}(0.00100 \ M), \ Sn^{++}(0.0600 \ M)$$

with a calomel half-cell.

*16-9.   Plot the following values of mv against ml of 0.100 *N* NaOH in the potentiometric titration of 2.50 g of an aq. soln. (sp. gr. 1.050) of a weak monobasic acid after dilution of the soln. to an appropriate vol. A hydrogen gas electrode and a calomel half-cell are used. 0.00 ml = 416 mv; 1.00 ml = 482; 2.00 ml = 511; 4.00 ml = 543; 7.00 ml = 570; 10.00 ml = 591; 12.00 ml = 606; 14.00 ml = 635; 15.00 ml = 661; 15.50 ml = 700; 15.60 ml = 750; 15.70 ml = 790; 15.80 ml = 845; 16.00 ml = 873; 17.00 ml = 912; 18.00 ml = 931; 20.00 ml = 952; 24.00 ml = 977; 28.00 ml = 988.

(*a*) At what vol. of NaOH is the soln. neutral? (*b*) What vol. of NaOH corresponds to the equivalence point? (*c*) What is the pH value at the equivalence point? (*d*) What is the voltmeter reading at the point halfway to the equivalence point?

(e) What, therefore, is the ionization const. of the acid?   (f) What is the acidity of the original undiluted soln. expressed as normality and (g) as percentage by wt. of total available hydrogen?

*16-10.   A sample weighing 0.800 g consists of Na_2CO_3 mixed with inert matter and either NaOH or $NaHCO_3$.   It is dissolved and titrated with 0.500 N HCl, using a pH meter equipped with a glass electrode and a calomel half-cell (with *satd.* KCl). The following pH readings were obtained for corresponding vols. of HCl: 0.00 ml = pH 11.60; 2.00 ml = 11.48; 4.00 ml = 11.16; 5.00 ml = 10.80; 5.50 ml = 10.48; 6.00 ml = 10.00; 6.50 ml = 8.98; 7.00 ml = 8.53; 8.00 ml = 8.11; 10.00 ml = 7.71; 12.00 ml = 7.52; 14.00 ml = 7.22; 16.00 ml = 6.88; 17.00 ml = 6.58; 17.50 ml = 6.30; 18.00 ml = 4.50; 18.50 ml = 2.95; 19.00 ml = 2.55; 20.00 ml = 2.11; 24.00 ml = 1.40.

(a) Draw the titration curve, and determine from it the percentage composition of the sample (see Sec. 11-19).   (b) A second sample consisting of equal parts by wt. of Na_2CO_3 and NaOH is dissolved and titrated as above.   It is found that the second equivalence point is identical in pH value and buret reading with the one obtained in the titration of the first sample.   Superimpose on the first graph the titration curve that would approximate that for the second titration.   (c) What voltmeter reading would be obtained at the neutral point if an antimony electrode and a calomel half-cell similar to the one above were used?

*16-11.   A sample of formic acid, HCOOH, is dissolved in water and titrated potentiometrically with 0.400 N NaOH (quinhydrone-calomel electrodes).   The following values of ml and corresponding mv were obtained: 0.00 ml = 273 mv; 2.50 ml = 242; 5.00 ml = 233; 10.00 ml = 226; 20.00 ml = 205; 25.00 ml = 177; 30.00 ml = 110; 31.50 ml = 60; 32.50 ml = −75; 33.00 ml = −150.   Plot the curve, and note that the point of maximum slope is at −75 mv.   Extrapolate the curve and determine from it (a) the approx. pH value of the soln. at 40.00 ml of NaOH, (b) the pH value at the equivalence point, (c) the pH value at 16.25 ml and from this value the ionization const. Ka of formic acid, (d) the hydrogen-ion concn. at the start of the titration and from it and the above Ka value the approx. initial molar concn. of formic acid in the soln., (e) the no. of g of HCOOH present in the original soln.

*16-12.   A cell is made up of a Pt wire dipping in a soln. of cerous and ceric ions and a calomel half-cell.   An emf of 1,425 mv is obtained.   Find the ratio of the concn. of Ce(IV) ions to that of Ce(III) ions in the soln.

*16-13.   In the potentiometric titration of 20.0 ml of 0.100 N $Ce(SO_4)_2$ (diluted with H_2O to 200 ml) with 0.100 N $FeSO_4$, what is the emf of the circuit (a) at the point where 5.0 ml of the $FeSO_4$ has been added, (b) at the point where 25.0 ml of the $FeSO_4$ has been added?   (c) What is the concn. of ferrous ions at the former point, and (d) what is the concn. of Ce(IV) ions at the latter point?

*16-14.   A sample of limonite weighing 0.350 g is dissolved in HCl, and the ferric ions are reduced by means of a slight excess of $SnCl_2$.   Without removing the excess stannous ions, the soln. is titrated potentiometrically with 0.100 N $K_2Cr_2O_7$ (Pt-calomel electrodes).   Plot the following values of ml of dichromate against corresponding mv, and from the graph find the approx. percentage of Fe_2O_3 in the limonite. The stannous ions are oxidized by the dichromate first. 0.0 ml = 190 mv; 1.00 ml = 218; 2.00 ml = 223; 3.00 ml = 240; 4.00 ml = 325; 5.00 ml = 342; 6.00 ml = 350; 9.00 ml = 363; 15.0 ml = 382; 20.0 ml = 388; 25.0 ml = 393; 30.0 ml = 417; 32.0 ml = 450; 34.0 ml = 510; 35.0 ml = 570; 36.0 ml = 910; 37.0 ml = 1,100; 39.0 ml = 1,155; 45.0 ml = 1,217; 50.0 ml = 1,229.

*16-15.   Calculate the voltmeter reading at the equivalence point in the potentio-metric titration of stannous ions with ceric ions ($Sn^{++} + 2Ce^{4+} \longrightarrow Sn^{4+} + 2Ce^{3+}$). A normal calomel half-cell is used.

*16-16.   Calculate from standard potentials given in the Appendix the electrode potential at the equivalence point in the titration of As(III) with $KMnO_4$ ($5HAsO_2 + 2MnO_4^- + 6H^+ + 2H_2O \longrightarrow 5H_3AsO_4 + 2Mn^{++}$). Assume that at the equivalence point the hydrogen-ion concn. is 1.00×10^{-2}.

*16-17.   Find the voltmeter reading at the equivalence point in the potentiometric titration of Sn^{++} with $KMnO_4$ (to give Sn^{4+} and Mn^{++}), using a normal calomel half-cell. Assume that at the equivalence point the soln. has a pH value of 2.00.

*16-18.   In the potentiometric titration (Pt electrode, calomel half-cell) of a certain soln. of $KMnO_4$ with $FeSO_4$ in the presence of acid, the pH value of the soln. is 1.00 at the point halfway to the equivalence point. (a) What is the emf of the circuit at this point? (b) What is the voltage of the circuit at the point 50% beyond the equivalence point?

*16-19.   What emf would be given by the circuit consisting of a calomel half-cell and each of the following solns.: (a) a 0.010 M soln. of a monobasic acid having an ionization const. of 1.0×10^{-4} (quinhydrone electrode), (b) a 0.010 M soln. of $Ce(SO_4)_2$ which has been titrated with $FeSO_4$ to a point one-fifth of the way to the equivalence point (Pt electrode), (c) a satd. soln. of AgBr (Ag electrode), (d) a satd. soln. of Ag_2CrO_4 (Ag electrode)? Use soly. products given in the Appendix.

*16-20.   A 25-ml pipetful of 0.200 N $AgNO_3$ is diluted to 250 ml and titrated potentiometrically with 0.200 N KBr (Ag electrode, calomel half-cell). Assuming the molar soly. of AgBr to be 5.9×10^{-7}, calculate the value of $E_{Ag} - E_{cal}$ (a) at the start of the titration, (b) at the equivalence point, (c) after 26.0 ml of the KBr has been added.

*16-21.   A 25-ml pipetful of 0.100 N KCl is diluted to 100 ml and titrated poten-tiometrically with 0.100 N $AgNO_3$ (Ag electrode, normal calomel half-cell). Deter-mine the voltage of the circuit at the following points in the titration: (a) at the start of the titration where a ppt. of AgCl has just begun to form, (b) when 15.00 ml of the $AgNO_3$ has been added, (c) at the equivalence point, (d) when 35.00 ml of the $AgNO_3$ has been added. Show the general form of the titration curve (soly. product AgCl = 1.0×10^{-10}).

*16-22.   A 0.250-g sample contg. a weak base (mol. wt. = 110) was dissolved in 100 ml of glacial acetic acid and titrated with 0.100 N $HClO_4$. 4.50 ml was required to reach the only inflection point in the titration curve. Calculate the percentage of the base in the sample.

*16-23.   A mixt. contains two weak organic acids, A (mol. wt. = 84) and B (mol. wt. = 140), together with inert matter.   A sample weighing 0.100 g was dissolved in 200 ml of a nonaqueous solvent.   A 100-ml aliquot was titrated with sodium aminoethoxide (5.00×10^{-2} M).   Equivalence points were indicated at 7.5 and 10.5 ml.   Calculate the percentage of each acid in the mixt. assuming acid B to be dibasic.

*16-24.   Several workers have described the analysis of monovalent cations by a titration procedure using calcium tetraphenylboron and an ion-sensitive electrode as the indicator electrode.   A 0.100-g sample known to contain cesium is dissolved in 250 ml of water, and this soln. is titrated with a 0.050 N soln. of calcium tetraphenylboron, requiring 14.0 ml to reach the equivalence point.   What is the percentage of cesium in the sample?

*16-25.   With a certain electrode it is found that the response for fluoride ion is linear from 10^{-5} to 10^{-1} M.   Two fluoride calibration solns. which are 1.0×10^{-2} and 1.0×10^{-4} M give readings of -350 and -50 mv, respectively.   Express the fluoride-ion concn. of an unknown soln. in p.p.m. if it gives a reading of -100 mv using the same system.

*16-26.   A certain soln. of NaOH is 5.20×10^{-4} M in OH^- ions.   With a hydrogen gas electrode and calomel half-cell what emf would be obtained?

16-27.   Two solns. are prepared, and with quinhydrone-calomel electrodes the voltmeter reads 100 mv in the case of one soln.   The reading is also 100 mv in the case of the other soln. provided the electrode connections are reversed.   (a) What are the pH values of the two solns.?   (b) What would be the hydroxyl-ion concn. if a satd. KCl calomel half-cell had been used and the readings were the same as indicated above?

16-28.   A certain monobasic acid has an ionization const. of 2.0×10^{-5}.   30.0 ml of a 0.300 N soln. is diluted to 200 ml and titrated with 0.200 N NaOH.   With a normal calomel half-cell used in each case, (a) what would be the pH reading of a pH meter (glass electrode) at the beginning of the titration, (b) what would be the voltmeter reading at the point where 10.00 ml of the NaOH has been added (quinhydrone electrode), (c) what would be the voltmeter reading at the equivalence point (antimony electrode), (d) what would be the voltmeter reading at the point where 50.00 ml of the NaOH has been added (hydrogen gas electrode)?

16-29.   With hydrogen gas–calomel electrodes, a 0.0100 M soln. of a certain monoacidic base gives an emf of 946 mv.   (a) What is the approx. ionization const. of the base?   (b) What emf would be obtained if 2.00 moles/liter of cation common to the base were introduced into the soln.?   (c) If the unbuffered base were titrated with acid, what would be the pH value at that point in the titration which is halfway to the equivalence point?

16-30.   Plot values on graph paper showing the relationship between mv and pH values (a) when using normal hydrogen-calomel electrodes, (b) when using quinhydrone-calomel electrodes.   Include the range between pH = 14 and pH = -2.

16-31. In the potentiometric titration of a weak monobasic acid with a strong base (hydrogen gas electrode, calomel half-cell), what numerical relationship exists between the emf E and the ionization const. Ka of the acid at that point in the titration which is halfway to the equivalence point?

16-32. In the potentiometric titration of 60.0 ml of 0.100 N ferrous sulfate (diluted with H_2O to 250 ml) with 0.200 N ceric sulfate, what would be the voltage reading (a) after 10.0 ml of ceric sulfate has been added, (b) after 30.0 ml of ceric sulfate has been added, (c) after 45.0 ml of ceric sulfate has been added? What is the ferrous-ion concn. of this last point?

16-33. An aq. soln. of a weak base of the general type ROH (where R represents an organic radical) has a specific gravity of 1.080. A 5.00-ml sample is diluted to about 250 ml and titrated potentiometrically with 0.150 N HCl (hydrogen gas electrode, calomel half-cell). From the following data showing no. of mv corresponding to no. of ml of acid, plot the titration curve and determine the following: (a) buret reading at the equivalence point, (b) buret reading at the neutral point, (c) pH value at the equivalence point, (d) voltmeter reading at the point in the titration halfway to the equivalence point, (e) ionization const. of the base, (f) normality as a base of the original undiluted soln., (g) basicity of the original undiluted soln. expressed as percentage by wt. of total available hydroxyl ions.

   0.00 ml = 982 mv; 1.00 ml = 921; 2.00 ml = 883; 4.00 ml = 837; 8.00 ml = 796; 12.00 ml = 763; 16.00 ml = 718; 17.00 ml = 694; 17.40 ml = 678; 17.80 ml = 657; 18.00 ml = 589; 18.20 ml = 517; 18.60 ml = 492; 19.00 ml = 477; 20.00 ml = 455; 24.00 ml = 420; 28.00 ml = 404.

16-34. A sample weighing 0.500 g consists of Na_2CO_3 mixed with inert matter and either NaOH and $NaHCO_3$. It is dissolved and titrated with 0.400 N HCl using a pH meter equipped with a glass electrode and a calomel half-cell (with *satd.* KCl). The following pH readings were obtained for corresponding vols. of HCl: 0.00 ml = pH 12.80; 3.00 ml = 12.62; 6.00 ml = 12.42; 9.00 ml = 12.20; 12.00 ml = 11.90; 15.00 ml = 11.43; 16.00 ml = 10.95; 17.00 ml = 9.40; 18.00 ml = 7.31; 19.00 ml = 6.90; 20.00 ml = 6.73; 21.00 ml = 6.59; 21.50 ml = 6.37; 22.00 ml = 4.50; 22.50 ml = 2.80; 23.00 ml = 2.60; 24.00 ml = 2.37; 26.00 ml = 1.98; 28.00 ml = 1.72; 30.00 ml = 1.56.

   (a) Draw the titration curve, and determine from it the percentage composition of the sample (see Sec. 11-19). (b) A second sample consisting of equal parts by wt. of $NaHCO_3$ and Na_2CO_3 is dissolved and titrated as above. It is found that the second equivalence point is identical in pH value and buret reading with the one obtained in the titration of the first sample. Superimpose on the first graph the titration curve that would approximate that for the second titration. (c) What voltmeter reading would be obtained at the start of the first titration if an antimony electrode and a calomel half-cell similar to the above were used?

16-35. Express the electrode potential at the equivalence point in the hypothetical titration of A$^+$ with B^{4+} (2A$^+$ + 3B^{4+} $\longrightarrow$ 2A^{4+} + 3B^{++}) assuming the standard potential of $A^{4+} + 3e = A^+$ to be E_A^0 and that of $B^{4+} + 2e = B^{++}$ to be E_B^0.

16-36.   Calculate from standard electrode values the electrode potential at the equivalence point in the titration represented by the equation $5H_2SO_3 + 2MnO_4^- \longrightarrow 5SO_4^= + 2Mn^{++} + 4H^+ + 3H_2O$.   Assume the pH value of the soln. at the equivalence point to be 2.50.

16-37.   Assume that at the equivalence point in the titration of A^{++} with B^{4+} (to give A^{4+} and B^{3+}) 99.9% of A^{++} has been oxidized.   Calculate (a) the numerical value of the equilibrium const. of the reaction, (b) the difference between the standard potential of A^{3+}—A^{++} and that of B^{4+}—B^{++}, and (c) the voltmeter reading at the equivalence point in the potentiometric titration of A^{++} with B^{4+}, using a normal calomel electrode and given that the standard potential of A^{4+}—A^{++} is $+0.20$ volt.

16-38.   Plot the following values of ml against mv in the potentiometric titration of 40.0 ml of 0.213 N H_3PO_4 diluted with water to 200 ml and titrated with 0.200 N NaOH (hydrogen gas electrode, calomel half-cell): 0.0 ml = 300 mv; 5.0 ml = 315; 10.0 ml = 350; 13.0 ml = 385; 13.8 ml = 405; 14.0 ml = 415; 14.2 ml = 450; 14.4 ml = 525; 14.8 ml = 555; 15.5 ml = 566; 17.0 ml = 580; 20.2 ml = 603. Complete the titration curve, assuming that it is known that the second inflection takes place at 750 mv.   (a) Find the pH values at which the first and second hydrogens of the H_3PO_4 occur.   (b) Also find the no. of g of combined P_2O_5 present in the original soln.

16-39.   The Cr in 5.00 g of steel is oxidized to dichromate and then titrated potentiometrically with 0.104 N $FeSO_4$ in the presence of acid.   (a) Show the general appearance of the titration curve.   (b) If the point of maximum slope of the curve is at 8.80 ml of $FeSO_4$, find the percentage of Cr in the steel.   (c) If at the point of adding 4.40 ml of $FoSO_4$ the H^+-ion concn. of the soln. is 0.10 M, calculate the voltage of the circuit at that point.

16-40.   A soln. consisting of 30.0 ml of 0.100 N KI is diluted to 100 ml and titrated potentiometrically with 0.100 N $AgNO_3$ (silver electrode, normal calomel half-cell).   Determine the voltage of the circuit at the following points in the titration, and show the general form of the titration curve: (a) at the start of the titration when AgI has just begun to form, (b) at the point halfway to the equivalence point, (c) at the point where 50.0 ml of the $AgNO_3$ has been added (soly. product AgI = 1.0×10^{-16}).

16-41.   Sketch the curves expected for the following titrations: (a) the titration of aniline dissolved in glacial acetic acid with perchloric acid; (b) the titration of trinitrophenol in methanol with tetrabutylammonium hydroxide; (c) the titration of sulfuric acid in glacial acetic acid with sodium methoxide; (d) the titration of a mixt. of pyridine and butylamine in glacial acetic acid with perchloric acid.

Conductometric Titrations

17-1 Conductance

Strong acids, strong bases, and most salts, when dissolved in a relatively large volume of water, are practically completely dissociated into ions. These ions are capable of transporting electricity, and because of them the solutions are good conductors of the electric current. The *conductance* of a solution is the reciprocal of its electrical resistance and is expressed in *reciprocal ohms* ($ohms^{-1}$) or *mhos*.

The *specific conductance* of a solution is the conductance of a cube of the solution of one-centimeter edge. The specific conductance at 25°C of 0.100 N HCl is 0.0394 ohm^{-1}; the specific conductance of 0.0100 N HCl is 0.00401 ohm^{-1}.

Equivalent conductance is the conductance of a solution containing one gram equivalent weight of dissolved electrolyte between electrodes one centimeter apart. It is therefore numerically equal to the product of the specific conductance of the solution and the number of milliliters containing one gram equivalent weight of electrolyte.

$$\text{Equivalent conductance} = \frac{1,000 \times \text{specific conductance}}{\text{normality}}$$

The equivalent conductance of 0.100 N HCl is 0.0394 × 10,000 = 394 $ohms^{-1}$; the equivalent conductance of 0.0100 N HCl is 0.00401 × 100,000 = 401 $ohms^{-1}$. As a solution becomes more dilute, its equivalent conductance becomes somewhat greater owing to the fact that in more dilute solutions interionic effects of electrolytes are lessened, which gives the apparent effect of increasing the degree of ionization of the dissolved substance.

By extrapolation it is possible to determine the equivalent conductance of a solution at infinite dilution.   For HCl this value at 25°C is 426.1 reciprocal ohms.   This is the theoretical conductance that would be given by a "perfect" solution containing 36.46 g of HCl between electrodes 1 cm apart.

17-2   Mobility of Ions

Different kinds of ions have different velocities, so that when an electric current is passed through a solution, the faster moving ions carry a relatively greater amount of the current.   In the case of very dilute HCl, the hydrogen ions, moving much faster than the chloride ions, carry about 82% of the current; the chloride ions carry only about 18%.   The *mobility* of an ion is the equivalent conductance of that ion, and the equivalent conductance of an electrolyte is equal to the sum of the mobilities of its ions.   Thus, the equivalent conductance at 25°C of HCl at infinite dilution ($= 426.1$) is equal to the sum of the mobility of the hydrogen ions ($= 349.8$) and the mobility of the chloride ions ($= 76.3$) at that temperature.   If several electrolytes are present in a solution, all the ions contribute to the conductance of the solution.   Mobilities increase by about 2% for each 1°C increase in temperature.

Table 4 gives the equivalent conductances, or mobilities, at 25°C of some of the common ions at infinite dilution.   From them can be calculated the equivalent conductances of corresponding electrolytes at infinite dilution.

Table 4   Equivalent ionic conductances (mobilities) (25°C)
(Averaged from various sources)

Na^+	50.1	Cl^-	76.3
K^+	73.5	Br^-	78.4
Ag^+	61.9	I^-	76.8
H^+	349.8	OH^-	198.0
NH_4^+	73.4	$C_2H_3O_2^-$	40.9
Li^+	38.7	$\frac{1}{2}SO_4^=$	79.8
$\frac{1}{2}Mg^{++}$	53.1	ClO_4^-	68.0
$\frac{1}{2}Ba^{++}$	63.6	NO_3^-	71.4
$\frac{1}{2}Ca^{++}$	59.5	$\frac{1}{2}C_2O_4^=$	74.0
$\frac{1}{2}Pb^{++}$	73.0	$\frac{1}{3}Fe(CN)_6^{3-}$	101.0
$\frac{1}{2}Fe^{++}$	54.0	$\frac{1}{4}Fe(CN)_6^{4-}$	110.5
$\frac{1}{3}Fe^{3+}$	68.0	$\frac{1}{2}CO_3^=$	70.0

17-3   Conductometric Acidimetric Titrations

Consider the titration of a dilute solution of HCl with NaOH solution:

$$H^+ + Cl^- + (Na^+ + OH^-) \longrightarrow Na^+ + Cl^- + H_2O$$

At the beginning of the titration, the HCl solution has a high conductance value, owing principally to the extremely high mobility of the hydrogen ions.   As NaOH is added, the concentration of the hydrogen ions is decreased, and although hydrogen ions are replaced by sodium ions, the mobility of the latter is much less, so that the conductance of the solution decreases rapidly.   At the equivalence point, the solution contains only NaCl, and the conductance is at a minimum, for, on further addition of NaOH, the hydroxyl ions with their high mobility give a rapidly increasing conductance to the solution.   If the titration is carried out under constant conditions of temperature, etc., and the volume of titrating solution is plotted against conductance, a curve of the appearance of line *ABC* in Fig. 11 is obtained.

In this figure, the portion of the conductance due to each ion present in the solution is indicated as a function of the quantity of titrant added.   Initially, the entire conductance is due to hydrogen ions and chloride ions; at the equivalence point, the conductance is due only to the sodium and chloride ions.   At the point where two equivalents of base have been added, the conductance is due to chloride, sodium, and hydroxyl ions.

Ideal titration curves applying to perfect solutions can be calculated from the mobilities of the ions involved.   Thus, in the titration of a very dilute solution containing a gram equivalent weight of HCl with a relatively concentrated solution of sodium hydroxide (so as to give no appreciable change in the total volume of the solution being titrated), the theoretical conductance of the original solution is 349.8 (H$^+$) + 76.3

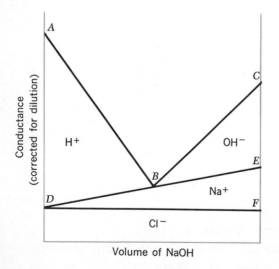

Fig. 11   Conductometric titration of dilute HCl with NaOH.

$(Cl^-) = 426.1$ ohms^{-1}.   At the equivalence point the solution contains only NaCl and its conductance is 50.1 $(Na^+) + 76.3$ $(Cl^-) = 126.4$ ohms^{-1}.   An excess of 1 g equiv. wt. of NaOH to the resulting solution would give a conductance of 50.1 $(Na^+) + 76.3$ $(Cl^-) + 50.1$ $(Na^+) + 198.0$ $(OH^-) = 375.5$ ohms^{-1}.   Plotting these conductance values against corresponding relative volumes of NaOH gives a titration curve like that of the resultant line ABC in the figure.   The equivalence point is the intersection of two straight lines.

In an actual titration of this type the lines are likely to be slightly curved because of (1) variation in temperature due, in part at least, to the heat of neutralization; (2) increase in the volume of the solution because of added reagent; and (3) interionic effects, such as hydrolysis. Foreign ions in the solution may distort the curve slightly, although their general effect is to increase the total conductance by a constant amount. In spite of this, the inflection is sharp, and three or four readings on each side of the equivalence point are usually sufficient to establish the point of intersection and hence the buret reading at the equivalence point.

The titration of a weak acid like acetic acid with a strong base like sodium hydroxide is shown in the curve AA of Fig. 12.   Here the first small amount of NaOH will, as before, cause a decrease in conductivity, but since the concentration of hydrogen ions in acetic acid is small, the conductance of the solution soon increases owing to the formation of sodium ions and acetate ions, the latter buffering the solution and thus cutting down the concentration of the highly mobile hydrogen ions.   The conductance values then follow closely those of the sodium acetate formed.   Beyond the equivalence point the addition of hydroxyl ions increases the slope of the titration curve but does not cause a sharp inflection in it.   If, on the other hand, a solution of NH_3 is used to titrate the acetic acid, a curve BB is obtained with a sharper inflection at the equivalence point, for the excess NH_4OH, owing to its slight degree of ionization, especially since it is buffered by the ammonium ions present, has little effect on the conductance of the solution.   In an actual titration of this type, the two parts of the conductance curve do not meet sharply at a point because of hydrolysis effects, but the equivalence point can be found by extending the straight parts of the titration graph to a common point [see C of Fig. 12].

The titration of a mixture of a strong acid and a weak acid with a standard base can often be carried out conductometrically, and the amount of each acid determined from the graph (see Prob. 17-6).   A similar type of titration curve is obtained in the titration of certain dibasic acids (see Prob. 17-18).

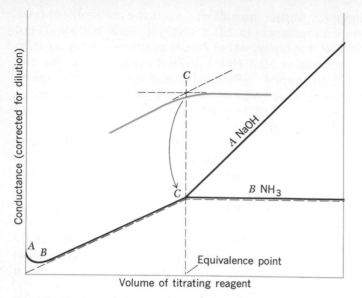

**Fig. 12   Conductometric titration of 0.01 N HC$_2$H$_3$O$_2$.   Curve A:
with NaOH.   Curve B: with NH$_3$.**

17-4   Conductometric Precipitation Titrations

Many precipitation titrations are also possible by conductometric
methods.   Consider, for example, a very dilute solution containing a
gram equivalent weight of sodium sulfate being titrated with a concentrated solution of barium acetate.   The theoretical conductance of the
original solution is 50.1 (Na$^+$) + 79.8 ($\frac{1}{2}$SO$_4^=$) = 129.9 ohms^{-1}.   At the
equivalence point the conductance is 50.1 (Na$^+$) + 40.9 (C$_2$H$_3$O$_2^-$) =
91.0 ohms^{-1}.   If an excess of a gram equivalent weight of barium acetate
is added, the conductance of the solution is 50.1 (Na$^+$) + 40.9 (C$_2$H$_3$O$_2^-$)
+ 63.6 ($\frac{1}{2}$Ba^{++}) + 40.9 (C$_2$H$_3$O$_2^-$) = 195.5 ohms^{-1}.   The titration curve
is therefore a flat V- shaped one with the equivalence point at the inter-
section of two straight lines.   Certain titration curves of this type are
illustrated in the accompanying problems.

17-5   Other Conductometric Titrations

Certain redox titrations are possible by conductometric methods provided there is a change in the hydrogen-ion concentration during the
progress of the titration (for example, 6Fe^{++} + Cr$_2$O$_7^=$ + 14$^+$ $\longrightarrow$
6Fe^{3+} + 2Cr^{3+} + 7H$_2$O).   Because of the high mobility of the hydrogen
ion, a marked decrease in conductance can be expected during the initial
part of the titration.   The precision of such titrations is satisfactory only
if the initial acidity is low.

Titrations involving certain complex-ion formations are possible.

Salts of strong bases and weak acids (for example, $NaC_2H_3O_2$) can be conductometrically titrated with strong acids, and salts of weak bases and strong acids (for example, NH_4Cl) can be titrated with strong bases.

Titration curves of some of these types are illustrated in the accompanying problems.

17-6 Conductometric Titration Apparatus

A common Wheatstone-bridge-type arrangement for determining the conductance of a solution is indicated in the diagram of Fig. 13, where D is usually a null detector, R_x is the conductivity cell, and S is a source of alternating current normally operated at 60 or 1,000 cps.

In measuring relative conductance values in a titration, the bridge is usually balanced, using the adjustable resistance and capacitance controls R_3 and C_3, respectively. Changes in the values of R_3 required to attain balance after each addition of titrant are then recorded.

Since in an ordinary titration we are not interested in the actual conductance values but only in the relative changes in conductivity as a means of establishing a titration curve, it is only necessary to plot the volume of titrating solution against the relative conductance values as obtained from the bridge readings. Unlike the potentiomotric graph, the conductometric titration curves are straight lines or nearly so, and they can therefore usually be fixed by a relatively few volume readings on each side of the equivalence point. In order for accurate values to be obtained

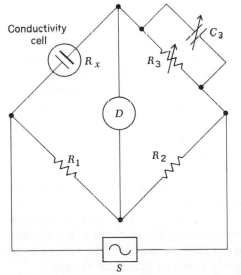

Fig. 13 Schematic diagram of a conducto-metric titration apparatus.

and in order for the lines to be straight or nearly so, it is important to keep the temperature of the solution as nearly constant as possible, and it is also theoretically necessary that the volume of the solution remains constant during the titration. This last condition is fulfilled approximately enough for ordinary titrations if the total volume of reagent does not exceed 1 or 2% of the solution titrated. The reagent should therefore be as concentrated, and the solution as dilute, as feasible. A solution 0.01 to 0.001 N titrated with a 1 N solution of reagent is a typical case. If the reagent volume exceeds 1 to 2% of the solution being titrated, the measured conductance should be corrected for the effect of dilution by means of an equation such as

$$\left(\frac{1}{R}\right)_{\text{actual}} = \frac{(V + v)}{V}\left(\frac{1}{R}\right)_{\text{observed}}$$

where V is the initial volume and v is the volume of titrant added up to that point in the titration.

17-7 High-frequency Titrations

The conductometric methods discussed above depended on ionic mobilities. At higher frequencies, in the megacycle range, the ion no longer has sufficient time to move within the time period of one-half cycle. However, the impressed electric field will cause a molecule or ion to become polarized as the electrons are attracted to one electrode and the nuclei to the other electrode. If the molecule has a dipole, the dipolar character will produce an additional polarization. For the very short period of time during which the polarization is being established, a current will flow as a result of both conductance and polarization effects.

For high-frequency measurements, the capacitive properties are considered; whereas in conductometric (low-frequency) methods, resistive properties are measured. Several different types of high-frequency devices have been designed. One commercially available unit places the sample between two plates of a capacitor with the capacitor forming part of a resonance circuit. If the material between the plates changes, for example, from air to water, the resonant condition will be destroyed. Precision capacitors are then added or removed so as to restore the resonant condition; the amount of capacitance change is directly related to the change in the properties of the solution in the cell.

The advantages of high-frequency techniques lie primarily in two areas: (1) It is not necessary to have electrodes in contact with the solution, and (2) nonaqueous solvents can be used. The type of titration curves obtained are similar to those found in conductance, permitting the analyst to obtain several points on either side of the equivalence point and to determine the equivalence point by graphical means.

PROBLEMS

*17-1.   If the specific conductance of $N/50$ HCl is 0.00792 ohm^{-1}, what is the equiv. conductance of $N/50$ HCl?

*17-2.   At 25°C what is the equiv. conductance at infinite dilution of a soln. of Ag_2SO_4?

*17-3.   A soln. contg. a g equiv. wt. of $BaCl_2$ at very high dilution is titrated at 25°C with Li_2SO_4.   From the mobilities of the ions involved, calculate the conductance of the soln. (*a*) at the start of the titration, (*b*) at the equivalence point, and (*c*) at the point where a total of 2.00 g equivs. of Li_2SO_4 has been added.   Plot these values to show the titration graph.   Make similar calculations and graph for the titration of $BaCl_2$ with Na_2SO_4.

*17-4.   A very dil. soln. of NaOH is titrated conductometrically with 1.00 N HCl. The following bridge readings representing relative conductances were obtained at the indicated points in the titration: 0.00 ml = 3.15; 1.00 ml = 2.60; 2.00 ml = 2.04; 3.00 ml = 1.40; 4.00 ml = 1.97; 5.00 ml = 2.86; 6.00 ml = 3.66.   Plot the titration curve, and determine from it the no. of g of NaOH present in the soln.

*17-5.   A soln. approx. $N/100$ in sodium acetate is titrated conductometrically with 1.00 N HCl.   From the following titration values showing relative conductances plot the curve, and calculate the no. of g of $NaC_2H_3O_2$ present in the soln.   (*Hint:* Extend the nearly straight parts of the curve to a point of intersection.)   0.00 ml = 218; 4.00 ml = 230; 8.00 ml = 243; 9.00 ml = 247; 10.00 ml = 256; 11.00 ml = 269; 12.00 ml = 285; 14.00 ml = 323; 17.00 ml = 380.   Show from mobilities and relative degrees of ionization why this form of curve is to be expected.

*17-6.   A sample of vinegar has been adulterated with HCl.   It is titrated with 0.500 N NH_4OH, and the following bridge readings representing relative conductances are obtained at the indicated buret readings: 0.00 ml = 2.87; 1.00 ml = 2.50;   2.00 ml = 2.10;   2.50 ml = 1.90;   3.00 ml = 1.70;   3.10 ml = 1.66; 3.20 ml = 1.70; 3.50 ml = 1.76; 4.00 ml = 2.00; 4.20 ml = 2.10; 4.50 ml = 2.15; 5.00 ml = 2.15; 6.00 ml = 2.14; 7.00 ml = 2.16, 8.00 ml = 2.18.   Calculate the no. of g (*a*) of HCl and (*b*) of $HC_2H_3O_2$ in the sample.   (*Hint:* Find the point of neutralization of the HCl by extending the nearly straight sides of the U-shaped part of the graph to a point of intersection.)

*17-7.   A dil. soln. contains a certain weak monoacidic base.   It is titrated conductometrically with 1.50 N HCl, and the following relative conductance readings are obtained: 0.00 ml = 128; 0.25 ml = 121; 0.50 ml = 116; 0.75 ml = 118; 2.00 ml = 139; 4.00 ml = 173; 5.00 ml = 197; 6.00 ml = 227; 8.00 ml = 288. (*a*) Plot these values, and determine the no. of meq. of base present in the original soln.   (*b*) Explain why the conductance decreases during the first part of the titration.   (*c*) What would be the general form of the titration curve if 1.50 N $HC_2H_3O_2$ was used in place of the HCl?

*17-8.   A soln. 0.0400 N in H_2SO_4 and contg. KI was titrated with 1.10 N $KMnO_4$ delivered from a microburet.   From the following results obtained for the relative conductance values corresponding to the buret readings, plot the curve, and determine from it the no. of g of KI present in the original soln.: 0.20 ml = 943; 0.40 ml = 872; 0.60 ml = 803; 0.80 ml = 737; 1.00 ml = 670; 1.20 ml = 622; 1.40 ml = 608; 1.60 ml = 609; 1.80 ml = 610; 2.40 ml = 614.

*17-9.   The analysis of a soln. contg. ammonium ions as the only singly charged cation is to be performed with sodium tetraphenylborate as the titrant; a 1:1 molar-ratio ppt. is formed.   An oscillometer is used as the detection device.   50.0 ml of the sample is placed in the cell and titrated with 2.00×10^{-2} M sodium tetra-phenylborate.   In such a titration the following data were obtained.   The pairs of values listed show in each case the reading corresponding to the total vol. used in the titration: 0.00 ml—29,600; 0.20 ml—28,000; 0.45 ml—25,600; 0.60 ml—24,000; 0.85 ml—22,700;   1.00 ml—22,900;   1.25 ml—26,500;   1.40 ml—28,500; 1.65—31,900.   Calculate the no. of g of ammonium ions present in the sample.

*17-10.   A 65.0-mg sample of an organic iodide salt contg. one iodine atom per organic molecule is dissolved in 50.0 ml of methanol and titrated with a methanol soln. of $AgNO_3$ which is 2.00×10^{-1} M.   The high-frequency conductance is meas-ured after each 0.10-ml increment.   The end point is found when 0.95 ml has been added.   (a) Calculate the mol. wt. of the organic salt.   (b) What shaped curve would you anticipate for this titration?

17-11.   At 25°C what is the equiv. conductance at infinite dilution of a soln. of $BaCl_2$?

17-12.   Show the general form of the titration curve one would expect to get in the conductometric titration of $N/100$ NH_4OH with (a) 1.00 N HCl, (b) 1.00 N $HC_2H_3O_2$.

17-13.   Using the equiv. conductance values obtained from the mobilities of the ions, show the general form of the titration curve in each of the following cases: (a) titration of NaOH with HNO_3, (b) titration of $BaCl_2$ with K_2SO_4, (c) titration of $BaCl_2$ with H_2SO_4, (d) titration of $Ba(OH)_2$ with H_2SO_4, (e) titration of $MgSO_4$ with $Ba(OH)_2$, (f) titration of NH_4Cl with NaOH, (g) titration of $AgNO_4$ with LiCl.

17-14.   In the titration of 80.0 ml of a soln. of HNO_3 with 4.85 N NaOH, the fol-lowing relative conductivities were obtained for the corresponding vols. of NaOH: 0.00 ml = 501; 1.00 ml = 340; 2.00 ml = 175; 3.00 ml = 180; 4.00 ml = 261; 5.00 ml = 338.   Plot the curve, and calculate the acid normality of the original acid soln.

17-15.   An aq. soln. of a certain weak organic monobasic acid is diluted and titrated conductometrically with 0.500 N NH_4OH.   The following relative conductiv-ities were obtained: 0.00 ml = 0.57; 0.50 ml = 0.32; 1.00 ml = 0.27; 1.50 ml = 0.40; 2.00 ml = 0.60; 3.00 ml = 0.95; 4.00 ml = 1.35; 5.00 ml = 1.75; 6.00 ml = 2.13; 7.00 ml = 2.48; 7.50 ml = 2.68; 8.00 ml = 2.78; 9.00 ml = 2.82; 10.00 ml = 2.83; 14.00 ml = 2.87.   (a) Plot these values, and determine the no. of meq. of the acid initially present.   (b) Show what the general appearance of the curve would have been had 0.500 N NaOH been used for the titration.

17-16.   A soln. approx. 0.01 N in NH_4Cl is titrated conductometrically with 1.25 N NaOH, and the following relative conductance values were obtained at the indicated buret readings: 0.00 ml = 451; 1.00 ml = 455; 2.00 ml = 459; 2.50 ml = 460;

2.75 ml = 462; 3.00 ml = 465; 3.25 ml = 472; 3.50 ml = 482; 3.75 ml = 497; 4.00 ml = 515; 4.50 ml = 575; 5.00 ml = 643; 6.00 ml = 776.   Plot the curve, and determine the no. of g of NH_4Cl present in the soln.

17-17.   A soln. contg. NaBr is titrated with 0.650 N $AgNO_3$.   The following relative values were obtained for the conductances of the soln. during the titration: 0.00 ml = 269; 0.50 ml = 255; 1.00 ml = 241; 1.50 ml = 227; 2.00 ml = 213; 2.50 ml = 197; 3.00 ml = 218; 3.50 ml = 237; 4.00 ml = 261; 4.50 ml = 282; 5.00 ml = 301.   Plot the curve on a large scale, and calculate the no. of g of NaBr originally present in the soln.

17-18.   Oxalic acid is a dibasic acid and can be considered as an equimolar mixt. of a fairly strong acid ($H_2C_2O_4 \rightleftharpoons H^+ + HC_2O_4^-$; $K' = 4 \times 10^{-2}$) and a weak acid ($HC_2O_4^- \rightleftharpoons H^+ + C_2O_4^=$; $K'' = 5 \times 10^{-5}$).   The following relative conductance values were obtained in the conductometric titration of a dil. soln. of oxalic acid with 0.640 N NH_4OH.   (a) Plot the curve, and calculate the no. of g of $H_2C_2O_4 \cdot 2H_2O$ present in the soln.   0.00 ml = 285; 0.20 ml = 235; 0.40 ml = 188; 0.60 ml = 141; 0.70 ml = 118; 0.80 ml = 109; 0.90 ml = 115; 1.00 ml = 123; 1.20 ml = 147; 1.40 ml = 173; 1.60 ml = 184; 1.80 ml = 183; 2.00 ml = 181; 2.20 ml = 181.   (b) What does the lowest point of the curve represent?   (c) Show how it would be possible in certain cases to analyze a mixt. of oxalic acid and sodium binoxalate, $NaHC_2O_4$.   (d) What would be the general appearance of the curve in this case?

17-19.   An acid soln. of uranyl nitrate, $UO_2(NO_3)_2 \cdot 6H_2O$, was passed through a Zn reductor, and after the soln. was aerated, the U was entirely as U(IV).   An aliquot portion of the soln. was titrated conductometrically with $K_2Cr_2O_7$ soln. (49.04 g/liter) back to the original oxidation state.   Plot the titration curve from the following data representing ml and corresponding relative conductance values, and determine from it the uranium content expressed in terms of g of U_3O_8 in the portion taken for titration.   0.00 ml = 820;   0.20 ml = 809;   0.40 ml = 798;   0.60 ml = 788; 0.80 ml = 778; 1.00 ml = 768; 1.20 ml = 762; 1.40 ml = 775; 1.60 ml = 788; 1.80 ml = 801, 2.00 ml = 814.

Polarography. Amperometric Titrations. Chronopotentiometry

18-1 The Polarographic Principle

Suppose a solution contains a reducible substance at low concentration (for example, 10^{-3} N) and in addition an inert electrolyte (*supporting electrolyte*) at a relatively high concentration (for example, 10^{-1} N), and suppose the unstirred solution is subjected to electrolysis, using one electrode of microdimensions. A convenient microelectrode consists of metallic mercury dropping at a steady rate from a capillary tube, thus exposing a constantly fresh surface of the metal to the solution. This electrode is called a *dropping mercury electrode* (DME). The other electrode, which must have a large surface area, serves as the reference electrode and in this case can be a pool of mercury at the bottom of the vessel. The supporting electrolyte contributes most to the conductance of the solution but is not affected at the electrodes.

If a DME is used as the cathode and the applied emf is increased gradually, the current remains near zero and increases only slightly until the decomposition potential is reached (see Sec. 15-4). This current is known as the *residual current*. At this point electrolytic reduction of the reducible substance starts at the cathode, the current increases, and an increased emf causes a sharp increase in the current in accordance with Ohm's law, $E = IR$. In spite of the fact that the reducible ion in the bulk of the solution diffuses slowly toward the electrode, as electrolysis progresses in the unstirred solution, a point is reached where the reducible ion or compound is nearly depleted at the electrode, and because of this concentration polarization, a further increase in emf causes practically no increase in current.

These steps are represented by the solid line in Fig. 14,

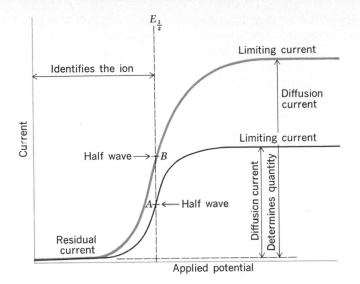

Fig. 14   Polarographic current-voltage relationship.

where current (in microamperes) is plotted against the applied voltage.

The nearly constant current corresponding to the upper right-hand part of the curve is called the *limiting current*. The increase in current from the residual current to the limiting current is called the *diffusion current*, and its magnitude is proportional to the concentration of the reducible substance in the solution.

Point A on the curve is the potential at which the current is one-half of the diffusion current. It is called the *half-wave potential*, and its significance is seen from the broken-line curve in the same figure. This represents the current-voltage curve obtained when a more concentrated solution of the same ion is electrolyzed. It is seen that the half-wave potential B in this case corresponds to the same point on the abscissa as the half-wave potential A. The half-wave potential of a reducible substance is therefore independent of the concentration and, with properly calibrated apparatus, serves as a means of identifying the substance being reduced or oxidized.

The magnitude of the diffusion current (height of the polarographic wave), on the other hand, is a measure of the quantity of the substance present in solution, so that a polarographic curve serves to identify an ion qualitatively and quantitatively. When several kinds of reducible substances are present in the same solution and the respective half-wave potentials are not too close together, the nature and approximate quantities of the substances can be established by a single run. The polarographic curve in such a case is a series of diffusion-current curves which are produced as the voltage is gradually increased, and the substances are reduced in order.   The general appearance of such a curve for the reduction of several inorganic ions is shown in Fig. 15.   In this figure, the value of the emf of the half wave at the end of the horizontal arrow identifies the lead.   The quantity of lead is revealed by the current spanned by the vertical arrow.

A schematic diagram of a polarographic hookup is shown in Fig. 16. In this case, the cathode consists of a dropping mercury electrode from which the metal emerges from a capillary tube in a steady flow of small drops.   A fresh surface of mercury is thereby constantly exposed to the solution, and there is therefore no effective change due to the formation of amalgams.   In many cases a saturated calomel half-cell is used as the anode and reference.

Actually, the current strengths vary between a minimum and a maximum for each drop of mercury as it forms, since there is a periodic change in the surface area of the drop.   Therefore the graph lines obtained are actually not the smooth lines shown in the accompaning figures but are sawtoothed lines.   The amplitude of the fluctuations is small, however, and smooth lines can easily be drawn between them to represent the mean positions.   Current-voltage curves can be automatically plotted by means of a mechanism called a *polarograph,* but satisfactory curves can also be obtained manually.

An important mathematical relationship pertaining to the diffusion current is shown in the *Ilkovic equation:*

$$i_d = 607nCD^{1/2}m^{2/3}t^{1/6}$$

where i_d = average diffusion current, μa, [10^{-6} amp]
$\quad\quad$ n = no. of faradays per mole involved in the electrode reaction
$\quad\quad$ C = concentration of the electroactive material, millimoles/liter
$\quad\quad$ D = diffusion coefficient of the electroactive material, cm^2/sec
$\quad\quad$ m = rate of flow of mercury through the capillary, mg/sec
$\quad\quad$ t = time between successive drops of mercury, sec

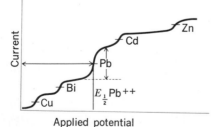

Applied potential   Fig. 15   Polarographic curve.

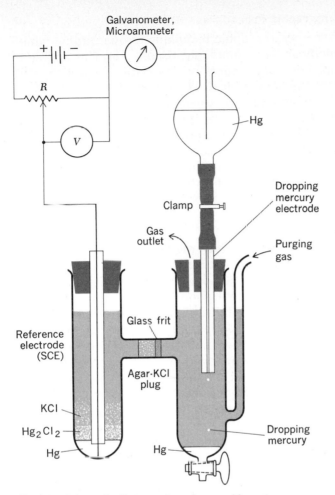

Fig. 16   Schematic diagram of a polarographic system.

The equation holds well only when t is between 3 to 7 sec.   The terms $m^{2/3}$ and $t^{1/6}$ are obviously dependent on the character and size of the capillary; the terms n, C, and $D^{1/2}$ are determined by the properties of the solute and solution.

Sometimes the factors pertaining to any one electrode process under a fixed set of experimental conditions are combined in a single factor I, called the *diffusion current constant*.

$$I = 607nD^{1/2} = \frac{i_d}{Cm^{2/3}t^{1/6}}$$

18-2   Analytical Polarographic Procedures

For the application of the polarographic technique to quantitative analysis, a number of methods are commonly used. (1) The absolute method involves simply the application of the Ilkovic equation and requires a knowledge of the values for n, D, m, and t. In most cases, the diffusion current is measured experimentally after the other terms have been determined. (2) Using a series of standard samples, and provided there are no interfering waves, it is possible to construct a graph of the diffusion-current values versus concentrations. The concentration of an unknown can then be read directly from the graph. An equation of the following type can also be utilized with a single standard solution:

$$C_{(unk)} = C_{(std)} \frac{i_{d(unk)}}{i_{d(std)}}$$

(3) The *internal standard method* (or pilot-ion method) is based on the fact that the ratio of two wave heights for two substances in the same solution is independent of most experimental parameters (temperature, m, t, viscosity, supporting electrolyte concentration). If one knows this ratio from a previous experiment (or the relative diffusion-current constants) and the concentration of one of the species, it is a simple matter to calculate the concentration of the unknown substance. (4) The *method of standard addition* is also frequently employed in polarographic analysis. Using this approach, a polarogram for an aliquot portion of the sample solution is obtained. To a second aliquot portion of the sample solution is added a known quantity of the species under investigation. The second solution is polarographed in the same manner as the first solution. Knowing the volumes of the aliquots and the quantity of material added, it is possible to calculate the concentration of the unknown in the sample solution. The following example illustrates one approach to standard addition techniques, although several different variations are frequently used. In most cases, a linear relationship between concentration and the quantity being measured is assumed; if this is not the case, slightly more complicated standard addition techniques are used.

Example 1   The analysis of an unknown cadium solution is to be carried out polarographically using a standard addition technique. The unknown sample yielded a diffusion current of 47.4 μa. When equal volumes of the unknown solution and a standard solution, 5.50×10^{-4} M, were mixed, a diffusion current of 58.5 μa was observed. Calculate the concentration of cadmium in the unknown. (Assume there are no species present in the unknown sample which complex with cadmium or reduce at the same potential.)

Solution   Remembering that equal volumes were used, an equation of the following type is applicable:

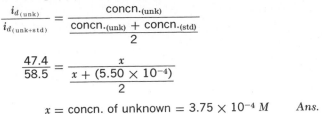

$$\frac{i_{d_{(unk)}}}{i_{d_{(unk+std)}}} = \frac{concn._{(unk)}}{\dfrac{concn._{(unk)} + concn._{(std)}}{2}}$$

$$\frac{47.4}{58.5} = \frac{x}{\dfrac{x + (5.50 \times 10^{-4})}{2}}$$

$$x = concn. \text{ of unknown} = 3.75 \times 10^{-4} \, M \qquad Ans.$$

18-3   Amperometric Titrations

The polarographic principle can be applied to certain titrations and produce results of a high precision, comparable to that obtainable in potentiometric and conductometric titrations. For some amperometric titrations, a DME is sufficiently sensitive; however, the use of a rotating platinum electrode (RPE) will usually result in increased sensitivity due to the larger diffusion currents. These result from the thinner diffusion layer produced by the rapid rotation.

Suppose a reducible substance in a solution is subjected to an initial emf which is of such magnitude as to give the current corresponding to the diffusion current, and suppose the solution is subjected to a precipitation titration with a nonreducible reagent. Such a case would be the titration of a solution of a lead salt with sulfate. The concentration of the reducible substance (Pb^{++}) is steadily diminished as the sulfate is added. The current, being proportional to the concentration of lead ions, likewise steadily diminishes as the titration proceeds, and if current values are plotted (as ordinates) against volumes of titrating solution added (as abscissas), a curve similar to that of Fig. 17 is obtained. The equivalence point corresponds to the point of intersection of the two arms of the curve. These arms are essentially straight lines, especially if the effect of dilution is corrected for. In the above case, the nearly horizontal portion of the curve corresponds to the diffusion current of a saturated solution of lead sulfate. Solubility effects may give a curved line in the close neighborhood of the equivalence point, but as in certain conductometric titration curves (see Fig. 12C), extension of the two straight parts of the curve will give a point of intersection corresponding to the equivalence point. As in conductometric titrations, it is advantageous to titrate a dilute solution with a relatively concentrated one.

An equally satisfactory titration curve is given in the amperometric titration of a nonreducible ion when it is titrated with a reagent capable of electrolytic reduction. This type of curve is illustrated in Prob. 18-15.

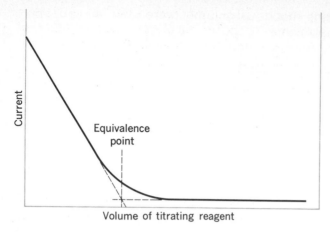

Current

Equivalence
point

Volume of titrating reagent

Fig. 17 **Amperometric titration curve (Pb^{++} + SO$_4^=$).**

The titration of a reducible ion with a reducible reagent (giving a V-shaped curve) is also feasible (Prob. 18-16).

18-4 Chronopotentiometry

Polarography differs from voltammetry in that the latter provides for rapid mass transport whereas the former relies on diffusion. Both methods assume a constant or continuously varied (scanned) applied potential, with the current being measured. If the reverse approach is followed, the current is held constant and the voltage is measured; this technique is called *chronopotentiometry*.

A cell containing the reducible or oxidizable substance, a supporting electrolyte, two working electrodes, and a reference electrode is used. A constant current is impressed across the two working electrodes. If a reducible substance is being studied, the resultant voltage between the cathode and the reference electrode is then measured. With the solution at rest, the reducible substance present within the volume near the electrode is quickly depleted. After this, the voltage changes rapidly to the value determined by the decomposition potential of the next reducible solute or of the supporting electrolyte. Figure 18 shows the appearance of the ''chronopotentiogram'' produced.

The *transition time* (τ), represented by the arrow, is the time required for the concentration of the reducible species in the vicinity of the electrode to be reduced effectively to zero. It is usually measured empirically. The value of the voltage at $\tau_{1/4}(E_{\tau_{1/4}})$ (see Fig. 18) is characteristic of the reducible substance and in certain instances is nearly equivalent to the standard potential or to the $E_{1/2}$ measured in polarography.

For quantitative applications, the square root of the transition time ($\tau^{1/2}$) is directly proportional to the concentration (in moles/milliliter) of the reducible substance, in accordance with the following equation:

$$\tau^{1/2} = \frac{\pi^{1/2}nFAD^{1/2}C}{2i}$$

where τ = transition time

n = number of electrons involved in the electrode reaction

F = faraday constant

A = area of the working electrode, in cm^2

D = the diffusion coefficient of the reducible substance, cm^2/sec

i = current, amp

The advantages of chronopotentiometry for quantitative analysis lie in the simplicity of the instrumentation and the speed of the determination (usually less than 60 sec for the measurement).

PROBLEMS

*18-1. It has been shown that F$^-$ ions in the presence of Cl$^-$ ions can be titrated amperometrically with the formation of a ppt. of PbClF. In one such titration at pH 6.5 in which 0.100 M Pb(NO$_3$)$_2$ was used, the equivalence point was established from the graph as corresponding to a buret reading of 5.95 ml. How many mg of F$^-$ ions were shown to be present? Show the general appearance of the titration curve.

*18-2. What is the approx. ratio of the concn. of Pb^{++} to that of Cu^{++} in the soln. giving the polarographic curve shown in Fig. 15?

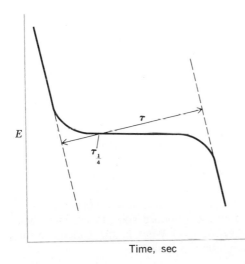

E

τ

$\tau_{\frac{1}{4}}$

Time, sec

Fig. 18   Schematic diagram of a chronopotentiogram.

*18-3.   An amperometric titration of 50.00 ml of an ammoniacal soln. of $NiCl_2$ contg. 2.0×10^{-4} mole of dissolved $NiCl_2$ is carried out with an ethanol soln. of dimethylglyoxime.   The values obtained were corrected for vol. changes.   The no. of μa at 0.00 ml was 18.20; that at 4.40 ml was 6.44; that at the equivalence point was 1.50.   What was the reading at 2.00 ml of titrant?

*18-4.   In a certain polarographic determination, using a dropping Hg electrode, the capillary is of such size that the Hg leaves the tip at a rate of 2 drops every 9.0 sec.   Each drop is found to weigh 6.1×10^{-3} g.   What is the product of the last two terms in the corresponding Ilkovic equation?

*18-5.   Lannoge [*Anal. Chem.*, **35**, 558 (1963)] has described an amperometric titration method for the detn. of vanadium in vanadium metal using a rotating platinum electrode (RPE).   A 1.00-g sample is dissolved, oxidized, and divided into four 200-ml samples.   To each is added 50.0 ml of 1.00×10^{-1} M ferrous ammonium sulfate, the excess of which is titrated with 2.00×10^{-2} N $K_2Cr_2O_7$. The potential of the RPE is set at 0.8 volt versus a saturated calomel electrode. (*a*) What type of titration curve would be obtained?   (*b*) What is the percentage of vanadium in the metal if an average of 11.0 ml of the $K_2Cr_2O_7$ soln. is required to titrate each of the four samples?

*18-6.   The amperometric analysis of some sympathomimetic amines is to be carried out using sodium tetraphenylborate as a pptg. agent.   Using a graphite electrode set at 0.550 volt versus a satd. calomel electrode (SCE), the titrant is electroactive, whereas the amines are not.   50.0 ml of an unknown soln. is mixed with 50.0 ml of an inert electrolyte-buffer combination, and the resultant soln. is titrated with 5.00×10^{-3} M sodium tetraphenylborate.   (*a*) Predict the shape of the titration curve.   (*b*) Calculate the concn. of amine in the unknown soln. when 3.60 ml of titrant is required, assuming a 1:1 reaction between the amine and titrant.

*18-7.   Calculate the diffusion coefficient of lead if the transition time for a 5.00×10^{-4} M soln. is 22.1 sec when $A = 2.4$ cm^2, $i = 144$ μa, and $n = 2$.

*18-8.   The analysis of hydroxylamine in acid soln. by chronopotentiometry has been described by Davis [*Anal. Chem.*, **35**, 764 (1963)].   In previous studies, it was shown that $n = 6$ and $D = 1.40 \times 10^{-5}$ cm^2/sec.   If the transition time was measured as 41 sec for a particular soln. with the current set at 1.50 ma through a 1.60-cm^2 electrode, calculate the concn. of hydroxylamine in the unknown soln.

*18-9.   Using a platinum disk electrode as the anode, triethylamine has been analyzed by chronopotentiometry.   A standard 4.00×10^{-4} M soln. yielded a transition time of 8.20 sec.   On running the unknown soln., the transition time was found to be less than 1 sec.   The const. current was therefore halved, and a working electrode of twice the area of the previous one was substituted.   (*a*) Predict the ratio of the transition time now exhibited by the standard soln. to the transition time exhibited before the changes were made.   (*b*) What is the concn. of the unknown soln. if it now exhibits a transition time of 1.9 sec?

*18-10. In a particular polarographic experiment, the diffusion current const. (I) for lead has been found empirically to be 8.25 when $m = 32.5$ mg/sec and $t = 4.3$ sec. Under exactly the same conditions, the lead diffusion current for an unknown soln. is measured and found to be 4.3 μa. Calculate the concn. of lead in the unknown soln. using the absolute method.

*18-11. The diffusion current for a standard 1.00×10^{-4} M soln. of hydroquinone is found to be 17.5 μa. An unknown soln. of hydroquinone when diluted tenfold and polarographed under the same conditions yielded a current of 27.9 μa. Calculate the concn. of hydroquinone in the unknown sample.

*18-12. A 1.00-g sample contg. some iron is dissolved and treated to make 100 ml of a ferrous soln. A 20.0-ml portion of this is polarographed, yielding a diffusion current of 42.0 μa. To the remaining portion of the initial soln., 5.00 ml of a 1.00×10^{-2} M ferrous ammonium sulfate soln. is added. A 20.0-ml-aliquot portion of the resulting soln. yields a diffusion current of 58.5 μa. Calculate the concn. of iron in the original sample.

*18-13. Zinc is to be used as an internal standard for the polarographic analysis of thallium. A standard soln., contg. twice the concn. of zinc as thallium, has diffusion currents of 1.89 μa for Tl^+ and 3.50 μa for Zn^{++}. A 10.0-g sample of an alloy contg. thallium but no zinc is dissolved to make 500 ml of soln. To 25.0 ml of this soln. is added 25.0 ml of a 1.00×10^{-3} M Zn^{++} soln. The diffusion currents are then measured and found to be 18.2 μa for Tl^+ and 14.5 μa for Zn^{++}. Calculate the percentage of thallium in the alloy.

*18-14. The concn. of sulfur in a liquid mercaptan can be determined amperometrically by titration with a 0.0200 N soln. of $AgNO_3$ (by a $1:1$ reaction) using a rotating platinum electrode. In a certain analysis 50.0 ml of an unknown sample, free of H_2S, is dissolved in 200 ml of acetone in which has been dissolved the supporting electrolyte and from which all O_2 has been removed. From the following data showing the no. of μa of current corresponding to the no. of ml of titrating soln. used, calculate the concn. of sulfur in the unknown: 0.00 ml = 0.40; 0.40 ml = 0.41; 0.60 ml = 0.40; 0.85 ml = 0.42; 1.05 ml = 0.41; 1.27 ml — 0.41; 1.49 ml = 0.42; 1.72 ml = 0.45; 1.85 ml = 0.70; 2.00 ml = 2.36; 2.17 ml = 3.80; 2.45 ml = 6.75; 2.70 ml = 8.89.

18-15. (a) In the following amperometric titration, plot the titration curve, and determine from it the vol. of titrant corresponding to the equivalence point. (b) Find the no. of g of K_2SO_4 shown to be present.

A certain vol. of 0.0100 M K_2SO_4 is titrated with 0.100 M $Pb(NO_3)_2$. The following values are the μa obtained at the corresponding vols. of titrant. Dilution effects have been corrected for. 0.0 ml = 0.8; 1.0 ml = 0.8; 2.0 ml = 0.8; 3.0 ml = 0.8; 4.0 ml = 0.9; 4.5 ml — 1.3; 5.0 ml — 4.2; 5.5 ml = 11.3; 6.0 ml = 20.0; 6.5 ml = 28.9; 7.0 ml = 37.5.

18-16. (a) Plot the following amperometric titration curve, and determine from it the vol. of titrant corresponding to the equivalence point. (b) How many g of Pb^{++} are shown to be initially present?

(c) A 50-ml pipetful of dil. $Pb(NO_3)_2$ (in 0.1 M KNO_3) is titrated with 0.0500 M

$K_2Cr_2O_7$ pptg. $PbCrO_4$. The following values are the no. of μa actually obtained at the corresponding vols. of titrant: 0.0 ml = 81.56; 1.0 ml = 66.22; 2.0 ml = 48.34; 3.0 ml = 31.66; 4.0 ml = 15.25; 4.8 ml = 3.79; 4.9 ml = 2.09; 5.0 ml = 2.90; 5.1 ml = 5.10; 5.3 ml = 12.03; 5.5 ml = 21.86; 6.0 ml = 43.86. Before plotting the curve, correct for dilution effect by multiplying each current reading by $(V + v)/V$ in which V = initial vol. of soln. and v = total vol. of reagent added.

18-17. Kolthoff and Langer [*J. Am. Chem. Soc.*, **62**, 3172 (1940)] report the amperometric titration of 50 ml of approx. 0.002 M $CoSO_4$ with α-nitroso-β-naphthol (approx. 0.1 M) in a medium 0.2 M in HAc and 0.2 M in NaAc to form a reddish-purple ppt. The titration curves obtained indicate the following readings: In the first series, the potential was -1.54 volts; in the second series, the potential was -0.06 volt. A satd. calomel electrode was used as the reference electrode.

Milliliters of reagent	Microamperes in series 1	Microamperes in series 2
0.00	5.90	0.10
2.00	3.45	0.12
3.00	2.25	0.13
4.00	1.05	0.14
4.50	3.40	2.70
5.00	8.90	7.90

(*a*) Plot these readings on graph paper, and determine the buret reading at the equivalence point in each case. (*b*) Give the reason for the difference in appearance between the curves obtained in the two titrations. (*c*) What approx. molar ratio between metal and precipitant is shown?

18-18. A soln. containing 1.0×10^{-3} mole/liter of reducible metal ion in a supporting electrolyte gives an average diffusion current of 6.00 μa. The diffusion current const. in this case is 4.00, and 1.25 mg/sec of Hg flow from the capillary. What is the drop time?

18-19. The diffusion coefficient of a certain reducible divalent ion at a concn. of 2.1×10^{-3} M in a soln. of supporting electrolyte is 1.0×10^{-5} cm^2/sec. (*a*) If the delivery capillary is of such size that the product of the last two terms of the Ilkovic equation is 2.60 and the ion is reduced to metal, calculate the average diffusion current. (*b*) If the drops fall every 5.0 sec, what is the rate of flow of the Hg?

Coulometric Titrations

19-1 Fundamental Principles of Coulometry

In a coulometric titration the equivalence point is established by potentiometric, conductometric, or color-indicator methods, but the reactant, instead of being added from a buret, is generated by electrolysis. In this way standard solutions are not required, and the generated reactant can be one (for example, Br_2 or Cl_2) that, because of instability, cannot be used as a standard solution in the conventional way. The amount of reactant is determined from the time and current required to reach the equivalence point, since from Faraday's law (see Sec. 15-3),

$$\frac{\text{Time (sec)} \times \text{no. of ma}}{96,500} = \text{no. of meq.}$$

Ordinarily, small quantities are determined in this way, and a device must be used to maintain a constant current. The time can be determined by means of an ordinary stopwatch, but it is better to use an electrical timer controlled by the current itself. It is also important in any given determination to make a blank run with a known quantity of constituent in order to establish the current efficiency.

As an example of a coulometric titration, consider the titration of an acid. The dilute solution of the acid to be titrated is added to a moderately concentrated solution of NaBr. A platinum anode and a silver cathode are used. Electrolysis is started, a constant current is maintained, and the pH value of the well-stirred solution is determined potentiometrically at frequent time intervals during the electrolysis. A titration curve (pH against time) can be plotted to determine the equivalence point, or the electrolysis can be carried only to the point where the appropriate pH value is reached. The reactions at the electrodes are

Anode: $2Ag + 2Br^- \longrightarrow 2AgBr + 2e$
Cathode: $2H_2O + 2e \longrightarrow 2OH^- + H_2$

The acid is, in effect, being titrated by the generated hydroxyl ions. If, for example, 350 sec is required for a current of 0.100 amp to bring the solution to the equivalence point under 100% current efficiency, then

$$\frac{350 \times 100}{96,500} = 0.363 \text{ meq. acid}$$

was present in the added sample.

By using a solution of an inert electrolyte (for example, Na_2SO_4), platinum electrodes, and separate anode and cathode compartments (connected only by an agar electrolyte bridge), the reactions at the electrodes are

Anode: $H_2O \longrightarrow 2H^+ + \frac{1}{2}O_2 + 2e$
Cathode: $2H_2O + 2e \longrightarrow 2OH^- + H_2$

In this case, an acid can, in effect, be titrated in the cathode compartment, and an alkali can be titrated in the anode compartment.

Certain reducing agents can be titrated coulometrically. With platinum electrodes and a two-compartment cell, the electrolysis of a solution of KBr or KI proceeds according to the equations

Anode: $2Br^- (2I^-) \longrightarrow Br_2 (I_2) + 2e$
Cathode: $2H_2O + 2e \longrightarrow 2OH^- + H_2$

If a solution of arsenic(III) is present in the anode compartment, it can be titrated by the liberated Br_2 or I_2:

$$AsO_3^{3-} + Br_2 (I_2) + 2OH^- \longrightarrow AsO_4^{3-} + 2Br^- (2I^-) + H_2O$$

The coulometric titration of an oxidizing agent like permanganate, dichromate, or ceric salt can be carried out by having present in the cathode compartment containing the oxidizing agent a considerable excess of ferric salt. The principal cathode reaction is the reduction of ferric ions (since they are present at high concentration). The ferrous ions formed, in turn, reduce the oxidizing agent being titrated:

Anode: $H_2O \longrightarrow 2H^+ + \frac{1}{2}O_2 + 2e$
Cathode: $2Fe^{3+} + 2e \longrightarrow 2Fe^{++}$

PROBLEMS

*19-1. A 0.200 M soln. of NaBr has a pH value of 6.50. To it is added a 25-ml pipetful of a dil. soln. of HCl. With a Pt cathode and an Ag anode the soln. is titrated coulometrically with a current maintained at 6.0×10^{-3} amp. At the end of 8 min 20 sec, a pH meter shows that the pH value of the soln. is again 6.50. Assuming 100% current efficiency, (*a*) what was the normality of the acid soln. added, and (*b*) what vol. of H_2 gas (dry, standard conditions) was evolved in the coulometer during the titration?

*19-2. In the coulometric titration of dichromate, how many g of $K_2Cr_2O_7$ correspond to 1.00 μa-sec? Write equations for the anode and cathode reactions in such a titration.

*19-3. A soln. contg. a moderate amt. of KI, a small amt. of $NaHCO_3$, and a minute amt. of Sb(III) salt is electrolyzed in the anode compartment of a coulometer cell. A soln. of Na_2SO_4 is used in the cathode compartment, and a salt bridge contg. Na_2SO_4 soln. connects the two compartments. Starch is added to the anode portion, and electrolysis is carried out until the soln. just turns blue. A pipetful of a soln. contg. 80 mg of Sb(III) is then introduced into the anode compartment, and the soln. is titrated coulometrically at a current strength maintained at 0.0500 amp until the blue color just reappears. (*a*) Assuming 100% current efficiency, how many min were registered during the titration by the timer inserted in the circuit? (*b*) Write equations for the anode and cathode reactions.

*19-4. A 1.05-g sample of a solid contg. an unknown quantity of arsenic is dissolved in water and the arsenic is converted to arsenite. The soln. is diluted to 100 ml and 25.0-ml portions are titrated, using electrogenerated iodine. The const. current exhibits a potential of 25 mv across a 10.0-ohm precision resistor and requires 125 sec to reach the starch end point. (*a*) Calculate the percentage of arsenic in the unknown sample. (*b*) Write balanced equations for the electrode reactions and for the titration reaction.

*19-5. Miller and Hume [*Anal. Chem.*, **32**, 524 (1960)] have described a coulometric titration of copper in brass using sulfhydryl. The sulfhydryl group is electrogenerated from the mercuric complex of thioglycollic acid. A 1.00-g sample of the brass is dissolved in 100 ml of acid. The electrolysis time required to reach the equivalence point of the blank (determined amperometrically with a mercury pM electrode) was 1.45 sec at a const. current of 22.5 ma. To this same blank soln. was added 10.0 ml of the unknown soln. The resultant solution required 65.7 sec to reach the equivalence point. Calculate the percentage of copper in the brass.

*19-6. The electrogeneration of the biphenyl radical anion and its application to the analysis of benzophenone have been described by Maricle [*Anal. Chem.*, **35**, 683 (1963)]. A 1.00-g solid sample contg. some benzophenone is dissolved in a soln. of dimethylformamide which contains biphenyl and tetra-n-butyl-ammonium bromide and which was pretitrated to the potentiometric end point. The sample was titrated with electrogenerated biphenyl radical anion, requiring 2 moles of monoradical anion per mole of benzophenone. A current of 18.5 ma for 142 sec was used. Calculate the percentage by wt. of benzophenone in the unknown sample.

19-7. In the coulometric titration of a dil. alkali, how many g of hydroxyl ions correspond to a μa-sec?

19-8. A soln. of $K_2Cr_2O_7$ was titrated coulometrically in the following manner. The soln. also contained 2 ml of 18 N H_2SO_4, 1 ml of 85% H_3PO_4, and 15 ml of 6 N ferric ammonium sulfate. Electrolysis was at 20.0 ma, and the end point, found potentiometrically, occurred at the end of 241.2 sec. (*a*) Find the no. of mg of Cr present in the sample, and show the general appearance of the titration curve (emf against time). (*b*) Write equations for the reactions at the anode and cathode.

FIVE
**Optical
Methods of
Analysis**

Absorption Methods

20-1 Principles

The unique absorption of light by a given compound has been used extensively as a means of analysis. The earliest work was carried out with color comparators which involved direct comparisons with standards. The development of instrumental methods has made possible many refinements in colorimetric methods and has enlarged the field to include absorption in many regions of the spectrum besides the visible. Depending on the compound and the type of absorption being measured, the sample may be in the gaseous, liquid, or solid state. In the ultraviolet and visible regions, the sample is usually dissolved to form a dilute solution; in the infrared region, a much wider variety of sample-handling techniques is used.

The following terms are frequently used in absorption methods:

P_0 or I_0 = intensity of incident light (i.e., light entering the sample)

P or I = intensity of transmitted light (i.e., light leaving the sample)

c = concentration of the solute in the sample medium

b = sample path length (usually in cm)

$T = \dfrac{P}{P_0}$ = transmittance of the sample (the ratio of the radiant power transmitted by the sample to the radiant power impinging on the sample)

$100T$ = percentage transmittance of the sample

$A = \log \dfrac{P_0}{P}$ = absorbance (optical density) of the sample

Two laws are fundamental to absorption methods. *Lambert's* (or *Bouguer's*) *law* states

> In a homogeneous sample the intensity of plane-parallel mono-chromatic light entering a sample normal to the surface is diminished exponentially as the path length of absorption increases arithmetically:

$$\frac{P}{P_0} = e^{-kb}$$

where k is a constant, the value of which depends on the nature of the solute, on the wavelength of light, on the concentration of the solution, and, frequently, on the nature of the medium. The symbol e is the base of natural (Naperian) logarithms (= 2.718···).

Beer's (or *Bernard's*) *law* states

> When parallel monochromatic light passes through a solution, the intensity of the transmitted light decreases exponentially as the concentration of the solution increases arithmetically:

$$\frac{P}{P_0} = e^{-k'c}$$

where k' is a constant, the value of which depends on the nature of the solute, on the wavelength of the light, on the length of the absorbing layer, and on the nature of the medium.

These laws are frequently combined into one law, commonly referred to as the *Beer-Lambert law*, which makes use of a single constant:

$$\log \frac{P_0}{P} = abc \qquad \text{or} \qquad A = abc$$

The constant a is called the *absorptivity*, and the concentration c is expressed in grams per liter. In cases where c is in molar units, the symbol ε is used in place of a and is called the *molar absorptivity*.

Example 1   If, with a beam of monochromatic light, 65.0% of the incident light is absorbed in its passage through a column of a certain colored solution, (a) what is the absorbance of the solution and (b) what fraction of the incident light would be transmitted if the column were only four-fifths as long?

Solution

(a) Percentage transmittance $= 100 \times \dfrac{I}{I_o} = 35.0$

Absorbance $= \log \dfrac{I_o}{I} = \log 2.86 = 0.456$ *Ans.*

(b) $\log \dfrac{I_o}{I} = \dfrac{4}{5} \times 0.456 = 0.365$

$\dfrac{I_o}{I} = 2.32$

$\dfrac{I}{I_o} = \text{transmittance} = 0.431$ *Ans.*

Numerous deviations from Beer's law, both chemical and instrumental, are known. For the law to be applicable, the precise chemical species present in the sample must not change as a function of concentration. In solution, one must be aware of solvent effects, dissociation, ionization, etc. Conversely, the degree of divergence from the law can offer a means of studying the particular phenomenon occurring.

Prior to the development of photoelectric devices for measuring light intensities, colorimetric methods were based almost exclusively upon the visual comparison of the color of a solution of known concentration with the color of the unknown solution. This was actually accomplished in a variety of ways. In one method, a series of long cylindrical tubes (*Nessler tubes*) was used; in another, the viewing depths were adjusted to obtain equal intensities (the *Duboscq colorimeter*).

Monochromatic radiation provides many advantages over white-light sources. For example, one colored component can be analyzed in the presence of several differently colored components. *Filter photometers*, incorporating filters to select the wavelength region for the measurement, are available in both single-beam and double-beam designs. As the name implies, a single-beam instrument has only one beam of light which is directed through the cell holder. The blank is placed in the cell holder first, and the instrument is set to read 100% transmittance. The blank is then removed, and the absorbance of the sample is measured. With a double-beam instrument, the light beam is usually split, and one portion is directed through the blank and the other through the sample simultaneously. Thus, a double-beam instrument inherently compensates for short-term changes in lamp intensity and detector response.

Spectrophotometers provide a major advantage over photometers in that the device used to select the wavelength of radiation (the monochromator) is much more versatile. These instruments can also be of either the single-beam or double-beam design. A double-beam recording spectrophotometer permits the direct measurement of an absorption spectrum, which frequently can be used for both qualitative and quantitative purposes.

Example 2   Solutions of fluorene (diphenylenemethane) in benzene can be analyzed by making use of its absorbance at 301 mμ, where

$\epsilon = 1.10 \times 10^4$ (log $\epsilon = 4.04$).   If a solution of fluorene of unknown concentration in benzene exhibits an absorbance of 0.720 in a 1.00-cm cell, what is the concentration of fluorene?

Solution   Using Beer's law,

$$A = \epsilon bc$$
$$0.720 = (1.10 \times 10^4)(1.00)(c)$$
$$c = 6.55 \times 10^{-5} M \qquad Ans.$$

The analysis of mixtures is also simple if each compound in the mixture exhibits an absorption in a region where no other species absorbs.   In these situations, the data are treated independently for each compound.   In most mixtures, however, more than one compound will absorb at a given wavelength; this does not make the analysis of the mixture an impossibility, provided the absorption spectrum for each pure compound present in the mixture is available.   If we assume that Beer's law holds, then since absorbances are additive, the total absorbance at any wavelength will be due to the sum of the absorbances of the individual components at that wavelength.   This is illustrated in Fig. 19.

By means of a series of simultaneous equations at different wavelengths (for example, at 300 and 400 mμ in Fig. 19), it is possible to analyze for several components present in a mixture by using absorption methods.

Example 3   A $1.0 \times 10^{-3} M$ solution of a dye (X) shows an absorbance of 0.20 at 450 mμ and an absorbance of 0.05 at 620 mμ.   A $1.0 \times 10^{-4} M$ solution of dye (Y) shows 0.00 absorbance at 450 mμ and an absorbance of 0.42 at 620 mμ.   Calculate the concentration of each dye

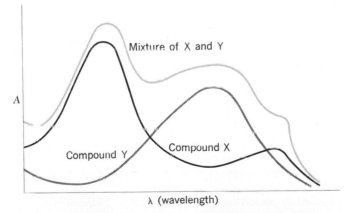

Fig. 19   Absorption spectra of two compounds, X and Y, and of an equimolar mixture of X and Y.

present in a solution which exhibits an absorbance of 0.38 and 0.71 at 450 and 620 mμ, respectively.   The same cell is used for all measurements.

Solution

1. Calculate the molar absorptivities of each species at both wavelengths.   Apply $A = \epsilon bc$ at each wavelength:
For dye (X):

$$\epsilon = \frac{0.20}{10^{-3}} = 200 \text{ at } 450 \text{ m}\mu$$

$$\epsilon = \frac{0.05}{10^{-3}} = 50 \text{ at } 620 \text{ m}\mu$$

For dye (Y):

$$\epsilon = 0.00 \text{ at } 450 \text{ m}\mu$$

$$\epsilon = \frac{0.42}{10^{-4}} = 4{,}200 \text{ at } 620 \text{ m}\mu$$

2. The absorption at each wavelength by the mixture will be equal to the sum of the individual absorptions.

$$A_{450} = (\epsilon_x)(c_x) + (\epsilon_y)(c_y)$$
$$A_{620} = (\epsilon_x)(c_x) + (\epsilon_y)(c_y)$$
$$0.37 = 200(c_x) + 0.00(c_y)$$
$$0.71 = 50(c_x) + 4{,}200(c_y)$$
$$c_x = \frac{0.38}{200} = 1.9 \times 10^{-3} \; M \qquad \textit{Ans.}$$
$$0.71 = (50)(1.9 \times 10^{-3}) + (4{,}200)(c_y)$$
$$c_y = \frac{(0.71) - (50)(1.9 \times 10^{-3})}{(4{,}200)} = 1.46 \times 10^{-4} \; M \qquad \textit{Ans.}$$

PROBLEMS

*20-1.   (*a*) What percentage of the incident light at a given wavelength is transmitted by a medium which at that wavelength has an absorbance of 1.176? (*b*) What is the absorbance of a soln. which absorbs two-thirds of the incident light?

*20-2.   A 250-ml sample of drinking water is to be analyzed for its percentage of NH_3.   It is diluted with 250 ml of NH_3-free water, Na_2CO_3 is added, and the mixt. is distilled.   Three separate fractions of 50 ml each are caught in 50-ml Nessler tubes contg. Nessler's reagent, which gives a yellow-orange color with small amts. of free NH_3.
    A stock soln. is prepared by dissolving 3.82 g of NH_4Cl in 1 liter of NH_3-free water, taking 10 ml of this soln., and again diluting to 1 liter.   A series of standards

is prepared by placing varying vols. of the stock soln. in 50-ml Nessler tubes, adding Nessler's reagent, and diluting to 50 ml.

The first fraction of the distillate from the sample is found to match in color with the standard contg. 1.7 ml of the stock soln.; the second fraction matches with the standard contg. 0.3 ml of the stock soln.; the third fraction is found to contain no appreciable NH_3.

Calculate the amt. in p.p.m. of nitrogen (present as NH_3) in the original drinking water.

*20-3.   A sample of Bureau of Standards steel contg. 0.410% Mn and weighing 1.00 g and a sample of similar steel of unknown Mn content weighing 1.10 g are separately dissolved in HNO_3, and the Mn oxidized to permanganate with periodate. The two solns. are diluted to the same vol. and are compared in a variable-depth colorimeter. The match of color intensities is at a point where the depth of the standard soln. is 10% less than that of the other soln. (*a*) Calculate the percentage Mn in the unknown, assuming Beer's law to hold over the small range of concns. involved. (*b*) Write an equation for the oxidation by the periodate.

*20-4.   A column of a soln. of $KMnO_4$ is found to have a transmittance of 0.340 for light of a wavelength of 525 mμ. What would be the transmittance of the light through a similar soln. in a column one-fifth as long?

*20-5.   A soln. of a certain colored substance at concn. A has a transmittance of 80.0%. If Beer's law holds, what would be the percentage transmittance at concn. 3A?

*20-6.   Manganese is determined colorimetrically as permanganate by measuring the absorption of monochromatic green light. A standard soln. in an absorption cell 5.00 cm long absorbs 10.0% of the light, while an unknown sample in a cell 1.00 cm long absorbs 50.0% of the light. The standard soln. contains 2.00 mg of Mn per liter. What is the concn. (in mg/liter) of the Mn in the unknown?

*20-7.   A certain soln. at concn. A absorbs 70.0% of the light passing through it. If Beer's law holds, what percentage of the light would be transmitted at a concn. one-third as great?

*20-8.   It has been shown that in the colorimetric detn. of silica in the form of blue silicomolybdate, the transmittance values of solns. of the compd. conform closely to Beer's law when light of appropriate wavelength is used. As determined by a spectrophotometer, the percentage transmittance of a soln. contg. 0.020 mg of SiO_2 was found to be 77.3; that of the same vol. of soln. contg. 0.10 mg of SiO_2 was 36.7. What is the calculated value of the percentage transmittance of the same vol. of soln. contg. 0.060 mg of SiO_2?

*20-9.   In the colorimetric detn. of Mn in an alloy, the unknown A and the standard alloy B of known composition were dissolved and analyzed in parallel. In each case the Mn was oxidized by periodate to permanganate and the solns. diluted to the same vol. In a spectrophotometer with a suitable filter the unknown and the standard registered 70.0 and 65.0% transmittance, respectively. Assuming Beer's law to hold, if the two permanganate solns. were placed in a colorimeter in which depths of solns. are varied until the intensities of transmitted light are matched, what would be the ratios of the depths of the two solns.?

*20-10.   The Coleman spectrophotometer has two adjacent scales, one marked "absorbance" and the other marked "% T." (a) What numerical value on the latter corresponds to 0.523 on the former? (b) What is the absorbance of a medium if 75.0% of the light is absorbed in its passage through the medium?

*20-11.   If the molar absorptivity of cyclopentadiene is 3.20×10^3 at 2400 Å, what will be the absorbance of a 5.00×10^{-5} M soln. in a 5.00-cm cell when measured at that wavelength?

*20-12.   Calculate the absorptivity of 2-naphthylamine if a 10.0-μg/ml soln. exhibits an absorbance of 0.400 when measured in a 1.00-cm cell.

*20-13.   The following data have been determined previously. Calculate the concn. of P and R in the mixt.

Compd.	Absorbance at 365 $m\mu$	Absorbance at 470 $m\mu$	Concn.
P	0.150	0.642	1.00×10^{-4} M
R	0.684	0.088	2.00×10^{-4} M
Unknown mixt.	0.721	0.604	?

*20-14.   The analysis of trace amts. of ruthenium as its 1-nitroso-2-naphthol complex has been discussed in the literature [Anal. Chem., 38, 221 (1966)]. The molar absorptivity is 1.83×10^4 at 645 $m\mu$. After treatment of a 20.2-mg zinc–magnesium ore sample in the proper way, including separation of the ruthenium tetroxide, the absorption of the 25.0-ml resultant sample is measured and found to be 0.250, using a 2.00-cm cell. Calculate the concn. of ruthenium in the ore (in percentage by wt.).

*20-15.   A 3.00-ml soln. of permanganate of unknown concn. is placed in a 1.00-cm absorption cell. Its absorbance is found to be 0.184. To the sample in the absorption cell is added 1.00 ml of a 5.00×10^{-3} M soln. of permanganate, and the absorption is again measured and found to be 0.424. Calculate the concn. of the unknown permanganate soln. in terms of (a) molarity, and (b) mg of MnO_4^- per ml.

*20-16.   Two compds., A and B, absorb radiation at 3660 Å. They can be distinguished because compd. A is decomposed by this radiation, while compd. B is not. The product of the photolysis of compd. A does not absorb at 3660 Å. Calculate the concn. ratio of A:B in an unknown mixt. using the following data (all measurements made with the same instrument and under the same conditions): Molar absorptivity of A at 3660 Å = 2,440; molar absorptivity of B at 3660 Å = 4,780; absorbance of the mixt. at 3660 Å = 0.754; initial absorbance of the mixt. at 3660 Å following complete photolysis of A = 0.555.

*20-17. A series of standard vanadium samples and an unknown sample are treated so as to form the peroxyvanadic ion which is yellow and absorbs at 455 mμ. The following data were obtained.   Each indicated pair of values shows the absorbance corresponding to the molar concn. of vanadium: 4.00×10^{-5}—0.140; 6.70×10^{-5}—0.234; 1.00×10^{-4}—0.350; 1.40×10^{-4}—0.490; 2.20×10^{-4}—0.769; unknown—0.385. (*a*) Is Beer's law obeyed? (*b*) What is the concn. of vanadium in the unknown?

20-2   Photometric Titrations

The application of absorption methods to determine the end point in a titration has proved to be a valuable technique.   Such so-called photometric titrations follow the change in the concentration of some light-absorbing species during the course of a titration.   A wide variety of photometric titration curves can be obtained; they have, in common with certain other titration methods, the property that only a few measurements on either side of the equivalence point need be made in order to obtain accurate results.   Figure 20 shows two typical curves.

PROBLEMS

*20-18.   Parry and Dollman have described a spectrophotometric titration for the detn. of alkaline earths in the presence of alkali halides [*Anal. Chem.*, **36**, 1783 (1964)].   The alkaline earth EDTA complex is formed first; then the EDTA complex of the alkali is formed, and this complex has a strong absorbance at 222 mμ.   A 1.25-g sample of sodium chloride is dissolved to prepare a 5.00-ml soln. contg. the necessary buffer.   2.00 ml of this soln. is titrated spectrophotometrically at 222 mμ in the absorption cell with a 1.00×10^{-3} M soln. of EDTA.   The following absorbance measurements were made:

Vol.:	0.0	0.5	1.0	2.0	2.5	3.0	3.5	4.0	5.0
Abs.:	0.10	0.11	0.11	0.12	0.13	0.17	0.23	0.27	0.36

Calculate the percentage of calcium present in the sodium chloride, assuming a negligible blank.

*20-19.   There are present in a mixt. two compds. (A and B) which exhibit absorption at 275 mμ.   With the addition of acid, the absorption of compd. B at

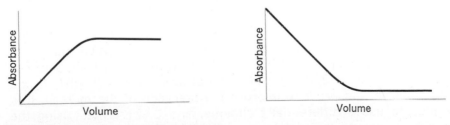

Absorbance / Volume   Absorbance / Volume

Fig. 20   Typical photometric titration curves.

275 mμ is eliminated, while that due to compd. A is unaffected.   (a) Sketch the general shape of the photometric titration curve when the mixt. is titrated with standard acid.   (b) Using the following data, calculate the ratio of the concns. of A:B.

Molar absorptivity of compd. A:	3.00×10^3 at 275 mμ
Molar absorptivity of compd. B:	8.00×10^2 at 275 mμ
Initial absorbance (1-cm cell):	0.655
Initial vol.:	50.0 ml
Vol. of titrant:	14.5 ml
Concn. of titrant:	0.0178 M

One mole of compd. B is equiv. to 1 mole of acid.

20-3   Precision Spectrophotometry

In the normal practice of spectrophotometry, errors become quite large at both extremes of the absorbance scale.   As a means of alleviating this situation, the technique of precision spectrophotometry, sometimes called differential spectrophotometry, is frequently employed.   For example, if it is known that the samples have about 5% transmittance, one is making use of only a very small portion of the scale.   If, however, one can prepare a standard solution of 10% transmittance and expand its scale to read 100% transmittance, yet not change the 0% transmittance, it should be possible to measure the unknown samples under conditions of much greater precision.

For trace analysis in the region of high percentage transmittance, a similar procedure can be followed: The solvent is used to set the instrument at 100% transmittance and a dilute solution of known concentration is used to set the 0% transmittance.   The expansion of the scale and the corresponding improvement in precision then depends on the concentration of the standardizing solution and the ability to vary the 0% transmittance settings of the spectrophotometer over a wide range.

If one wishes to analyze a solution of intermediate absorbance under conditions of high precision, two standard solutions (one slightly more concentrated and one slightly less concentrated than the unknown) are prepared and used to set the 0% and 100% transmittances, respectively.

Example 1 p-Nitroanisole in water exhibits an intense absorption (log ϵ = 4.00) at 313 mμ which can be used for analytical purposes. The samples, when prepared in the standard fashion, show absorbances greater than one at 313 mμ, where the absorption is due solely to the p-nitroanisole.   In order to improve the precision of the method, it is decided to use a differential technique, and 0% T is set, using the opaque shutter on the instrument.   A 1.00×10^{-4} M solution of the anisole in a 1.00-cm cell is used to set the 100% T. On this scale under the same conditions, an unknown reads 30.2% T. Calculate the concentration of this unknown.

Solution The standard solution would read 10.0% T on the normal scale:

$$A = (1.00 \times 10^4)(1.00)(1.00 \times 10^{-4}) = 1.00$$
$$\% \, T = 10.0\%$$

Therefore the scale has been expanded by a factor of 10, and the true % T for the unknown should be 3% T. Using this value, it is a simple matter to calculate its concentration.

$$-\log 0.03 = (10^4)(1)(\text{concn.})$$
$$\text{concn.} = 1.52 \times 10^{-4} \, M \qquad Ans.$$

PROBLEMS

*20-20. The ferrous ion–orthophenanthroline complex can be used to analyze for iron(II), using the absorption of this complex at 508 mμ. A group of samples is known to contain between 0.1 and 0.2 g of Fe. A known sample with 0.100 g of Fe per liter was treated in the proper way, and the absorbance on a filter photometer was set at 0. The absorbance of a second standard (0.200 g of Fe per liter) was then measured and found to be 0.795. Calculate the concn. of an unknown which exhibits an absorbance of 0.650 when prepared and analyzed in a manner similar to that of the standards.

*20-21. Styphnic acid exhibits an absorption maximum at 400 mμ (log $\epsilon = 4.20$). An investigator wishes to analyze for styphnic acid with high precision in the concn. range from 4.00×10^{-5} M to 4.10×10^{-5} M. Two standard solns. at these concns. were prepared and used to set the 100 and 0% T positions, respectively. The unknown soln. was then run under similar conditions, exhibiting 82.5% T. Calculate the concn. of the unknown, assuming that Beer's law holds throughout this concn. range.

*20-22. Compd. X shows only a very weak absorption maximum at 330 mμ (log $\epsilon = 1.40$). For the trace analysis of this compd., it is essential that the scale be expanded as much as possible. 100% T is set using the solvent, and a 1.00×10^{-4} M soln. is used to set the 0% T. Quadruplicate detns. are then performed on a soln. of unknown concn., and the following results are obtained: 38.6, 38.2, 39.0, and 38.6% T. Calculate the concn. of the unknown soln.

20-4 Evaluation of Physical Properties Using Spectrophotometric Data

Spectrophotometric methods can be used for the determination of a wide variety of physical constants and properties. The dissociation constant of an indicator or other compound can frequently be measured using spectroscopic data. For example, to determine the pK_a value of an organic acid, it is necessary to evaluate the molar absorptivities of the acid and base forms of the compound at the wavelengths of maximum absorption for both species. Then, using a buffered solution of the compound, the pH of which is within 0.5 pH units of the pKa value, the absorption is measured at the two wavelengths determined previously. Calculation of the concentration of each of the two species present and insertion into the following equation permits one to calculate the pKa value for the organic acid.

$$pKa = pH - \log \frac{[base]}{[acid]}$$

pKa values can also be obtained by plotting the absorbance at a specific wavelength versus pH for a series of solutions. At the wavelength selected, there should be a considerable change in the absorbance on going from one species to the other.

Example 1   β-Naphthol is a weak organic acid with a dissociation constant in the region from pH 9 to 10.   The following data are pertinent to the system:

	$\log \epsilon$ (285 $m\mu$)	$\log \epsilon$ (346 $m\mu$)
β-Naphthol	3.49	0.00
β-Naphtholate anion	3.70	3.47

In a solution of a transparent buffer (ionic strength, 1.1) and containing 1.00×10^{-4} M β-naphthol, the pH was measured and found to be 9.20; the absorbance at 285 $m\mu$ was 0.373 and at 346 $m\mu$ was 0.0981.   Calculate the pKa of β-naphthol.   (All measurements were made using a 1-cm cell and conform to Beer's law.)

Solution

ROH: $\epsilon_{285} = 3,087$ $\epsilon_{346} = 0$

RO$^-$: $\epsilon_{285} = 5,010$ $\epsilon_{346} = 2,950$

$$[RO^-] = \frac{(0.0981)}{(2,950)(1)} = 3.33 \times 10^{-5} \ M$$

$$0.373 = [RO^-](1)(5,010) + [ROH](1)(3,087)$$

Substituting 3.33×10^{-5} for [RO$^-$],

$$[ROH] = 6.67 \times 10^{-5} \ M$$

$$pKa = 9.20 - \log \left(\frac{3.33 \times 10^{-5}}{6.67 \times 10^{-5}} \right) = 9.20 - \log 0.5 = 9.50 \qquad \textit{Ans.}$$

Spectroscopic measurements are frequently used to evaluate complex-formation equilibria and to measure the metal-to-ligand ratio for a particular complex. Various methods have been described for this purpose: the mole-ratio method, the continuous variation method, and the slope-ratio method. Although it is beyond the scope of this work to discuss these in detail, the example below illustrates how the mole-ratio method can be used to determine the metal-to-ligand ratio of a complex.

Example 2   Clem and Huffman [*Anal. Chem.*, **37**, 86 (1965)] have described the use of an azide complex of palladium for analytical purposes. They found that a particular complex exhibited an absorption maximum at 315 $m\mu$ in aqueous solution. Data such as the following might have been obtained and used to determine the formula for the complex. Calculate the ligand-to-metal ratio for this complex.

Solution   Solutions of Pd^{++} ions plus azide were prepared, and the absorbance of each was measured. The following values show in each case the molar ligand-to-metal ratio and the corresponding absorbance at 315 $m\mu$: 1:1—0.12; 2:1—0.24; 3:1—0.36; 4:1—0.46; 5:1—0.48; 6:1—0.48; 7:1—0.48.

Plot the absorbance versus mole ratio of ligand to metal and extrapolate the straight portions on both sides of the break. The point at which these two lines intersect indicates the ligand-to-metal ratio, which is 4.0 in this case.   *Ans.*

PROBLEMS

*20-23.   A sample of a certain organic acid weighing 0.500 g is dissolved in water to make 100 ml of soln. and is then titrated photometrically with 0.100 N base. Calculate the equiv. wt. of the acid from the following data which show the absorbance corresponding to each of the total vols. of base used: 0.00 ml = 0.72; 4.00 ml = 0.63; 7.91 ml = 0.55; 12.10 = 0.46; 16.15 ml = 0.40; 20.02 ml = 0.40; 24.15 ml = 0.39.

*20-24.   A 0.200-g sample of a certain dibasic acid is dissolved in 100 ml of water and is titrated with 0.300 M NaOH. The course of the titration is followed by measuring the absorption of the acid species at 315 $m\mu$. Calculate the mol. wt. of the acid from the following data which show the absorbance corresponding to each of the total vols. of NaOH used: 0.00 ml = 0.62; 0.10 ml = 0.57; 0.20 ml = 0.53; 0.30 ml = 0.47; 0.40 ml = 0.44; 0.50 ml = 0.41; 0.60 ml = 0.39; 0.70 ml = 0.37; 0.80 ml = 0.35; 0.90 ml = 0.34; 1.00 ml = 0.34; 1.10 ml = 0.34; 1.20 ml = 0.33.

*20-25.   An acid-base indicator shows a max. absorption at 615 $m\mu$ which can be used for the detn. of its pKa value. The following values were obtained when the absorbance of a 1.0×10^{-5} M soln. was measured at each of the indicated pH values. Calculate the pKa value of the indicator. pH 1.00 = 1.10; pH 2.00 = 1.08; pH 3.00 = 1.04; pH 3.75 = 0.96; pH 4.00 = 0.84; pH 4.50 = 0.32; pH 5.00 = 0.11; pH 6.00 = 0.08; pH 7.00 = 0.06.

*20-26. The basic form of a monobasic acid exhibits a max. absorption at 450 mμ (log ϵ = 4.20), while the acid form shows no absorption at this wavelength. In a buffered soln. of pH 2.85, the absorption of a 2.55 $\times$ 10^{-5} M soln. of the acid was 0.201 at 450 mμ. Calculate the pKa and the Ka values for this acid. The same cell and spectrophotometer were used for all measurements.

*20-27. It is known that the pKa value of the 2-naphthylammonium ion is approx. 4.00 and that the free base compd. shows two absorption maxima, 340 mμ and 280 mμ, which are useful for spectroscopic measurements. 2-Naphthylammonium ions does not absorb at the former wavelength but does at the latter. Using the following data, calculate two values for the pKa of 2-naphthylammonium ion. The same equipment was used for all measurements.

	log ϵ (280 mμ)	log ϵ (340 mμ)
2-Naphthylamine	3.82	3.32
2-Naphthylammonium ion	3.48	0.00

A 1.00 $\times$ 10^{-4} M soln. of 2-naphthylamine, buffered to pH 3.91, gave an absorbance (280 mμ) value of 0.440 and an absorbance (340 mμ) value of 0.0805.

*20-28. The following data were obtained for the percent transmittance as a function of pH exhibited by the conjugate base of a monobasic acid. From these values, calculate the pKa value of the acid. pH 3.00 = 100% T; pH 4.00 = 100%; pH 5.00 = 98%; pH 6.00 = 95%; pH 7.00 = 64%; pH 7.20 = 54%; pH 7.60 = 36%; pH 8.00 = 25%; pH 9.00 = 17%; pH 10.00 = 16%; pH 11.00 = 16%.

*20-29. The infrared absorption spectra of the silver cyanide complex has been studied, and there appears an absorption at 2,146 cm^{-1} which is distinctive for the complex. Using this frequency, the following data were obtained, and each pair of values given shows the absorption corresponding to the indicated ligand-to-metal ratio: 0.5:1—0.15; 1.0:1—0.30; 1.5:1—0.45; 2.0:1—0.59; 2.5:1—0.60; 3.0:1—0.60; 3.5:1—0.60.

(a) Calculate the ligand-to-metal ratio for this complex. (b) Suggest possible reasons why the intersection of the extrapolated lines does not agree exactly with the experimentally determined value at that point.

*20-30. Lead dithizonate is a very stable complex with a strong absorbance at 510 mμ. In order to determine the metal-to-ligand ratio for this complex, the method of continuous variation is chosen. Solns. are prepared in which the mole fraction of the metal is varied from zero to one, while the ligand mole fraction goes from one to zero. The absorption of the complex for each soln. is listed below. Calculate the ligand-to-metal ratio for this complex.

Mole fraction of Pb	Mole fraction of ligand	Absorption
0.0	1.0	0.00
0.1	0.9	0.24
0.2	0.8	0.48
0.3	0.7	0.70
0.4	0.6	0.69
0.5	0.5	0.60
0.6	0.4	0.48
0.7	0.3	0.36
0.8	0.2	0.24
0.9	0.1	0.12
1.0	0.0	0.00

*20-31.   The metal M is known to form a complex with the ligand X, but the exact formula of the complex is not known.   In an attempt to determine the ligand-to-metal ratio for the complex, the following data were obtained: 100 ml of a soln., 2.00×10^{-4} M in the metal, properly buffered, was titrated with a soln. of the ligand, 2.00×10^{-2} M in X.   Only the complex absorbs at the wavelength used. The following obtained pairs of values show in each case the absorption corresponding to the vol. of ligand titrant used: 1.00 ml—0.18; 1.80 ml—0.32; 3.10 ml—0.54; 3.95 ml—0.69; 4.10 ml—0.70; 4.85 ml—0.72; 5.60 ml—0.72; 7.00 ml—0.72. Calculate the ligand-to-metal ratio for the complex.

*20-32.   Cu(II) is found to form a complex with a certain new complexing agent. When attempting to use the mole-ratio method, investigators found that the max. absorption of the complex occurred at 455 mμ at which wavelength the ligand individually showed only slight absorption.   Calculate the ligand-to-metal ratio for the complex from the following data which show for each pair of values the absorption corresponding to the indicated ligand to metal ratio: 0.5:1—0.14; 1.0:1—0.28; 1.5:1—0.42; 2.0:1—0.55; 2.5:1—0.61; 3.0:1—0.66; 3.5:1—0.71.

20-5   Absorption in the Infrared Region

The principal application of infrared spectroscopy has been for the identification of organic compounds; the technique has received less attention as a quantitative method.   Formerly, it was usually necessary to operate with large slit widths in order to compensate for the weaker sources and detectors then available.   With the recent advent of much improved infrared spectrophotometers, the quantitative analysis of mixtures is more feasible.   The wide variety of vibrational modes found in most molecules dictates that most infrared spectra will be very complex.   This should make possible the quantitative analysis of numerous components in a complicated mixture.

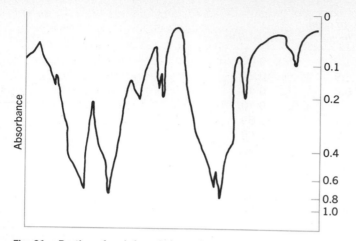

Fig. 21   Portion of an infrared absorption spectrum.

In Fig. 21 is shown part of an infrared absorption spectrum, and in theory any of the principal bands could be used for the quantitative analysis of the compound.   Because of the sharp and narrow character of many infrared absorption bands, it is often not feasible to measure the absorption at only the wavelength of maximum absorption.   Therefore, the spectrum is usually scanned in the region of interest, and the transmittance or absorbance of the appropriate peak is obtained by a graphical approach (base-line technique) illustrated in Fig. 22.

A base line is drawn tangentially across the base of the absorption peak.   If it is assumed that the absorption curves of all other substances present are linear in this short range, then the difference between the base line and the peak represents the absorption due to the compound in question.   In addition to peak heights, peak areas have frequently been used as a more precise measure of the absorption attributed to a particular band.   Since Beer's law holds in the infrared region, the determination of an unknown concentration is handled in a manner similar to that used in the ultraviolet and visible regions of the spectrum.

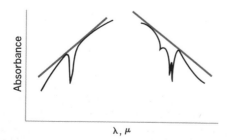

λ, μ

Fig. 22   Graphical approach to the determination of the base line of an infrared absorption peak.

For cases where absorption bands of other species do not cause a serious interference, the use of a properly selected internal standard is frequently advantageous. It is customary to use a constant concentration of the internal standard which permits samples of varying path length to be analyzed. Frequently an absorption band of the main constituent can be used in place of a separate substance used as the internal standard. A plot of the ratio of the absorbance of the given species to the absorbance of the internal standard versus the concentration of the given species becomes the calibration curve for the analysis of the unknown.

The infrared absorption of solid compounds is frequently measured by using KBr disks. In order to perform quantitative studies with these, it is necessary to know the thickness of the disk used. In many cases, it is easier and much more accurate to include an internal standard in the KBr disk. [Potassium thiocyanate with a strong absorption at 4.70 μ (2,125 cm^{-1}) is frequently chosen for use as the internal standard.]

Example 1   The concentration of silicon in a polymeric film was to be analyzed using the Si–H stretching vibration of approximately 2,200 cm^{-1}. Very carefully prepared films indicated that there was almost no interference at this frequency. The following data were obtained with a series of standards:

% Silicon	Absorbance
0.0	0.04
0.8	0.11
1.4	0.16
2.2	0.22
3.0	0.29

The absorption of an unknown sample of the film was measured, exhibiting an absorbance of 0.18. Calculate the concentration of Si in the film.

Solution   By plotting the given data, a straight line is obtained with a slope of 0.90. Using this calibration curve, the concentration of silicon in the film is calculated to be 1.7%.   *Ans.*

In those cases where a mixture of known composition is being analyzed, it is frequently possible to analyze as many as five or six components using the necessary simultaneous equations to solve for the concentration of each species. As with the approach used in the ultraviolet and visible regions, it is necessary to have available samples of the pure materials or else to know the absorptivities at the wavelengths to be used for the analysis.   Matrix methods are usually used to facilitate the solving of the mathematical expressions in the more complicated systems.

PROBLEMS

*20-33.   Mixts. of 2-hydroxy- and 3-hydroxystearic acids were to be analyzed, using their carbonyl absorptions at 5.73 and 5.94 μ, respectively.   A standard soln. (0.50 M) of each acid was run using the same cell.   The measured absorbances were 0.32 and 0.44 for the 2- and 3-derivatives, respectively.   An unknown sample weighing 5.00 g was extracted.   The extractant was evaporated to dryness, the residue was dissolved in 1.00 ml of solvent, and its absorption was measured in the same manner, using the same cell, as in the case of the standard solns.   The absorption at 5.73 μ was 0.14, and at 3.94 μ it was 0.27.   Calculate the percentage of each stearic acid present in the sample, assuming that the extraction was 100% efficient and that, of the species extracted, only these compds. absorb at the wavelengths used.

*20-34.   The presence of ethylene in samples of ethane is easily determined using the absorption of ethylene in the vicinity of 5.2 μ.   A series of standards was prepared and gave the following data:

% Ethylene	% Transmittance
0.50	75.8
1.00	57.5
1.50	43.6
2.00	33.1
2.50	25.1
3.00	19.1

Calculate the percentage of ethylene in an unknown sample if its percent transmittance at 5.2 μ is 38.7% when using the same cell and the same instrument.

*20-35.   The presence of water in a particular organic solvent is to be measured, using the near-infrared absorption of the water at 1.43 μ.   Five samples, each contg. 5.00 ml of the solvent, are prepared.   The quantity of water added to each sample and the absorbance measured for each sample are listed below.   Calculate the concn. of water in the sample in mg of water per ml of sample.

Mg of water added to sample	Absorbance at 1.43 μ
0.0	0.21
1.0	0.38
2.0	0.55
3.0	0.72
4.0	0.89

*20-36. In a particular synthesis, it is anticipated that a small amt. of an aromatic impurity would be present in the final product. After further work, the impurity was identified, and it was shown that only the impurity exhibited absorption at 2.48 μ due to the presence of an aromatic —CH group. On the basis of this, a quantitative method for the analysis of the impurity was developed. The unknown sample was analyzed and exhibited an absorbance of 0.49. To 1.34 g of the unknown was added 0.10 g of the impurity. This mixt. was then analyzed in a manner similar to the unknown and exhibited an absorbance of 0.90. Calculate the percentage of the impurity in the unknown.

*20-37. One product produced in a particular synthesis is an aliphatic aldehyde which exhibits a strong absorption at 9.72 μ. All the products of the synthesis are solids, so it is decided that the analyses should be made using KBr disks. Even with extreme care, the investigators found that their results depended on too many variables, and they were forced to use KSCN as an internal standard. A series of standards was prepared and gave the following results:

A due to aldehyde	A due to KSCN	Concn. of the aldehyde, %
0.11	0.07	1.0
0.45	0.14	2.0
0.53	0.11	3.0
0.58	0.09	4.0

An unknown sample analyzed in a similar manner to those above yielded an absorbance at 9.72 μ of 0.84, and the absorbance at 4.70 μ due to the internal standard KSCN was 0.18. Calculate the percentage of the aldehyde in the unknown.

*20-38. A method has been described in the literature [*Anal. Chem.*, **35**, 1489 (1963)] for the analysis of calcium sulfate hydrates with an internal standard in mineral oil mulls. It was shown that the absorption at 3,390 cm^{-1} was due to the dihydrate of the calcium sulfate only. Using a series of standards contg. known quantities of calcium sulfate dihydrate and the unknown sample, the following data were obtained. Calculate the percent water in a sample if it exhibits absorption of 0.47 and 0.37 at 875 and 3,390 cm^{-1}, respectively.

A (std)	A (sample)	Water, %
0.75	0.15	4.0
0.60	0.23	8.0
0.31	0.19	12.0
0.70	0.57	16.0
0.45	0.43	20.0

(The standard was calcium carbonate, and its absorption at 875 cm^{-1} was used.)

*20-39. The composition of a copolymer is to be determined by infrared spectroscopy. One of the two polymers present, S, has a unique and moderately intense absorption at 1,450 cm^{-1}; the other polymer, Y, has a less strong but unique absorption at 890 cm^{-1}. A pure sample of compd. S of thickness 5.0 mil shows an absorbance of 0.65 at 1,450 cm^{-1}. A sample of pure polymer Y shows an absorbance of 0.47 at 890 cm^{-1} when an 8.0-mil sample is analyzed. Calculate the bulk ratio of S:Y in a copolymer of S and Y if its thickness is 5.00 mil and shows an absorbance of 0.34 at 1,450 cm^{-1} and 0.14 at 890 cm^{-1}. (*Note:* 1 mil = 0.001 in. = 0.0254 mm.)

*20-40. Compd. X is the principal product in a certain manufacturing process. Compd. Y is the only important impurity. Compd. X has a weak but very sharp absorption at 7.42 μ where compd. Y shows no absorption. Compd. Y has a strong, sharp absorption at 5.72 μ where compd. X has no absorption. The method of analysis makes use of the principal component, compd. X, as the internal standard. Beer's law has been found to apply to both compds. A standard soln. contg. 1.00% of compd. Y in compd. X exhibits an absorption of 0.95 at 7.42 μ and 0.34 at 5.72 μ. An unknown is analyzed and exhibits an absorption of 0.73 at 7.42 μ and 0.28 at 5.72 μ. (*a*) What is the percentage of Y in the unknown mixt.? (*b*) Why is a weak absorption band used for compd. X rather than a strong one?

20-6   Atomic Absorption

The analysis of metal ions, making use of the absorption properties of their solutions, has been used extensively. In recent years, however, a far more selective method of analysis for metal ions has been developed. In atomic absorption spectroscopy, the absorption of radiation is by neutral metal atoms found in the flame.

The sample, usually in solution form, is aspirated into a burner. In the ideal case, the solvent is evaporated, the salt particles are vaporized, and neutral atoms are produced by dissociation. Thus the flame represents the sample in atomic absorption. Commonly used sources which emit elemental spectra or "lines" rather than continuous spectra are hollow-cathode lamps or metal-vapor lamps. The lines emitted depend upon the materials from which the lamp or tube is made.

Calculations involved with atomic absorption are similar to those used with other absorption methods. However, due to variations between flames and between individual instruments, it is usually necessary to prepare a calibration curve. Even though percent transmittance or percent absorption are quantities usually measured, it is a simple matter to convert to absorbance and plot the absorbance versus concentration, which should yield straight lines at moderate to low concentrations.

PROBLEMS

*20-41. The following data were obtained in the detn. of cadmium in an ore, using atomic absorption. The pairs of values show in each case the absorbance corresponding to the indicated concn. of Cd: 0.00 p.p.m.—0.000; 2.00 p.p.m.—

0.053; 3.80 p.p.m.—0.104; 5.80 p.p.m.—0.160; 8.00 p.p.m.—0.220; 9.60 p.p.m.—0.260; 11.20 p.p.m.—0.310.   Calculate the concn. in p.p.m. of cadmium in an unknown which exhibits an absorbance of 0.179.

⋆20-42.   In order to check the detn. outlined in Prob. 20-41, there was added to the unknown sample sufficient cadmium to increase its concn. in the soln. by 3.00 p.p.m.   The sample was then reanalyzed and gave an absorbance of 0.261. Does this confirm the result found in the previous problem?   Show your calculations.

⋆20-43.   A sample of silver-contg. alloy weighing 5.00 g was dissolved and treated to produce 500 ml of soln.   In the following data the given pairs of values show in each case the recorded % T values corresponding to the concn. of Ag in p.p.m. in a series of standard solns.: 0.00 p.p.m.—100.0%; 5.00 p.p.m.—86.8%; 10.0 p.p.m.—75.5%;   15.0 p.p.m.—65.3%;   20.0 p.p.m.—56.5%;   25.0 p.p.m.—49.0%; 30.0 p.p.m.—42.6%.   If the transmittance of the unknown soln. was 68.5%, what was the concn. of silver in the alloy (a) in p.p.m., and (b) in percent?

⋆20-44.   On some instruments, percent absorption is read directly from the meter, where percent absorption equals $100 - \% T$.   Assuming that the following data for the detn. of magnesium were obtained on such an instrument, calculate the concn. (in p.p.m.) of magnesium in the unknown.   The pairs of values given show in each case the percent absorption corresponding to the indicated concn. of Mg: 0.00 p.p.m.—0.0%; 0.20 p.p.m.—11.8%; 0.40 p.p.m.—22.4%; 0.60 p.p.m.—31.8%; 0.80 p.p.m.—39.9%; 1.00 p.p.m.—47.3%; 1.20 p.p.m.—53.5%; unknown—25.0%.

⋆20-45.   A series of calcium standards gave the following absorbance values. The pairs of values listed show in each case the absorbance corresponding to the concn. of Ca in p.p.m.: 0.00 p.p.m.—0.000; 1.00 p.p.m.—0.090; 2.20 p.p.m.—0.194; 3.10 p.p.m.—0.273; 3.90 p.p.m.—0.340; 5.00 p.p.m.—0.440; 6.00 p.p.m.—0.525.   A 1.00-g sample of an unknown soil was dissolved after decomposition and gave 150 ml of soln.   This soln. was analyzed in the same manner as the standards and on the same instrument, giving an absorbance of 0.380.   Calculate the concn. of calcium (a) in the unknown soln. in p.p.m. and (b) in the soil in percentage by wt.

21 Emission Methods

21-1 Flame Photometry

In the application of flame photometry, as well as of emission spectroscopy, to the analysis of inorganic species, emitted lines are used. From the frequencies of the lines, the analyst is able to identify the species producing the radiation. The line intensities are used in quantitative analysis.

The sample is injected or aspirated into the flame. The solvent is quickly lost by evaporation, and the remaining salt particles are vaporized and dissociated into neutral atoms which are then excited. A valence electron of the atom is excited to a higher energy state by the energy of the flame, and in the process of returning to a lower energy state, it may give off radiant energy. The measurement of the emitted radiation is the basis for the flame photometric methods.

The temperature obtained in the average flame is in the vicinity of 2500 to 3000°C; this is sufficient to excite the valence electrons of many elements. However, the character of the flame, its temperature, and the design of the burner affect the tendency of many elements to form in the flame compounds which are refractory, with the result that the free atom is not obtained and no emission is observed. Nevertheless, for the many elements that can be studied and analyzed by flame photometry, the method is sensitive and generally convenient to use.

Qualitative analysis, utilizing flame photometry, is simplified since the temperature of most flames is so low that usually only one or a few characteristic lines will appear for each element. Quantitative analysis by flame photometry is simple in theory but is complicated by instability in the flame, chemical and optical interferences, variations in the rate of aspiration, etc.   In order to overcome many of these difficulties, the internal standard method and the method of standard addition are frequently used, though a direct intensity method can be used in certain cases.

In the internal standard method, a known constant quantity of a metal which is not present in the unknown sample and which has chemical and electronic properties similar to those of the metal being analyzed is added to each sample.   The intensities of the lines of both the internal standard and the unknown are measured under the same operating conditions.   Calibration plots are then made of the logarithm of the intensity ratio (sample:standard) versus the logarithm of the concentration.

The method of standard addition requires the analysis of the unknown sample and then the addition to the unknown sample of a known amount of the material being analyzed.   The solution containing the sample plus the added standard is then analyzed under the same conditions previously used for the analysis of the unknown.   The increase in the observed signal is proportional to the known quantity of material added, and from this it is possible to calculate the amount of material initially present in the unknown.   The method of standard addition is particularly applicable to those cases where interferences are known to exist in the sample because of the matrix from which it came.

Example 1   An industrial analyst wishes to compare the internal standard method with the method of standard addition for the analysis of potassium in a process stream.   He has previously decided to use lithium as the reference element in the internal standard method.   In part (*a*) below is given the data for the analysis by the internal standard method; in part (*b*) is given the data using the method of standard addition.   Calculate the concentration of potassium in the stream, using both methods.

(*a*) The unknown, when run under similar conditions and with the same concentration of the lithium internal standard, gave readings of 10.5 for the lithium intensity and 38.0 for the potassium intensity.   All emission intensities were corrected for background.

Concn. of K p.p.m	K intensity	Li intensity
1.0	10.0	10.0
2.0	15.3	10.5
5.0	22.2	9.5
10.0	35.4	10.0
20.0	56.4	11.0
50.0	77.5	10.0

(*b*) Standard solutions containing 0.0, 1.0, 2.0, 5.0, 10.0, 20.0, and 50.0 p.p.m. of potassium were prepared. A 10.0-ml sample of each solution was mixed with 10.0 ml of the unknown, and the following data were obtained:

Concn. of K p.p.m.	Intensity
0.0	18.0
1.0	19.5
2.0	21.0
5.0	25.5
10.0	33.0
20.0	48.0
50.0	93.0

Solution

(*a*) The logarithm of the ratio (K:Li intensity) is plotted against the logarithm of the K concentration. The logarithm of the emission ratio for the unknown is 0.60. Reading from the graph, this gives log [K$^+$] = 1.08. The concentration of the unknown is therefore 12.0 p.p.m.   *Ans.*

(*b*) The intensity reading for the unknown is 18.0 units. The addition of potassium in an amount equal to the unknown should therefore increase the intensity reading by 18.0 units. This corresponds to a reading of 36.0 units and represents a concentration of 12.0 p.p.m.   *Ans.*

PROBLEMS

*21-1.   The following data were obtained in the analysis of water samples for Ca using the 4229-Å line. Calculate the concn. of Ca present in the unknown water sample. The pairs listed show in each case the intensity corresponding to the indicated Ca concn. in p.p.m.: 0.0 p.p.m.—4.0; 2.0 p.p.m.—9.6; 4.0 p.p.m.—15.0; 6.0 p.p.m.—20.7; 8.0 p.p.m.—26.5; 10.0 p.p.m.—31.9; unknown—11.5.

*21-2.   The same unknown given in Prob. 21-1 was also analyzed using a standard addition technique on a different instrument. The unknown alone gave an intensity of 44.5 units, of which 31.5 were due to background. Increasing the concn. of Ca present in the sample by 2.0 and 4.0 p.p.m. resulted in emission intensities of 53.8 and 63.1 units, respectively, including the same background. Calculate the concn. of Ca present in the unknown.

*21-3.   Calcium can be analyzed using lithium as an internal standard. The following corrected emission intensities were obtained for calcium in soil samples.

Ca concn. p.p.m.	Ca intensity	Li intensity
Unknown	74.0	88.5
1.00	28.0	87.0
2.00	41.4	88.0
3.00	50.8	84.0
4.00	60.7	81.0
5.00	76.4	89.0
6.00	80.5	85.5

Calculate the concn. of Ca in the soil sample.

*21-4. Strontium is determined routinely by flame photometry in a particular industrial laboratory using the following calibration data obtained at 4607 Å. The pairs listed show in each case the intensity value corresponding to the Sr concn. in p.p.m. 50.0 p.p.m.—85.0; 40.0 p.p.m.—68.0; 30.0 p.p.m.—51.0; 20.0 p.p.m.—34.1; 10.0 p.p.m.—16.9; 0.0 p.p.m.—0.0. In the analysis of a sample from a new source, perhaps contg. an interfering substance, two measurements were made. In the first, an aliquot portion of the sample was measured, producing an intensity reading of 42.0. To another aliquot, sufficient Sr was added to increase the concn. by 5.0 p.p.m. The resultant soln. produced an intensity reading of 49.0. Calculate the Sr concn. in the unknown.

*21-5. Manganese can be determined flame photometrically at 4033 Å. In a certain analysis the following calibration data were obtained. The pairs listed show in each case the intensity value corresponding to the Mn concn. in p.p.m. 0.0 p.p.m.—4.5; 4.0 p.p.m.—21.0; 8.0 p.p.m.—38.5; 12.0 p.p.m.—56.5; 16.0 p.p.m.—73.0; 20.0 p.p.m.—90.0. Calculate the concn. of Sr in an unknown sample which exhibits an emission intensity of 43.5.

*21-6. The analysis of indium can frequently be carried out flame photometrically using the 4511-Å line of indium. An unknown of 500 g is dissolved in water to form 1.00 liter of soln., and of this a 3.00-ml aliquot is taken and the flame emission measured. The measured intensity is found to be 48.0 units. 5.00 mg of indium as a soluble salt is added to the remaining sample; the flame emission intensity is again measured and is found to be 53.5 units. Calculate the percentage of indium in the unknown, assuming negligible background.

21-2 Emission Spectroscopy

Basically, emission spectroscopy is very similar to flame photometry. Atoms are excited into states of higher energy, and measurement is made of the emission produced when the atom, or some ion produced from the atom, returns to a lower energy state. In the details, however, the techniques are very different.

The means of excitation used in emission spectroscopy are of three basic types. The dc arc, the ac arc, and the ac spark are all used. For the most sensitive determinations, the dc arc is usually preferred; for analyses requiring high precision, the ac spark is generally the chosen method. The electrodes between which the arc or spark occurs may be of a wide variety of types. If a conducting material is to be analyzed, the sample is fashioned in such a way as to form an electrode, and a carbon or graphite electrode is usually used as the second electrode. Various other types of electrodes for working with liquids and solids have been designed and are in common use.

The instrument used to separate the different wavelengths of light produced are either grating or prism monochromators. With grating instruments which give linear dispersion, it is a relatively simple matter to calculate the wavelengths of unknown lines, provided some reference lines are available. An additional level of complexity enters into the use of grating instruments in the form of overlapping spectra due to different orders; this is particularly serious with concave gratings. Though some instruments are equipped with "order sorters," the analyst must be careful not to confuse lines due to different orders. With prism instruments which give a nonlinear dispersion, the determination of the wavelength of an unknown line is frequently a more difficult process; standard graphs are usually constructed for a particular instrument. An alternate approach is to use the *Hartmann dispersion formula:*

$$\lambda = \lambda_0 + \frac{c}{d_0 - d}$$

where λ_0, c, and d_0 = constants

d = measured distance from a reference line

λ = wavelength of the unknown line

By using three known lines in the vicinity of the unknown line, it becomes a simple matter to calculate the constants and then determine the wavelength of the unknown line. The constants have to be redetermined in different parts of the spectrum.

Because of the variability of the arc produced and unavoidable differences in the development of photographic films, internal standards are usually used in quantitative emission spectroscopy. As with flame photometry, the line selected for the internal standard element should have properties which are similar to the line selected for the element being analyzed; such a pair of lines is termed a *homologous pair.*

Measurement of the intensities of the selected lines of radiation produced in the arc or spark permits the emission spectrographic procedure to be used for quantitative analysis. The use of direct readers, i.e., photoelectric devices with amplifiers and readout systems, is increasing in those cases where rapid and routine analyses are required.   In these cases, many of the same procedures are used that have been discussed in flame photometry.   In those cases where photographic recording is used, it is usually necessary to prepare an emulsion calibration curve in order to relate quantitatively line density and incident intensity.   In the simplest case, quantitative estimates are made by comparing line densities for the unknown element and the internal standard element with the line densities obtained for a large series of standards containing the element in question and the internal standard.   This obviously depends upon having available a considerable supply of standard samples of similar composition to the unknown.

The log-sector method for quantitative analysis permits the comparison of line lengths rather than line densities.   A working curve for the log-sector method can then be prepared, using standards, by plotting the difference in lengths of the unknown and internal standard lines versus the logarithm of the concentration.   However, in most cases it is difficult to determine just where a line ends, and this makes the procedure only semiquantitative.

If a densitometer is available, it is possible to measure the densities of the unknown and internal standard lines directly.   (The density is defined as the logarithm of the ratio of the intensity of the measuring beam of light passing through a clear portion of the film to the intensity of the same beam passing through the center of the line.)   For most emulsions, there is a region of exposures in which the density is directly proportional to the logarithm of the intensity of the incident light as determined from an emulsion calibration curve.   Using the intensities thus determined, a working curve can be prepared by plotting the logarithm of the ratio of the intensities of the homologous lines versus the logarithm of the concentration of the unknown element.   For purposes of calculations, it will be assumed that the proportionality between density and the intensity holds in all cases (i.e., that the emulsion calibration curve is linear in the region of interest).   It will also be assumed that corrections have been applied for any background density.   This permits one to form a working curve by plotting the difference in the densities for the homologous lines versus the logarithm of the unknown's concentration.

PROBLEMS

*21-7.   Because of the large no. of lines obtained, iron is frequently used to make a reference plate for calibration purposes.   In the following table, distances from a common reference point to a particular line are given.   Calculate the wavelengths for the unknown lines assuming that a grating instrument was used.

	Å	mm
Iron	4156.8	23.5
Iron	4134.7	59.7
Iron	4118.6	86.1
Iron	4107.5	104.3
Unknown A		51.0
Unknown B		93.4

*21-8. In an iron alloy, the following iron lines were positively identified: 2453.5, 2483.3, 2488.2, 2501.1, 2522.2, 2535.6, 2549.6, 2562.5, 2598.4, and 2623.5 Å. Additional prominent lines were found in this region of the spectrum, and their wavelengths were determined by comparison with the iron lines.   The wavelengths found were 2463.5, 2491.5, 2515.8, 2542.5, 2567.9, 2570.0, 2576.1, 2582.5, 2593.7, 2605.7, and 2608.6 Å.   Determine what other three elements were present in the alloy as indicated by these particular lines.   (Consult necessary tables.)

*21-9. (*a*) If a monochromator equipped with a plane grating is adjusted to transmit electromagnetic radiation of 5248 Å, a second-order line of what wavelength would also be transmitted?   (*b*) Would the third order of a line at 1748 Å be transmitted?

*21-10. Three lines of a spectrum obtained with a prism spectrograph are identified as being 3405.1, 3524.5, and 3719.9 Å, respectively.   The line at 3405.1 Å was chosen as an arbitrary reference line, and the distances to the other two lines were found to be 24.8 and 59.3 mm, respectively.   Calculate the wavelength of a line appearing at 42.2 mm from the reference line at 3405.1 Å.

*21-11. A sample of tissue underwent a spectrographic analysis for lead content. After proper treatment, the following data were obtained for a series of standard samples in which tin was added as the internal standard.

Pb p.p.m.	Sn *intensity* 3034.1 Å	Pb *intensity* 2833.1 Å
1.00	1.114	0.223
2.00	0.835	0.535
3.00	1.190	1.544
Unknown	0.825	0.635

Calculate the concn. of Pb in the sample.

*21-12. Plant extracts were analyzed for their magnesium content, using the 2795.5-Å Mg line.   The samples were ground and extracted, and molybdenum was added as the internal standard.   Three magnesium standards were prepared with concns. of 2.00, 4.00, and 6.00 mg/ml.   The intensity ratios for these three solns.

were 0.140, 0.240, and 0.330, respectively.   Calculate the concn. of Mg in an unknown sample in which the microphotometer readings were $I_{Mg} = 0.325$ and $I_{Mo} = 1.142$.   (All intensities were corrected for background.)

*21-13.   The analysis of cadmium solns. from samples of leaf tissue was carried out spectrographically, using tin as an internal standard.   The spectrograph was equipped with a log-sector attachment, and the heights of the various lines were measured on the photographic plates.   The following data were obtained for a series of standard solns. and for an unknown soln.:

% Cd	Cd–line height mm	Sn–line height mm
1.0×10^{-3}	7.6	4.2
1.0×10^{-2}	9.0	4.5
1.0×10^{-1}	9.9	4.4
1.0	10.7	4.1
Unknown	9.0	4.3

Calculate the percentage of cadmium in the unknown leaf sample soln.

*21-14.   A high-grade steel was analyzed for its manganese content, the iron serving as the internal standard.   Three standard samples contg. 0.047, 0.104, and 0.254% Mn, respectively, gave readings of intensity ratios [I_{Mn} (2933 Å): I_{Fe} (2932 Å)] of 0.182, 0.531, and 1.980, respectively.   An unknown sample of a similar steel was treated in the same way as the above standards, and its measured intensity ratio was 0.685.   What was the manganese content of the unknown steel?

*21-15.   The iron content in certain silica samples is determined spectroscopically with a direct-reading instrument.   The 2813.3-Å line of iron is used in this detn. while the silicon line at 2881.6 Å serves as the internal standard.   To prepare the standards, 1.00-g samples of iron-free silica were treated to dissolve the samples. Then 1.00, 2.00, 4.00, and 8.00 ml of a 1.00% iron soln. were added, and the final soln. vol. was adjusted to 100 ml.   The intensity ratios $I_{Fe}:I_{Si}$ obtained for the above four iron solns. were 0.150, 0.271, 0.504, and 0.930, respectively.   Calculate the percentage of iron present in a silica sample which gave an intensity ratio (Fe:Si) of 0.755 when analyzed in the same way as the standards.

*21-16.   For the detn. of X in wood samples, it is necessary first to ash the sample and then to add a predetermined amt. of internal standard Y.   The total sample is then mixed with a known quantity of specially purified powdered graphite. Using an emission spectrograph equipped with photographic detection, the following densities were measured for a series of standard samples:

% X	Density X	Density Y
0.10	8.0	6.8
0.32	8.7	6.6
1.20	9.8	6.7
4.0	10.9	6.9
9.8	11.5	6.7

Calculate the percentage of X in an unknown wood sample which when treated in the same manner as the standards gave densities of 8.4 for X and 6.5 for Y.

*21-17. A series of iron lines of known intensity, as determined by an absolute method, were used to calibrate an emulsion. The following data were obtained in which each pair of values shows the percentage transmission corresponding to the indicated intensity: 0.126—88.0%; 0.219—72.0%; 1.18—15.1%; 0.519—42.0%; 1.92—8.8%; 1.00—19.5%; 0.619—35.7%. Plot on log-log paper an emulsion calibration curve in the form of percent transmission versus relative intensity. Using this curve, translate the following % T values for a series of steels with known silicon content into intensity ratios ($I_{Si}:I_{Fe}$), and plot against percent Si on log-log paper.

% Si	% T for Si line	% T for Fe line
0.18	78.3	20.8
0.35	62.5	23.0
0.80	28.0	21.3
1.50	10.6	19.4
2.19	9.0	24.1

Calculate the percent Si in a similar unknown steel sample, the spectrum of which shows 45.5% T at the Si line and 22.5% T at the Fe line. Note that the emulsion calibration curve is not linear.

21.3 Fluorescence and Phosphorescence

The tendency of certain molecules to absorb radiation in the ultraviolet or visible regions of the spectrum and then to emit radiation, usually at longer wavelengths, is quite common. The term *fluorescence* is used to describe the emission which accompanies a transition from a higher electronic state to a lower electronic state (usually the ground state) of the same multiplicity. If the two states are of different multiplicities (for example from triplet to singlet), then the process is referred to as *phosphorescence.*

Quantitative applications of fluorescence and phosphorescence arise because the emitted light is proportional to the amount of material which undergoes fluorescence or phosphorescence.   In most applications of fluorescence analysis, the solution is so dilute that only a very small fraction (less than 5%) of the exciting light is absorbed.   Under these conditions, the intensity of fluorescence (I_f) can be expressed as follows:

$$I_f = kI_o \epsilon c \phi$$

where ϵ = molar absorptivity
     I_o = intensity of the exciting light
     c = molar concentration of the solute
     ϕ = quantum yield defined as the number of quanta emitted per number of quanta absorbed
     k = constant

It is obvious therefore that, for one compound, the fluorescence intensity should be directly proportional to the concentration of the fluorescing species, provided one is working with a solution dilute enough so that only a small fraction of the exciting light is absorbed.   In the event that a greater proportion of the exciting light is absorbed, other effects (inner-filter effects or so-called "concentration quenching") occur which limit the linear relation between the fluorescence intensity and the concentration of the solute.   This is shown in the accompanying graph (Fig. 23), where at low concentration there is a linear relationship and at the higher concentrations the linear dependence breaks down.   In cases where opaque samples are to be analyzed, the fluorescence is usually viewed from the front surface as opposed to the more commonly used right-angle geometry which is amenable to the measurement of fluorescence from dilute solutions.

The limit of detection for many compounds, assuming carefully purified solvents and reagents, is frequently in the vicinity of from 0.1 to 0.001 μg/ml.   This is a greater sensitivity than is obtainable with most absorption methods and explains much of the interest in fluorescent methods.   If the species under consideration is not fluorescent, it is sometimes possible to convert it quantitatively into a fluorescent com-

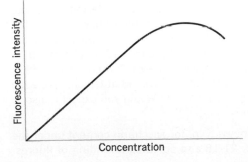

Fig. 23   Fluorescence intensity versus concentration.

pound or to couple it with some compound or metal ion such that the resulting complex is fluorescent (or phosphorescent).

The equation given above also indicates that the intensity of fluorescence depends upon the intensity of the exciting light. Since the excitation sources do not maintain constant output with continued use, it is usually necessary to compare the fluorescence intensity of the unknown sample with that of a standard measured on the same instrument immediately preceding or following the measurement of the unknown. Using the equation,

$$\text{Concn. of unknown} = \frac{I_{unk}}{I_{std}} \times \text{concn. of standard}$$

it is a simple matter to calculate the concentration of the unknown, provided the analyst is working in the linear region of the calibration curve.

Example 1   The analysis of tyrosine in protein hydrolyzates has been studied by Duggan and Udenfriend [*J. Biol. Chem.*, **223**, 313 (1956)] and excitation occurs at 275 mμ and emission at 303 mμ. Using standard solutions of tyrosine, it was shown that the fluorescence was directly proportional to the tyrosine concentration in the concentration range from 0.5 to 5.0 μg/ml and that there appeared to be no interference from other species found in the hydrolyzate. Using a 1.00-μg/ml standard solution of tyrosine, the fluorescence intensities of the standard and unknown were measured and found to be 73 and 62 units, respectively. Calculate the concentration of tyrosine in the unknown.

Solution

$$\text{Concn. (unk)} = \frac{62}{73} \times 1.00$$

$$= 0.85 \ \mu\text{g/ml} \qquad Ans.$$

PROBLEMS

*21-18.   Saccharin reacts with resorcinol in the presence of sulfuric acid to give a highly fluorescent product. With known concns. of saccharin, the following data were obtained, using the accepted method and a standard filter fluorometer. The pairs listed show in each case the fluorescence intensity corresponding to the concn. of saccharin in p.p.m.   1.0 p.p.m.—2.40; 5.0 p.p.m.—12.0; 10.0 p.p.m.—25.0; 15.0 p.p.m.—36.5; 20.0 p.p.m.—49.0; 25.0 p.p.m.—61.0; 30.0 p.p.m.—68.5; 35.0 p.p.m.—66.0; 40.0 p.p.m.—63.4.   (*a*) Determine over what concn. range the fluorescence intensity is a linear function of concn.   (*b*) Would you expect it also to be linear at concns. less than 1.0 p.p.m.?

*21-19.   If you were analyzing an unknown soln. for saccharin content under the same conditions as those used in Prob. 21-18 and obtained a reading of fluorescence intensity equal to 7.75 units, what would be the concn. of saccharin in the unknown soln.?

*21-20.   The concn. of cholesterol in serum can be analyzed fluorometrically. Using the accepted procedure, a standard sample contg. 20.0 mg/100 ml yielded an uncorrected fluorescence intensity of 78.8 units (the blank read 2.0 units). (a) What would be the concn. of an unknown soln. having an uncorrected fluorescence intensity of 63.5 units, assuming that the blank still reads 2.0 units? (b) What would be the concn. of cholesterol in the serum used to produce the unknown sample in part (a) if it were derived from a 50.0-ml sample of serum?

*21-21.   The analysis of selenium by complexing it with 2,3-diaminonaphthalene and measuring the fluorescence of the complex has been described [Allaway and Cary, *Anal. Chem.*, **36**, 1359 (1964)].   A 5.00-g sample is treated by the oxygen flask technique and several subsequent steps until it has reacted with the ligand to form a final 10.0 ml of soln.   A standard soln. contg. 10.0 $\mu g/ml$ of Se produces a fluorescence intensity of 64.0 units.   If the unknown soln. gives a fluorescence intensity of 74.5 units, what is the concn. of Se in the initial sample?

*21-22.   The identification and analysis of phenothiazine drugs by fluorescence methods is commonly used.   In the analysis of chlorpromazine, the following data were obtained, and the pairs listed show in each case the fluorescence intensity corresponding to the concn. of the standard: 0.0 p.p.m.—0.00; 0.10 p.p.m.—7.50; 0.20 p.p.m.—14.8; 0.30—22.6; 0.40 p.p.m.—30.0; 0.50 p.p.m.—37.7.   Calculate the concn. of chlorpromazine in a soln. exhibiting a fluorescence intensity of 18.7 with a blank reading of 2.4.

*21-23.   In some fluorometric methods, the quenching of the fluorescence is proportional to the concn. of the desired species; for example, the metal X can be assumed to quench the fluorescence of ligand L.   The following data were obtained from a series of runs:

Solution	Fluorescence intensity
Blank	0.0
5.0×10^{-6} M in L	84.0
5.0×10^{-6} M in L and 1.0×10^{-6} M in X	67.2
5.0×10^{-6} M in L and 2.0×10^{-6} M in X	50.5
5.0×10^{-6} M in L and 3.0×10^{-6} M in X	33.6
5.0×10^{-6} M in L and 4.0×10^{-6} M in X	16.9
5.0×10^{-6} M in L and 5.0×10^{-6} M in X	0.50
5.0×10^{-6} M in L and 6.0×10^{-6} M in X	0.00

Find (a) the molar ratio of the complex formed between X and L, and (b) the concn. of X in a soln. which, when treated in the same way, gives a reading of 26.8 units.

*21-24.   Phenylketonuria (pku) is a disease which is characterized by high levels of phenylalanine in the blood due to the faulty metabolism of this compd.   Since the disease is congenital and has serious consequences, it is essential to detect it as soon after birth as possible.   Using a standard fluorometric method for phenyl-alanine in blood plasma, the following data were obtained:

Std., 1.00 mg/ml	20.0 *units* fluorescence
Blank	0.0
Child A: normal	18.5
B: normal	21.0
C: normal	19.7
D: diseased	390
E: diseased	710
F: diseased	534

The following samples were taken from five children.   (*a*) Which do you think has pku?   (*b*) What is the concn. of phenylalanine in child 4?

Child	Fluorescence intensity
1	21.1
2	365
3	19.4
4	20.3
5	604

*21-25.   The drug morphine can be converted to pseudomorphine using alkaline oxidation.   The pseudomorphine can be analyzed fluorometrically using excitation at 250 mμ and measuring the emission at 440 mμ.   The limit of detection is reported to be 0.02 $\mu g/ml$ of plasma or tissue extract.   1.00 g of tissue is extracted and treated according to the prescribed procedure to produce 10.0 ml of soln.   This is analyzed fluorometrically, producing a reading of 67.5 units with a blank reading of 3.40 units.   Under the same conditions, a 1.40-$\mu g/ml$ standard sample gave a fluorescence intensity of 55.5 units when the blank read 3.20 units. Calculate the percentage of morphine in the tissue.

X-ray Methods

22-1 Principles

If a beam of electrons or photons of sufficient energy is directed at a material, ionization of the material may result. If the photons (or electrons) are of even greater energy, a K- or L-shell electron may be ejected from the atom. This vacancy is then filled by an electron from one of the outer shells of the same atom. In the course of this process of an electron "jumping" from an outer shell to an inner shell, an x-ray photon will be given off. Due to the precise energy distribution of the shells and subshells for each element, the energy of the x-ray emitted will be uniquely dependent on the element involved. With most x-ray techniques, the physical state of the atom or its state of combination has no effect; however, using the newer instrumentation with low-energy x-rays, it is possible to study chemical combination, valence, and coordination.

Instrumentally, the production and detection of x-rays present some problems very different from those found in ultraviolet and visible spectroscopy. A source of x-rays, an x-ray tube, usually contains a target against which a beam of high-energy electrons is directed. The x-rays produced from this target will be composed of a continuum, on which are superimposed the very intense lines of the source element. These lines can be used for both qualitative and quantitative analysis of the target element (as with the electron probe microanalyzer), or they may be used for measuring x-ray absorption. In addition, the continuum is frequently used to excite x-ray fluorescence. In all the above techniques, whether the target is the sample or the secondary source, an x-ray detection device is needed.

In the ultraviolet region, photons of various energies are usually differentiated, using a prism or grating monochromator. With x-rays a diffraction technique is also used, but it is much more complicated in practice. The x-rays are focused upon an "analyzing crystal" which acts in the same manner as a dispersion grating. The spectrum produced can then be recorded photographically or with some type of counter.

22-2   Absorption

If a beam of x-rays is collimated and directed toward a target, the absorption is a first-order process described by the following equation:

$$P = P_0 e^{-(\mu/\rho)\rho x}$$

where P_0 = initial intensity of the x-ray beam
P = transmitted intensity
x = thickness of the sample (usually in cm)
ρ = density of the sample

The terms μ and μ/ρ are referred to as the *linear absorption coefficient* and the *mass absorption coefficient,* respectively. The quantity μ/ρ has also been found empirically to fit the following equation:

$$\frac{\mu}{\rho} = \frac{CZ^4\lambda^{5/2}N}{A}$$

where N = Avagadro's number
A = atomic weight of the element
Z = atomic number of the element
C = constant over a narrow region of wavelengths

If the sample contains more than one element, then the absorption of each element at the wavelength in use contributes to the total absorption. More specifically, the mass absorption coefficient for the sample is related to the mass absorption coefficient for each element present, in the following manner:

$$\left(\frac{\mu}{\rho}\right)_T = \left(\frac{\mu}{\rho}\right)_1 W_1 + \left(\frac{\mu}{\rho}\right)_2 W_2 + \cdots$$

where W_1 is the weight fraction of element 1 and similarly for all other elements present. Using this relationship and known mass absorption coefficients for certain elements at particular lines, the percentage of each species in a sample can be calculated. Because of instrumental variations and matrix effects in the samples, calibration curves are usually used in quantitative work.

Example 1   Calculate the mass absorption coefficient for benzoic acid at the $K_{\alpha 1}$ x-ray line of copper (1.54 Å) if the mass absorption coefficients for carbon, hydrogen, and oxygen are 4.52, 0.48, and 11.1, respectively, at this line.

Solution   The percentage composition of benzoic acid is 68.9% C, 26.2% O, and 4.9% H.   The mass absorption coefficient for benzoic acid can then be calculated directly:

$$\left(\frac{\mu}{\rho}\right)_T = (0.689 \times 4.52) + (0.262 \times 11.1) + (0.049 \times 0.48)$$

$$= 6.03 \text{ cm}^2/\text{g}   Ans.$$

Example 2   The percentage of lead tetraethyl in a gasoline sample is determined, using absorption of the $K_{\alpha 1}$ x-ray line of copper.   Gasoline samples are prepared containing varying amounts of lead tetraethyl in pure gasoline, and the absorption is measured.   The following values are obtained showing the absorption reading for each percentage of lead tetraethyl in the sample: 0.00%—22.0; 0.10%—27.5; 0.20%—32.8; 0.30%—38.6; 0.40%—44.1; 0.50%—49.4.   Calculate the percentage of lead tetraethyl in a gasoline sample which shows an absorption reading of 41.0.   What is the cause of the absorption reading when no lead tetraethyl is present?

Solution   A calibration curve is drawn, and from it the percentage of lead tetraethyl in the sample is found to be 0.34%.   The absorption with no lead tetraethyl added is due simply to the absorption by carbon, oxygen, and hydrogen in the gasoline.   *Ans.*

22-3   Emission

The traditional approach to x-ray analysis involves using the sample material as the target and analyzing the x-rays emitted by this target when it is bombarded with the exciting electrons.   Although this approach is sometimes used in qualitative work, it is seldom used in quantitative procedures.

A different approach which has found wide acceptance is the electron-probe technique.   In this method, a beam of collimated electrons is focused on the sample which is in a vacuum.   The x-rays produced are then analyzed using a goniometer and a counter.   This method provides a qualitative and a quantitative record of the atomic composition of the sample.   Electron-probe microanalysis provides one of the most sensitive methods available for the detection of a specific element.   At the same time it gives excellent quantitative data for elements that are present at greater concentration than a few percent.   Since the electron beam is small and can be focused very precisely, this method is useful in those applications where it is important to analyze differences in atomic composition occurring in very small volumes.

The most commonly used analytical x-ray technique is x-ray fluorescence. In this method, the electron beam is focused on the target, usually tungsten, from which the primary x-rays are directed to the sample. In the sample, secondary, or fluorescent, x-rays will be produced for those elements which are capable of being excited by the primary x-rays. The fluorescent emission is then usually measured with a goniometer and some type of counting device. A typical x-ray fluorescence spectrum is shown in Fig. 24. Note that the continuum which is part of the emission from the target is now absent.

With both the absorption and emission methods, it is usually necessary to work with standard samples in order to minimize a variety of effects which seriously affect the method. Multiple excitation, where fluorescence from one element excites fluorescence in another element, and phenomena dependent upon differences in the matrix of the sample are two of the most difficult problems associated with x-ray spectrochemical analysis.

Example 1   A particular alloy contains iron and nickel. When the alloy is excited, the x-ray fluorescences are readily detected and can be used for identification and quantitative analysis. The data obtained for a series of standards encompassing the percentage range found in the alloys are shown below. (The values have been corrected for background and instrumental errors.) These listed pairs of values show in each case the fluorescent emission (1.65 Å) corresponding to the percentage of nickel present: 1.0%—5.6; 2.0%—10.6; 3.0%—14.7; 4.0%—18.2; 5.0%—21.7; 6.0%—24.4; 7.0%—26.6; 8.0%—28.3. An unknown alloy containing only iron and nickel was analyzed and gave a fluorescent emission of 22.4 at the nickel $K_{\alpha 1}$ line, with a background correction of 1.7. Calculate the percentage of nickel in the alloy.

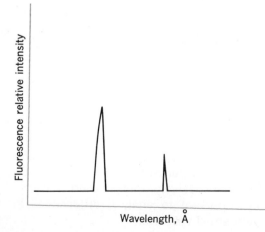

Wavelength, Å

Fig. 24   Typical x-ray fluorescence spectrum.

Solution   The calibration data are plotted as intensity versus percentage of nickel, and a nonlinear working curve is obtained.   The value for the unknown (22.4) is corrected for background (1.7) to give a corrected intensity of 20.7.   This corresponds to a nickel concentration of 4.7%.

Ans.

PROBLEMS

*22-1.   If it is assumed that compd. X shows a mass absorption coefficient of 4.75 cm^2/g at the $K_{\alpha 1}$ line for copper (1.54 Å), what would be the approx. mass absorption coefficient at the zinc $K_{\alpha 1}$ line (1.43 Å)?

*22-2.   The detn. of cobalt in certain biological samples was carried out using x-ray absorption.   A series of standards known to be free of cobalt gave absorption readings in the range from 10 to 14 units.   Data for a calibration curve were then obtained using solns. of known cobalt concn.

% Co *concn.*	*Absorption*
0.00	10, 11, 14
0.50	17, 19, 17
1.00	23, 25, 25
1.50	28, 29, 29
2.00	34, 37, 36
2.50	42, 40, 40

An unknown sample was then treated in the prescribed way and yielded absorption values of 22, 23, 22.   Calculate the percentage of cobalt in this unknown sample.

22-3.   The analysis of organically bound chlorine using x-ray absorption has been described by Griffen [*Anal. Chem.*, **34**, 606 (1962)].   Using the K-line x-rays of manganese, the mass absorption coefficient of chlorine is 102 cm^2/g, while hydrogen, carbon, and oxygen have values of 0.2, 4.5, and 11.4 cm^2/g, respectively. Make a plot showing absorbance vs. ml of trichloroethylene added to 50 ml of a solvent mixt. of average composition 68.2% C, 13.6% H, and 18.2% O for the range from 0 to 5 ml of trichloroethylene (density = 1.46).   The sample area is 4.25 cm^2; the solvent has a density of 0.74 g/cm^3 and is 0.5 cm thick.   (Assume no vol. change on mixing.)

*22-4.   Bartkiewicz and Hammatt [*Anal. Chem.*, **36**, 833 (1964)] have described an x-ray fluorescence procedure for the detn. of cobalt, zinc, and iron in organic matrices.   The organics are first taken into soln., to which is added a known quantity of copper naphthenate to serve as the internal standard.   Using standard solns., the following data were obtained for a zinc calibration curve (all intensities are corrected):

% Zn	Zn intensity	Cu intensity
0.10	15.6	26.0
0.20	27.0	27.0
0.30	39.2	28.0
0.40	46.7	27.0
0.50	50.0	25.0

A 0.50-g unknown sample was treated in the recommended manner and yielded the following intensities: copper, 25.0; zinc, 27.5. Calculate the percentage of zinc in the unknown.

*22-5. In order to measure the thickness of a lead paint, lead x-ray fluorescence from the paint is analyzed. With increasing thickness of the paint, the x-ray fluorescence signal from the lead increases in the manner indicated by the following data in which the pairs of values show in each case the units of fluorescence intensity corresponding to in. of thickness of the paint. 0.00 in.—0.0 units; 0.02 in.—14.5 units; 0.04 in.—28.8 units; 0.06 in.—43.6 units; 0.08 in.—58.2 units; 0.10 in.—71.5 units; 0.12 in.—85.0 units. Calculate the thickness of a paint sample which exhibits a lead x-ray fluorescence intensity of 47. 5 when measured under the same conditions.

*22-6. The analysis of zinc in oil sludge was studied, using x-ray fluorescence. The zinc (K_{a1}) line at 1.43 Å had been selected, and the following calibration data were obtained, using gallium as an internal standard:

% Zn	Zn count rate	Ga count rate
0.10	91	700
0.20	185	710
0.30	272	680
0.40	374	705

The above rates are in counts per second (c.p.s.) and have been corrected for background. Analysis of an unknown yielded the following corrected count rates: Zn, 235 c.p.s.; Ga, 710 c.p.s. Calculate the percentage of zinc in the unknown oil sludge.

*22-7. A piece of fractured steel is to be analyzed for elemental discontinuities at the place of fracture, using an electron probe. Previous analyses have shown that in the bulk of the steel the nickel concn. is 2.05%. With the microprobe the following data were obtained at various points in the steel sample removed from the fracture.

Time to obtain 10,000 counts Ni ($K_{\alpha 1}$) 1.54 Å, sec	Background; time to obtain 100 counts, sec
68.4	24.5
69.3	24.9
67.0	24.1
68.5	24.7
69.0	25.1

The five measurements shown below were made along the line of fracture.

Time to obtain 1,000 counts Ni ($K_{\alpha 1}$) 1.54 Å, sec	Background; time to obtain 100 counts, sec
68.7	24.3
69.5	24.2
67.3	24.5
67.4	24.7
68.8	24.2

Calculate the average percentage of nickel in the vicinity of the fracture.

**Nuclear
Magnetic
Resonance**

23-1 Principles

If the axial spin of the nucleus and its corresponding magnetic moment are nonzero for a sample subjected to a strong magnetic field, absorption in the radio-frequency region of the electromagnetic spectrum may occur. This condition is fulfilled for many nuclei, including H^1, C^{13}, N^{14}, O^{17}, F^{19}, and P^{31}, and most of the applications of nuclear magnetic resonance (nmr) have been with these nuclei.

In the presence of an external magnetic field, the nuclear angular momentum (I) is quantized. In those instances where $I = \frac{1}{2}$, there are only two possible energy levels, and the nuclear spins of the nuclei will be nearly equally divided between the two levels. For a specific field strength, the nuclear transition from one energy level to the other corresponds to a specific absorption in the radio-frequency region. This absorption forms the basis for nuclear-magnetic-resonance spectroscopy.

In the application of nmr to chemical problems, it has been common practice to use instruments which incorporate a fixed radio frequency and then to vary the magnetic field. The applied magnetic field also induces magnetic moments in the electrons around the nucleus, which in turn affect the resonance conditions for the specific nucleus. Under conditions of a fixed radio-frequency field, nuclei in different electronic environments will each require a specific and different magnetic field in order for resonance to occur. For example, in the proton magnetic-resonance spectrum of ethanol obtained with an instrument such as the Varian A-60 under normal operating conditions, the C_1 protons exhibit absorption in the vicinity of 3.6 p.p.m. but those on C_2 absorb in the vicinity of

1.2 p.p.m.   The difference is due to the different electronic environments of the methylene and methyl groups, which in turn are a result of the proximity of the hydroxyl group to the C_1 protons.   Thus, by use of nmr, similar nuclei may be distinguished from each other in environments that may also be very nearly similar—a fact that has been responsible for the extremely rapid application of nmr techniques to a wide variety of chemical problems.

The principle application of nmr spectroscopy has been in the area of structure elucidation.   For example, the technique readily permits distinguishing vicinal from geminal hydrogens.   Nuclear magnetic resonance has also been applied to kinetic problems and in certain instances to conformational analysis.   The application of nmr to quantitative problems has developed more slowly.   With most commercial instrumentation, it is possible to measure directly an integrated absorption curve. For the curve to have meaning, however, it is essential for it to be run with great care to avoid difficulties due to saturation and base-line drift; for this reason both internal and external standards are frequently used when doing quantitative work.   An integrated absorption curve has the shape of a number of steps of differing heights, where the total height is proportional to the total number of analyzed nuclei present in the molecule under study.   The difference in height between any two steps is proportional to the number of nuclei responsible for that specific absorption.   Figure 25 shows the nmr absorption spectrum for 2,6-dimethylphenol and its integrated absorption spectrum.   In the general case, it is possible by using the electronic integrator to analyze for compound A

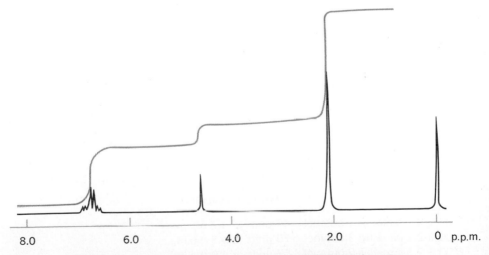

Fig. 25   NMR absorption spectrum of 2,6-dimethylphenol and integrated spectrum.

in the presence of compound B, provided compound A exhibits absorption in a region where compound B does not.

An advantage of using nmr for analysis is that the method is non-destructive and convenient. If the sample is a liquid, it can be run directly; if it is a solid, it is dissolved in an appropriate solvent. Until recently it was necessary to work with rather large quantities of material (e.g., 50 mg) in order to achieve a good signal. Various approaches have been taken to alleviate this difficulty. One has been the development of smaller sample tubes; another has been the development of signal-averaging techniques which permit the treatment in a statistical manner of the poor signal-to-noise ratio obtained at low concentrations.

Example 1   The analysis of alanine in the presence of β-alanine can be accomplished by making use of their nmr spectra run in D_2O. A 5.00% solution of alanine in D_2O exhibits an integrated intensity of 980 at 1.48 p.p.m. because of the α-methyl group. A 5.00% solution of β-alanine under the same conditions exhibits an integrated intensity of 650 at 2.54 p.p.m. because of the α-methylene group present in this molecule. A 5.00% solution of an unknown mixture containing only alanine and β-alanine in D_2O exhibited integrated intensities of 377 at 1.48 and 400 at 2.54 p.p.m. Calculate the percentage of alanine in the mixture.

Solution

$$\frac{377}{980} \times 100 = 38.5\% \text{ alanine} \qquad \textit{Ans.}$$

A check can be made using the β-alanine:

$$\frac{400}{650} \times 100 = 61.5\% \text{ } \beta\text{-alanine} \qquad \textit{Ans.}$$

PROBLEMS

*23-1.   In the analysis of a series of butanol derivatives [Z. *Anal. Chem.*, **205**, 194 (1964)], it was found that because of steric effects, the OH group signal appears at a different field strength for each compd. The following data were obtained under identical operating conditions:

Soln. in benzene	Integrated intensity
5.00% 2,2-dimethyl-1-butanol	47 units at 4.7 p.p.m.
8.00% 2,2-dimethyl-3-butanol	75 units at 4.3 p.p.m.
6.00% 2,3-dimethyl-2-butanol	57 units at 4.0 p.p.m.

Calculate the percentage of each compd. present in a mixt. which exhibits integrated intensities of 65 units at 4.7 p.p.m., 55 units at 4.3 p.p.m., and 20 units at 4.0 p.p.m.

*23-2.   Hydrogen analysis by nmr spectroscopy has become a powerful tool due to its inherent simplicity and relative speed.   The total integrated area (measured on a standard proton-magnetic-resonance spectrometer) can be described by the following equation:

$$\text{Total area (or integrated intensity)} = kWH$$

where k = proportionality const.
   W = wt. of sample dissolved in a standard vol.
   H = % hydrogen in sample
   A standard sample was prepared contg. 0.320 g/ml of n-decane in CCl_4.   It exhibited an integrated intensity of 922 units.   An unknown sample was prepared contg. 0.285 g/ml of the unknown compd. in CCl_4.   Its intensity was measured in a tube of identical diameter on the same instrument, yielding 325 units.   Calculate the percentage of hydrogen in the unknown sample.

*23-3.   The quantitative detn. of 1-phenyl-1-bromopropane (I) in the presence of 1-phenyl-2-bromopropane (II) using nmr has been described [*J. Org. Chem.*, **29,** 1503 (1964)].   For this system, nmr has been found to be superior to gas chromatography because of the similar thermal properties of the compds. and the difficulty of separating them.   The absorption from the proton in the   CHBr— group occurs at 4.77 and 5.85 τ for the compds. I and II, respectively.   0.540 g of an unknown mixt. contg. both bromopropanes and other compds. is dissolved in 10.0 ml of CCl_4 which already contains tetramethylsilane.   This soln. is run directly, and the integrated intensity at 5.85 τ is 40% greater than the integrated intensity at 4.77 τ. The integrated intensity at 4.77 τ is only 25% as great as when a soln. of 0.20 g of pure II, treated similarly to the unknown, is measured.   Calculate the percentage of I and the percentage of II in the mixt.

*23-4.   The analysis of fluorine in organic compds. is frequently long and tedious. A method has been described [*Anal. Chem.*, **36,** 1713 (1964)] which makes use of the fluorine nuclear magnetic resonance, provided the fluorine concn. in the prepared sample solns. is greater than 1 M.   The article also describes the use of fluorobenzene as an internal standard.   Using CCl_4 as the solvent, the following data were obtained.

Wt. of fluorobenzene taken	1.94 g
Wt. of unknown taken	0.57 g
Vol. of solvent used	5.00 ml
Integrated intensity due to fluorobenzene	784 units
Integrated intensity due to unknown	387 units

Calculate the percentage by wt. of fluorine in the unknown compd.

*23-5.   The detn. of replaceable hydrogens by nmr has been described by several workers. It has also been shown that for systems where the exchange with D_2O is rapid, there results only one peak from both the active hydrogen and the water. In order better to describe a complicated natural product, an investigator wished to determine the no. of easily replaceable hydrogens. In the method used, the external standard contained 0.50% methanol in pyridine in which the concn. of D_2O was 1.0 M. Under these conditions, the integrated intensity for the active hydrogen–HDO peak was 745 units. A 2.00% soln. of the unknown natural product was treated in a similar manner and the integrated intensity for the corresponding peak was found to be 227 units. Assuming that the instrument was stable and that the tubes were of the same diameter, etc., calculate the percentage by wt. of active hydrogen in the unknown natural product.

*23-6.   The quantitative analysis of certain nonionic surfactants by nmr has been described [*Anal. Chem.*, **35,** 1283 (1963)]. Specifically, interest centered on the length of the alkyl side chains as substituents of phenol–ethylene oxide condensates. It was shown that the four protons found on the benzene ring could be used for calibration purposes. Absorption in the vicinity of 6.1 τ was ascribed to the protons of the ethylene oxide chain plus the terminal OH group, and the absorption at still higher τ was said to result from the alkyl side chain. For a particular surfactant, the integrated intensity for the benzene protons was 240 units, while the intensities at 6.1 τ and 8.9 τ were 440 and 540 units, respectively. (*a*) Calculate the average number of protons found in the alkyl group. (*b*) What is the ratio of ethylene oxide plus terminal hydroxyl protons to the no. of aromatic protons?

*23-7.   Classification of alcohols by nmr spectroscopy has been described in the literature [*JACS*, **86,** 1256 (1964)]. The solvent used for these studies was dimethylsulfoxide (DMSO). Under the conditions used, the hydroxyl proton resonance of *cis*-4-*t*-butylcyclohexyl alcohol (10% soln.) occurs at $\tau = 5.89$ and is of equal magnitude (51 units) with that of the *trans* isomer, the absorption of which is at $\tau = 5.55$. In a particular analysis, these two compds. are the only ones extracted which have absorption in the region from 5.4 to 6.1 τ, and they can be analyzed using nmr. A 5.00-g sample is extracted at 90% efficiency and then concd. The resulting material is dissolved to make 6.0 g of a DMSO soln. The nmr spectrum obtained has integrated intensities of 78 and 34 units at 5.89 and 5.55 τ, respectively. Calculate the percentage by wt. of each isomer in the starting material.

23-8.   The analysis of cryptopine found in samples of "pure" thebaine has been discussed in the literature. Thebaine exhibits absorption due to three protons between 4.8 and 5.75 p.p.m. and absorption due to two protons between 5.75 and 7.15 p.p.m. Cryptopine exhibits no absorption between 4.8 and 5.75 p.p.m. and absorption due to six protons between 5.75 and 7.15 p.p.m. Derive an expression for determining quantitatively the concn. of cryptopine in thebaine.

Mass Spectrometry

24-1 Principles

Since its beginning, mass spectrometry has been associated with both qualitative and quantitative analysis. From the quantitative standpoint, mass spectrometry is being successfully applied to an increasing number of problems.

Many different types of mass spectrometers have been designed, and several are available as commercial instruments, but certain basic components are common to all of them. The means of placing the sample, in whatever physical state it exists, into the chamber where it can be ionized has proved to be difficult in many cases. Since at first only gases were analyzed, it was possible by using standards and applying Dalton's law to measure the number of moles of a particular gas present in a mixture. However, because of the need to analyze compounds of low volatility, a variety of other techniques and "sample introduction systems" were developed. Heated inlet systems are frequently used, and solid samples may be placed in a small crucible or on a wire and then heated directly in the ion source.

A means of producing ions from the neutral molecules or atoms present in the ion source is necessary. This is usually accomplished by having the gaseous species pass through an electron beam. As a result of electron-molecule collisions, the molecule loses an electron and becomes positively charged. This is indicated schematically by the following:

$$\text{Molecule} + e^- \longrightarrow \text{molecule}^+ + 2e^-$$

The energy of the electron beam that is just sufficient to cause a single ionization of the molecule, usually producing the molecular ion, is referred to as the *appearance potential*.

When the energy of the electron beam is increased, however, the magnitude of the molecular-ion peak is seen to decrease and a large number of fragment peaks appear, resulting from fragmentation of the molecule to form ions other than the molecular ion. A mass spectrum as normally obtained includes all these fragment peaks and, in addition, peaks resulting from the presence of naturally occurring isotopes. Other sources, such as those due to thermal ionization, field-emission, photo-ionization, arc discharge, and spark have been successfully used.

In order to separate an ion of a certain mass-to-charge ratio from another ion of different mass-to-charge ratio, a wide variety of techniques have been used. Three of the more common ones are the time-of-flight, the magnetic single-focusing, and the double-focusing instruments. The time-of-flight mass spectrometer separates ions on the basis of their velocities in an evacuated drift tube. If all ions start the path at the same time, then the ion of smallest mass-to-charge ratio will reach the detector first. The time-of-flight on an ion in the commercially available Bendix instrument can be approximated by the equation $t = 2m/e$, where m is the mass of the ion and e is its charge (assuming an accelerating potential of 3,000 volts and a drift tube of 100 cm). Most single-focusing instruments depend upon a magnetic field to separate ions of different mass. Under the influence of a magnetic field, the ion of lowest mass-to-charge ratio will be deflected the farthest, assuming all ions have the same initial velocity. This property can then be utilized in a variety of ways, but the most common method is to bring into focus on the exit slit ions of increasing or decreasing mass-to-charge ratios by changing the magnetic field.

In the use of single-focusing instruments, several difficulties become apparent. Among these is the fact that all the ions produced in the source do not have the same velocity; hence the deflected beam is not completely homogeneous. Mattauch and Herzog overcame this difficulty by designing a double-focusing instrument. In it were incorporated an electrostatic analyzer which yields ions of nearly homogeneous energy and a magnetic analyzer which operates in the normal manner (magnetically) and follows the electrostatic analyzer. This incorporation of two analyzers into one mass spectrometer produces mass spectra of an entirely different type, with many useful applications which are inaccessible to single-focusing instruments.

Several methods of detecting ions in a mass spectrometer have been used. The photographic plate was used on many of the early instruments and is also used on some of the double-focusing instruments. More frequently, some form of electrical detection is incorporated, such as the faraday cup, which is usually linked with an electrometer. Electron multipliers are also often used. With electrical detection, the output signal is usually displayed on a strip chart recorder or on an oscillo-graphic recorder.

   In Fig. 26 is shown a portion of a typical mass spectrum obtained with a single-focusing instrument incorporating electrical detection. To avoid running more spectra than are necessary, it is common practice to record the spectrum, using a recorder equipped with several channels. Such oscillographic recorders incorporate several optical galvanometers, each of which is set at a different sensitivity; thus each line shown corre-sponds to a different sensitivity. Similarly, with photographic detection, the spectrum obtained will usually contain many spectra, corresponding to spectra of different sensitivities plotted on the same graph. These spectra as obtained directly from the mass spectrometer are difficult to handle and inconvenient to interpret. For this reason, the spectra are usually transformed into one of two forms, either manually or by means of a computer.

   For the purpose of interpreting a mass spectrum, it is customary to

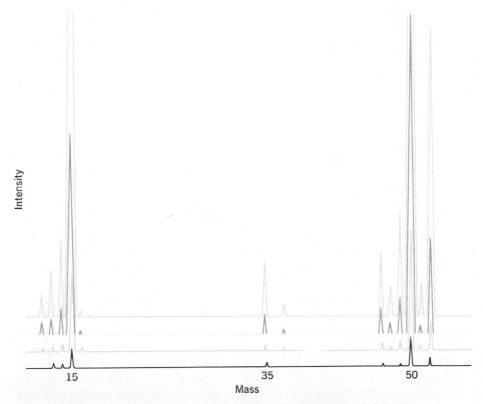

Fig. 26   Mass spectra of monochloromethane (ratios of sensitivities $= 1:3:10:30$).

plot the relative abundance of a particular ion against the mass-to-charge (m/e) ratio.   To the ion of greatest abundance (the "base peak") is assigned a value of 100, and the abundances of the other ions are calculated relative to this.   For purposes of quantitative work, these data are frequently arranged in tabular form as illustrated below for the case of the mass spectral data for monochloromethane.

m/e	Rel. abundance	m/e	Rel. abundance
12	3.3	47	7.1
13	5.4	48	3.4
14	8.4	49	11.4
15	72.3	50	100
16	1.0	51	3.8
35	6.2	52	31.0
37	1.9		

Comparison of spectra, particularly those obtained with different instruments, is a much more difficult process.   It is then important to know what contribution each peak makes to the total ion current (i.e., to the sum of all peaks).   For this reason, spectra are sometimes presented as percent Σ_m versus m/e, where Σ_m is the percentage of the total ion current due to a single peak and where the total ion current is measured from any specific m/e peak to the peak of highest molecular weight in the spectrum.   Figure 27 illustrates both graphical forms of presentation in one plot; the left-hand axis is the relative abundance (in percent of the base peak) and the right-hand axis is percent Σ_m.

The increased use of double-focusing instruments has added a new dimension to mass spectrometry.   Because of their very great resolving power, usually greater than 1 part in 25,000, it is now possible to determine precisely the mass of a particular ion as opposed to knowing simply the nearest whole-number mass.   This permits the determination of the elemental composition of the ion and frequently of the molecule.   For quantitative analysis, it makes certain that the analysis of a mixture can be based for each species upon the intensity of a single peak due to only one ion, and this peak is sharply defined from all surrounding peaks.

24-2   Applications

Taking the simple case of two compounds present in a mixture, it is not difficult to imagine that each compound would have at least one peak in its spectrum which would be unique and could be used for the analysis

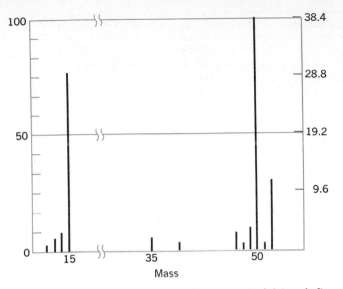

Fig. 27   Methods of presentation of mass spectral data. Left-hand axis: percent relative abundance (relative to "base peak"). Right-hand axis: percent Σ_m.

of that compound.   In order to use this approach, it is imperative that there be available samples of the pure compounds so that the mass spectrum of each component and its sensitivity can be determined. Sensitivity is used in this case to mean the height of the particular mass peak per unit pressure of the molecule in the ion source if one is working with a gaseous sample.   In the event that one is working with some other means of sample introduction, it becomes much more difficult to describe a precise sensitivity for a particular compound, and in fact it is usually necessary to use an internal standard.

Another method of quantitative analysis which is frequently used is isotope dilution.   As opposed to radioactive methods, analyses using a mass spectrometer can make use of both stable and unstable isotopes. However, from a practical standpoint the method is identical to that discussed in the section on radiochemical techniques.

Example 1   A mixture of 1-α-naphthylpentadecane and its saturated analog are analyzed with a mass spectrometer.   The following data were obtained for the unknown and for the pure compounds under the same operating conditions on the same instrument:

m/e	1-α-Naphthylpentadecane	1-α-Decalylpentadecane	Unknown
81	0.3	49.0	48.9
95	0.2	43.0	43.0
137	0.1	100	100
141	100	0.1	9.3
338	48.0	0.0	4.4
348	0.0	8.4	8.4
Sens.	0.797	0.910	

Calculate the mole percent of each compound in the mixture.

Solution

1. Call 1-α-naphthylpentadecane compound A and 1-α-decalylpenta-decane compound B.

2. Decide which peaks to use for the calculation. For compound A, the peak at $m/e = 338$ is obviously preferred. For the analysis of compound B, the peak at $m/e = 137$ is chosen since compound A presents the least interference at this mass-to-charge ratio.

3. Determine the uncorrected partial pressure due to each compound by setting up two simultaneous equations:

$$100 = 0.1(X_A) + 100(X_B)$$
$$4.4 = 48(X_A) + 0.0(X_B)$$

4. Solving,

$$X_A = 0.08 \qquad X_B = 0.92$$

5. Divide by the appropriate sensitivity factors to yield the partial pressures of the two gases:

$$\frac{0.08}{0.797} = 0.10 = P_A$$

$$\frac{0.92}{0.910} = 1.01 = P_B$$

6. The partial pressure multiplied by 100 and divided by the sum of the partial pressures (ΣP_i) yields the mole-percent composition of the mixture:

$$\frac{0.10 \times 100}{1.11} = 9 \text{ mole \% of A} \qquad Ans.$$

$$\frac{1.01 \times 100}{1.11} = 91 \text{ mole \% of B} \qquad Ans.$$

Quantitative analysis of more complicated mixtures using a single-focusing instrument is frequently far more involved. The basic assumption upon which these analyses are made is that peaks heights are strictly additive and the procedure is therefore similar to that used in ultraviolet absorption analysis of multicomponent mixtures. However, in mass spectrometry it is frequently possible to analyze mixtures containing as many as 10 or 20 components. Two basic approaches are used: the subtraction method and the method of linear simultaneous equations. In the example below, both of these methods are illustrated with a three-component mixture; the same principles would apply for mixtures of greater complexity.

Example 2   A mixture contains three species (A, B, C) in unknown proportions. The mass spectra of the pure compounds and their sensitivities have been run previously. The data from this and the data obtained on the unknown are listed below as relative abundances. Calculate the percentage composition of the mixture (*a*) by the subtraction method and (*b*) by the method of linear simultaneous equations.

m/e	A	B	C	Unknown
52	100	24.4	5.7	69.6
71	0.0	18.5	0.0	23.9
75	17.3	8.2	69.4	100
84	28.4	40.0	27.0	93.3
Sens.	0.425	0.780	0.940	

Solution (*a*)

1. A peak in the mass spectrum due to only one component must be found. The peak at $m/e = 71$ for compound B fulfills this requirement. The uncorrected partial pressure of component B can then be calculated:

$$X_B = \frac{23.9}{18.5} = 1.29$$

2. Using this value, a new spectrum of component B can be calculated:

m/e	B (*new spectrum*)
52	31.5
71	23.9
75	10.6
84	51.6

3. By subtracting this spectrum from the spectrum of the unknown, one obtains a difference spectrum which is due only to components A and C:

m/e	Unknown
52	38.1
71	0.0
75	89.4
84	41.7

4. The remaining data can be set up as two equations in two unknowns using the peaks at $m/e = 52$ and $m/e = 75$, since these show the greatest difference in peak magnitudes for the two components. [The above procedures, (1) through (3), would normally be carried out successively until only two components remained.]

$$38.1 = 100(X_A) + 5.7(X_C)$$
$$89.4 = 17.3(X_A) + 69.4(X_C)$$

Solving,

$$X_A = 0.31 \quad \text{and} \quad X_C = 1.21$$

5. Calculate the partial pressure of each component by dividing the uncorrected partial pressure of each compound by the appropriate sensitivity:

$$0.31/0.425 = 0.73 = P_A$$
$$1.29/0.780 = 1.65 = P_B$$
$$1.21/0.940 = 1.29 = P_C$$
$$\Sigma P_i = 3.67$$

6. Calculate the mole percent of each component by dividing each partial pressure by the total pressure and multiplying by 100:

$$\frac{0.73}{3.67} = 20.0 \text{ mole \% of A}$$

$$\frac{1.65}{3.67} = 45.0 \text{ mole \% of B} \quad \Bigg\} \quad Ans.$$

$$\frac{1.29}{3.67} = 35.0 \text{ mole \% of C}$$

Solution (b)   This solution makes use of matrix algebra.
    1. For three compounds, it is necessary to set up three linear

simultaneous equations in three unknowns.   The same three peaks are used as in the previous solution.

$$69.6 = 100(X_A) + 24.4(X_B) + 5.7(X_C)$$
$$23.9 = 0.0(X_A) + 18.5(X_B) + 0.0(X_C)$$
$$100 = 17.3(X_A) + 8.2(X_B) + 69.4(X_C)$$

2. Using matrix algebra (a computer can also be used),

$$A = \begin{bmatrix} 100.0 & 24.4 & 5.7 \\ 0.0 & 18.5 & 0.0 \\ 17.3 & 8.2 & 69.4 \end{bmatrix}$$

which can then be inverted to yield

$$A^- = \begin{bmatrix} 0.0101 & -0 & -0.0025 \\ -0.0130 & 0.0540 & -0.0031 \\ -0.0083 & -0 & 0.0146 \end{bmatrix}$$

3. These values can then be utilized to set up three new equations into which are substituted the heights of the appropriate m/e peaks:

$$(X_A) = (0.0101)(69.9) + (-0.0130)(23.9) + (-0.0083)(100) = 0.31$$
$$(X_B) = (0.0540)(23.9) = 1.29$$
$$(X_C) = (-0.0025)(69.6) + (-0.0031)(23.9) + (0.0146)(100) = 1.21$$

4. These values are then treated in the same manner as in the previous solution.

PROBLEMS

*24-1.   A sample of specially purified argon gas was analyzed in a mass spectrometer and gave the following data:

m/e	% Abundance	Mass
36	0.337	35.968
38	0.063	37.963
40	99.600	39.962

Calculate the at. wt. of argon which would appear on a periodic table.

*24-2.   The following data were obtained for a series of known compds. and for a mixt. of them.

m/e	A	B	C	D	Unknown
67	100	16.0	17.0	12.3	100
84	0	25.0	0	0	14.9
97	0	7.0	0	44.0	80.8
105	5.4	0	42.0	8.5	26.1
109	4.8	4.2	100	1.5	26.6
Sens.	1.42	0.82	0.94	1.08	

(*a*) Calculate the mole percent of each species in the mixt. using the method of subtraction. (*b*) Calculate the mole percent of each species in the mixt. using the method of linear simultaneous equations. (*c*) Do the results by the two methods agree?

*24-3. Below are given the principle portions of the mass spectra of several hydrocarbons and of an unknown composed of the four compds. Calculate the mole percent of each of the hydrocarbons present in the unknown mixt. (Data are given as relative abundances.)

m/e	2-Methyl-pentane	3-Methyl-pentane	2,2-Dimethyl-butane	2,3-Dimethyl-butane	Unknown
29	17.6	61.0	50.0	9.77	41.5
39	16.9	18.1	26.4	16.5	23.9
42	53.3	5.53	5.16	86.7	43.3
43	100	28.4	100	100	100
56	4.20	75.7	28.9	1.00	30.8
57	10.0	100	97.1	0.66	66.4
70	6.34	1.47	3.22	0.63	2.72
71	27.0	5.39	72.0	15.5	49.1
86	2.98	3.03	0.05	3.37	2.88
Sens.	1.47	1.05	0.84	1.57	

24-4. Using the same data that appears in Prob. 24-3, make a plot of relative abundance versus *m/e* for the principle component and the unknown. (*a*) Do they look similar? (*b*) Should they?

*24-5. The following data showing relative abundances were obtained for a four-component gas mixt. and for the four pure compds. A, B, C, and D.

m/e	A	B	C	D	Unknown
83	18.2	0.0	12.0	24.0	78.5
94	0.0	12.1	7.2	11.1	48.5
108	92.0	0.2	1.7	0.0	27.8
127	0.0	100	0.7	1.2	36.7
145	0.0	1.4	0.0	92.4	18.2
168	0.0	0.1	17.0	0.3	100
172	0.0	6.8	4.2	0.0	27.0
Sens.	1.21	1.04	0.97	1.51	

(a) What four peaks would you choose for the analysis of this mixt.?   (b) Calculate the percentage composition of the unknown mixt.   Neglect the contribution from the peak of any other compd. the magnitude of which is less than 2% of the peak being used for the analysis.

*24-6.   (a) Calculate more accurately the percentage composition of the unknown in Prob. 24-5, using the method of linear simultaneous equations.   Compare your answer with that obtained in Prob. 24-5.   (b) Could the subtraction technique have been applied to Prob. 24-5?

*24-7.   The analysis of compd. X, whose base peak is at $m/e = 187$, is carried out by mass spectrometry using an internal standard (substance Y) which gives a major peak at $m/e = 182$. 5 ml of the unknown mixt. is mixed with 0.50 ml of the soln. contg. 10% of the internal standard.   (All components are sufficiently volatile at the temp. used.)   The following calibration data were obtained:

Peak height $m/e = 187$	Peak height $m/e = 182$	Concn. of compd. X in the calibration mole % solns.
8.10	19.3	1.3
64.9	79.0	2.6
47.5	44.0	3.4
77.0	55.0	4.5
38.2	22.6	5.3

An unknown sample (5.00 ml) is mixed with 0.50 ml of a new soln. of the internal standard which contains only 5% of compd. Y; ratio of peak heights [$m/e\,(187/182)$] is 0.96.   Calculate the mole percent of compd. X in the unknown mixt.

*24-8.   The analysis of an important industrial compd. M is complicated by the extremely poor yield in its synthesis.   The material in question shows a large peak at $m/e = 188$.   By another procedure it is possible to prepare a small quantity of the pure compd. M with the only N atom replaced by ^{15}N.   To the impure unknown sample weighing 0.50 g is added 5.00 mg of the ^{15}N-contg. compd. M, and the materials are mixed thoroughly.   A mass spectrum is run on the resultant mixt. The relative peak height at $m/e = 188$ is 71.5, while that at $m/e = 189$ is 240. (a) Calculate the percentage of compd. M present in the unknown sample, assuming that the naturally-occurring ^{15}N is insignificant.   (b) Calculate the percentage of compd. M present in the unknown, taking into consideration the presence of naturally occurring ^{15}N.   (The natural abundance of ^{15}N is 0.36%.)

Refractometry
and Polarimetry

25-1 Refractometry

Refractive index measurements have been used for a variety of purposes, both qualitative and quantitative. The refractive index, n, is the quantity which is usually measured, where $n = \dfrac{\sin i}{\sin r}$ and where the angles i and r are best illustrated by noting Fig. 28. Thus n is a measure of the extent to which the direction of a ray of light is changed on going from one medium into another. The symbol n_{D}^{20} is frequently encountered; D indicates that the sodium D line was used for the measurement, and the number 20 represents the temperature in degrees centigrade. Since the refractive index depends on the wavelength of light used and on the temperature, it is imperative that these facts be explicitly stated.

Two basic types of refractometers are used: the Abbe and the immersion. In the *Abbe refractometer*, two prisms are used and the sample is placed between them. By means of additional lenses and prisms, the instrument reads the refractive index directly. The *immersion refractometer* contains only one prism plus associated compensators and lenses. The prism is placed directly in the solution being analyzed, but it is necessary that 10 to 20 ml of sample solution be available, whereas the Abbe instrument requires only a drop or two. The scale of the immersion refractometer is in divisions which must be correlated with either the refractive index or the concentration, using reference standards or published tables. With both instruments, it is imperative that the temperature be held constant.

For the quantitative analysis of mixtures, a linear relationship is assumed between the mole fraction and the refractive index.

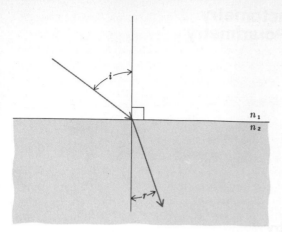

Fig. 28 Refraction of a light beam. (n_1 = medium number 1; n_2 = medium number 2; i = angle of incidence; r = angle of refraction.)

PROBLEMS

*25-1. Calculate the refractive index of a soln. contg. 35.0 mole percent of propanal ($n_D^{20} = 1.3636$) and 65.0 mole percent of 1-propanol ($n_D^{20} = 1.3850$).

*25-2. If a linear relationship between the refractive index and mole fraction is assumed, what would be the percentage-by-wt. composition of a toluene and α-aminotoluene mixt. which has a refractive index of $n_D^{20} = 1.5195$? (Toluene: $n_D^{20} = 1.4961$; α-aminotoluene: $n_D^{20} = 1.5402$.)

*25-3. The alcohol content in a fermentation broth is analyzed by distilling the alcohol from the broth, diluting to a known vol. with distilled water, and measuring its refractive index, using an immersion refractometer. The reading can be correlated with percent alcohol by vol., using standard tables. The distillate from a 450-ml sample is collected and diluted to 100 ml with distilled water. The scale reading obtained, using a standard immersion refractometer, with this soln., is 18.8, which corresponds to 3.45% alcohol by vol. What is the percentage of alcohol in the broth?

*25-4. A mixt. of pentanoic and heptanoic acids is analyzed by refractometry; its refractive index is found to be 1.4120 (n_D^{20}). Calculate the mole percent and wt.-percent composition of the mixt. (Heptanoic acid: $n_D^{20} = 1.4216$; pentanoic acid: $n_D^{20} = 1.4086$.)

25-2 Polarimetry

It is a known characteristic of certain compounds that the rates of propagation of the left- and right-hand components of a plane-polarized light ray through the material are different. The result is that the plane of polarized light will have been rotated on passing through a solution of such a compound. The compound responsible for this phenomenon is referred to as being *optically active*. As with refractometry, the choice of the wavelength of light and the maintenance of a known constant temperature are extremely important.   Under the proper conditions and using a good polarimeter, the specific rotation $[\alpha]$ (that is, the rotation measured under standard conditions) is proportional to the measured rotation in degrees (a), the concentration of the solute in grams per 100 ml of solution (C), and the path length in decimeters (b), according to the following equation:

$$[\alpha]_\lambda^t = \frac{100a}{bC}$$

As with refractometry, the temperature is indicated by a superscript and the wavelength of light used by a subscript.

Optical activity has been used for a variety of qualitative and structural identification problems.   In quantitative analysis it has been shown that the extent of rotation depends on the concentration of the optically active solute in a variety of ways, depending on the specific compound. Three basic quantitative relationships have been proposed by Biot:

$$[\alpha] = A + Bq$$
$$[\alpha] = A + Bq + Cq^2$$
$$[\alpha] = A + \frac{Bq}{C + q}$$

where $[\alpha]$ = specific rotation
A, B, C = constants
q = weight fraction of solvent present in the sample

The three equations represent a straight line, a parabola, and a hyperbola, respectively.   Since it is not possible to predict which relationship between concentration and rotation will be followed by any particular compound, it is necessary to prepare a series of standards of different concentrations in order to determine first the nature of the curve for that compound.

Polarimetry in various forms has found wide application in the analysis of sugars, in which case the specially designed instrument employed is called a saccharimeter.

Polarimeters consist of only a very few parts: a light source, a polarizing prism, a sample tube, an analyzing prism, a scale, and an eyepiece.   The rotation of the analyzing prism with respect to the polarizing prism permits the direct measurement of the rotatory power.   The introduction of a half-shade device permits one to compare two portions of the field in order to reach the balance point.   More refined photoelectric polarimeters and recording spectropolarimeters are also frequently used.

PROBLEMS

*25-5. An organic compd. has a specific rotation of 45.20°. A soln. of this compd. is placed in a 10.0-cm tube, and its rotation is found to be 13.20°. (*a*) What is the concn. of the compd. in the unknown soln.? (*b*) What are the units of the concn.?

*25-6. If the measured rotation in Prob. 25-5 was then checked with the sample tube filled with solvent and was found to be 1.08°, what would be the corrected concn. of the compd. in the unknown soln.?

*25-7. Calculate the specific rotation of brucine if its rotation (*a*) is −3.50° when 9.88 g is dissolved in 94.6 g of ethanol, assuming no vol. change on mixing. The soln. was measured in a 5.0-cm sample tube. What would be the composition of a soln. of brucine in ethanol if it exhibited a rotation of −11.5° when measured under the same conditions as the soln. above?

*25-8. Three standard solns. of compd. X are prepared with 20, 50, and 80% of X, respectively. The specific rotations of the three samples are 5.95, 5.70, and 5.44, respectively. (*a*) Which of Biot's equations applies? (*b*) Calculate the values of the applicable consts.

*25-9. The following data were obtained in an attempt to determine the relationship between specific rotation and concn. for turpentine dissolved in alcohol:

Turpentine g	Alcohol g	Specific rotation
10	90	−37.061
50	50	−37.566
90	10	−38.486

(*a*) Which of Biot's equations does this data fit? (*b*) Calculate the numerical values for the appropriate consts.

*25-10. The analysis of a mixt. known to contain primarily turpentine is based upon the information given in Prob. 25-9 and the assumption that turpentine is the only optically active species present. 10.0 g of the unknown mixt. is dissolved in ethanol and diluted to 100 ml with ethanol. The rotation of the resulting soln. when measured in a 20.2-cm tube is found to be −6.789°. Calculate the approx. concn. of turpentine in the sample.

*25-11. An amino acid has a specific rotation of 78.32° in a 1 *N* HCl soln. A certain soln. is known to contain a small quantity of amino acid, but the rotation of the soln. is too small to be measured directly. A vol. of 10.0 liters of the unknown is concd. to 50 ml and is then passed through a chromatographic column. That portion of the eluent contg. only the amino acid has a vol. of 150.0 ml, which is then concd. to a vol. of 10.0 ml. This soln. is mixed with an equal vol. of 2 *N* HCl, and the rotation of the resultant soln. is found to be 14.55° when measured in a 19.8-cm tube. Calculate the concn. of amino acid in the initial unknown soln.

SIX
Specialized
Methods

 **Radiochemical Methods**

The particles or rays produced in radioactive decay form the basis for numerous analytical methods. The choice of detector depends on the particle (or ray) being measured and on the purpose of the particular experiment. We are not concerned here with differences between various types of detectors but rather with the quantitative aspects of the radioactive-decay phenomenon and with its application to chemical problems in a variety of techniques.

26-1 Counting Statistics

For each radioactive disintegration, a particle will be emitted. However, because of such effects as coincidence and geometry, the measured counting rate is usually proportional but not equal to the disintegration rate. Since the radioactive-decay process is statistical in nature, the analyst is concerned with the utilization of probability theory and statistics. If the assumption is valid that the half-life of the radioactive species is long compared with the counting time, then it can be shown that the standard deviation in the total count, σ, is approximately equal to $\sqrt{N}$, where N is the number of counts taken. The standard deviation in the counting rate or activity (σ_r) is simply $\sqrt{\dfrac{r}{t}}$, where r is the counting rate (in counts per unit time) and t is the time. It would then be correct to express the activity as $r \pm \sigma_r$.

In order to know the count due to the sample alone, it is almost always necessary to measure the background and then subtract it from the total count.

Example 1 What is the activity of a sample containing C^{14} if the measured activity is 4,000 counts per min (cpm) and the background activity is 800 counts per 2 min?

Solution

$$4,000/1 - 800/2 = 3,600 \text{ cpm} \qquad Ans.$$

In the above problem, the analyst should have included the standard deviations in order to give an indication of the precision of the measurements. The results would then be

$$(4,000 \pm 63) - \left(400 \pm \frac{14}{2}\right) = 3,600 \pm \sigma_s$$

and σ_s, the standard deviation of the sample's activity, can be calculated according to the following equation:

$$\sigma_s = \sqrt{\sigma_{r(sample)}^2 + \sigma_{r(background)}^2}$$

In the above example then, σ_s would be equal to 64.5, and the activity of the sample would be properly expressed as $3,600 \pm 64.5$ cpm. *Ans.*

The standard deviation of a group of observations with a mean that approximates the true mean would be represented by σ if the value included both background and sample activity (σ_s would be used if only sample activity is considered). If only random errors are present, then up to 68% of a large number of measurements may deviate by an amount equal to $\pm\sigma$. From the standpoint of an individual observation, one datum will deviate by an amount equal to or less than $\pm\sigma$ 68% of the time. The limits corresponding to $\pm2\sigma$ and $\pm3\sigma$ are 95 and 99%, respectively.

The relative standard deviation expressed in percent is also frequently used. It is

$$\frac{\sigma}{N} \times 100$$

The one other term which is sometimes applied to radiochemical methods is the probable error of a determination; it is defined as 0.68σ.

PROBLEMS

*26-1. A radioactive species when counted with a scintillation counter gives a counting rate of 8,500 cpm. Estimate the standard deviation of the counting rate.

*26-2. In Prob. 26-1 the background was also measured and found to be 1,960 counts per 5 min. What is the activity of the radioactive species?

*26-3.   Calculate (*a*) the absolute magnitude and (*b*) the percent variation at the 1σ, 2σ, and 3σ levels for a species showing a corrected activity of 7,900 cpm.

*26-4.   A sample shows a count rate of 12,000 cpm, while the background registers 2,000 counts in 5 min.   (*a*) Calculate the activity of the sample.   (*b*) What is the probable error in this measurement?

*26-5.   A particular radioisotope is being analyzed and shows an activity of 6,400 cpm.   What is the relative standard deviation for this measurement expressed in percent?

*26-6.   If the counting rate for a particular sample of radioactive silver is 5,200 cpm, (*a*) would a counting rate of 5,340 cpm be within the "probable error"? (*b*) Show why.

*26-7.   Would the 5,340 rate be within the 95% confidence limit for the same detn. as is indicated in Prob. 26-6?

*26-8.   For a particular detn., the relative standard deviation must not exceed $\pm1\%$ at the 99% confidence limit (3σ).   (*a*) Determine the no. of counts which are needed to fulfill this condition.   (*b*) If the counting rate is 3,600 counts per sec, how long will the counting require?

*26-9.   A radioactive sample exhibits a count of 350 for a 6-min counting period and the background count is 60 for $2\frac{1}{2}$ min.   What is the relative standard deviation of the sample measurement?

*26-10.   The sample analyzed in Prob. 26-9 is again analyzed and gives 370 counts for 6 min while the background remains the same.   Outside what confidence limit (68, 95, 99%) does this observation fall?

26-2   Half-life

In working with any particular radioactive isotope, one must be concerned with its half-life, a means of detecting the isotope, and the specific activity of the sample in question.   The standard method for expressing the strength of a radioactive material, regardless of the particle or ray emitted, is the *curie*.   The curie is defined as an activity of 3.70×10^{10} disintegrations per second; however, the millicurie (mc) and microcurie (μc) are more frequently used.   The half-life is also of primary concern, since it determines precisely the change in activity of the sample with time.   The decay of a radioactive nuclide follows a first-order rate law, such that

$$\frac{dN}{dt} = -\lambda N$$

where N is the number of radionuclides present at time t and λ is the characteristic decay constant.   With integration, rearrangement, and substitution of certain boundary conditions (that $N = N_0$ when $t = t_0$), the following equation is obtained:

$$N = N_0 e^{-\lambda t}$$

In most measurements, the activity is the measured quantity, and it is assumed that it is proportional to the disintegration rate. The activity then becomes $A = \lambda N$, and the corresponding rate expression is

$$A = A_0 e^{-\lambda t}$$

At the time when one-half of the radionuclides has disintegrated, $t = t_{1/2}$, $N = \frac{1}{2}N_0$, and $\lambda = \dfrac{0.693}{t_{1/2}}$. Expressed in terms of the counting rate, this becomes

$$A = A_0 e^{-0.693(t/t_{1/2})}$$

Example 1   A sample contains 5 mc (millicuries) of potassium-42 (half-life = 12.4 hr). Calculate (a) the initial disintegration rate in disintegrations per minute (dpm), (b) the disintegration rate after 40.0 hr, and (c) the number of grams of potassium-42 initially present.

Solution

(a) $5 \times 10^{-3} \times 60 \times 3.70 \times 10^{10} = 1.11 \times 10^{10}$ dpm   *Ans.*

(b) $A = 1.11 \times 10^{10} e^{-0.693(40.0/12.4)}$

   $= 1.11 \times 10^{10} e^{-2.23}$

   $= 1.20 \times 10^9$ dpm   *Ans.*

(c) $N = \dfrac{(5 \times 10^{-3})(3.7 \times 10^{10})}{0.693/12.4 \times 3,600} = 1.19 \times 10^{13}$

   $= \dfrac{1.19 \times 10^{13}}{6.02 \times 10^{23}} \times 42.0 = 8.30 \times 10^{-10}$ g   *Ans.*

PROBLEMS

*26-11.   How many curies are present in each of the following if all the atoms indicated are radioactive?   (a) 1.0 mg of $Cl_{\frac{38}{2}}$ (half-life of Cl^{38} is 37.3 min); (b) 6.0 μg of $I_{\frac{1}{2}}^{131}$ (half-life of I^{131} is 8.05 days); (c) 1.0 g of Cs^{137} (half-life of Cs^{137} is 30 years).

*26-12.   What is the wt. in g of each of the following?   (a) 1.0 μc of Ca^{45} (half-life of Ca^{45} is 164 days); (b) 2.5 mc of Y^{90} (half-life of Y^{90} is 64 hr); (c) 3.0 μc of Sr^{90} (half-life of Sr^{90} is 30 years).

*26-13.   A 25.0-mg ppt. of AgCl contg. radioactive silver (half-life 270 days) has a measured activity of 148 cps using a detection system which is 40.0% efficient. Calculate the percentage of radioactive silver in the ppt.

*26-14.   A sample of Na^{22} ($t_{1/2} = 15.0$ hr) exhibits an activity of 1,580 cpm. What will be its activity in (a) 7.5 hr, (b) in 22.5 hr, and (c) in 4.5 days?

*26-15.   What will be the activity of 10 mc of S^{35} ($t_{1/2} = 60$ days) after 65 days?

*26-16.   Both Sb^{122} ($t_{1/2} = 2.8$ days) and Sb^{124} ($t_{1/2} = 60$ days) are β-particle emitters.   If a mixt. of equal amts. of each isotope is present initially, what will be the ratio of $Sb^{122} : Sb^{124}$ after 30 days?

26-3   Analytical Applications

The application of radioactive tracers to analytical problems involves a wide variety of techniques and methods.   Both organic and inorganic tracers are used in radiometric titrations, in isotope dilution experiments, and for the development and evaluation of other analytical methods.   In each of these methods, a molecule or ion containing the radioactive isotope is present during the course of the reaction or chemical change under investigation.   By taking measurements of the activity before and after the reaction, it is possible to determine the end point of a titration, the course of a reaction, the completeness of a separation, etc.

In a radiometric titration, the titrant is frequently a radioactive species.   If, for example, the titration involves a precipitation, measurements of the activity of the solution during the course of the titration will remain nearly constant and then increase after the end point has been reached.   Alternatively, it is possible to measure the solubility of a particular compound by incorporating a radioactive isotope in the species being precipitated and then measuring the activity of the precipitate itself or measuring the residual activity of the solution.

Isotope dilution methods are frequently used where it is difficult to measure the yield of a specific reaction or process or to separate all a specific compound from a reaction mixture.   However, if it is possible to isolate a portion of the material in a pure form, then a small amount of the material under investigation is added in which has been incorporated a radioactive isotope, the separation procedure is followed, and the activity of the purified material is compared with the activity of the material added.   A comparison permits one to calculate the concentration of the material in the original mixture.

If we assume that W g of the compound is present in the reaction mixture and that W' g of the same compound containing a radioactive isotope (specific activity A') is added to the mixture, then by isolating in a pure form a small amount of the compound and measuring its specific activity (A), it is possible to calculate the value of W from the other three measured values, using the following equation:

$$W = W'\left(\frac{A'}{A} - 1\right)$$

Example 1   The determination of mercury present as $HgCl_2$ in carbon catalysts has been studied, using an isotopic dilution method with Hg^{203}.

To a 1.00-g sample of the carbon catalyst was added 1.00 g of a synthetic mixture containing 1.00% Hg^{203} and having a specific activity of 2,400 (cpm/g).   Following the proper treatment, 100 mg of mercury was separated and counted (30.0 cpm).   Calculate the percentage of mercury in the carbon catalyst sample.

Solution

> W' is 0.0100 g
> A' is 2400 cpm/g
> A is 30 cpm/0.100 g or 300 cpm/g

Using the above equation, W is found to be 0.0700 g and the percentage of mercury in the carbon catalyst is 7.00%.   *Ans.*

PROBLEMS

*26-17.   The detn. of calcium by pptn. with C^{14}-labeled oxalic acid and measurement of the activity of the ppt. has been studied.   The following data were obtained for a calibration curve:

Calcium	
µg	cpm
50	78
100	165
150	235
200	313

A 0.500-g unknown sample was ashed, and calcium was separated by ion exchange and pptd. as the oxalate labeled with C^{14}.   The sample yielded a count rate of 204 cpm.   Calculate the percentage of calcium in the sample.

*26-18.   The detn. of the chloride content of tissue in various animals can be made by an isotopic dilution method using Cl^{36}.   A 0.800-g sample of tissue was taken and to it was added 1.00 ml of a 1.00×10^{-2} M soln. of $NaCl^{36}$ which had an activity of 185 cpm.   The entire sample was treated to remove the protein and ashed; after further treatment, 0.100 g of HCl was separated and counted (400 cpm).   Calculate the chloride content of the tissue in terms of percent chlorine.

*26-19.   The detn. of sulfate using Cr^{51} as a radiotracer has been described by Armento and Larson [*Anal. Chem.*, **35**, 918 (1963)].   The sulfate unknown soln. is treated with an HCl soln. of barium chromate.   After neutralization, the pptd. barium sulfate and the excess barium chromate are filtered off, and the activity of the remaining chromate, equivalent to the sulfate, is measured.

To 10.0 ml of an unknown soln. contg. sulfate was added 1.00 ml of 0.200 M

$BaCrO_4$ which was counted just prior to the addition, yielding 170×10^3 cpm. The mixed soln. diluted to 25.0 ml in a volumetric flask was permitted to stand for 30 min; the acid was neutralized with 5.00 ml of base, centrifuged, and 1.00 ml of the supernatant soln. was counted (2.41×10^3 cpm). Calculate the concn. of sulfate in the unknown soln. (The half-life of Cr^{51} is 27.8 days, and corrections for decay during the time involved can be neglected since the method requires just over 1 hr.)

*26-20.   In order to develop a separation technique, the distribution of cobalt between the liquid and resin phase for an ion-exchange resin is being investigated. Co^{60} is being used as a convenient means of measuring the distribution coefficient:

$$K_d = \frac{(Co)_{resin}}{(Co)_{soln.}} = \frac{cpm/g \ resin}{cpm/ml \ soln.}$$

A cobalt soln. is prepared by taking 50 ml of a 1.00×10^{-4} M soln. of Co^{++}, adding 1.00 ml of a Co^{60} soln. (142×10^3 cpm) and diluting to 100 ml. To this is added 5.00 g of resin, the mixt. is equilibrated, and the resin is filtered. 1.00 ml of the remaining soln. is counted in the same apparatus as was used for the tagging soln. initially and yields 1.23×10^3 cpm. Calculate the K_d value.

*26-21.   Phosphorus (P^{32}) is to be used to determine the extent to which phosphate is adsorbed on different clays. 5.00 g of a particular clay is crushed, ground, dried, sieved, and mixed with 500 ml of a 0.0200 M soln. of sodium phosphate. To this mixt. is added 10.0 ml of a sodium phosphate soln. (2.00×10^{-2} M) contg. P^{32} and exhibiting an activity of 7450 cpm/ml. Following equilibration with the clay, the sample is centrifuged, and 1.00 ml of the supernatant soln. is counted, yielding a rate of 135 cpm. Calculate (a) the no. of g of phosphate adsorbed by the clay and (b) the concn. of phosphate remaining in the soln.

*26-22.   The detn. of fluoride ion by a radiotracer technique has been described. Under specialized conditions, tantalum (Ta^{182}) is extracted as the fluoride from a sulfuric acid soln. into diisobutylketone. The following data were obtained using the prescribed technique and standard solns. of fluoride contg. 400 to 800 μg of fluoride.

Quantity of fluoride, μg	Activity of extract cpm
400	4,760
500	6,290
600	7,800
700	9,330
800	10,880

An unknown sample of water, treated in the same manner as the standards, exhibited an activity of 7,110 cpm. Calculate the quantity of fluoride present in the unknown sample.

*26-23. One step in the manufacture of compd. X has consistently low yields unless conditions are maintained very precisely. In order to monitor the conditions, it was decided to use an isotopic dilution procedure to measure the concn. of one of the reactants, phenylalanine. 10.0 ml of the reaction mixt. was withdrawn and to it was added 1.00 ml of a 5.00×10^{-3} M soln. of phenylalanine–C^{14} (specific activity = 145×10^3 cpm/g). The soln. mixt. was equilibrated, and from it there was extracted and purified 18.2 mg of phenylalanine (activity = 576 cpm). Calculate the concn. of phenylalanine in the reaction mixt.

26-4 Activation Analysis

In this technique a sample is subjected to a large dose of neutrons, which produces radioactive nuclides of 1 mass unit higher than the element bombarded. The radioactive nuclides are then analyzed to provide both qualitative and quantitative data for the system.

During the course of the activation, the number of radioactive atoms (N^*) present in the sample is being increased by the flux of neutrons, but it is being decreased by the natural radioactivity of the radionuclides produced. The rate of production (R) follows the expression

$$R = N\Phi\sigma$$

where N = number of nuclei available
Φ = slow neutron flux, neutrons cm^{-2} sec^{-1}
σ = slow neutron capture cross section, cm^2
It is then possible to derive an expression for N^* in terms of R and time t:

$$N^* = \left(\frac{Rt_{1/2}}{0.693}\right)(1 - e^{-0.693t/t_{1/2}})$$

From this equation, it can be deduced that it would be useless to bombard the sample for a period of time greater than six half-lives; for many purposes irradiation times of two half-lives would be adequate since this would produce approximately 75% of saturation. Two limiting cases exist which make possible a much simpler approach to the calculation of the irradiation time. (1) If the half-life of the isotope being produced is long relative to the irradiation time, then the above equation simplifies to $N^* = Rt$. (2) If the half-life is short relative to the time of bombardment, the above equation can be simplified differently to become

$$N^* = \frac{Rt_{1/2}}{0.693}$$

When a sample composed of more than one element is subjected to activation analysis, a number of different radionuclides will usually be produced. The different particles and rays emitted can be detected, using various different types of counters. Alternatively, it is possible to resolve the decay curve obtained by measuring the total radioactivity produced by the sample as a function of time. The logarithm of the activity is plotted against time, and the individual slopes are determined mathematically. One limitation of the latter method is that only those isotopes of moderately long half-lives can be positively identified. The use of activation analysis for quantitative analysis usually requires a comparison with a known standard in order to know the strength of the neutron beam and to minimize errors in the counting, in chemical treatment, and in geometrical considerations.

Example 1 Calculate the activity produced in a sample of an iron alloy containing small amounts of chromium under the following conditions. A 5.00-mg sample, containing $2.00 \times 10^{-2}\%$ Cr, is irradiated for 60.0 hr at a neutron flux of 2.00×10^{11} neutrons cm^{-2} sec^{-1}. The half-life of chromium-51 is 27.8 days, and the cross section for thermal neutron absorption is 17.0 barns for Cr^{50}. (1 barn $= 10^{-24}$ cm^2 and is the unit used to express the cross-sectional area of the target nuclei.)

Solution

$$A = \lambda N^*$$

Using expressions given previously for λ, N^*, and R, the following expression is obtained by substitution:

$$A = N\Phi\sigma(1 - e^{-0.693t/t_{1/2}})$$

$$A = \frac{(5.00 \times 10^{-3})(2.00 \times 10^{-4})(6.023 \times 10^{23})}{(52.0)}$$

$$\times \frac{(17.0 \times 10^{-24})(1 - e^{-0.693[60/(27.8)(24)]})}{1}$$

$A = 2.28 \times 10^3$ dps   *Ans.*

PROBLEMS

*26-24. A 1.40-g sample of rock contg. 1.24% Al is placed in a vial and irradiated with thermal neutrons having a flux of 1.00×10^8 neutrons cm^{-2} sec^{-1}. The aluminum is converted to Al^{28} which has a half-life of 2.27 min. After 30.0 min of irradiation, what percentage of the aluminum is Al^{28}? (Assume that initially all the aluminum was Al^{27}. The cross section for thermal neutrons by Al^{27} is 0.21 barns.)

*26-25. The following data were obtained as the decay curve for an unknown compd. Neglecting the very short-lived components, determine the half-life of each of the longer-lived components. The given pairs of values show in each case the activity in cps corresponding to the time in min. 0 min—1,459 cps; 10 min—376 cps; 20 min—217 cps; 30 min—133 cps; 40 min—90 cps; 50 min—59 cps;

60 min—39 cps; 70 min—35 cps; 80 min—31 cps; 90 min—27 cps; 100 min—24 cps; 110 min—21 cps; 120 min—19 cps. (*Hint:* Plot activity versus time on semi-log graph paper.)

*26-26.   The detn. of the concn. of zirconium in a nickel-base high-alloy steel by neutron activation analysis has been described by Gruverman and Henninger [*Anal. Chem.*, **34**, 1680 (1962)]. Zr^{95} (half-life, 65 days) was produced, using a neutron beam with a flux of 8.00×10^{12} neutrons cm^{-2} sec^{-1}.   The cross section for thermal neutron absorption by Zr^{94} is 0.08 barns, and its isotopic abundance is 17.4%.   If a 1.00-g sample of the steel was activated for 25 hr, calculate the percentage by wt. of zirconium in the steel if the activity of the sample 30 days after completion of the activation was 19 cpm above background.   (Assume the counter is 100% efficient for the γ rays produced by the Zr^{95}.)

*26-27.   A 0.55-g biological sample contains 6.20% P^{31}.   The sample is irradiated with thermal neutrons, flux $= 6.0 \times 10^{10}$ neutrons cm^{-2} sec^{-1} for a period of 20 hr. The cross section for the (n, γ) reaction is 0.23 barns, and the P^{32} produced has a half-life of 14.2 days.   (*a*) Calculate the specific activity of the phosphorus in the sample upon completion of the irradiation.   (*b*) What would be the specific activity 1 week later?

*26-28.   A radioactive sample yielded the following activity data in which the given pairs of values show in each case the activity in cpm corresponding to the time in hours: 0 hr—12,000 cpm; 0.5 hr—7,000 cpm; 1.0 hr—4,000 cpm; 1.5 hr—2,400 cpm; 2.0 hr—1,450 cpm; 2.5 hr—910 cpm; 3.0 hr—570 cpm; 3.5 hr—285 cpm; 4.0 hr—185 cpm; 4.5 hr—137 cpm; 5.0 hr—102 cpm.   Calculate the decay constants for the different radioisotopes identified by the data.

*26-29.   There are two stable isotopes of gallium, Ga^{69} and Ga^{71} (natural abundance $= 39.6\%$).   Both can undergo thermal neutron absorption producing Ga^{70} and Ga^{72} which have half-lives of 21 min and 14.1 hr, respectively, and cross sections of 1.9 and 5.0 barns, respectively.   Calculate the min. wt. of gallium in an unknown sample which can be detected, assuming that the neutron flux available is 4.0×10^{11} neutrons cm^{-2} sec^{-1}, that irradiation takes place for 6.0 hr, and that it is possible to distinguish between the β particles given off by the two radioactive isotopes.   The activity of the sample cannot be measured until 6.0 hr after the termination of the irradiation because of the need for prior separations.   Assume that the detector is 50% efficient and that the minimum significant count rate is 10 cpm above background.

Thermal Methods

27-1 Thermogravimetry (TGA)

The principle of measuring loss or gain in weight with changes in temperature is quite old, and with the introduction of improved instrumentation, the technique of thermogravimetry has found increasing application. A small quantity of sample is subjected to a temperature change (either a "steplike" change in temperature or a linearly increasing temperature), and the weight changes are recorded automatically. A thermogram results in which the weight or weight change is plotted against the temperature (see Fig. 29). For the quantitative application of the method, it is most common to change the temperature by a fixed amount and measure the weight change after the new constant weight has been achieved. The weight change can then be related quantitatively to the thermochemical reaction occurring. Conversely it is possible to analyze quantitatively for the amount of a particular species present in a mixture if that species is the only one undergoing a thermochemical reaction the stoichiometry of which is known. In all applications of thermogravimetry, the conditions under which the measurement is made are extremely important. The composition of the surrounding atmosphere, the type and design of the furnace and sample chamber, and whether the sample is exposed to the atmosphere are all important considerations.

27-2 Differential Thermal Analysis (DTA)

This technique strongly complements thermal gravimetry by providing information about changes which do not involve weight, for example, phase transitions and crystalline transitions. In this technique, a sample is placed in a small tube or other container which is located in a block. Also located in

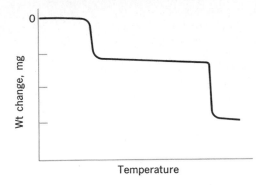

Fig. 29   Thermogram (thermogravimetric analysis curve) for a compound showing two thermal decompositions.

the block is an identical tube or container filled with an inert reference material or air.   The block is placed in a furnace which can be programmed to give a linearly increasing temperature.   The difference between the outputs of two thermocouples, one placed in the sample and the other placed in the reference, is amplified and recorded as a function of the temperature.   If any change occurs which is endothermic, the heat being applied to the sample will be consumed, and a difference in temperature will result.   As soon as the change has taken place, the sample temperature will quickly increase until it again equals the reference temperature.   In Fig. 30 a typical differential thermogram shows both endothermic and exothermic peaks.

For analysis it is more difficult to use the differential thermogram, but the peak height can be used as a measure of the quantity of material reacted.   It must be stressed, just as with thermogravimetry, that the conditions under which DTA measurements are made must be controlled and reproduced very carefully.   With some of the newer instrumentation it has become possible to obtain both TGA and DTA data simultaneously on the same sample.   This has the distinct advantage that the operating conditions are identical.

27-3   Thermometric Titrations

This technique is entirely different from the previous ones in that the measured quantity is the heat of a reaction, usually occurring in the liquid phase but sometimes in the gas phase.   The titrations take place in a Dewar or thermostated vessel equipped with a stirrer and a sensing thermocouple.   The temperature of the titrant is also controlled.   If the reaction involves a heat change, it will be sensed by the thermocouple and recorded.   Most frequently the titrant is added at a constant rate by a motor driven syringe.   The two general types of plots obtained are shown in Fig. 31.   By measuring the time involved from the first break in the curve to the second and knowing the rate of titrant delivery, the

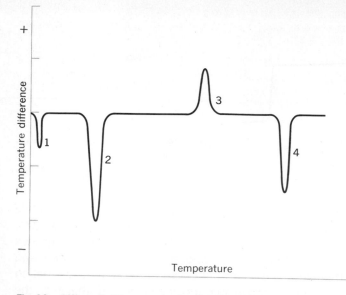

Fig. 30   Differential thermogram for the same compound shown in Fig. 29. Note that there are two additional transitions which do not involve changes in weight.   1, 2, and 4—endothermic; 3—exothermic.

consumed volume of titrant required to reach the end point can be readily calculated.

With thermometric titrations, the heat changes are generally small; hence it is difficult to titrate very dilute solutions.   Also it is sometimes necessary to take into account heat effects due to mixing and dilution.

The sensitivity of the technique is actually enhanced by the use of organic solvents because of their low specific heats.   For many compounds, thermometric titrations provide one of the few methods of analyzing concentrated solutions.   The range of systems which can be analyzed by thermometric titrations includes acid-base titrations in aqueous and nonaqueous media, precipitation reactions, and complexation reactions.

PROBLEMS

*27-1.   Petrocelli and coworkers [*Anal. Chem.*, **36,** 2509 (1964)] have described a thermogravimetric method for the detn. of potassium ozonide based on the following reaction:

$$KO_3(s) \longrightarrow KO_2(s) + \tfrac{1}{2}O_2(g)$$

If a sample weighing 0.2546 g was heated to 70°C for 1 hr and the final wt. was found to be 0.2123 g, what was the percentage of potassium ozonide in the sample? (It can be assumed that all other species in the sample, particularly the potassium superoxide, are stable at this temp.)

*27-2.   Everson [*Anal. Chem.*, **36,** 854 (1964)] has described a thermometric titration method for the detn. of butyllithium in hydrocarbon solvents.   In the method described, the butyllithium is titrated with a 1.20 *M* standard hydrocarbon soln. of *n*-butanol, the product being lithium butoxide.   40.0 ml of toluene as solvent is placed in the titration vessel and to this is added 10.0 ml of sample.   The chart drive is energized at time $t = 0$, and a straight horizontal line is obtained.   At time $t = 1$ min, the motor-driven syringe delivering the titrant is started.   An increase in temp. occurs until an inflection point is reached at 1.8 min, after which the temp. decreases slowly.   The rate of delivery of the motor-driven syringe is 0.240 ml/min. Calculate the concn. of butyllithium in the sample.

*27-3.   Having available an apparatus for thermometric titrations, it was decided to analyze for Cu(II) using a method described by Billingham and Reed [*Anal. Chem.*, **36,** 1148 (1964)].   In the reaction vessel there was 100 ml of soln. contg. excess sodium iodide; the titrant was 1.03 *M* sodium thiosulfate.   To the soln. in the vessel was added 10.0 ml of the sample, the iodine produced was titrated in 0.840 min using an automatic syringe that delivered 0.280 ml/min.   Calculate the concn. of Cu(II) in the unknown sample.

*27-4.   Keily and Hume [*Anal. Chem.*, **36,** 543 (1964)] described a method for the thermometric titration of very weak acids.   The solvent used in all cases was specially prepared anhydrous glacial acetic acid; the titrant was perchloric acid in glacial acetic acid.   To a titration vessel was added 50.0 ml of solvent and 10.0 ml of an acetic acid soln. contg. 85.4 mg of diphenylamine.   Using standard procedure, this soln. was titrated with 0.500 *M* perchloric acid, and 0.995 ml of titrant was required.   Calculate the percentage purity of the diphenylamine.

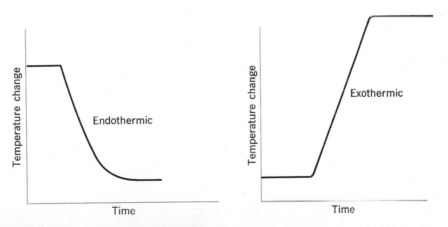

Fig. 31   Thermometric titration curves.

*27-5.   In the making of certain polymers, the organic component is mixed with a "filler" of inert material.   Light and coworkers [*Anal. Chem.*, **37,** 79 (1965)] have described a thermogravimetric method for the analysis of silica-filled Teflon.   The method is based on the fact that the Teflon is vaporized at 600°C while the silica is not.   A stream of helium is passed over the crucible to ensure removal of the decomposition products.   Using a 97.5-mg sample, the wt. loss was found to be 63.2 mg.   With another sample weighing 109 mg, the wt. loss was 71.6 mg. (*a*) What is the percentage by wt. of silica in each sample?   (*b*) Sketch the type of thermogram you would expect.

*27-6.   Differential thermal analysis has been applied by Venuto and coworkers [*Anal. Chem.*, **38,** 1267 (1966)] to the estimation of nitrogen in synthetic zeolites, particularly ammonium Y faujasite.   The differential thermograms were run under an oxygen atmosphere, and an exotherm in the region of 400°C was indicative of the loss of zeolitic ammonium groups.   Using a standardized instrument and procedure, it was shown that for the range from 0 to 4 percentage by wt. of nitrogen there was a linear increase in the height of the exotherm from 0 to 88 mm.   If an unknown sample exhibited an exotherm at about 400°C with a height of 27 mm, what was the percentage by wt. of nitrogen in the zeolite sample?

*27-7.   Precipitation and complexation reactions have been used as the basis for many thermometric titrations.   Everson and Ramirez [*Anal. Chem.*, **37,** 812 (1965)] described a method for diethylzinc using the 1:1 complex with *o*-phenanthroline (PHEN).   To 50.0 ml of specially purified and dried toluene was added 1.98 g of sample contg. an unknown quantity of diethylzinc.   When titrated with a soln. of PHEN, it required 1.27 ml.   When the PHEN titrant had been previously standardized under identical conditions, 1.67 ml of PHEN was required to titrate 2.00 ml of a standard soln. contg. 77.0 mg of diethylzinc per ml.   Calculate the concn. of diethylzinc in the unknown in millimoles per g of sample.

Kinetic Methods

(See Secs. 5-1 to 5-7 for an introduction to some of the theory applicable to kinetic analysis.)

28-1 Principles

A wide variety of kinetic methods of analysis have been developed, and many are in common use. For the determination of a single component, kinetic methods can be fast and simple. If we assume that reactant A and reagent R undergo a reaction to form product P, and if the reaction is pseudo first order when there is a large excess of reagent present, the initial rate of reaction will be directly proportional to the concentration of reactant A. Enzyme reactions, as a result of their speed and specificity, are frequently utilized. By preparing a calibration curve of the initial rate versus the concentration of reactant A, all measured under carefully controlled conditions, it is possible to analyze an unknown containing the reactant.

The rate of the reaction with respect to time can be expressed in the form

$$\ln\left(\frac{C_0}{C_0 - C}\right) = kt$$

where C_0 = initial concentration of A, moles/liter

C = number of moles/liter of A that have reacted after time t

k = first-order or pseudo first-order rate constant

In these methods it is possible to measure either the disappearance of reactant A or the appearance of product P in order to obtain the initial rate. It is however essential that the stoichiometry of the reaction be known and that the method chosen for the measurement be sufficiently fast to yield a reliable initial rate for the reaction. The introduction of electronic equipment to measure the slope of a rate curve or to measure the time required to consume a predetermined amount of reagent has also increased the speed with which routine analyses can be carried out.

If there are two reactants (A and B) which undergo the same reaction with a particular reagent R, it is still a relatively simple matter to analyze the mixture kinetically if one component reacts at a much faster rate than the other.

$$A + R \xrightarrow{k_a} P'$$
$$B + R \xrightarrow{k_b} P'' \qquad k_a \gg k_b$$

If we assume that the ratio of rate constants is 500, that the concentrations of reactants are equal, and that there is a large excess of reagent, then the slower reaction can be neglected. If the conditions with respect to the reagent concentrations and the temperature are set properly, it is frequently possible to analyze either the faster- or the slower-reacting component without significant interference from the other reacting species.

In many cases the difference in reaction rates is not very large but is nevertheless significant. In this situation a variety of approaches has been used for the simultaneous determination of the two reactants. It is not feasible to discuss all of them here; however, the following example should be considered as an introduction to one approach.

Example 1   The reaction scheme for compounds A and B with reagent R is as follows:

$$A + R \xrightarrow{k_a} P' + HCl$$
$$B + R \xrightarrow{k_b} P'' + HCl$$

The chloride concentration of the system is measured as a function of time. A differential kinetic plot is made from the data. This plot shows the relationship between $\ln (C_0 - C)$ and time, where C is the number of moles per liter of both reactants which have reacted at time t and C_0 is the total concentration of A and B in moles per liter or the number of moles per liter reacted at completion.

Ten (10.0) milliliters of an unknown containing A and B plus solvent was reacted with an excess of R, and the following data were obtained. The listed pairs of values show in each case the molar chloride-ion concentration corresponding to the time in seconds: 0 sec—0.000 M; 20 sec—0.347 M; 50 sec—0.519 M; 100 sec—0.577 M; 150 sec—0.613 M; 200 sec—0.644 M; 250 sec—0.670 M; completion—0.800 M.

Calculate the following: (a) the rate constant k_b, (b) the concentration of B in the unknown sample, (c) the ratio of A to B in the unknown sample, and (d) the time necessary for 90% reaction of B.

Solution

(a) Plot the data as $\ln(C_0 - C)$ versus t. Calculate the slope of the straight-line portion of the curve after the break; the slope $= -k_b = 0.216$ min^{-1}.   *Ans.*

(b) The initial concentration $[B_0]$ is determined by extrapolating the straight-line portion of the curve back to zero time; the numerical value of the intercept is then equal to $\ln[B_0]$.

$[B_0] = 0.316\ M$ *Ans.*

(c) The total concentration of A and B can be calculated from the total chloride concentration at completion:

$[A] + [B] = 0.800\ M$ $[B] = 0.316\ M$

Therefore

$[A] = 0.484\ M$

and the ratio

$[A]:[B] = 1.53.$ *Ans.*

(d) If $[B_0] = 0.316\ M$, 90% reaction would constitute the reaction of 0.284 M. Using the expression given previously,

$$\ln\left(\frac{C_0}{C_0 - C}\right) = k_b t$$

Substituting,

$$2.303 \log \frac{0.316}{0.316 - 0.284} = 0.216t$$

$t = 10.6$ min   *Ans.*

PROBLEMS

*28-1.   A 1.00×10^{-2} M soln. of A reacts with an excess of R to produce P; the first-order rate constant for the reaction is 0.600 sec^{-1}. Calculate the time required to reach (a) 10.0, (b) 50.0, and (c) 99.0% reaction.

*28-2.   If the concn. of the limiting reagent in a first-order reaction is decreased by one quarter in 25.0 sec, what is the first-order rate const.?

*28-3.   Calculate the ratio of rate consts. necessary to ensure that 99.0% of a faster-reacting species has reacted before 1.0% of a slower-reacting species has reacted.

*28-4.   Blaedel and coworkers [*Anal. Chem.*, **34**, 388 (1962); **36**, 343 (1964)] have described a method for the detn. of glucose using the enzyme glucose oxidase. In the presence of oxygen and water, the enzyme catalyzes the production of gluconic acid and hydrogen peroxide from glucose, the limiting reagent.   The hydrogen peroxide oxidizes potassium ferrocyanide to potassium ferricyanide, which is analyzed by a variety of methods.   Instead of measuring the change from time zero to a preset time, they arranged their experimental setup so that the sample soln. and reagent soln. were mixed at the beginning of a reaction line.   Early in the line was one detector and later in the same line was another detector, and the difference in signal between the two detectors was recorded.   If glucose is present, it will react as it moves through the line, and the difference signal gives an indication of the quantity of glucose measured.   A standard soln. of glucose, 100 p.p.m., was prepared and analyzed; an unknown soln. after fivefold concn. was analyzed by the same procedure, yielding a difference signal of 18.0 divisions.   Assuming that the recorder was set to read 100 divisions for the standard glucose soln., what was the concn. of glucose in the unknown?

*28-5.   Malmstadt and Pardue [*Anal. Chem.*, **33**, 1040 (1961)] attacked the problem of the detn. of glucose in a slightly different manner from that given in Prob. 28-4.   The hydrogen peroxide produced in the reaction of glucose with oxygen and water and catalyzed by glucose oxidase was reacted with iodide in the presence of a molybdate catalyst to produce iodine, which was measured potentiometrically. In this system, the time required to produce a certain fixed quantity of product was measured.   The reciprocal of this reaction time should then be proportional to the concn. of glucose in the sample.   0.200 ml of a sample of blood was diluted and deproteinized; the final vol. was 10.0 ml.   1.00 ml of this soln. was added to the cell contg. 1.00 ml of a composite soln. contg. everything except the glucose.   The reaction time for the above unknown blood sample was 18.5 sec.   To 1.00 ml of the unknown blood sample was added an equal vol. of saline soln. contg. 40.0 p.p.m. of glucose.   0.200 ml of this resulting soln. was treated in the same manner as the unknown blood sample, yielding a time of 16.0 sec.   Calculate the concn. of glucose in the unknown blood sample.

*28-6.   Cystine acts as a catalyst for the reduction of iodine by azide.   Pardue [*Anal. Chem.*, **36**, 633 (1964)] has described a kinetic method for the analysis of cystine in which the change in the iodine concn. is measured potentiometrically. By automatically comparing the initial rate of change of the potentiometric signal with that produced by an electronic integrator, he was able to obtain a readout numerically equivalent to the cystine concn. in p.p.m.   A 5.00-g biological sample was denatured, extracted, centrifuged, and further treated to produce a 10.0-ml sample which contained the cystine.   To the reaction cell containing the azide, iodine, and iodide in 1.00 ml of soln., 1.00 ml of the cystine soln. was added.   The readout was 5.20.   Calculate the concn. of cystine in the biological sample in (*a*) p.p.m. and (*b*) percentage by wt.

*28-7.   Compd. X reacts with an excess of reagent Y to produce a highly colored soluble product.   A series of standard solns. in ether, each of 100 ml, are prepared contg. 0 to 1.56 g of X; 10.0 ml of each soln. is reacted with 50.0 ml of a reagent soln. contg. excess Y. The absorbance of the resultant soln. is measured 1.00 min after mixing, during the initial period of the reaction. The corresponding absorbances increase linearly from 0.00 to 1.20. 0.500 g of a solid contg. X is dissolved in 50.0 ml of an aq. soln., and compd. X is extracted into 25.0 ml of ether. 10.0 ml of the ether soln. is analyzed kinetically in the same manner as the standards; the resultant absorbance is 0.42. (a) Plot the calibration curve as absorbance versus wt. of X. (b) Calculate the percentage of X in the solid sample.

*28-8. Parsons and coworkers [*Anal. Chem.*, **27,** 21 (1955)] have described a method for the analysis of 1-naphthol present in 2-naphthol at low concns. The method is based on the faster rate of diazotization of 1-naphthol as compared to that of 2-naphthol. In this method the naphthols are dissolved in an alkaline soln., acid is added to ppt. most of the 2-naphthol, and the remaining soln. (primarily 1-naphthol with a little 2-naphthol) is reacted with a diazonium salt. At a preset time after mixing, the absorbance of the dye produced in the reaction is measured and compared with a calibration curve. The following data were obtained for standards and for an unknown. The listed pairs of values show in each case the absorbance corresponding to the wt. percent of 1-naphthol: 0.00%—0.06; 0.10%—0.13; 0.20%—0.21; 0.30%—0.27; 0.40%—0.35; 0.50%—0.41; 0.60%—0.48; unknown—0.31. Calculate the percentage of 1-naphthol present in the 2-naphthol.

*28-9. The hydrolysis rate consts. for two compds. (A + B) are 3.30×10^{-2} and 22.4/sec, respectively, in a soln. of 80% ethanol and 20% water. For the following calculations, assume equal concns. (0.100 M) of the two species in the soln. (a) Calculate the time required for 99.0% of the faster-reacting compd. to react. (b) At the time determined in part (a), how much of the other species would have reacted? (c) Make a differential kinetic plot for the hydrolysis of a mixt. of A and B, showing both portions of the curve. (d) If you wished to analyze only for B in an unknown mixt., would it be necessary to obtain all the data required to establish the curve obtained in part (c)? (e) Describe the procedure you would use to analyze only for A.

*28-10. The analysis of mixts. of sugars by a differential kinetic approach utilizing dialysis has been described by Siggia, Hanna, and Serencha [*Anal. Chem.*, **36,** 638 (1964)]. The sample mixt. (1.45 g) of fructose and dextrose was placed in a dialyzing tube with deionized water as solvent. (Fructose dialyzes more rapidly than dextrose.) The dialyzing tube was placed in a beaker of deionized water. At 5.00-min intervals, 2.00-ml samples of the outside soln. were withdrawn, dried, and the remaining sugar weighed. The following data were obtained. In the data the listed pairs of values show in each case the wt. corresponding to the total time: 10 min—0.27 mg; 20 min—0.47 mg; 30 min—0.59 mg; 40 min—0.66 mg; 50 min—0.69 mg; 100 min—0.87 mg; 150 min—1.01 mg; 200 min—1.10 mg. (a) Calculate the initial percentage of dextrose (the slower-diffusing compd.) present in the sample. (b) Calculate the rate const. for the dialysis of dextrose under the conditions used. (c) For how long would the dialysis need to be carried out in order for 99.0% of the dextrose to have dialyzed? (d) Estimate the rate const. for the dialysis of fructose in this analysis.

Extraction Methods

Extraction of a solute from one liquid phase into another is used to separate many different classes of compounds, particularly polar solutes from nonpolar solutes and complexed metals from the free ions. A separatory funnel is the device most frequently used, although more complicated instruments are also employed, especially for multiple extractions.

29-1 Distribution Law

From the quantitative standpoint, the *distribution coefficient* (or partition coefficient) is the determining factor. The distribution coefficient, K, is an equilibrium constant of a special type, and it is related to the concentration, C, of the species under investigation in the two phases:

$$K = \frac{C_x'(\text{nonaqueous phase})}{C_x''(\text{aqueous phase})}$$

In many applications, an organic phase immiscible with water is used in conjunction with water as the second phase. Under these conditions, most metal ions and polar organic compounds are more soluble in the aqueous phase, and the nonpolar species are found chiefly in the organic phase. Unless specified otherwise, the distribution coefficient is usually given with the concentration of the species in the aqueous phase in the denominator. For dilute solutions, it is assumed that the activity coefficients are constant.

An immediate practical question which arises is whether it is better to perform one extraction with a large quantity of solvent, for example with 100 ml, or two extractions with a smaller quantity of solvent, for example 50 ml each time. The following example indicates that it is better to carry out the extraction in as many small batches as is practically feasible.

Example 1   Between water and carbon tetrachloride, chlorine has a distribution coefficient of 10.   If 0.30 g of chlorine is dissolved in 100 ml of water, calculate the percentage of the chlorine extracted (a) by one extraction with 100 ml of carbon tetrachloride and (b) by two extractions with 50 ml each of carbon tetrachloride.

Solution

(a) Moles of chlorine present $= \dfrac{0.30}{71} = 4.22 \times 10^{-3}$

Let a = moles extracted

$$10 = \frac{\dfrac{a}{100}}{\dfrac{(4.22 \times 10^{-3}) - a}{100}}$$

$a = 3.84 \times 10^{-3}$ moles Cl_2

Percentage of Cl_2 extracted $= \dfrac{3.84 \times 10^{-3}}{4.22 \times 10^{-3}} \times 100 = 91.0\%$ *Ans.*

(b) Let a = moles extracted in first 50.0 ml extraction.
Let b = moles extracted in second 50.0 ml extraction.

$$10 = \frac{\dfrac{a}{50}}{\dfrac{(4.22 \times 10^{-3}) - a}{100}}$$

$a = 3.52 \times 10^{-3}$ moles Cl_2

There remains in the aqueous phase, 0.70×10^{-3} moles of chlorine after the first extraction.   For the second extraction,

$$10 = \frac{\dfrac{b}{50}}{\dfrac{(0.70 \times 10^{-3}) - b}{100}}$$

$b = 0.58 \times 10^{-3}$ moles Cl_2

Total moles extracted $= 4.10 \times 10^{-3}$

Percentage of Cl_2 extracted $= \dfrac{4.10 \times 10^{-3}}{4.22 \times 10^{-3}} \times 100 = 97.2\%$ *Ans.*

In general it can be shown that after one equilibration

$$W_0 - C_x V_x + C_y V_y \tag{1}$$

where W_0 = initial weight of material present
C_x = concn. of material in phase x
C_y = concn. of material in phase y
V_x and V_y = vols. of phases x and y, respectively

Equation (1) can be rearranged to

$$W_0 = (KV_x + V_y)C_y \tag{2}$$

by using the distribution coefficient (K), where

$$K = \frac{C_x}{C_y} \tag{3}$$

The amount of material remaining after the first extraction is

$$W_1 = C_y V_y$$

where W_1 is the number of grams remaining in phase y.   By proceeding in like manner, it can be shown that

$$W_2 = W_1\left(\frac{V_y}{KV_x + V_y}\right)$$

where W_2 is the number of grams of material remaining in phase y after two extractions.   This can be extended still further to yield a general expression:

$$W_n = W_0\left(\frac{V_y}{KV_x + V_y}\right)^n$$

where W_n is the number of grams remaining in phase y after n extractions.

   In order to accomplish a separation by means of an extraction, it is necessary that the two species which are to be separated have apprecia-bly different distribution coefficients.   The ratio of the two distribution coefficients is used to define the separation factor α, which is equal to K_A/K_B.   In addition to the separation factor, the volume ratio (the volume of organic phase to the volume of aqueous phase) frequently has a considerable effect on the ability to separate two species.

PROBLEMS

*29-1.   If the separation factor for two compds., A and B, between water and ether is 2.00, calculate how many extractions would be required in order to achieve a concn. ratio for B:A of 10.0 in the remaining aq. phase. (Assume equal volumes for extraction, i.e., that $V_x = V_y$ and that equal amounts of A and B were present initially.)

29-2.   A statement frequently encountered in discussions of extraction is that there is little point in carrying out more than five successive extractions.   Using a distribution coefficient of three and a total of 100 ml of each phase, show why this statement is valid.

*29-3.   Compd. X has a distribution coefficient of 2.7 between water and benzene. If a 50.0-ml aq. sample contains 4.5 mg of X, calculate (a) how many ml of benzene should be needed for a single extraction to remove 99.0% of compd. X and (b) how many extractions of 50.0 ml of benzene would be needed to extract 99.0% of compd. X.

29-4.   The distribution coefficient for fumaric acid between water and ether is 1.11. Make a plot showing on the vertical axis the percentage of fumaric acid extracted versus the no. of the extraction.   Use vol. ratios ($V_{org} : V_{aq}$) of 0.33, 1.00, 3.00, and 10.00, and include sufficient extractions to remove 99.9% of the fumaric acid.

*29-5.   Using the data obtained in the previous problem and assuming a 100-ml aq. sample contg. 1.50 g of fumaric acid, how many extractions with 100 ml of ether would be required to remove all but 0.01 g of the fumaric acid?

*29-6.   If, after one extraction, 90.0% of compd. A is in the organic phase and only 5.00% of compd. B is in the organic phase, calculate the separation factor, assuming (a) the vol. ratio was 1.0 and (b) the vol. ratio was 0.5.

*29-7.   Given an aq. soln. contg. compds. A and B.   In an extraction with an organic solvent, the distribution coefficient for compd. A is 10.0, while that of compd. B is 0.1, and in each case the extraction vol. ratio is 1.0.   (a) Calculate the percentage of A and the percentage of B extracted into the organic phase by a single extraction.   (b) A second extraction will increase the total yield of compd. A to what percentage, and the total amt. of compd. B extracted will now be what percentage?   (c) On a ratio basis (total percent of A in the extract versus total percent of B in the extract), has the purity of A in the extract been improved by the second extraction?   (d) If the organic extract from the first extraction had been reequilibrated with water, what percentage of compd. A and what percentage of compd. B would have remained in the organic phase?   (e) On a ratio basis as in part (c), has the purity of compd. A in the extract been enhanced by the reequilibration with water?

*29-8.   Compds. X and Y have distribution coefficients of 5.00 and 0.50, respectively.   (a) What vol. ratio must be used to ensure that 99.0% of compd. X is removed in a single extraction?   (b) What percentage of compd. Y would be extracted under these circumstances?   (Assume that equal amts. of X and Y were initially present.)

*29-9.   When an HCl soln. of ferric chloride is equilibrated with twice its vol. of ether satd. with HCl, 99.0% of the ferric chloride is extracted.   Determine the distribution coefficient for ferric chloride between an HCl soln. and HCl-satd. ether.

*29-10.   Complex M has a distribution coefficient of 48.0 between water and carbon tetrachloride, while that of complex N is 1.0.   (a) In an aq. soln., equimolar in both complexes, what vol. ratio should be used to provide 99.0% extraction of complex M?   (b) Under these conditions, what percentage of complex N would also be extracted?   (c) Would decreasing the volume ratio improve the "purity" of the extracted complex M?

*29-11.   Acetylacetonate is a chelating agent for many metal ions.   50.0 ml of an aq. soln. of M^{++}, 5.00×10^{-3} M, is equilibrated with 20.0 ml of ether contg. an excess of acetylacetonate.   The reaction can be abbreviated as $M^{++} + 2AAc^- \rightleftharpoons$ $M(AAc)_2$.   If 94.0% of the metal is extracted into the ether phase, calculate K' where $K' = \dfrac{[M(AAc)_2]}{[M^{++}]}$.

*29-12.   Assume the following two systems: System I: separation factor of 1.5 for compds. A and B; System II: separation factor of 9.0 for compds. W and X.   The distribution coefficients for B and X are 1.00 and 0.500, respectively.   Calculate the vol. ratio which would be necessary to produce a separation characterized by (*a*) 99.0% of A extracted and (*b*) 99.0% of W extracted.   For extractions with a vol. ratio of 1.0, calculate the purity of each extract in terms of the ratio of (*c*) percentage of A extracted to percentage of B extracted and (*d*) percentage of W extracted to percentage of X extracted.   Compare the two systems.

*29-13.   The analysis of gold by extraction and spectrophotometry has been described by Holbrook and Rein [*Anal. Chem.*, **36,** 2451 (1964)].   A 0.500-g sample was treated to dissolve the gold.   The final vol. of the soln. was 500 ml.   Standard solns. of gold contg. 100 μg of gold per 5.00 ml were also prepared.   To 25.0 ml of a soln. contg. bromide ion and phosphoric acid was added 5.00 ml of the gold soln. and 5.00 ml of a trioctyl-phosphine oxide in chloroform soln.   The bromoaurate-trioctyl-phosphine oxide complex was formed and extracted into the chloroform layer.   The absorbance of the complex at 395 mμ in the chloroform layer gives a measure of the gold present.   In the above case, the absorbances for the reference and unknown were 0.380 and 0.740, respectively. Calculate the percentage by wt. of gold present in the sample.

Chromatographic Methods

The common ground for all chromatographic techniques is the differential migration of a solute due to a stationary phase providing a competing attraction with that of a moving phase. Even though there exists this common ground, there are many differences between the various chromatographic methods. This chapter deals first with column chromatography utilizing adsorption and includes a more detailed discussion of differential migration. Other chromatographic methods and some representative applications are then discussed.

30-1 Column Chromatography (Adsorption)

If a column is packed with an adsorbent, such as silica gel in petroleum ether, there results a two-phase system—the stationary phase (the adsorbent) and the liquid phase (the solvent). If a stopcock on the bottom of the column is opened, the liquid phase becomes the moving phase. The introduction of a mixture of solutes dissolved in petroleum ether or some other moving phase (or *eluent*) is the first step of the separation. Remembering that the liquid phase is continuously moving at a slow rate past the adsorbent, each molecule "chooses" between the moving phase and the stationary phase on the basis of its adsorption and solution properties. Chromatographic methods depend on only very small differences in adsorption or solution properties; hence molecules which are only slightly different may be separated. The more strongly adsorbed species (in this example, the more polar solute) will spend a higher proportion of the time adsorbed to the silica gel than will the less polar solute. The less polar solute therefore is spending more time in the moving phase and is carried down the column by the moving phase at a faster rate than the more polar solute. This process of differential migration is referred to as the *development of the chromatogram*. If there is sufficient difference in the adsorptive and solution properties of the different solutes, there will appear in the column completely separate bands, each of which is a different solute. Figure 32 illustrates this process.

The choice of adsorbent, eluent (moving phase, solvent), and length of column are the three principal variables in determining whether or not one obtains a satisfactory chromatogram. For an analysis to be practical, the properties of the eluent and the length of the column must be properly balanced. In many cases, it is necessary to increase the polarity of the moving phase gradually in order to elute all the solutes from the column in a reasonable length of time.

30-2   Column Chromatography (Partition)

In certain instances another type of column chromatography is used, namely, *partition chromatography*. In place of the adsorbent, an inert phase coated with a stationary liquid phase is used. The solute mole-

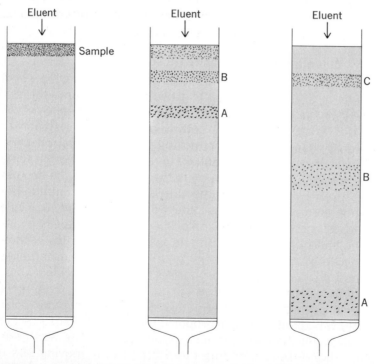

Fig. 32   Chromatographic columns at various stages of development.

cules must then partition between the moving liquid phase and the stationary liquid phase. With the exception of this change, the results obtained are nearly identical to those found with adsorption column chromatography.

Although the size of the band and the intensity of its color (if it is colored) give an approximation of the quantity of the material present for both adsorption and partition column chromatography, it is necessary to use some independent means of analysis in order to obtain a quantitative analysis for a particular solute.

30-3   Paper and Thin-layer Chromatography

In paper chromatography, the stationary phase is a piece of special chromatographic paper. The mixture to be separated is placed on one end of the paper as a very small spot or fine line; as the eluting solvent moves along the paper, usually only by capillary action, the solutes move at different rates. The exact mechanism of the differential migration is not clear; it may be adsorption on the paper or a partitioning between the eluting solvent and polar solvents, principally water, adherred to the paper. Probably it is a combination of these, depending on the solutes being separated. The technique of paper chromatography represents a big improvement over that of column chromatography for many applications. It is much faster and requires much less sample. To determine where on the paper a solute is located after elution can be difficult, and a number of methods are used: inherent color of the solute, reaction with a color-producing reagent (such as ninhydrin), ultraviolet or infrared absorption, fluorescence, radioactivity, or extraction coupled with another analytical method.

For identification of a species in a mixture, the R_f value is used. It is defined as follows:

$$R_f = \frac{\text{distance moved by the solute (spot)}}{\text{distance moved by the solvent front}}$$

This is shown in Fig. 33. If a standard and a solute have the same R_f value, it is probable but not certain that they are the same compound; however, to be certain, one should also run both the standard and the solute mixture, using a different eluting agent. If they again have the same R_f value, then one can be certain that the solute is in fact the same material as the standard.

A component can be definitely identified also by using two-dimensional chromatography in which a chromatogram is developed first in one direction and then in the other direction, using a different solvent system as eluent. If the spots of the solute and reference behave identically, the solute is identified. Figure 34 illustrates a two-dimensional

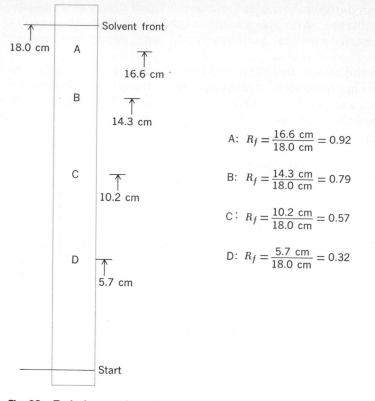

Fig. 33   Typical paper chromatogram and R_f values.

chromatogram.   Many of the methods used for qualitative identification are easily adapted for quantitative analysis, usually following extraction of the solute from the paper by some suitable solvent.

More recently, thin-layer chromatography (TLC) is being used for many applications in preference to paper chromatography, because of a further increase in speed and more convenient manipulation of the differential migration mechanism.   With paper chromatography, the exact role of the paper in the separation process has always been of concern; with TLC, a glass plate is coated with an extremely thin layer of an adsorbent (alumina is frequently used) or of an inert support (such as a diatomaceous earth) coated with a stationary phase.   Thus either an adsorption mechanism or a partitioning mechanism can be chosen with TLC.

A very small sample spot is applied and the solutes are eluted by an appropriate solvent or solvent mixture.   For qualitative identification of the solute under consideration, the same techniques are used with

TLC as are used with paper chromatography. For quantitative analyses, thin-layer chromatography has presented a major advantage; the "spot" can be easily scraped from the plate and placed in a solvent. The resulting solution, containing only the one solute, can then be analyzed by any of the standard analytical techniques. In many instances this procedure represents a major saving of time and an improvement in convenience over what has been possible with paper chromatography.

Example 1   A 500-g sample of fruit is to be analyzed for a particular pesticide, using TLC and fluorescence. The fruit is washed to dissolve the pesticide; the solvent is evaporated to dryness, and the solute is dissolved in a volume of 1.00 ml. Then 100 μl of this mixture is placed on an alumina TLC plate and eluted. The pesticide is identified by comparison with a standard. The spot is scraped from the plate and dissolved in 100 ml of ethanol. This solution gives a reading of 47.5 units on a standard filter fluorometer, with a blank reading of 3.0 units. Using standards, it had previously been determined that under identical conditions 5.00 μg of the pesticide produced a reading of 87.0 units above background. Calculate the concentration of the pesticide on the fruit in p.p.m.

Solution

47.5 − 3.0 = 44.5 units due to fluorescence of the pesticide

$$\frac{44.5}{87.0} = \frac{x}{5.0}$$

$x = 2.56$ μg of pesticide

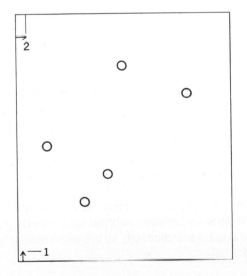

Fig. 34   **A two-dimensional chromatogram.**

Therefore

2.56 μg of pesticide in the 500-g sample = 0.00512 p.p.m.   *Ans.*

30-4   Gas Chromatography (Gas-Liquid and Gas-Solid)

The application of the chromatographic principle to volatile systems has resulted in a major advance in the case of both qualitative and quantitative analyses.   In gas-liquid chromatography, a column is prepared containing an inert support coated with a stationary liquid phase.   The moving phase is an inert gas, usually helium, although argon and nitrogen are sometimes used.   The sample mixture is introduced into the gas stream and hence onto the column.   The injector, the column, and the detectors are usually heated.   The differential migration process is governed by the partitioning of the solute between the moving gas phase and the stationary liquid phase.   Therefore the rate of travel for a solute through the column depends on the flow rate of the carrier gas, the temperature, and the stationary liquid phase.   As with the other chromatographic techniques, there are a large number of encounters between the moving phase and the stationary phase for each solute molecule, with the result that compounds that are almost identical can nevertheless be separated.

The efficiency of a column in separating nearly identical species is usually expressed in terms of its HETP, or "height equivalent to a theoretical plate."   The HETP for a particular column is that region of the column, expressed in units of length, in which an equilibration occurs between the moving or gas phase and the stationary phase.   The smaller the HETP, the more efficient is the column.   The HETP of a column depends on a variety of parameters (such as the packing density of the stationary phase and its loading, the size of the stationary phase, and the velocity of the carrier gas) and on the specific properties of the solute being eluted.   From a practical standpoint, it is sometimes desired to determine the number of theoretical plates in a particular column.   This is readily accomplished since, as a peak moves through a column, the band-broadening is a measure of the column's efficiency.   One equation frequently used for this purpose is $N = (4t/W)^2$, where N is the number of plates in the column, t is the retention time to the peak maximum, and W is the distance on the base line between the tangents extrapolated from the sides of the two peaks in units of time.   Slightly different equations can be used for unsymmetrical peaks.   Once N is known, the HETP $= L/N$, where L is the length of the column.   In order to calculate the number of plates in a column, the specific solute chromatogrammed under specified conditions should always be indicated, since the value obtained depends on the solute used.

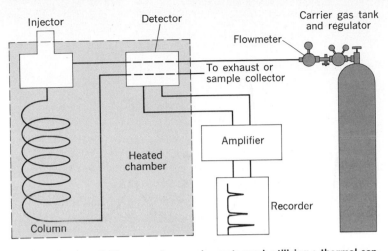

Fig. 35   Schematic diagram of a gas chromatograph utilizing a thermal conductivity detector.

Figure 35 depicts the basic components of a gas chromatograph. A variety of different detectors are used with gas-liquid chromatography, although by far the most common one is the thermal conductivity detector.   The two sides of the detector, one reference and one sample, form two arms of a Wheatstone bridge.   As long as pure carrier gas is passing through both sides, the bridge is balanced.   With the passage of some other gas in addition to some of the carrier gas through one side of the detector, the thermal conductivity of that side changes, and the bridge is out of balance.   The imbalance signal is amplified and fed to a strip chart recorder.

In gas-solid chromatography, a solid adsorbent material is used to pack the column, and the process of adsorption is responsible for the differential migration of solutes.   Solute molecules choose between the moving gaseous phase and the surface of the stationary solid phase. Although gas-solid chromatography has found a number of important applications, gas-liquid chromatography has proved to be by far the more versatile and convenient.

For purposes of qualitative identification, the retention time (time from injection to the maximum of a given peak) is the measured value. Figure 36 shows a typical chromatogram.   If the retention times agree for a solute and a standard when measured under identical column conditions at two significantly different temperatures, one can be almost certain that the solute and the standard are the same compound.   To be certain, it is essential that the retention times agree on two columns having significantly different stationary liquid phases.

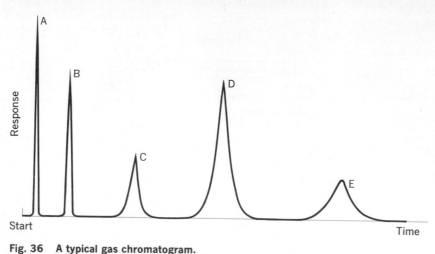

Response

A

B

C

D

E

Start

Time

Fig. 36   A typical gas chromatogram.

For quantitative analysis, the best measure of the quantity present is the area under the peak as opposed to the height of the peak or the peak width at half-peak height.   For those cases where thermal conductivity is used as the detection mechanism, it has been found that peak area correlates best with weight percent of the species present in the sample as opposed to volume percent or mole percent.   Naturally, if the species under consideration have nearly identical densities, the area percent will also agree closely with the volume percent.   The area under the peak can be measured in a variety of ways: with a polar planimeter, by triangulation (assuming symmetrical or nearly symmetrical peaks), by mechanical devices which are part of the recorder, or by electronic devices coupled directly to the detector or the detector's amplifier.   For samples in different matrices or in those cases where the detector's response is not the same for each component, calibration curves are usually prepared.   If properly used, gas chromatography provides a very convenient and highly accurate means of chemical analysis for systems that are volatile under reasonable operating conditions.

Example 1   The accompanying figure (Fig. 37) is a gas chromatogram of a commercial product.   The areas under each peak are tabulated. Calculate the retention time for each component and the percentage composition of the sample.   (Assume equivalent detector response for each component.)

Solution

Retention times: A = 2.9 min; B = 6.2 min; C = 10.1 min.   The percentage composition of this sample can only be obtained with the available data by using the "area normalization method" in which it is assumed that all species exhibit the same response characteristics or that corrections have been made for differences in response and that all components in the mixture are represented in the chromatogram.

Composition: Total area $= 31.0 + 53.2 + 14.5 = 98.7$

$$A = \frac{31.0}{98.7} \times 100 = 31.4\%$$

$$B = \frac{53.2}{98.7} \times 100 = 53.9\%$$ *Ans.*

$$C = \frac{14.5}{98.7} \times 100 = 14.7\%$$

30-5   Ion-exchange Chromatography

The ability to separate ions of similar chemical properties has been made possible by the introduction of ion-exchange methods.   An ion-exchange resin is in most cases an insoluble organic polymer on which are located a large number of ionizable groups.   Depending on the polymer and on the type of groups, the resin can exchange either cations or anions, and its selectivity for specific ions can be altered   The operative mechanism in this case is very different from that found with the chromatographic methods discussed previously.   In the ion-exchange process, the dominant force is one of electrostatic attraction.   For example, there might exist an equilibrium of the following type:

$$HR + M^+ \rightleftharpoons MR + H^+$$

where R is the resin.   In chromatographic applications of ion exchange, the resin becomes the stationary phase, and the solvent or eluent is the moving phase.

For example, the resin could be a polymeric chain containing sulfonic acid groups.   If metal ions are available, the protons on the sulfonic acid groups may be displaced into the solvent and the metal ion will be held by the resin.   If more than one metal ion is present in the solution phase, the metal which is most strongly attracted will spend the highest

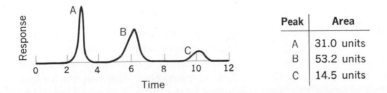

Peak	Area
A	31.0 units
B	53.2 units
C	14.5 units

Fig. 37

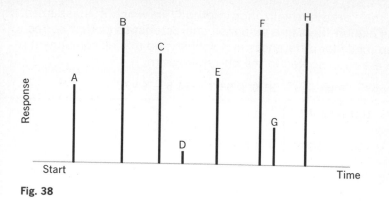

Fig. 38

proportion of time attached to the resin. In quantitative terms, the strength of the attraction is measured as a distribution ratio:

$$C = \frac{\text{quantity of ion in the resin phase}}{\text{quantity of ion in the solution phase}}$$

The distribution ratio is usually measured in a batch process where a specific quantity of resin is mixed with a specific quantity of metal ion. The metal ion concentration in each phase is then measured independently. In a chromatographic situation, differences in attraction result in the desired separation. Elution from an ion-exchange resin depends on the nature of the ions and the pH of the eluent as well as on the presence of any complexing agents.

Analytical applications of ion-exchange methods can be grouped under several general categories: separations of metal ions or other ions, concentration of an ionic constituent, removal of an ionic species, and preparation of reagents. Some of the following problems illustrate these applications.

PROBLEMS

*30-1. A mixt. contains (*a*) *n*-butane, (*b*) isobutane, (*c*) *n*-hexane, and (*d*) 3-methylpentane. When chromatographed, the areas were measured and found to be, respectively, 4.3 cm², 3.8 cm², 12.5 cm², and 1.2 cm². Calculate the percentage composition of the mixt. (Assume equal detector responses.)

*30-2. A sample of gasoline was analyzed, using gas chromatography, and gave the chromatogram shown in Fig. 38. A standard sample contg. equal quantities of the known components W, X, Y, and Z was then run, and the retention times for the peaks corresponded to peaks B, C, F, and H, respectively. The heights for the known peaks obtained under the same conditions as the unknown sample were 18, 14, 18, and 19 cm², respectively. Assuming that the detector's response for components A, D, E, and G was the same as for components B and F, calculate the relative percentage-by-wt. composition of the gasoline.   (Assume that the peak heights given are proportional to the peak areas.)

*30-3.   A mixt. of three components is separated using paper chromatography, and each component is analyzed using absorption.   With standards contg. 100 p.p.m. of each component run simultaneously, the following data were obtained; Compd. A, 0.72 absorbance; B, 0.55; C, 0.80.

For the unknown mixt., the data obtained when the sample was run under identical conditions were as follows: Compd. A, 0.15 absorbance; B, 0.84; C, 0.75.

(a) Calculate the relative percentage composition of the unknown mixt.   (b) If the R_f values for the three components were 8.5, 6.3, and 5.5 cm, respectively, sketch the appearance of the paper chromatogram.   Label each spot.

30-4.   A three-component mixt. is eluted first with solvent A and then with solvent B in a two-dimensional thin-layer chromatogram.   The R_f values with the two solvent systems are as follows:

Compd.	Solvent A	Solvent B
I	15.4	6.3
II	15.2	9.2
III	9.1	6.5

Show what the thin-layer chromatogram would look like after the first development and then after the second.   Label each spot.

*30-5.   A mixt. contg. only ethanol and methanol was analyzed, using a gas chromatograph, and gave the chromatogram shown in Fig. 39.   In this chromatogram the area of I is 5.6 cm² and that of II is 1.2 cm².   The major peak is due to ethanol.   Calculate the percentage composition of the mixt. (a) assuming that the thermal conductivities of the alcohols are the same and (b) assuming that the thermal conductivity of methanol is 0.70 times as great as that of ethanol.

*30-6.   The components in 10.0 ml of a biological extract were separated, using adsorption chromatography (column) with silica gel.   The eluent was monitored continuously by ultraviolet absorption and produced the chromatogram shown in Fig. 40.   The vol. of eluent including component D (mol. wt. = 194) was evaporated to dryness, and the residual solid was dissolved in 3.00 ml of CCl₄.   This soln. gave an absorbance of 0.57 A.   A 1.00×10^{-4} M standard soln. of component D was prepared in CCl₄, and it gave an absorbance of 0.68 A.   Calculate the concn. (as mg per ml) of component D in the biological fluid.

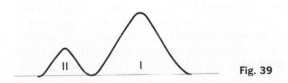

Fig. 39

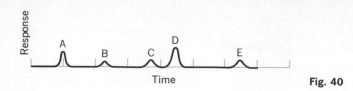

Fig. 40

*30-7. Three isomeric xylenols present in automobile exhausts can be separated by gas chromatography [*Anal. Chem.*, **36**, 2442 (1964)]. In an attempt to make the method quantitative, a series of standards was run and gave the data shown below (for that portion of the calibration curve which is linear). Upon injecting a 0.50 μl sample of the phenolic fraction of an automobile exhaust into the same gas chromatograph under the same conditions, the data listed in the third column of the table were obtained. Calculate the percentage by vol. of each xylenol in the unknown phenolic fraction.

	Area	
	Standard	*Unknown*
	cm²/μl	cm²
2,3-xylenol	1,300	45
3,5-xylenol	1,200	54
3,4-xylenol	1,150	24

*30-8. The following calibration data were obtained for the gas chromatographic analysis of benzoic acid and phenylacetic acid in cyclohexane:

Concn.	*Calibration peak areas*	
%	(*sample* = 0.50 μl)	
	Benzoic acid	*Phenylacetic acid*
	cm²	cm²
0.20	8.4	6.8
0.50	21.0	16.8
1.00	41.9	34.0
2.00	84.1	67.8

A sample known to contain these two acids as well as other compds. in cyclohexane was chromatographed, yielding very small peaks at the proper retention times for these acids. The sample size was increased to 2.5 μl, and there resulted peak areas of 11.5 cm² for benzoic acid and 13.0 cm² for phenylacetic acid. (*a*) What is the percentage-by-wt. composition of each acid in the unknown? (*b*) Another sample is known to contain twice as much benzoic acid and seven times as much phenylacetic acid as the first. What peak areas should be found if this sample were chromatographed under the same conditions as above except for using a sample size of 1.0 μl?

30-9. Equal vols. of chlorobenzene, 1,2-dichlorobenzene, and 1,3-dichlorobenzene are mixed, and the resulting mixt. is injected into a gas chromatograph. The following areas are obtained: 6.36, 7.55, and 7.45 cm^2, respectively. Assuming that the thermal conductivities of the three compds. are the same, show that the percentage area does not agree well with either the percentage-vol. composition or with the percentage-mole composition of the sample but that it agrees best with the wt.-percentage composition of the sample. (The densities of the three components are 1.106, 1.305, and 1.288 g/ml, respectively.)

*30-10. Morie and Sweet [*Anal. Chem.*, **37**, 1552 (1965)] have described a method for the analysis of aluminum, gallium, and indium by complexation with trifluoroacetylacetonate and extraction of the complexes into benzene; the benzene soln. is then analyzed by gas chromatography. A 1.00-g sample of ore was dissolved, treated, and the final vol. adjusted to 25.0 ml; the chelates were extracted into 5.00 ml of benzene which contained the ligand. 5.00 μl of the benzene extract was injected into the gas chromatograph. Peak areas of 12.5, 6.8, and 19.0 cm^2 were measured for aluminum, gallium, and indium, respectively. Standard solns. contg. 5.00 mg of the metal per 25.0 ml were treated similarly, yielding peak areas of 15.0, 13.5, and 10.0 cm^2, respectively. Calculate the wt. percent of each metal in the ore.

*30-11. The analysis of trace levels of naturally occurring fluoride ion is to be attempted using an ion-exchange method. In the proposed method, two identical columns of an anion-exchange resin are prepared. Through one is passed 100 ml of a standard soln. contg. 0.100 mg/liter of fluoride ion. Through the other is passed 1 liter of the unknown soln. The fluoride is then eluted from the columns as the beryllium fluoride complex ion, and the fluoride complex is analyzed spectrophotometrically. The standard soln. yields an absorbance of 0.480, while that of the unknown is 0.560. Calculate the concn. of fluoride ion in the unknown soln. in p.p.m.

*30-12. Roberts and Ryterband [*Anal. Chem.*, **37**, 1587 (1965)] have described a method for the analysis of cerium in cast iron. The method depends on the retention of the iron(III) chloride complex on an ion-exchange resin and the nonretention of cerium, which is then extracted as the 8-quinolinol chelate into chloroform; the chelate is analyzed spectrophotometrically. Using a series of standards, it was established that Beer's law holds up to at least 4.00×10^{-3} M chelate and that a 1.00×10^{-3} M soln. of the chelate gave an absorbance of 0.680. A 1.00-g sample of cast iron was treated as directed, resulting in a final vol. of 20.0 ml of chloroform soln. The absorbance recorded for the extracted chelate was 0.18. Calculate the wt. percent of cerium in the cast iron. (Assume all the cerium passes through the ion-exchange column and is then extracted.)

*30-13. A standard soln. of HCl (5.00×10^{-2} M, 100 ml) is to be prepared by passing a standard soln. of sodium chloride through a cation exchange resin in its hydrogen form; the eluted hydrogen chloride soln. is to be used as the acid. In

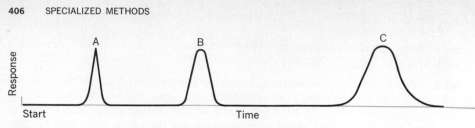

Fig. 41

order to be certain that all the hydrogen and chloride ions have been eluted, 25.0 ml of the standard NaCl soln. is passed through the column, followed by 50.0 ml of distilled water, and the total eluent is diluted to 100 ml.   How many g of NaCl should be dissolved in what vol. of distilled water to produce the required standard NaCl soln.?

*30-14.   A mixt. contg. three components yielded a chromatogram shown in Fig. 41 when run using a 6-ft column.   (a) Determine the no. of plates in the column, using each peak individually.   (b) Determine the average no. of plates in the column.   (c) What is the average value for the HETP for this column?   (d) Should the values necessarily be identical?

Gas-volumetric Analysis

31-1 Fundamental Gas Laws

Problems involving the determination of the proportional amounts of the components of a gaseous mixture and the determination of the amount of a given substance by measuring the quantity of gas which that substance can be made to evolve in chemical reaction are the only phases of gas analysis considered in this book.

Calculations of gas analyses make use of the following gas laws, most of which apply strictly only to the so-called "perfect" or "ideal" gases but which can be applied to ordinary analyses with results that are usually in keeping with the precision of analytical manipulation. These laws should already be more or less familiar to the student.

It will be recalled that to be under "standard conditions" a gas must be dry, under a pressure equal to 760 mm of mercury, and at a temperature of $0°C$ ($= 273°K$).

Boyle's Law. The volume of a fixed mass of a gas at constant temperature is inversely proportional to the pressure to which it is subjected; that is,

$$pv = p'v' = k$$

where pv and $p'v'$ are pairs of simultaneous values of pressure and volume of a given mass of gas and k is a constant.

Charles's Law. The volume of a fixed mass of a gas at constant pressure is directly proportional to the absolute temperature to which it is subjected; that is,

$$\frac{v}{v'} = \frac{T}{T'}$$

where vT and $v'T'$ are pairs of simultaneous values of volume and temperature expressed on the absolute scale. Zero on the absolute scale is at $-273°C$; hence, the temperature in absolute units can be found by adding 273 to the temperature in centigrade units. Charles's law can therefore be written

$$\frac{v}{v'} = \frac{273 + t}{273 + t'}$$

where t and t' represent the respective temperatures in degrees centigrade.

The formulas expressing the two gas laws mentioned above can be combined to give

$$\frac{pv}{T} = \frac{p'v'}{T'}$$

Dalton's Law. The pressure exerted by a mixture of gases is equal to the sum of the pressures of the individual components, and the pressure exerted by a single component is the same as the pressure that component would exert if existing alone in the same volume.

Gay-Lussac's Law. Whenever gases unite or gaseous products are formed, the proportions by volume measured at the same temperature and pressure of all the gaseous products concerned can be represented by ratios of small integers. Thus, in the reaction

$$2H_2 + O_2 \longrightarrow 2H_2O$$

two parts by volume of hydrogen unite with one part by volume of oxygen to give two parts by volume of water vapor.

Avogadro's Law. Equal volumes of all perfect gases under identical conditions of temperature and pressure contain the same number of molecules. The number of molecules in 1 mole of the gas is 6.023×10^{23} (*Avogadro's number*).

31-2   Correction for Water Vapor

Evolved gases are frequently collected and measured over liquids which exert an appreciable vapor pressure, and in such cases the barometric pressure does not represent the pressure of the pure gas. It can be assumed that the gas will be saturated with the vapor of the liquid over which it is measured, and in such cases the vapor pressure of the liquid depends only upon the temperature. According to Dalton's law, the pressure of the pure gas can be found simply by subtracting the vapor pressure of the liquid at the given temperature from the barometric pressure. The values of the vapor pressure of water at different temperatures are given in Table 7 (Appendix).

Example 1   (Incorporating the first two laws in Sec. 31-1.) If at 755 mm barometric pressure and 26°C a dry gas occupies 50.0 ml, what volume would it occupy under standard conditions?

Solution   To convert to standard conditions, the pressure must be increased from 755 to 760 mm and the temperature decreased from 26 (= 26 + 273 = 299°K) to 0°C (= 273°K). Each change results in a decrease in volume.   The new volume becomes

$$50.0 \times \tfrac{755}{760} \times \tfrac{273}{299} = 45.4 \text{ ml} \qquad Ans.$$

Example 2   If the gas described in Example 1 was not dry but was confined over water, what would be the volume of the dry gas under standard conditions?

Solution   At 26°C the vapor pressure of water is equal to that of 25 mm of mercury (Table 7, Appendix).   The partial pressure of the gas is therefore 755 − 25 = 730 mm.   The volume under standard conditions is therefore

$$50.0 \times \tfrac{730}{760} \times \tfrac{273}{299} = 43.9 \text{ ml} \qquad Ans.$$

31-3   Gas-volumetric Analyses

Under gas-volumetric methods may be included those methods in which a gas is evolved by means of a chemical reaction, and from the volume of the gas the weight of the substance producing it is calculated.

From Avogadro's law it is evident that the weights of equal volumes of gases will be in direct proportion to the respective molecular weights. The weight in grams of 22.4 liters of any gas, when measured under standard conditions, i.e., at 0°C and under a pressure of 760 mm of mercury, represents the molecular weight of the gas. If the molecular weight of a gas and the volume that a certain quantity of it occupies under standard conditions are known, the weight of that quantity can be readily determined.   That is the principle underlying gas-volumetric analysis.   Since it is usually inconvenient actually to measure the volume of a gas at 0°C and under 760 mm pressure, it is customary to measure the gas at any convenient temperature and pressure and by means of Boyle's and Charles's laws to calculate the volume that the gas would occupy under standard conditions.

Example 1   A 0.500-g sample of limestone on treatment with acid liber ates 98.7 ml of CO_2 when measured over water[1] at 23°C and 761 mm pressure.   What is the percentage of CO_2 in the sample?

---

[1] Because of the appreciable solubility of CO_2 in water, it is desirable to use water that has been previously saturated with CO_2.

Solution

Vapor pressure of water at 23°C = 20.9 mm
Pressure of the pure CO_2 = 761 − 20.9 = 740 mm
Vol. of CO_2 under standard conditions

$$= 98.7 \times \frac{740}{760} \times \frac{273}{273 + 23} = 88.6 \text{ ml} \qquad Ans.$$

The gram-molecular weight (44.0 g) of CO_2 would occupy under standard conditions a volume of 22.4 liters = 22,400 ml. The weight of CO_2 evolved is, therefore,

$$44.0 \times \frac{88.6}{22,400} = 0.174 \text{ g}$$

Percentage of CO_2 in the sample is

$$\frac{0.174}{0.500} \times 100 = 34.8\% \qquad Ans.$$

Alternative Method. Some chemists prefer to solve problems involving molar relationships of gases by means of the following general formula:

$$pv = NRT$$

where p = pressure of the gas, atm

$$= \frac{\text{pressure, mm}}{760}$$

v = volume, ml

N = no. of moles of gas

$$= \frac{\text{wt. of gas}}{\text{mol. wt.}}$$

T = temperature on the absolute scale

R = "gas const." = 82.07, when p, v, N, and T are expressed in the units given here

Applying this formula to the problem under consideration,

$$\frac{740}{760} \times 98.7 = \frac{\text{wt. of gas}}{44.0} \times 82.07 \times 296$$

Wt. of CO_2 = 0.174 g

$$\text{Percentage} = \frac{0.174}{0.500} \times 100 = 34.8 \qquad Ans.$$

31-4   Absorption Methods

Absorption methods of gas analysis apply to the determination of the proportionate amounts of the components of a gaseous mixture.   The mixture of gases is treated with a series of absorbents, and the temperature and pressure are usually kept constant throughout the entire determination.   In cases where these are allowed to vary, corrections for their effect can be made by applying the principles outlined in Sec. 31-1.   The difference in the volume of the gas before and after it has been acted

Gas	*Reagent*
Carbon dioxide	Sodium hydroxide
	Potassium hydroxide
Unsaturated hydrocarbons ("illuminants")	Bromine water
	Fuming sulfuric acid
Oxygen	Alkaline pyrogallol solution
	Yellow phosphorus
Carbon monoxide	Ammoniacal cuprous chloride
Hydrogen	Palladium sponge
	Palladous chloride solution
	Colloidal palladium solution

upon by each absorbing agent represents the amount of gas absorbed, and the amount is usually expressed on a percentage-by-volume basis. The many forms of apparatus used for carrying out gas absorptions are described in the textbooks on the subject, but the fundamental principles are identical.   The reagents commonly employed are shown in the accompanying table.

Example 1   A sample of illuminating gas occupying a volume of 80.0 ml is treated in succession with potassium hydroxide solution, fuming sulfuric acid, alkaline pyrogallol solution, and ammoniacal cuprous chloride solution.   After each treatment, the volume of the residual gas at constant temperature and pressure is measured as 78.7, 75.5, 75.1, and 68.3 ml, respectively.   What is the percentage composition of the gas as shown by these results?

Solution

$$\text{Vol. of } CO_2 = 80.0 - 78.7 = 1.3 \text{ ml}$$
$$\text{Vol. of illuminants} = 78.7 - 75.5 = 3.2 \text{ ml}$$
$$\text{Vol. of } O_2 = 75.5 - 75.1 = 0.4 \text{ ml}$$
$$\text{Vol. of } CO = 75.1 - 68.3 = 6.8 \text{ ml}$$

The percentages of the various components are therefore

$$\left.\begin{array}{l} \dfrac{1.3}{80.0} \times 100 = 1.6\% \ CO_2 \\[2em] \dfrac{3.2}{80.0} \times 100 = 4.0\% \ \text{illuminants} \\[2em] \dfrac{0.4}{80.0} \times 100 = 0.5\% \ O_2 \\[2em] \dfrac{6.8}{80.0} \times 100 = 8.5\% \ CO \\[2em] \dfrac{68.3}{80.0} \times 100 = 85.4\% \ \text{inert gases} \end{array}\right\} \quad Ans.$$

31-5   Combustion Methods

If a gas mixture contains one or more components capable of combustion with oxygen, it is usually possible to determine the percentages of these components by allowing combustion to take place and measuring the contraction in volume, the amount of carbon dioxide formed, the volume of oxygen used, or combinations of these measurements, depending upon the number and character of the combustible components present.   Gay-Lussac's law underlies calculations involving contractions in volume.   Thus, in the combustion of carbon monoxide with oxygen,

$$2CO + O_2 \longrightarrow 2CO_2$$

two volumes of carbon monoxide unite with one volume of oxygen to form two volumes of carbon dioxide.   The combustion is therefore accompanied by a contraction equal to one-half the volume of the carbon monoxide present and produces a volume of carbon dioxide equal to the original volume of carbon monoxide.

The equations in Table 5 represent combustion reactions commonly encountered in gas analysis, and the right-hand columns show the volume relationships in each case.

With this table little difficulty should be experienced in formulating the necessary equations for the determination by combustion of various mixtures of gases.   It is only necessary to set up and solve simultaneously as many independent equations as there are unknown components in the gas mixture.

In case air is used for combustion, it can be assumed to consist of 20.9% by volume of oxygen.

Example 1   A gas mixture consists of CO, CH_4 (methane), and N_2. Twenty (20.0) milliliters is taken, 80.0 ml of O_2 is added, and combustion is allowed to take place over mercury.   After cooling, the volume of the gas is 79.0 ml.   After this gas is passed through KOH solution, the

Table 5   Some gas combustion relationships

	Vol. gas	O_2 con- sumed	Con- trac- tion	CO_2 pro- duced
Hydrogen $2H_2 + O_2 \longrightarrow 2H_2O$	1	$\frac{1}{2}$	$1\frac{1}{2}$	0
Carbon monoxide $2CO + O_2 \longrightarrow 2CO_2$	1	$\frac{1}{2}$	$\frac{1}{2}$	1
Methane $CH_4 + 2O_2 \longrightarrow CO_2 + 2H_2O$	1	2	2	1
Acetylene $2C_2H_2 + 5O_2 \longrightarrow 4CO_2 + 2H_2O$	1	$2\frac{1}{2}$	$1\frac{1}{2}$	2
Ethylene $C_2H_4 + 3O_2 \longrightarrow 2CO_2 + 2H_2O$	1	3	2	2
Ethane $2C_2H_6 + 7O_2 \longrightarrow 4CO_2 + 6H_2O$	1	$3\frac{1}{2}$	$2\frac{1}{2}$	2
Propylene $2C_3H_6 + 9O_2 \longrightarrow 6CO_2 + 6H_2O$	1	$4\frac{1}{2}$	$2\frac{1}{2}$	3
Propane $C_3H_8 + 5O_2 \longrightarrow 3CO_2 + 4H_2O$	1	5	3	3
Butane $2C_4H_{10} + 13O_2 \longrightarrow 8CO_2 + 10H_2O$	1	$6\frac{1}{2}$	$3\frac{1}{2}$	4

volume of the residual gas is 61.0 ml.   What is the volume of each component making up the original gas mixture?

Solution   Let

$$x = \text{vol. of CO}$$
$$y = \text{vol. of } CH_4$$
$$z = \text{vol. of } N_2$$
$$x + y + z = 20.0 \tag{1}$$

Contraction due to combustion (see Table 5):

$$\tfrac{1}{2}x + 2y = 100 - 79 = 21.0 \tag{2}$$

CO_2 produced (see Table 5):

$$x + y = 79 - 61 = 18.0 \tag{3}$$

Solving these three equations simultaneously,

$$\left. \begin{array}{l} x = 10.0 \text{ ml CO} \\ y = 8.0 \text{ ml } CH_4 \\ z = 2.0 \text{ ml } N_2 \end{array} \right\} \quad Ans.$$

Example 2   The residual gas mentioned in the example in Sec. 31-4 consists entirely of hydrogen, methane, and nitrogen.   To a 20.0-ml sample is added 100.0 ml of air, and the mixture is exploded.   After the carbon dioxide is absorbed in potassium hydroxide, the volume of the gas is found to be 88.0 ml, and after the excess oxygen is absorbed in pyrogallol, the volume of the gas is 82.1 ml.   What is the percentage of each component in the gas mixture and in the original illuminating gas?

Solution   Let

$$x = \text{vol. of } H_2$$
$$y = \text{vol. of } CH_4$$
$$z = \text{vol. of } N_2$$

Then

$$x + y + z = 20.0 \tag{1}$$

Contraction in vol. plus CO_2 produced $= (100.0 + 20.0) - 88.0 = 32.0$

$$(1\tfrac{1}{2}x + 2y) + y = 32.0 \tag{2}$$

Vol. of O_2 taken $= 100.0 \times 0.209 = 20.9$
Vol. O_2 consumed $= 20.9 - (88.0 - 82.1) = 15.0$

$$\tfrac{1}{2}x + 2y = 15.0 \tag{3}$$

Solving these equations simultaneously,

$$x = 12.7 \text{ ml } H_2$$
$$y = 4.3 \text{ ml } CH_4$$
$$z = 3.0 \text{ ml } N_2$$

The percentages by volume of these components are found by dividing these volumes by 20.0 and multiplying by 100.

$$\left.\begin{array}{l} 63.5\% \ H_2 \\ 21.5\% \ CH_4 \\ 15.0\% \ N_2 \end{array}\right\} \quad \textit{Ans.}$$

In the original illuminating gas (Example 1, Sec. 31-4) the percentages of these components are

$$\left.\begin{array}{l} 12.7 \times \dfrac{68.3}{20.0} \times \dfrac{100}{80.0} = 54.2\% \ H_2 \\[2mm] 4.3 \times \dfrac{68.3}{20.0} \times \dfrac{100}{80.0} = 18.3\% \ CH_4 \\[2mm] 3.0 \times \dfrac{68.3}{20.0} \times \dfrac{100}{80.0} = 12.8\% \ N_2 \end{array}\right\} \quad \textit{Ans.}$$

PROBLEMS

*31-1.   (a) If 500 ml of H_2 gas is cooled at const. pressure from 26 to $-10°C$, what is the resulting vol.?   (b) If now the pressure is increased from 758 to 774 mm, what is the resulting vol.?

*31-2.   If 360 vols. of H_2 measured dry at $-13°C$ are heated at const. pressure, the vol. is found to increase by 10%. What is the increase in temp.?

*31-3.   If 1.00 g of $CaCO_3$ is dissolved in HCl, what vol. of gas is evolved (a) when measured dry at 15°C and 780 mm pressure, (b) when measured over H_2O at 30°C and 748 mm pressure?

*31-4.   (a) How many moles and how many g of O_2 occupy a vol. of 8.00 liters when measured over water at 40°C and at a barometric pressure of 750 mm? (b) What pressure would be exerted by the O_2 alone if the same mass occupies a vol. of 7.00 liters when measured over water at 14°C?   (c) What would be the total pressure in the container?   (d) At what temp. would the same mass of dry O_2 occupy a vol. of 9.00 liters at a pressure of 720 mm?

*31-5.   The average mol. wt. of air is 29.   (a) How many molecules, (b) how many g, and (c) how many g moles of air are present in 100 ml of air at 20°C and at a pressure of 1.0×10^{-6} mm of Hg?

*31-6.   A 25-liter vessel is filled with N_2 satd. with water vapor at 50°C and under a barometric pressure of 750 mm.   The temp. is now lowered to 15°C, and the pressure again brought to 750 mm.   (a) How many g of pure N_2 are present in the vessel, and (b) how many g of H_2O have condensed?

*31-7.   How many g of $KClO_3$ must be ignited to KCl in order to produce 290 ml of O_2 gas when measured over H_2O at 17°C and 777 mm pressure?

*31-8.   What wt. of limestone should be taken for analysis so that when strongly ignited, the vol. in ml of evolved CO_2 measured dry at 20°C and 780 mm equals the percentage of CO_2 present?

*31-9.   Calculate the vol. of H_2O that can be obtained from 8.0 g of $H_4Ca_{12}Al_6Si_{10}O_{43}$ (f. wt. = 1616) measured at (a) 20°C and 750 mm pressure, (b) 750 mm pressure and 900°C.

*31-10.   A sample of pyrite ore weighing 0.2500 g yields 0.7783 g of $BaSO_4$. (a) How many cu ft of air measured at 130°F and 27 in. of Hg pressure would theoretically be required to burn 1.25 lb of the pyrite?   (b) What would be the vol. of the gaseous residue (SO_2 and residual N_2) measured at the same temp. and pressure? ($4FeS_2 + 11O_2 \longrightarrow 2Fe_2O_3 + 8SO_2$; air = 20.9% O_2 by vol.; 1 cu in. = 16.39 ml; 1 lb = 0.4536 kg.)

*31-11.   The following measurements of a gas are made under identical conditions: Sample taken = 100.0 ml; vol. after KOH treatment = 91.5 ml; vol. after pyrogallol treatment = 81.4 ml; vol. after $Cu(NH_3)_2^+$ treatment = 81.1 ml.   Calculate the percentages of CO_2, O_2, CO, and N_2 in the gas if no other components are present.

*31-12.   A flue gas is known to contain 3.8% O_2, 15.0% CO_2, and the rest N_2.   A 95.0-ml sample is drawn into a multiple absorption apparatus.   What would be the vol. reading after absorption in the following absorbents in the order stated: (a) KOH, (b) pyrogallol, (c) ammoniacal CuCl?

*31-13.   (a) Calculate the percentage composition of a mixt. of H_2 and N_2 from the following measurements made under identical conditions: Vol. of gas taken = 58.2 ml; vol. of O_2 added = 32.0 ml; vol. of O_2 consumed by combustion = 6.1 ml. (b) What vol. of gas remains after combustion and cooling?

*31-14.   What is the percentage composition of a mixt. of H_2, CH_4, and N_2 if the contraction in vol. due to combustion with O_2 and cooling is the same as the vol. of the sample taken?

*31-15.   What is the percentage of CH_4 in a mixt. of H_2, CH_4, and C_2H_2 if a contraction of 26.0 ml results when 16.0 ml of the mixt. is burned with an excess of air and cooled to room temp.?

*31-16.   The following measurements are made under identical conditions: Vol. of gas taken = 10.5 ml; vol. of air added = 137.4 ml; total vol. after combustion and cooling = 136.1 ml; vol. after removing CO_2 = 129.6 ml.   Calculate the percentage composition of the gas assuming it to be a mixt. of H_2, CO, and CH_4.

*31-17.   What is the percentage of propane, C_3H_8, in a mixt. of propane, CO, and CH_4 if a 13.7-ml sample on combustion produces 23.7 ml of CO_2?

*31-18.   What is the percentage composition of a mixt. of CO, C_2H_6, and N_2 if, on combustion with O_2 and cooling, the contraction in vol. and the vol. of CO_2 produced are each numerically equal to the vol. of the sample taken?

*31-19.   To 40.8 ml of a mixt. of H_2, N_2, and CO is added 150.0 ml of air, and the mixt. is exploded and cooled.   If 4.8 ml of CO_2 is produced and the residual O_2 requires 42.0 ml of H_2 for combustion, (*a*) what is the percentage composition of the original mixt., and (*b*) what was the total vol. of cooled gas after the first combustion?

*31-20.   A mixt. of C_2H_6, H_2, CO, and N_2 has a vol. of 28.0 ml.   After combustion with 72.0 ml of O_2 and cooling, the residual vol. is 60.0 ml, and after this is passed into KOH soln., the residual gas occupies 34.0 ml.   When this gas is passed over yellow phosphorus, only 4.0 ml remains.   Find the percentage composition of the original gas.

*31-21.   From the following data, calculate the percentage composition of a sample of illuminating gas: Sample taken = 100.6 ml; vol. after KOH treatment = 98.4 ml; after Br_2 treatment = 94.2 ml; after pyrogallol treatment = 93.7 ml; after CuCl treatment = 85.2 ml; residual gas taken for combustion = 10.3 ml; vol. of air added = 87.3 ml; vol. after combustion and cooling = 80.1 ml; CO_2 produced = 5.2 ml.

*31-22.   A mixt. of gases consists of carbon monoxide, methane, and acetylene. To a 50.0-ml sample is added 140 ml of O_2, and the mixt. is burned.   After cooling, the vol. is 116.0 ml, and after passing this gas through KOH soln., the vol. becomes 54.0 ml.   Find the percentage (by vol.) composition of the original gas.

*31-23.   Coke-oven gas usually consists of moderate amts. of hydrogen, methane, ethane, unsatd. hydrocarbons ("illuminants"), carbon monoxide, carbon dioxide, nitrogen, and oxygen.   In a certain analysis of such material a 100-ml vol. of the gas is used.   After passing it in succession through KOH, fuming H_2SO_4, and alkaline pyrogallol, the vol. readings are 96.7, 95.2, and 95.0 ml, respectively.   The residual gas is then passed over heated CuO ($\underline{CuO} + H_2 \longrightarrow \underline{Cu} + H_2O$; $\underline{CuO} + CO \longrightarrow \underline{Cu} + CO_2$), and after cooling to room temp., the vol. is found to be 35.5 ml, of which 5.5 ml is then absorbed by KOH soln.   Of the residual gas 10.0 ml is then burned in 90.0 ml of O_2, and the vol. shrinks to 83.5 ml.   KOH soln. absorbs 9.0 ml of this.

Calculate the percentage (by vol.) of each component of the original gas.

31-24. If a gas measured dry at 27°C and 758 mm pressure occupies a vol. of 500 ml, find its vol. if the temp. is increased to 87°C and the pressure increased to 775 mm.

31-25. If H_2 gas when measured over H_2O at 23°C and 772 mm pressure occupies 97.3 ml, what would be the vol. under standard conditions?

31-26. A gas has a vol. of 222 ml over H_2O at 12°C and 751 mm pressure.   What vol. would it occupy over H_2O at 31°C and 770 mm pressure?

31-27. (a) What is the temp. of 14.0 g of dry N_2 occupying a vol. of 10.0 liters under a pressure of 745 mm?   (b) What vol. would be occupied by 7.00 g of N_2 if satd. with water vapor at 30°C and at a total pressure of 760 mm?

31-28. How many atoms of H_2 are present in a liter of the pure gas at -30°C and at a pressure of 1.00×10^{-7} mm?

31-29. What is the max. no. of g of H_2O that can be introduced into a 20-liter evacuated vessel maintained at 30°C without effecting a condensation of liquid water?

31-30. $BaCO_3$ and $MgCO_3$ are mixed in the proportion by wt. of $2:1$.   (a) Calculate the vol. of 6.00 N HCl required to decompose a 5.00-g sample.   (b) Find also the vol. of CO_2 formed when measured dry at 22.4°C and 758 mm pressure. (c) What would be the vol. of the gas if it were collected under the same conditions over H_2O (previously satd. with CO_2)?

31-31. What wt. of sample consisting of $CaCO_3$ + SiO_2 should be taken so that the no. of ml of CO_2 obtained by treating the sample with acid and measuring the CO_2 dry at 18°C and 763 mm pressure will equal the percentage of CaO in the sample?

31-32. What total vol. of gas (N_2 + CO_2) measured dry at 20°C and 755 mm pressure could be obtained by the combustion of 0.2010 g of $CO(NH_2)_2$ (urea)?

31-33. If, in the analysis of a 1.00-g sample of a carbonate, 18.0 ml of CO_2 measured over H_2O (previously satd. with CO_2) at 18°C and 763 mm pressure was obtained, find the percentage of combined C in the sample.

31-34. Calculate the vol. of O_2 required to oxidize a sample of Fe weighing 0.9000 g, assuming that the product of combustion is 60.0% Fe_2O_3 and 40.0% Fe_3O_4 and that the gas is measured dry at 21°C and 756 mm pressure.

31-35. Decomposition of A g of indole gave 16.42 ml of N_2 when measured over H_2O at 27°C and 758 mm pressure.   Combustion in O_2 of a sample weighing 1.333A g increased the wt. of a KOH bulb by 0.6026 g and that of a $CaCl_2$ tube by 0.1078 g.   Calculate the empirical formula of indole.

31-36. A water gas has the following composition: 33.4% CO, 8.9% unsatd. hydrocarbons, 3.9% CO_2, 7.9% N_2, 10.4% satd. hydrocarbons, 34.6% H_2, and 0.9% O_2.   If a sample of 100 ml is passed through the following absorbents, in the order stated, until const. vol. is reached in each case, what is the vol. reading after each treatment: (a) KOH, (b) Br_2–H_2O, (c) pyrogallol, (d) ammoniacal CuCl?

31-37.   If the combustion reaction and vol. relationships of butene, C_4H_8, were included in Table 5, what would be the equation and the numerical values?

31-38.   If 12.0 g of carbon undergoes combustion in 31.3 liters (standard conditions) of O_2, what is the percentage-by-vol. composition of the gas mixt. after combustion?

31-39.   Assume air to contain 20.9 parts (by vol.) of O_2 and 79.1 parts of N_2.   If 100 parts of air is mixed with 95 parts of H_2 (both measured at 20°C and 760 mm) and the mixt. exploded, what are the relative vols. of the components of the residual gas after cooling to 20°C and 760 mm pressure?

31-40.   The following measurements were made under the same conditions: Vol. of gas taken = 95.3 ml; vol. of O_2 added = 40.8 ml; vol. of gas after combustion and cooling = 40.1 ml.   Find the percentage of composition of the gas assuming it to consist of a mixt. of H_2 and N_2.

31-41.   What is the percentage composition of a mixt. of H_2, CO, and CH_4 if the vol. of the O_2 consumed in combustion and the vol. of CO_2 produced are each equal to three-fourths of the vol. of the original gas taken?

31-42.   A known vol. of a mixt. of CH_4, CO, and N_2 is exploded with an excess of air.   Show by equations that the percentage composition of the mixt. cannot be determined by measuring the contraction in vol. and the vol. of O_2 consumed.

31-43.   A certain illuminating gas is known to contain the following components: H_2, CH_4, CO_2, N_2, O_2, CO, and unsatd. hydrocarbons.   Calculate the percentage composition of the gas from the following data: Sample taken = 99.5 ml; vol. after KOH treatment = 97.6 ml; after Br_2 treatment = 94.4 ml; after pyrogallol treatment = 93.8 ml; after CuCl treatment = 85.1 ml; residual gas taken for combustion = 12.0 ml; vol. of O_2 added = 20.2 ml; residual vol. after combustion and cooling = 11.8 ml; combined $CO_2 + O_2$ remaining = 11.4 ml.

31-44.   A certain natural gas is known to contain CH_4, N_2, and CO_2.   A 50-ml sample is passed into KOH, and the vol. of the residual gas is found to be 49.6 ml. Of this residual gas, 20.0 ml is taken, and an excess of air is added.   Combustion and cooling cause a shrinkage in the total vol. of 38.4 ml.   Find the percentage composition of the original gas.

31-45.   A blast-furnace gas is of the following composition: 12.5% CO_2, 26.8% CO, 3.6% H_2, 57.1% N_2.   If a 100-ml sample was passed through a soln. of KOH, what would be the vol. of the residual gas?   If to 50.0 ml of this residue was added 25.0 ml of O_2 and the mixt. exploded, what would be the new vol. of the gas after cooling and what would be its percentage composition?

Functional Group Determinations

32-1 Applications of Inorganic Procedures to Organic Determinations

Many functional groups of organic compounds can be determined quantitatively by utilizing, in part at least, conventional analytical methods. Such determinations are illustrated in the problems given in this chapter. In each case the necessary descriptive material is incorporated in the statement of the problem. Only a very elementary knowledge of organic chemistry is required.

PROBLEMS

*32-1. Primary, secondary, and tertiary amines (RNH_2, $RN \cdot R'H$, $RN \cdot R'R''$) in glacial acetic acid soln. can be titrated quantitatively with standard $HClO_4$ (for example, $RNH_2 + H^+ \longrightarrow RNH_3^+$). The end point can be determined potentiometrically or by means of a suitable indicator.

Primary and secondary, but not tertiary, amines can be acetylated (reacted upon by acetic acid anhydride) (for example, $C_6H_5NH_2 + (CH_3CO)_2O \longrightarrow C_6H_5NH \cdot OCH_3 + CH_3COOH$, and $C_6H_5NHCH_3 + (CH_3CO)_2O \longrightarrow C_6H_5NCH_3 \cdot OCH_3 + CH_3COOH$), and the acetylated products do not titrate with $HClO_4$. Furthermore, primary, but not secondary or tertiary, amines react with salicylaldehyde, $HO \cdot C_6H_4 \cdot CHO$, to form weak Shiff bases which do not titrate with $HClO_4$.

Given a mixt. of aniline (f. wt. = 93), methyl aniline (f. wt. = 107), dimethyl aniline (f. wt. = 121), and inert material. The sample mixt. weighing 1.20 g is dissolved in glacial acetic acid, and three separate $\frac{1}{5}$-aliquot portions are treated as follows: One portion is titrated with 0.100 M $HClO_4$ in glacial acetic acid soln., and 17.0 ml is required. A second portion is acetylated, and the resulting soln. requires 11.0 ml of the $HClO_4$. The third portion is treated with salicylaldehyde, and the resulting soln. requires 15.0 ml of the $HClO_4$. (a) What is the percentage of inert material in the original mixt.?

The $HClO_4$ soln. is conveniently standardized against a weighed amt. of potassium biphthalate which, in glacial acetic acid, acts as a base and is titrated to normal phthalic acid.   (b) What is the normality of the above $0.100\ M\ HClO_4$ when used as an acid in a conventional aq. soln. titration?

32-2.   In Prob. 32-1, substitute for aniline and its derivatives toluidine ($CH_3 \cdot C_6H_4 \cdot NH_2$) and its similar methyl and dimethyl derivatives, and determine the percentage of each in the original mixt.

*32-3.   An acid soln. of Ti(III) is a very powerful reducing agent and is useful in determining iron by reduction titration, using KCNS indicator.   It is even more useful in the volumetric detn. of nitro, nitroso, and azo groups in organic compds. Generalized equations for these titrations are $Fe^{3+} + Ti^{3+} \longrightarrow Fe^{++} + Ti^{4+}$; $RNO_2 + 6Ti^{3+} + 6H^+ \longrightarrow RNH_2 + 6Ti^{4+} + 2H_2O$; $RNO + 4Ti^{3+} + 4H^+ \longrightarrow RNH_2 + 4Ti^{4+} + H_2O$; $RN{=}NR' + 4Ti^{3+} + 4H^+ \longrightarrow RNH_2 + R'NH_2 + 4Ti^{4+}$. All such titrations are carried out in an inert atmosphere.

An acid soln. of $TiCl_3$ is prepared, and it is found that 1.00 ml will just reduce 1.02 ml of a soln. of ferric sulfate of which 1.00 ml $\approx$ 7.98 mg of Fe_2O_3.   A $\frac{1}{5}$-aliquot portion of an ethanol-water soln. of p-nitroaniline is treated with 25.0 ml of the Ti(III) soln., and the excess Ti(III) requires 15.0 ml of the standard ferric soln. How many millimoles of nitroaniline were in the original ethanol-water soln.?

32-4.   In the titration of the following compds. with $TiCl_3$ (see Prob. 32-3), what fraction of the f. wt. represents the equiv. wt. in each case?   (a) Nitrosobenzene, (b) dinitroaniline, (c) benzyl nitrate, (d) phenylhydroxylamine, (e) azobenzene, (f) 2,4-dinitrophenylhydrazine.

*32-5.   Many compds. contg. a methoxy group ($-OCH_3$) or an ethoxy group ($-OC_2H_5$) can be determined by the Zeisel method in which the compd. is heated with HI, whereby the alkyl radical of the alkoxyl group is evolved as a gaseous iodide: $R \cdot OCH_3 + HI \longrightarrow R \cdot OH + CH_3I$; $R \cdot OC_2H_5 + HI \longrightarrow R \cdot OH + C_2H_5I$. Although the methyl or ethyl iodide, after suitable purification steps, can be converted to AgI and weighed as such, it is more feasible to use a volumetric process on the purified product.   Here the alkyl iodide is absorbed and oxidized with Br_2 according to the overall reaction equation: $RI + 3Br_2 + 3H_2O \longrightarrow RBr + HIO_3 + 5HBr$.   After destroying any excess Br_2 with formic acid, the HIO_3 is determined iodimetrically in the conventional way ($IO_3^- + 5I^- + 6H^+ \longrightarrow 3I_2 + 3H_2O$) using thiosulfate as titrant.

A sample of anisole ($C_6H_5OCH_3$, f. wt. = 108) contains inert matter and weighs 20.0 mg.   When carried through the Zeisel procedure, 20.0 ml of $Na_2S_2O_3$ soln. (1.00 ml $\approx$ 12.5 mg $CuSO_4 \cdot 5H_2O$) is required.   (a) What is the percentage purity of the anisole?   (b) Write the equation for the action of the formic acid mentioned in the above discussion.

32-6.   A sample of a pure compd. weighing 21.0 mg and contg. several OCH_3 groups has a mol. wt. of 266.   When analyzed by the Zeisel method (see Prob. 32-5), 28.4 ml of $Na_2S_2O_3$ soln. (of which each ml is equiv. in an iodimetric process to 0.100 millimole of Cu) is required.   (a) Calculate the no. of methoxy groups per molecule of the compd.   (b) What wt. of AgI would have been obtained if the same wt. of sample had been analyzed by the gravimetric modification?

*32-7. Amino acids can be determined by measuring the vol. of N_2 gas evolved by their reactions with nitrous acid (Van Slyke method), for example, $CHCH_3NH_2COOH + HNO_2 \longrightarrow CHOHCH_3COOH + N_2 + H_2O$ (compare $NH_3 + HNO_2 \longrightarrow N_2 + 2H_2O$; note that only one-half of the liberated N_2 comes from the amine).

A second method is to titrate the amino acid in a nonaqueous solvent like glacial acetic acid. In this case the titrant is perchloric acid which titrates the amino group (for example, $CHCH_3NH_2COOH + HClO_4 \longrightarrow (CHCH_3NH_3COOH)^+ + ClO_4^-$).

A sample of glycine, CH_2NH_2COOH, is titrated in glacial acetic acid soln., and a 50.0-ml pipetful of 0.100 N $HClO_4$ is used. The excess $HClO_4$ is then titrated with a glacial acetic acid soln. which is 0.150 N in dissolved sodium acetate, and 16.0 ml of the latter is required to give a color change with an appropriate indicator ($HClO_4 + CH_3COONa \longrightarrow NaClO_4 + CH_3COOH$). What vol. of N_2 gas (when measured over water at 770 mm and 20°C) would have been evolved if the same wt. of sample had been analyzed by the Van Slyke method?

*32-8. The detn. of ethylene glycol can be carried out by allowing it to stand in aq. soln. in contact with a measured vol. of periodate: $CH_2OH \cdot CH_2OH + IO_4^- \longrightarrow 2HCHO + IO_3^- + H_2O$. The soln. contg. the excess IO_4^- is then treated with a measured vol. of As(III) soln. which, in the presence of $NaHCO_3$, reduces IO_4^- but not IO_3^-. The excess As(III) is then titrated with standard I_2. From the following data, calculate the no. of g of glycol present in the original soln. (*Note:* The concn. of the periodate is not needed in the calculation.) Aliquot portions of sample taken for analysis $= \frac{1}{10}$; vol. of $NaIO_4$ added $= 25.00$ ml; vol. of standard As(III) added $= 23.50$ ml; As soln. contained 40.00 millimoles of As_2O_3 per liter; vol. of 0.1300 N I_2 required for excess As(III) $= 2.00$ ml. In a blank run on 5.00 ml of the $NaIO_4$, 15.00 ml of the As(III) was added and the excess required 3.08 ml of the standard I_2.

*32-9. Phenol, C_6H_5OH, and certain substituted phenols can be determined by the process of bromination in which a measured amt. of an excess of $KBrO_3 + KBr$ is added to the acid soln. and the liberated Br_2 ($BrO_3^- + 5Br^- + 6H^+ \longrightarrow 3Br_2 + 3H_2O$) replaces a definite number of hydrogens on the benzene ring. Phenol itself forms 2,4,6-tribromophenol ($C_6H_5OH + 3Br_2 \longrightarrow C_6H_4Br_3OH + 3HBr$). The Br_2 left over liberates I_2 from an added excess of KI ($Br_2 + 2I^- \longrightarrow I_2 + Br^-$), and the I_2 is titrated with standard thiosulfate. Salicylic acid is a phenol with a carboxyl group ortho to the hydroxyl group. It forms tribromophenol with Br_2 as in the above case, together with CO_2 from the carboxyl group. Acetylsalicylic acid (aspirin) reacts in a similar fashion. Some phenols (e.g., paranitrophenol) form dibromo products; others (e.g., β-naphthol) take on only one bromine atom per molecule.

A soln. of sodium salicylate (mol. wt. $= 160.1$) is brominated with a 25.0-ml pipetful of $KBrO_3$ soln. contg. 33.33 millimoles of $KBrO_3$ and 80 g of KBr per liter. After reaction is complete, the soln. is treated with excess KI and the liberated I_2 requires 26.0 ml of $Na_2S_2O_3$ soln. which is 0.150 N as used in iodimetric processes. How many g of sodium salicylate were present in the original soln.?

*32-10. Many aromatic amines, like phenols, can be determined by bromination (see Prob. 32-9), and in most cases bromine atoms replace three hydrogens of the benzene ring. This is true of a certain amine weighing 0.0434 g which is treated with KBr and 0.800 millimole of $KBrO_3$. The resulting soln., when treated with excess KI, liberates an amt. of I_2 which would be capable of oxidizing in neutral soln. 0.500 millimole of As_2O_3. What is the mol. wt. of the amine?

32-11. (*a*) A 5-grain aspirin tablet should theoretically require what *net* vol. of $KBrO_3$ soln. (0.0500 N as a potassium salt) for bromination (see Prob. 32-9)? (*b*) How many g of β-naphthol would be brominated by that net vol. of the $KBrO_3$? (Mol. wts.: acetylsalicylic acid = 180; β-naphthol = 144.   1.000 g = 15.43 grains.)

*32-12.   A common method for the quantitative detn. of hydroxyl groups in primary and secondary alcohols and in phenols consists first of replacing the hydrogen of the hydroxyl group with an acetyl group by means of acetic anhydride ("acetylation") and then adding water and titrating with NaOH the acetic acid resulting from the acetylation and from the excess acetic anhydride:

$$R(OH)_n + n(CH_3CO)_2O \longrightarrow R(OCOCH_3)_n + nCH_3COOH$$
$$(CH_3CO)_2O + H_2O \longrightarrow 2CH_3COOH$$

A blank run is made on the reagent. For purposes of calculation it is important to note that each organic hydroxyl group gives one molecule of acetic acid and that each molecule of acetic anhydride gives two molecules of acetic acid.

   A sample of benzyl alcohol, $C_6H_5CH_2OH$, dissolved in an inert solvent, is acetylated with 3.00 ml of acetic anhydride mixt., and the resulting soln., after adding water, requires 3.30 ml of 0.550 N NaOH for neutralization. A separate 3.00-ml portion of the acetylating mixt., after adding water, requires 7.50 ml of the NaOH. How many g of benzyl alcohol were present in the original soln.?

32-13.   Phenols, like alcohols, can be acetylated (see Prob. 32-12). A pure substituted phenol contg. only one hydroxyl group weighs 0.222 g and in an inert solvent is treated with a certain vol. of acetic anhydride mixt. The resulting soln. after dilution requires 7.00 ml of NaOH (1.00 ml $\approx$ 0.600 millimole of potassium biphthalate). A blank run on the same vol. of the reagent requires 10.33 ml of the NaOH. What is the mol. wt. of the phenol?

*32-14.   Primary and secondary alcohols can be determined not only by acetylation (see Prob. 32-1) but also by a similar process of "phthalation" in which the alcohol reacts with phthalic anhydride according to the general equation

$$R(OH) + C_6H_4(CO)_2O \longrightarrow C_6H_4COORCOOH$$

When treated with water, the excess anhydride hydrolyzes:

$$C_6H_4(CO)_2O + H_2O \longrightarrow 2C_6H_4(COOH)_2$$

and the combined phthalic acid and phthalic acid ester are titrated with standard NaOH. A blank run is made on an equal vol. of the reagent.

   A sample contg. 10.0 meq. of alcoholic hydroxyl is treated with five times the vol. of phthalic anhydride reagent theoretically necessary to carry out the phthalation, and the mixt. is warmed with water and titrated with standard NaOH. (*a*) How many meq. of NaOH would be required in the titration? (*b*) What is the difference between the no. of meq. of NaOH used in the titration of the sample and that of a blank on a similar vol. of reagent?

*32-15.   Polyhydric alcohols in which the hydroxyl groups are attached to adjacent carbon atoms can be quantitatively oxidized by an excess of periodic acid (Malaprade reaction).   Although the commonest form of periodic acid is H_5IO_6, it can be considered as a hydrated form of metaperiodic acid, HIO_4.

Common polyhydric alcohols are glycol and glycerol.   Their reactions with metaperiodic acid are, respectively, $CH_2OH-CH_2OH + HIO_4 \longrightarrow 2HCHO + HIO_3 + H_2O$ and $CH_2OH-CHOH-CH_2OH + 2HIO_4 \longrightarrow 2HCHO + HCOOH + 2HIO_3 + H_2O$.   Since HIO_4 and HIO_3 liberate different amts. of I_2 from an acid soln. of KI ($IO_4^- + 7I^- + 8H^+ \longrightarrow 4I_2 + 4H_2O$; $IO_3^- + 5I^- + 6H^+ \longrightarrow 3I_2 + 3H_2O$), an iodimetric process can be used for the detn. of alcohols of this type.

An aq. soln. of glycerol (mol. wt. = 92.07) is treated with 50.0 ml of HIO_4 soln. which is 0.0500 N as an acid.   After oxidation is complete, the addition of acid and an excess of KI liberates sufficient iodine to require 60.0 ml of 0.200 M $Na_2S_2O_3$ soln. for reduction.   How many g of glycerol were present in the original aq. soln.?

32-16.   The Malaprade reaction (see Prob. 32-15) is applied to an aq. soln. contg. 0.150 g of glycol (mol. wt. = 62.07).   A 50.0-ml pipetful of 0.0600 M H_5IO_6 is used.   What vol. of $Na_2S_2O_3$ soln. which is 0.500 N as a sodium salt would be required to titrate the liberated iodine?

*32-17.   A sample of glycerol (f. wt. = 92.0) is known to contain water as its only impurity.   The sample weighing 0.1000 g is treated with a pipetful of periodic acid, the amt. being in excess of that required to bring about the oxidation of the glycerol which takes place according to the equation given in Prob. 32-15.   The resulting mixt. is then treated with excess KI + acid, and both the iodic acid formed by the reaction and the excess periodic acid above that added liberate free iodine (see equations in Prob. 32-15).   The total liberated I_2 is found to require 80.0 ml of $M/5$ $Na_2S_2O_3$ for a conventional iodimetric titration.   In a separate blank run, a similar pipetful of the HIO_4, when treated with an excess of KI + acid, liberates an amt. of I_2 requiring 20.0 millimoles of $Na_2S_2O_3$ for titration.   What percentage of water is shown to be present in the glycerol sample?

*32-18.   If the water present in the glycerol of Prob. 32-17 had been determined by a Karl Fischer titration in which a sample weighing 0.1000 g had been titrated with a specially prepared soln. of I_2 and SO_2 in a methanol-pyridine mixt., how many millimoles of I_2 would have been used up in the titration?   The *net* titration reaction can be represented by the equation $H_2O + I_2 + SO_2 + CH_3OH \longrightarrow 2HI + CH_3HSO_4$.   (The end point is indicated by the initial appearance of the brown color of excess I_2, although a potentiometric titration is more commonly used.)

SEVEN

Common Analytical Determinations

Common
Analytical
Determinations

The following methods are those in common use in the gravimetric and volumetric determinations of the more common elements and radicals. They are given here in barest outline principally to serve as a reference in solving problems in this book. They also serve as background material to aid the instructor in devising problems for quizzes and other special assignments. Only a few colorimetric methods (applying in general to constituents at very low concentration) are included. Special instrumental methods are omitted.

ALUMINUM

Precipitated with NH_4OH as $Al(OH)_3$, ignited, and weighed as Al_2O_3.

Precipitated with 8-hydroxyquinoline (oxine) as $Al(C_9H_6NO)_3$ and weighed as such or ignited and weighed as Al_2O_3.

Precipitated with oxine as in the preceding case and the precipitate dissolved in HCl. KBr added and the oxine titrated with standard $KBrO_3$ to disappearance of color of methyl red or other suitable dye indicator. The indicator is oxidized by the excess bromate + bromide to a colorless product. Net equation for the oxine titration: $3C_9H_6NOH + 2BrO_3^- + 4Br^- + 6H^+ \longrightarrow 3C_9H_4NBr_2OH + 6H_2O$. See Sec. 12-9.

Colorimetric. Red color with ammonium salt of aurintricarboxylic acid or with alizarin.

AMMONIUM

(See under Nitrogen.)

ANTIMONY

Precipitated as Sb_2S_3 or Sb_2S_5, ignited in an inert atmosphere, and weighed as Sb_2S_3.

Precipitated as Sb_2S_3 or Sb_2S_5, heated with $NH_4OH + H_2O_2$, ignited in air, and weighed as Sb_2O_4.

In alloys.   Left as a residue of hydrated Sb_2O_5 on treating alloy with HNO_3 ($6\underline{Sb} + 10NO_3^- + 10H^+ \longrightarrow 3\underline{Sb_2O_5} + 10NO + 5H_2O$). Residue ignited in air to Sb_2O_4.   Tin must be removed.

Titrated in ice-cold HCl solution from valence 3 to 5 with standard $KMnO_4$ ($5SbCl_4^- + 2MnO_4^- + 12H_2O \longrightarrow 5H_3SbO_4 + 2Mn^{++} + 20Cl^- + 9H^+$).

Titrated from valence 3 to 5 with standard $KBrO_3$ ($+KBr$) in HCl solution to disappearance of color of methyl red or other suitable dye indicator.   The dye is oxidized by the excess $KBrO_3 + KBr$ to a color-less product.   Net titration equation: $3SbCl_4^- + BrO_3^- + 9H_2O \longrightarrow 3H_3SbO_4 + Br^- + 12Cl^- + 9H^+$.

Titrated from valence 3 to 5 with I_2 in a solution kept nearly neutral with excess $NaHCO_3$ ($SbO_3^{3-} + I_2 + 2HCO_3^- \longrightarrow SbO_4^{3-} + 2I^- + 2CO_2 + H_2O$).   The antimony is often held as a tartrate complex in this titration.

Titrated in strong HCl solution from valence 3 to 5 with standard KIO_3 ($2SbCl_4^- + IO_3^- + 5H_2O \longrightarrow 2H_3SbO_4 + ICl_2^- + 6Cl^- + 4H^+$). Free I_2 is formed as an intermediate product and gives a violet color with chloroform.   Titration is to disappearance of this color.

Brought to 5-valent form and the HCl solution treated with KI.   The liberated I_2 titrated with standard $Na_2S_2O_3$ ($H_3SbO_4 + 2I^- + 4Cl^- + 5H^+ \longrightarrow SbCl_4^- + I_2 + 4H_2O$).

Colorimetric.   Intensity of color of colloidal suspension of Sb_2S_3.

ARSENIC

Precipitated as As_2S_3 from 9 N HCl solution with H_2S and weighed as such.

Arsenate precipitated from ammoniacal solution as $MgNH_4AsO_4 \cdot 6H_2O$, ignited, and weighed as $Mg_2As_2O_7$.

Precipitated with uranyl ions as $UO_2NH_4AsO_4 \cdot xH_2O$ which is ignited to U_3O_8 and weighed.

Arsenate precipitated from neutral solution as Ag_3AsO_4.   Precipitate dissolved in HNO_3 and the Ag^+ titrated with standard KCNS with ferric alum indicator ($Ag^+ + CNS^- \longrightarrow \underline{AgCNS}$).

Titrated from valence 3 to 5 with standard I_2 in a solution kept nearly neutral by excess $NaHCO_3$ ($AsO_3^{3-} + I_2 + 2HCO_3^- \longrightarrow AsO_4^{3-} + 2I^- + 2CO_2 + H_2O$).

Titrated in strong HCl solution with standard KIO_3 ($2As^{3+} + IO_3^- + 2Cl^- + 5H_2O \longrightarrow 2H_3AsO_4 + ICl_2^- + 4H^+$).   Free I_2 is formed as an intermediate product and gives violet color with chloroform indicator. Titration is to disappearance of this color.

Titrated from valence 3 to 5 with standard $KBrO_3$ ($+KBr$) in HCl solution to disappearance of color of methyl red or other suitable dye indicator. The dye is oxidized by the excess $KBrO_3 + KBr$ to a colorless product. Net titration equation: $3As^{3+} + BrO_3^- + 9H_2O \longrightarrow 3H_3AsO_4 + Br^- + 9H^+$.

Small amounts. Reduced in acid solution with Zn and evolved as AsH_3 gas. The arsine decomposed to As and color compared to standards. Or AsH_3 absorbed in measured volume of I_2 solution. Excess I_2 titrated with standard $Na_2S_2O_3$ ($AsH_3 + 4I_2 + 4H_2O \longrightarrow H_3AsO_4 + 8I^- + 8H^+$).

Colorimetric. Evolved as AsH_3, which gives dark stain on $HgBr_2$ paper or on $AgNO_3$ crystal.

BARIUM

Precipitated as $BaSO_4$, ignited, and weighed as such.

Precipitated as $BaCrO_4$ and weighed as such.

Precipitated with $(NH_4)_2CO_3$ as $BaCO_3$, ignited, and weighed as such.

Precipitated as $BaCrO_4$. Precipitate dissolved in excess standard $FeSO_4$ ($+H_2SO_4$) and excess Fe^{++} titrated with standard $KMnO_4$ ($\underline{BaCrO_4} + 3Fe^{++} + 8H^+ + SO_4^= \longrightarrow 3Fe^{3+} + Cr^{3+} + \underline{BaSO_4} + 4H_2O$).

Precipitated as $BaCrO_4$ and precipitate dissolved in KI + dilute HCl. Liberated I_2 titrated with standard $Na_2S_2O_3$ ($2\underline{BaCrO_4} + 6I^- + 16H^+ \longrightarrow 2Ba^{++} + 3I_2 + 8H_2O$).

BERYLLIUM

Precipitated with NH_4OH as $Be(OH)_2$, ignited, and weighed as BeO.

Precipitated from ammoniacal solution with 8-hydroxyquinoline, as $Be(C_9H_6NO)_2$, ignited, and weighed as BeO.

Precipitated as $BeNH_4PO_4$, ignited, and weighed as $Be_2P_2O_7$.

BISMUTH

Precipitated with H_2S as Bi_2S_3 and weighed as such.

Precipitated as basic carbonate, ignited, and weighed as Bi_2O_3.

Precipitated as BiOI with KI from hot, very weakly acid solution and weighed as such.

Precipitated with cupferron, ignited, and weighed as Bi_2O_3.

Precipitated as $BiPO_4$ and weighed as such.

Electrolyzed and weighed as Bi.

Precipitated as oxalate, $(BiO)_2C_2O_4$, the precipitate dissolved in dilute H_2SO_4, and the oxalate titrated with standard $KMnO_4$.

Reduced with hypophosphorous acid to Bi and weighed as such.

Colorimetric.   Yellow color with KI + dilute HNO_3.

BORON

Borate heated with methanol and the volatile methyl borate passed through a weighed amount of ignited lime: $2B(OCH_3)_3 + \underline{CaO} + 3H_2O \longrightarrow$ $6CH_3OH + \underline{Ca(BO_2)_2}$. The material is reignited and weighed.   Gain in weight = B_2O_3.

Borate treated with methanol as above and the methyl borate hydrolyzed: $B(OCH_3)_3 + 3H_2O \longrightarrow H_3BO_3 + 3CH_3OH$. The CH_3OH is removed by evaporation and the H_3BO_3 titrated with standard NaOH in the presence of glycerol (or other polyhydric alcohol).   Only one hydrogen of H_3BO_3 reacts.

Colorimetric.   Red stain on turmeric paper.

BROMINE

Bromide.   Precipitated as AgBr and weighed as such.

Bromide.   *Volhard method.*   Precipitated as AgBr with measured amount of $AgNO_3$ and the excess Ag^+ titrated with standard KCNS using ferric alum indicator ($Ag^+ + CNS^- \longrightarrow \underline{AgCNS}$).

Bromide.   Titrated with standard $AgNO_3$ using eosin or other adsorption indicator.

Free bromine.   Excess KI added and the liberated I_2 titrated with standard $Na_2S_2O_3$ ($Br_2 + 2I^- \longrightarrow I_2 + 2Br^-$).

Bromate.   Excess KI added in the presence of acid and the liberated I_2 titrated with standard $Na_2S_2O_3$ ($BrO_3^- + 6I^- + 6H^+ \longrightarrow 3I_2 + Br^- + 3H_2O$).

Bromate.   Measured amount of As_2O_3 (dissolved in $NaHCO_3$) added. The solution is acidified, boiled, neutralized with $NaHCO_3$, and the excess arsenite titrated with standard I_2 ($BrO_3^- + 3H_3AsO_3 \longrightarrow 3H_3AsO_4 + Br^-$; $AsO_3^{3-} + I_2 + 2HCO_3^- \longrightarrow AsO_4^{3-} + 2I^- + 2CO_2 + H_2O$).

Bromate.   Reduced with H_2SO_3 to bromide, which is determined by precipitating with $AgNO_3$ and weighing as AgBr.

CADMIUM

Precipitated as CdS, converted to $CdSO_4$, and weighed as such.

Electrolytically deposited as Cd and weighed as such.

Precipitated as CdS and the precipitate titrated with standard I_2 in the presence of HCl ($\underline{CdS} + I_2 \longrightarrow Cd^{++} + \underline{S} + 2I^-$).

Precipitated as $CdNH_4PO_4 \cdot H_2O$ and weighed as such or ignited and weighed as $Cd_2P_2O_7$.

Precipitated with 8-hydroxyquinoline (oxine) as $Cd(C_9H_6NO)_2 \cdot 2H_2O$ and the precipitate dissolved in HCl. KBr is added and the oxine titrated with $KBrO_3$ as in the case of magnesium (*q.v.*).

CALCIUM

Precipitated as $CaC_2O_4 \cdot H_2O$, ignited at low heat, and weighed as $CaCO_3$.

Precipitated as $CaC_2O_4 \cdot H_2O$, ignited strongly, and weighed as CaO.

Precipitated as $CaC_2O_4 \cdot H_2O$, ignited, moistened with H_2SO_4, reignited, and weighed as $CaSO_4$.

Precipitated as $CaWO_4$ and weighed as such.

Precipitated as $CaC_2O_4 \cdot H_2O$, the precipitate dissolved in dilute H_2SO_4, and the oxalate titrated with standard $KMnO_4$.

Precipitated as $CaC_2O_4 \cdot H_2O$ with a measured amount of oxalate. The precipitate is filtered and the excess oxalate in the filtrate titrated with standard $KMnO_4$.

Precipitated as $CaC_2O_4 \cdot H_2O$, and the ignited material (CaO, or $CaCO_3$, or CaO + $CaCO_3$) titrated with standard acid.

CARBON

In organic compounds. Substance is burned in O_2 and the CO_2 caught in an absorbing agent (e.g., "Ascarite") and weighed.

In iron and steel. Alloy is burned in O_2. The CO_2 is caught in absorbing agent (e.g., "Ascarite") and weighed. Or the CO_2 is caught in a measured volume of standard $Ba(OH)_2$ solution and (1) the $Ba(OH)_2$ filtrate or supernatant liquid titrated with standard acid or (2) the change in conductivity of the $Ba(OH)_2$ is measured.

CO_2 *in carbonates (Alkalimeter method).* Sample is treated with acid in a weighed alkalimeter and the loss in weight measured.

CO_2 *in carbonates.* Sample is treated with acid and the evolved CO_2 caught in an absorbing agent (e.g., "Ascarite") and weighed.

CO_2 *in gas mixture.* CO_2 absorbed in KOH solution and the decrease in volume of gas mixture measured.

CO in gas mixture. CO absorbed in ammoniacal cuprous chloride solution and the decrease in volume of gas mixture measured. Or volume change measured before and after combustion with O_2.

Oxalate. Precipitated as CaC_2O_4, ignited to CaO, or $CaCO_3$, or $CaSO_4$ (see under Calcium), and weighed.

Oxalate. Titrated with standard $KMnO_4$ ($5C_2O_4^= + 2MnO_4^- + 16H^+ \longrightarrow 10CO_2 + 2Mn^{++} + 8H_2O$).

Formate. Titrated in essentially neutral solution with $KMnO_4$ ($3CHO_2^- + 2MnO_4^- + H_2O \longrightarrow 3CO_2 + \underline{2MnO_2} + 5OH^-$).

CERIUM

Precipitated as $Ce(OH)_4$ or $Ce(OH)_3$ or $Ce_2(C_2O_4)_3$, ignited, and weighed as CeO_2.

Precipitated as $Ce(IO_3)_4$, converted to $Ce_2(C_2O_4)_3$, ignited, and weighed as CeO_2 ($2Ce(IO_3)_4 + 24H_2C_2O_4 \longrightarrow \underline{Ce_2(C_2O_4)_3} + 4I_2 + 42CO_2 + 24H_2O$; $2\underline{Ce_2(C_2O_4)_3} + 4O_2 \longrightarrow 4\underline{CeO_2} + 12CO_2$).

Cerous oxidized to ceric with $NaBiO_3$ or $(NH_4)_2S_2O_8$ and excess oxidizing agent removed. Measured amount of $FeSO_4$ added and the excess ferrous titrated with standard $KMnO_4$ ($2Ce^{3+} + \underline{NaBiO_3} + 6H^+ \longrightarrow 2Ce^{4+} + Bi^{3+} + Na^+ + 3H_2O$; $Ce^{4+} + Fe^{++} \longrightarrow Ce^{3+} + Fe^{3+}$).

CHLORINE

Chloride. Precipitated as $AgCl$ and weighed as such.

Chloride (Volhard method). Precipitated as $AgCl$ with measured amount of $AgNO_3$ and the excess Ag^+ titrated with standard $KCNS$ using ferric alum indicator ($Ag^+ + CNS^- \longrightarrow \underline{AgCNS}$).

Chloride. Titrated with standard $AgNO_3$ using dichlorofluorescein or other adsorption indicator.

Chloride (Mohr method). Titrated in neutral solution with standard $AgNO_3$ using K_2CrO_4 indicator.

Free chlorine. Excess KI added and the liberated I_2 titrated with standard $Na_2S_2O_3$ ($Cl_2 + 2I^- \longrightarrow I_2 + 2Cl^-$).

Hypochlorite. Excess KI added in the presence of acid and the liberated I_2 titrated with standard $Na_2S_2O_3$ ($OCl^- + 2I^- + 2H^+ \longrightarrow I_2 + Cl^- + H_2O$).

Hypochlorite. Titrated with standard Na_3AsO_3 using KI + starch as outside indicator ($OCl^- + AsO_3^{3-} \longrightarrow Cl^- + AsO_4^{3-}$).

Chlorate. Reduced to chloride with Zn, $FeSO_4$, or H_2SO_3 and chloride determined gravimetrically as $AgCl$.

Hypochlorite. Reduced to Cl^- with $FeSO_4$ and the chloride determined gravimetrically as $AgCl$.

Chlorate. Excess KI added in the presence of acid and the liberated I_2 titrated with standard $Na_2S_2O_3$ ($ClO_3^- + 6I^- + 6H^+ \longrightarrow Cl^- + 3I_2 + 3H_2O$).

Perchlorate. Precipitated as $KClO_4$ and weighed as such.

CHROMIUM

Chromic ions precipitated with NH_4OH as $Cr(OH)_3$, ignited, and weighed as Cr_2O_3.

Chromate precipitated as $BaCrO_4$ from neutral or buffered acid solution, ignited gently, and weighed as such.

Dichromate reduced with measured amount of $FeSO_4$ and the excess ferrous titrated with standard $KMnO_4$, $K_2Cr_2O_7$, or $Ce(SO_4)_2$.

Dichromate reduced with excess KI and the liberated I_2 titrated with standard $Na_2S_2O_3$ ($Cr_2O_7^= + 6I^- + 14H^+ \longrightarrow 2Cr^{3+} + 3I_2 + 7H_2O$).

Colorimetric. Purple color of chromate with diphenylcarbazide.

COBALT

Electrolytically deposited as Co from ammoniacal solution.

Precipitated with α-nitroso-β-naphthol as $Co[C_{10}H_6O(NO)]_{2-4}$ and the precipitate (1) ignited in O_2 to Co_3O_4 and weighed or (2) ignited in H_2 to Co and weighed.

The naphthol precipitate is digested with $HNO_3 + H_2SO_4$, evaporated, and the cobalt weighed as $CoSO_4$.

Precipitated with 8-hydroxyquinoline (oxine) as $Co(C_9H_6NO)_2 \cdot 2H_2O$ and the precipitate dissolved in HCl. KBr is added and the oxine titrated with $KBrO_3$ as in the case of magnesium (*q.v.*).

Measured amount of NH_4CNS and some pyridine added. Precipitate of $Co(C_5H_5N)_4(CNS)_2$ filtered and the excess CNS^- titrated with standard $AgNO_3$ using ferric indicator.

Colorimetric. Red color with α-nitroso-β-naphthol. Blue color with NH_4CNS + acetone.

COPPER

Electrolytically deposited as Cu.

Precipitated with H_2SO_3 + KCNS and weighed as CuCNS ($2Cu^{++} + H_2SO_3 + 2CNS^- + H_2O \longrightarrow \underline{2CuCNS} + SO_4^= + 4H^+$).

Precipitated with α-benzoinoxime (cupron) and weighed as $Cu(C_{14}H_{11}O_2N)$.

HCl solution passed through silver reductor ($CuCl_4^= + Ag \longrightarrow CuCl_2^- + \underline{AgCl} + Cl^-$) into unmeasured amount of ferric alum ($\overline{Fe^{3+}} + CuCl_2^- + \underline{2Cl^-} \longrightarrow CuCl_4^= + Fe^{++}$) and the reduced iron titrated with standard ceric sulfate using ferroin indicator.

Excess KI added and the liberated I_2 titrated with standard $Na_2S_2O_3$ ($2Cu^{++} + 4I^- \longrightarrow 2\underline{CuI} + I_2$).

Ammoniacal solution titrated with standard KCN to the point of decolorization [$2Cu(NH_3)_4^{++} + 7CN^- + H_2O \longrightarrow 2Cu(CN)_3^= + CNO^- + 6NH_3 + 2NH_4^+$].

Precipitated as CuCNS (see above) and the precipitate titrated with standard KIO_3 forming I_2 which gives a violet color with chloroform ($10\underline{CuCNS} + 14IO_3^- + 14H^+ \longrightarrow 10Cu^{++} + 10SO_4^= + 7I_2 + 10HCN + 2H_2O$). Titration continued to disappearance of this color ($2I_2 + IO_3^- + 10Cl^- + 6H^+ \longrightarrow 5ICl_2^- + 3H_2O$). Net reaction: $4\underline{CuCNS} + 7IO_3^- + 14H^+ + 14Cl^- \longrightarrow 4Cu^{++} + 4SO_4^= + 7ICl_2^- + 4HCN + 5H_2O$.

Colorimetric. Brown color with $K_4Fe(CN)_6$. Blue color with NH_4OH.

CYANIDE

(See under Nitrogen.)

FLUORINE

Precipitated as CaF_2, ignited, and weighed as such.

Precipitated as PbFCl from acid solution and weighed as such.

Precipitated PbClF dissolved in HNO_3 and the chloride determined by the Volhard method (see under Chlorine).

Titrated with standard $Th(NO_3)_4$ using zirconium-alizarin indicator ($4F^- + Th^{4+} \longrightarrow ThF_4$).

Evolved as SiF_4 by action with quartz and concentrated H_2SO_4, the gas absorbed in water, and the solution titrated with standard NaOH using phenolphthalein ($4HF + SiO_2 \longrightarrow SiF_4 + 2H_2O$; $3SiF_4 + 3H_2O \longrightarrow 2H_2SiF_6 + \underline{H_2SiO_3}$; $H_2SiF_6 + 6OH^- \longrightarrow 6F^- + \underline{H_2SiO_3} + 3H_2O$).

Colorimetric. Partial bleaching of orange color of Ti(IV) + H_2O_2.

GOLD

Chemically or electrolytically reduced to Au and weighed as such.

Reduced to metal by measured amount of reducing agent (e.g., oxalate) and excess titrated with standard $KMnO_4$.

Colorimetric. Brown or purple color with $SnCl_2$.

HYDROGEN

Volatilized as water and loss in weight determined.

Volatilized as water and measured by gain in weight of absorbing agent (for example, $CaCl_2$).

Gas analysis.   Absorbed on Pd sponge and loss in volume of gas mixture determined.   Or volume change measured before and after combustion with O_2.

Water.   Sample dissolved in CH_3OH and titrated with Karl Fischer reagent (I_2 + CH_3OH + pyridine + SO_2); (H_2O + I_2 + SO_2 + CH_3OH $\longrightarrow$ $2HI$ + CH_3HSO_4).

Hydrogen peroxide.   Titrated directly with standard $KMnO_4$ ($5H_2O_2$ + $2MnO_4^-$ + $6H^+$ $\longrightarrow$ $5O_2$ + $2Mn^{++}$ + $8H_2O$) or with standard ceric sulfate.

Hydrogen peroxide.   Measured amount of standard Na_3AsO_3 added in presence of NaOH (HO_2^- + AsO_3^{3-} $\longrightarrow$ OH^- + AsO_4^{3-}) and the excess arsenite titrated with KIO_3 using chloroform indicator (see under Arsenic).

Hydrogen peroxide.   Excess KI added in presence of acid and liberated I_2 titrated with thiosulfate (H_2O_2 + $2I^-$ + $2H^+$ $\longrightarrow$ I_2 + $2H_2O$).

Hydrogen peroxide (Colorimetric).   Yellow color with Ti(IV) or with Mo(VI).

IODINE

Iodide.   Precipitated as AgI and weighed as such.

Iodide.   Precipitated as PdI_2 and weighed as such (Br^- and Cl^- not precipitated).

Iodide (Volhard method).   Measured amount of $AgNO_3$ added and the excess Ag^+ titrated with standard KCNS (Ag^+ + CNS^- $\longrightarrow$ AgCNS).

Iodide.   Excess $Fe_2(SO_4)_3$ added, liberated I_2 caught in KI solution and titrated with standard $Na_2S_2O_3$ ($2I^-$ + $2Fe^{3+}$ $\longrightarrow$ I_2 + $2Fe^{++}$) (Br^- and Cl^- not affected).

Iodide.   Excess KIO_3 added in presence of acid and liberated I_2 boiled out.   Excess IO_3^- determined in cooled solution by adding KI and titrating the liberated I_2 with standard $Na_2S_2O_3$ ($5I^-$ + IO_3^- + $6H^+$ $\longrightarrow$ $3I_2$ + $3H_2O$).

Iodide.   Titrated with standard KIO_3 in presence of concentrated HCl using chloroform as indicator. I_2 is first liberated and colors $CHCl_3$ violet.   Color fades away at end point.   Net reaction: $2I^-$ + IO_3^- + $6Cl^-$ + $6H^+$ $\longrightarrow$ $3ICl_2^-$ + $3H_2O$.

Iodide.   Titrated directly with standard $AgNO_3$ using eosin adsorption indicator.

Iodate.   Excess KI added and the liberated I_2 titrated with standard $Na_2S_2O_3$ (IO_3^- + $5I^-$ + $6H^+$ $\longrightarrow$ $3I_2$ + $3H_2O$).

Free iodine.   Titrated with standard $Na_2S_2O_3$ using starch indicator (I_2 + $2S_2O_3^=$ $\longrightarrow$ $2I^-$ + $S_4O_6^=$).

Free iodine.   Titrated with standard Na_3AsO_3 using starch indicator in solution kept nearly neutral with excess $NaHCO_3$ ($I_2 + AsO_3^{3-} + 2HCO_3^- \longrightarrow AsO_4^{3-} + 2I^- + 2CO_2 + H_2O$).

Free iodine.   Titrated with standard KIO_3 in presence of concentrated HCl to formation of iodine chloride and disappearance of violet color of chloroform indicator ($2I_2 + IO_3^- + 6H^+ + 10Cl^- \longrightarrow 5ICl_2^- + 3H_2O$).

Iodate.   Reduced to iodide with H_2SO_3 and precipitated and weighed as AgI.

IRON

Precipitated as $Fe(OH)_3$ with NH_4OH or $NaOH$, ignited, and weighed as Fe_2O_3.

Precipitated with cupferron as $(C_6H_5NONO)_3Fe$ from acid solution, ignited, and weighed as Fe_2O_3.

Ferrous titrated with standard $KMnO_4$, $K_2Cr_2O_7$, or $Ce(SO_4)_2$ (for example, $5Fe^{++} + MnO_4^- + 8H^+ \longrightarrow 5Fe^{3+} + Mn^{++} + 4H_2O$).

Ferric treated with large excess KI and liberated I_2 titrated with standard $Na_2S_2O_3$ ($2Fe^{3+} + 2I^- \longrightarrow I_2 + 2Fe^{++}$).

Ferric titrated with standard $TiCl_3$ solution using KCNS indicator ($Fe^{3+} + Ti^{3+} \longrightarrow Fe^{++} + Ti^{4+}$).

Colorimetric.   Red color with dimethylglyoxime.   Blue color with ferrocyanide.   Amethyst color with salicylic acid.   Red color with KCNS. Red color with *o*-phenanthroline.

LEAD

Precipitated as $PbSO_4$, $PbCrO_4$, or $PbMoO_4$ and weighed as such.

Electrolytically oxidized and deposited as PbO_2, and weighed as such ($Pb^{++} + 2H_2O \longrightarrow PbO_2 + 4H^+ + 2\epsilon$).

Precipitated and weighed as $Pb(IO_3)_2$.

Titrated with standard $(NH_4)_2MoO_4$ using tannin as outside indicator ($Pb^{++} + MoO_4^{=} \longrightarrow PbMoO_4$).

Precipitated as $PbCrO_4$, the precipitate dissolved in acid, and the $Cr_2O_7^{=}$ determined volumetrically as under Chromium above.

Colorimetric.   Red color with dithizone.

MAGNESIUM

Precipitated from ammoniacal solution as $MgNH_4PO_4 \cdot 6H_2O$ and weighed as such, or ignited and weighed as $Mg_2P_2O_7$.

Precipitated with 8-hydroxyquinoline, dried, and weighed as $Mg(C_9H_6NO)_2$.

Precipitated with 8-hydroxyquinoline (oxine) as $Mg(C_9H_6NO)_2 \cdot 2H_2O$ and the precipitate dissolved in HCl. KBr is added and the oxine titrated with $KBrO_3$ to disappearance of color with methyl red or other suitable dye indicator. The dye is oxidized by the excess $KBrO_3 + KBr$ to a colorless product. Net equation for the oxine titration: $3C_9H_6NOH + 2BrO_3^- + 4Br^- + 6H^+ \longrightarrow 3C_9H_4NBr_2OH + 6H_2O$. (See Sec. 12-9.)

MANGANESE

Manganous ions oxidized by $KClO_3$ or $KBrO_3$ to MnO_2. Precipitate ignited in air and weighed as Mn_3O_4.

Precipitated as $MnNH_4PO_4$, ignited, and weighed as $Mn_2P_2O_7$.

Bismuthate method. Oxidized with $NaBiO_3$ or BiO_2 to permanganate. Measured amount of $FeSO_4$ added, and excess ferrous titrated with standard $KMnO_4$ ($2Mn^{++} + 5\underline{NaBiO_3} + 14H^+ \longrightarrow 2MnO_4^- + 5Bi^{3+} + 5Na^+ + 7H_2O$).

Chlorate method. Oxidized with $KClO_3$ in presence of concentrated HNO_3 to MnO_2. Measured amount of $FeSO_4$ added, and the excess ferrous titrated with standard $KMnO_4$ ($\underline{MnO_2} + 2Fe^{++} + 4H^+ \longrightarrow Mn^{++} + 2Fe^{3+} + 2H_2O$).

Persulfate method. Oxidized with $(NH_4)_2S_2O_8$ ($+AgNO_3$) to permanganate, and then titrated with standard Na_3AsO_3 to indefinite valence of $3+$. Arsenite standardized against similar sample containing known Mn.

Volhard method. Manganous ions titrated directly with standard $KMnO_4$ in solution kept neutral with ZnO ($3Mn^{++} + 2MnO_4^- + 2\underline{ZnO} \longrightarrow 5\underline{MnO_2} + 2Zn^{++} + 2H_2O$).

Colorimetric. Purple color of permanganate formed with KIO_4.

MERCURY

Precipitated as HgS and weighed as such.

Electrolytically precipitated as Hg and weighed as such.

Titrated with standard KCNS in absence of chloride using ferric alum indicator [$Hg^{++} + 2CNS^- \longrightarrow Hg(CNS)_2$].

Precipitated as $HgZn(CNS)_4$ with $\underline{ZnSO_4} + NH_4CNS$ and weighed as such.

Precipitated as $Hg_5(IO_6)_2$ with periodate and weighed as such, or the precipitate dissolved in KI + HCl (forming $HgI_4^= + I_2$) and the liberated iodine titrated with standard thiosulfate.

Precipitated as Hg_2Cl_2 and the precipitate titrated with standard KIO_3 in the presence of concentrated HCl ($2Hg_2Cl_2 + IO_3^- + 6H^+ +$

$6Cl^- \longrightarrow 4HgCl_2 + ICl_2^- + 3H_2O$). Free I_2 is formed as an intermediate product and gives a violet color with chloroform indicator. Titration is to disappearance of this color.

MOLYBDENUM

Precipitated as $PbMoO_4$ and weighed as such.

Precipitated as Hg_2MoO_4 or as MoS_3, ignited, and weighed as MoO_3.

Precipitated with α-benzoinoxime (cupron), ignited, and weighed as MoO_3.

Precipitated with 8-hydroxyquinoline and weighed as $MoO_2(C_9H_6NO)_2$.

Reduced from valence 6 to 5 with silver reductor and titrated with standard ceric sulfate, using ferroin indicator.

Reduced with Zn and passed directly into ferric alum. The solution is then titrated with standard $KMnO_4$. The molybdenum is reduced by the Zn to Mo(3). Ferric ions oxidize it to Mo(5), and the permanganate oxidizes the reduced iron to ferric and the Mo(5) to Mo(6).

Colorimetric. Red color with $SnCl_2$ + KCNS. Red-brown color with tannic acid. Red-brown color with NH_4OH + H_2O_2.

NICKEL

Precipitated with dimethylglyoxime as $[(CH_3)_2 \cdot CNOH \cdot CNO]_2Ni$ and weighed as such.

Electrolytically precipitated as Ni and weighed as such.

Measured amount of KCN added to ammoniacal solution and the excess CN^- titrated with standard $AgNO_3$ using KI indicator $[Ni(NH_3)_6^{++} + 4CN^- \longrightarrow Ni(CN)_4^= + 6NH_3; 2CN^- + Ag^+ \longrightarrow Ag(CN)_2^-]$.

Measured amount of NH_4CNS and some pyridine added. Precipitate of $Ni(C_5H_5N)_4(CNS)_2$ filtered, and the excess CNS^- titrated with standard $AgNO_3$, using ferric indicator.

Precipitated with 8-hydroxyquinoline (oxine) as $Ni(C_9H_6NO)_2 \cdot 2H_2O$, and the precipitate dissolved in HCl. KBr is added and the oxine titrated with $KBrO_3$ as in the case of magnesium (*q.v.*).

Colorimetric. Red color with dimethylglyoxime. Red color with thiocarbonate. Blue color with NH_4OH. Red color with dithiooxalate.

NITROGEN

Organic nitrogen (Kjeldahl method). Converted by digestion with concentrated H_2SO_4 + catalyst to NH_4HSO_4. Excess NaOH is then added, the liberated NH_3 distilled into measured amount of acid, and the excess acid titrated with standard NaOH using methyl red indicator.

Ammonium.   Excess NaOH added, the liberated NH_3 distilled into measured amount of acid, and the excess acid titrated with standard NaOH using methyl red indicator.

Ammonium.   Precipitated as $(NH_4)_2PtCl_6$ and weighed as such, or ignited to Pt.

Nitrate, nitrite.   Reduced to NH_4^+ with Zn or with Devarda alloy; then by Kjeldahl method above.

Nitrite.   Titrated with standard $KMnO_4$ ($5NO_2^- + 2MnO_4^- + 6H^+ \longrightarrow 5NO_3^- + 2Mn^{++} + 3H_2O$).

Cyanide.   Precipitated with $AgNO_3$ as $Ag[Ag(CN)_2]$ and weighed as such.

Cyanide (Volhard method).   Measured amount of $AgNO_3$ added and the excess Ag^+ titrated with standard KCNS using ferric alum indicator ($2CN^- + 2Ag^+ \longrightarrow \underline{Ag[Ag(CN)_2]}$).

Cyanide (Liebig method).   Titrated with standard $AgNO_3$ to faint turbidity of $\underline{Ag[Ag(CN)_2]}$ [$2CN^- + Ag^+ \longrightarrow Ag(CN)_2^-$].

Gas analysis.   Volume of residual nitrogen measured after absorbing other gases.

Ammonium (Colorimetric).   Orange color with K_2HgI_4 + KOH (Nessler's reagent).

Nitrate (Colorimetric).   Blue color with diphenylamine or with diphenylbenzidine.

Nitrite (Colorimetric).   Red color with sulfanilic acid + α-naphthylamine.

OXALATE

(See under Carbon.)

OXYGEN

Gas analysis.   Volume of gas mixture determined before and after absorbing in alkaline pyrogallol.

PHOSPHORUS

Phosphate.   Precipitated as $MgNH_4PO_4 \cdot 6H_2O$, ignited to $Mg_2P_2O_7$, and weighed.

Phosphite.   Treated with $HgCl_2$ and the precipitated Hg_2Cl_2 weighed ($H_3PO_3 + 2HgCl_2 + H_2O \longrightarrow \underline{Hg_2Cl_2} + H_3PO_4 + 2Cl^- + 2H^+$).

Phosphite.   Oxidized with HNO_3 and determined as in the case of phosphate.

Iron and steel.   Precipitated as $(NH_4)_3PO_4 \cdot 12MoO_3$ and weighed as such, or ignited and weighed as $P_2O_5 \cdot 24MoO_3$.

Iron and steel (Ferric alum method).   Precipitated as $(NH_4)_3PO_4 \cdot 12MoO_3$, dissolved, the Mo reduced with Zn in a reductor and passed directly into excess ferric alum.   The solution is then titrated with standard $KMnO_4$.   The molybdenum is reduced by the Zn to Mo(3).   Ferric ions oxidize it to Mo(5), and the permanganate oxidizes the reduced iron to ferric and the Mo(5) to Mo(6).

Iron and steel (Blair method).   As in the preceding method except that the reduced solution is caught in an open flask where slight oxidation by the air occurs.   The Mo, now having an average valence corresponding to the oxide $Mo_{24}O_{37}$, is titrated to $MoO_4^=$ with standard $KMnO_4$.

Iron and steel (Alkalimetric method).   Precipitated as $(NH_4)_3PO_4 \cdot 12MoO_3$, dissolved in a measured amount of standard NaOH, and the excess alkali titrated with standard HNO_3 using phenolphthalein indicator.   Net   reaction: $(NH_4)_3PO_4 \cdot 12MoO_3 + 23OH^- \longrightarrow 12MoO_4^= + HPO_4^= + 3NH_4^+ + 11H_2O$.

Phosphate (Colorimetric).   Yellow color with ammonium molybdate $+ HNO_3$.

PLATINUM

Precipitated as K_2PtCl_6 and weighed as such.

Precipitated as $(NH_4)_2PtCl_6$ and weighed as such, or ignited to Pt and weighed.

Electrolytically reduced to Pt and weighed as such.

Reduced by formic acid to Pt and weighed as such.

POTASSIUM

Precipitated as K_2PtCl_6 and weighed as such, or the precipitate reduced to Pt and weighed, or the precipitate ignited and weighed as Pt + 2KCl.

Precipitated as $KClO_4$ and weighed as such.

Small amounts precipitated as $K_2Na[Co(NO_2)_6] \cdot H_2O$ and weighed in the anhydrous form or determined by adding measured amount of standard $KMnO_4$ and back-titrating with standard oxalate $(5K_2Na[Co(NO_2)_6] + 11MnO_4^- + 28H^+ \longrightarrow 10K^+ + 5Na^+ + 5Co^{++} + 30NO_3^- + 11Mn^{++} + 14H_2O)$.

Precipitated as $(C_6H_5)_4BK$ with tetraphenylboron salt and weighed as such.

Precipitated as $(C_6H_5)_4BK$, ignited in air, and the resulting KBO_2 titrated with standard acid.

SELENIUM

Reduced by H_2SO_3, KI, etc., to Se and weighed as such.

Selenious acid treated with measured amount of $KMnO_4$, and the excess permanganate titrated with standard $FeSO_4$ ($5H_2SeO_3 + 2MnO_4^- \longrightarrow 5SeO_4^= + 2Mn^{++} + 4H^+ + 3H_2O$).

Selenious acid treated with KI, and the liberated I_2 titrated with standard thiosulfate ($H_2SeO_3 + 4I^- + 4H^+ \longrightarrow \underline{Se} + 2I_2 + 3H_2O$).

Selenious acid treated with measured amount of thiosulfate and the excess titrated with standard iodine ($H_2SeO_3 + 4S_2O_3^= + 4H^+ \longrightarrow S_4SeO_6^= + S_4O_6^= + 3H_2O$).

Colorimetric.   Red color with KI + acid.

SILICON

Precipitated as H_2SiO_3, ignited to SiO_2, and weighed.   The impure SiO_2 is then treated with HF, evaporated, reignited, and impurities are weighed.   Loss in weight = $\underline{SiO_2}$ ($SiO_2 + 4HF \longrightarrow SiF_4 + 2H_2O$).

SILVER

Precipitated as AgCl and weighed as such.

Volhard method.   Titrated with standard KCNS using ferric alum indicator ($Ag^+ + CNS^- \longrightarrow \underline{AgCNS}$).

Titrated with standard NaCl using dichlorofluorescein as an adsorption indicator.

SODIUM

Silicates (J. Lawrence Smith method).   Silicate decomposed by heating with $CaCO_3 + NH_4Cl$.   Leached with water, Ca^{++} removed, filtrate evaporated, and residue ignited.   NaCl + KCl weighed.   K then determined as $KClO_4$ or K_2PtCl_6.   Na determined by difference.

Small amounts.   Precipitated as $NaZn(UO_2)_3(C_2H_3O_2)_9 \cdot 6H_2O$ or as $NaMg(UO_2)_3(C_2H_3O_2)_9 \cdot 6\frac{1}{2}H_2O$ and weighed as such.

STRONTIUM

Precipitated as $SrSO_4$ and weighed as such.

Precipitated as the oxalate, $SrC_2O_4 \cdot H_2O$, ignited to SrO, and weighed as such.

SULFUR

Sulfate.   Precipitated as $BaSO_4$ and weighed as such.

Sulfate (Hinman method).   Excess acid solution of $BaCrO_4$ added ($SO_4^= + Ba^{++}CrO_4^= \longrightarrow BaSO_4 + CrO_4^=$).   Excess NH_4OH added to precipitate excess $BaCrO_4$.   Combined $BaSO_4 + BaCrO_4$ filtered.   Filtrate acidified, treated with excess KI, and liberated I_2 titrated with standard $Na_2S_2O_3$ ($Cr_2O_7^= + 6I^- + 14H^+ \longrightarrow 2Cr^{3+} + 3I_2 + 7H_2O$).   In the titration each $Cr_2O_7^=$ is equivalent to $2SO_4^=$.

Sulfate.   Precipitated with benzidine hydrochloride giving $C_{12}H_8(NH_2)_2 \cdot H_2SO_4$.   Suspension of precipitate titrated with standard NaOH which acts only on the H_2SO_4.

Sulfide (Evolution method for alloys).   Evolved as H_2S by action of HCl and caught in ammoniacal solution of $ZnSO_4$.   The solution is acidified and the H_2S titrated with standard I_2 or standard KIO_3 + KI using starch indicator ($H_2S + I_2 \longrightarrow S + 2H^+ + 2I^-$).

Sulfide.   Oxidized to sulfate, precipitated as $BaSO_4$, and weighed.

Sulfite.   Oxidized with Br_2 or with $H_2O_2 + NH_4OH$, precipitated as $BaSO_4$ and weighed as such.

Sulfite.   Titrated with standard I_2 using starch indicator ($SO_3^= + H_2O + I_2 \longrightarrow SO_4^= + 2I^- + 2H^+$).

Peroxydisulfate.   Measured amount of $FeSO_4$ added and excess ferrous titrated with standard $KMnO_4$ ($S_2O_8^= + 2Fe^{++} \longrightarrow 2SO_4^= + 2Fe^{3+}$).

Thiosulfate.   Titrated with standard I_2 ($2S_2O_3^= + I_2 \longrightarrow S_4O_6^= + 2I^-$).

Thiocyanate.   Measured amount of $AgNO_3$ added and excess Ag^+ titrated with standard KCNS ($CNS^- + Ag^+ \longrightarrow AgCNS$).

Thiocyanate.   Precipitated as $Cu_2(CNS)_2$ with $H_2SO_3 + CuSO_4$ and weighed as such.

Thiocyanate.   Titrated with standard $AgNO_3$ using adsorption indicator as in the case of chloride and bromide.

Hyposulfite.   Ammoniacal $AgNO_3$ added [$S_2O_4^= + 2Ag(NH_3)_2^+ + 2H_2O \longrightarrow 2Ag + 2SO_3^= + 4NH_4^+$].   The precipitated silver is dissolved in HNO_3 and titrated with standard KCNS using ferric alum indicator.

Thiocyanate (Colorimetric).   Red color with ferric ions.

THORIUM

Precipitated as $Th(C_4H_8CO_2)_2$ with sebacic acid, ignited, and weighed as ThO_2.

Precipitated as $Th(IO_3)_4$, converted to oxalate, ignited to ThO_2, and weighed as such.

Precipitated as oxalate, $Th(C_2O_4)_2$, ignited, and weighed as ThO_2.

TIN

Precipitated as H_2SnO_3 by hydrolysis, ignited, and weighed as SnO_2.

Precipitated as SnS_2, ignited, and weighed as SnO_2.

In alloys.   Alloy treated with HNO_3 leaving H_2SnO_3 as residue.   This is ignited to SnO_2 and weighed.   ($3\underline{Sn} + 4NO_3^- + 4H^+ + H_2O \longrightarrow 3H_2SnO_3 + 4NO$).

Precipitated with cupferron, ignited, and weighed as SnO_2.

Titrated from valence 2 to 4 with standard $KBrO_3$ ($+KBr$) in HCl solution to disappearance of color of methyl red or other suitable dye indicator.   The dye is oxidized by the excess $KBrO_3 + KBr$ to a colorless product.   Net titration equation: $3Sn^{++} + BrO_3^- + 6H^+ + 18Cl^- \longrightarrow 3SnCl_6^= + Br^- + 3H_2O$.

Titrated from valence 2 to 4 in cold HCl solution in current of CO_2 with standard I_2 ($Sn^{++} + I_2 + 6Cl^- \longrightarrow SnCl_6^= + 2I^-$).

Titrated to yellow color with standard $FeCl_3$ ($Sn^{++} + 2FeCl_4^- \longrightarrow SnCl_6^= + 2Fe^{++} + 2Cl^-$).

Titrated with standard KIO_3 in presence of concentrated HCl, with chloroform indicator.   Titration is to disappearance of purple color caused by intermediate formation of free iodine.   Net reaction: $2Sn^{++} + IO_3^- + 6H^+ + 14Cl^- \longrightarrow 2SnCl_6^= + ICl_2^- + 3H_2O$.

TITANIUM

Precipitated as $Ti(OH)_4$, ignited, and weighed as TiO_2.

Precipitated with cupferron, ignited, and weighed as TiO_2.

Reduced by Zn (but not reduced by $SnCl_2$) to Ti^{3+} and titrated with standard $KMnO_4$, or passed from zinc reductor into ferric alum and the reduced iron titrated with standard $KMnO_4$ ($2Ti^{4+} + \underline{Zn} \longrightarrow 2Ti^{3+} + Zn^{++}$; $5Ti^{3+} + MnO_4^- + 8H^+ \longrightarrow 5Ti^{4+} + Mn^{++} + 4H_2O$).

Reduced to Ti^{3+} and titrated with standard ferric alum using NH_4CNS indicator ($Ti^{3+} + Fe^{3+} \longrightarrow Ti^{4+} + Fe^{++}$).

Precipitated with 8-hydroxyquinoline (oxine) as $TiO(C_9H_6NO)_2$ and weighed as such, or dissolved in HCl and the liberated oxine titrated in the presence of KBr with standard $KBrO_3$ as in the case of magnesium (*q.v.*).

Colorimetric.   Yellow color with H_2O_2 + acid.   Red color with thymol.

TUNGSTEN

Precipitated with acid as H_2WO_4 or with cinchonine as cinchonine tungstate, ignited, and weighed as WO_3.

Precipitated with 8-hydroxyquinoline (oxine) and weighed as $WO_2(C_9H_6NO)_2$, or the oxine in the precipitate liberated and determined volumetrically with standard $KBrO_3$ as with magnesium (*q.v.*).

Reduced from valence 6 to 3 with hot lead amalgam and titrated back to 6 with standard $KMnO_4$.

URANIUM

Precipitated with NH_4OH as $(NH_4)_2U_2O_7$, ignited in air, and weighed as U_3O_8.

Reduced from valence 6 to 4 with Zn and precipitated with cupferron.   The precipitate ignited in air to U_3O_8 and weighed as such.

Precipitated as $UO_2NH_4PO_4$, ignited, and weighed as $(UO_2)_2P_2O_7$.

Reduced with Zn and titrated back with standard $KMnO_4$ (UO_2^{++} +

$Zn + 4H^+ \longrightarrow U^{4+} + Zn^{++} + 2H_2O$; $5U^{4+} + 2MnO_4^- + 2H_2O \longrightarrow 5UO_2^{++} + 2Mn^{++} + 4H^+$).

Colorimetric.   Orange color with $NaOH + Na_2O_2$.

VANADIUM

Precipitated as $HgVO_3$, ignited, and weighed as V_2O_5.

Precipitated as $Pb(VO_3)_2$, fumed with H_2SO_4, filtered, ignited, and weighed as V_2O_5.

Measured amount of KI added to HCl solution of vanadate ($2H_3VO_4 + 2I^- + 6H^+ \longrightarrow 2VO^{++} + I_2 + 6H_2O$).   The excess iodide plus the liberated iodine titrated with standard KIO_3 using chloroform indicator (see under Iodine).   Equation for net reaction: $4H_3VO_4 + 4I^- + IO_3^- + 18H^+ + 10Cl^- \longrightarrow 4VO^{++} + 5ICl_2^- + 15H_2O$.

Reduced from valence 5 to 4 by SO_2 or H_2S and titrated back with standard $KMnO_4$ ($2VO_3^- + SO_2 + 4H^+ \longrightarrow 2VO^{++} + SO_4^- + 2H_2O$; $5VO^{++} + MnO_4^- + 6H_2O \longrightarrow 5VO_3^- + Mn^{++} + 12H^+$).

Colorimetric.   Red color with H_2O_2 + acid.   Violet color with strychnine.

ZINC

Precipitated as ZnS, ignited, and weighed as ZnO.

Precipitated as $ZnNH_4PO_4$ and weighed as such or ignited to $Zn_2P_2O_7$ and weighed.

Reduced electrolytically in NaOH solution to Zn and weighed as such.

Precipitated with 8-hydroxyquinoline (oxine) and the precipitate dissolved in HCl.   The liberated oxine titrated with standard $KBrO_3$ as in the case of magnesium (*q.v.*).

Titrated with standard $K_4Fe(CN)_6$ using $Fe_2(SO_4)_3$ as internal indicator or $UO_2(NO_3)_2$ as external indicator.   The net equation is: $3Zn^{++}$ + $2Fe(CN)_6^{4-} + 2K^+ \longrightarrow \underline{K_2Zn_3[Fe(CN)_6]_2}$.

Colorimetric.   Blue color with NH_4OH + resorcinol.

ZIRCONIUM

Precipitated as $Zr(OH)_4$, ignited, and weighed as ZrO_2.

Precipitated with cupferron or phenyl-arsonic acid, ignited, and weighed as ZrO_2.

Precipitated with H_2SeO_3 as $ZrOSeO_3$, ignited, and weighed as ZrO_2.

Precipitated as $Zr(HPO_4)_2$, ignited, and weighed as ZrP_2O_7.

EIGHT
Miscellaneous Problems

Miscellaneous Problems

The problems in this section are mostly of the "noninstrumental" type, and many of them are of a composite nature in that they involve more than one type of calculation. The first group pertains to mathematical principles ordinarily taken up in elementary courses in qualitative analysis; the remaining problems pertain mostly to quantitative determinations of specific elements and substances. Problems to which answers are given in Part IX are indicated by asterisks.

I. QUALITATIVE ANALYSIS

*A-1.   A neutral soln. contg. 0.0170 g of dissolved $AgNO_3$ is treated with 6.00 ml of 0.100 N HCl, and the pptd. AgCl is filtered off and washed with water. (a) How many meq., how many g ions, and how many g of Cl^- are present in the filtrate? (b) How many ml of NH_4OH (sp. gr. 0.960, contg. 9.90% NH_3 by wt.) would theoretically be required to neutralize the acid in the filtrate? (c) What is the normality of this NH_4OH? (d) If the above pptd. AgCl is suspended in H_2O at a certain temp. and the soly. product of AgCl at that temp. is A, what (in terms of A) would be the molar concn. of Ag^+ ions in the satd. soln.? (e) How many ml of 0.200 N NH_4OH would theoretically be required to dissolve the AgCl to form the complex ammino ion? (f) What is the pH value of the 0.200 N NH_4OH?

*A-2.   Given: 17.0 mg $AgNO_3$, 26.2 mg $HgNO_3$, and 5.00 millimoles of HNO_3, all in aq. soln. (a) How many ml of 1.00 N NH_4Cl are required to ppt. all the Ag and Hg as AgCl and Hg_2Cl_2? (b) How many ml of NH_4OH contg. 1.00 mole of dissolved NH_3 per liter are required to neutralize the acid in the filtrate from these ppts.? (c) What total vol. of the NH_4OH is theoretically required to dissolve the AgCl and form Hg + $HgNH_2Cl$ with the Hg_2Cl_2? (d) What is the soly. product of Hg_2Cl_2 if its soly. is A moles/liter?

A-3.   To a soln. contg. 50.0 mg of Ag^+ and 50.0 mg of Pb^{++} is added sufficient NH_4Cl to give ppts. of AgCl and $PbCl_2$ and make the surrounding soln. 0.500 N in Cl^- ions. If the vol. of the soln. is 30.0 ml and the soly. products of AgCl and $PbCl_2$

are 1.0×10^{-10} and 2.4×10^{-4}, respectively, how many mg of Ag and of Pb will remain unpptd.? How many ml of boiling water are required to dissolve the pptd. $PbCl_2$ if its satd. soln. at that temp. is $0.120 M$? How many mg of AgCl would be dissolved by this treatment if its soly. at 100°C is 0.150 millimole/liter?

A-4. (a) How many ml of $2.00 M$ NH_4Cl soln. would be required to ppt. all the Ag from a soln. contg. 85.0 mg of dissolved $AgNO_3$? (b) How many millimoles and how many mg of NH_4Cl does each ml of the reagent contain? (c) How many ml of $5.00 N$ NH_4Cl should be taken in order to prepare 500 ml of the $2.00 M$ soln. by dilution with water?

A-5. If the AgCl in the preceding problem is dissolved in $0.300 N$ NH_4OH, (a) how many ml are theoretically required? (b) How many mg of dissolved NH_3 are in the required amt. of soln.? (c) How many g ions of Cl^- are in the resulting soln. of AgCl? (d) Express by symbols the dissociation const. of the complex ion in the soln. (e) What is the pH value of the $0.300 N$ NH_4OH?

A-6. In qualitative separations, an equimolar mixt. of Hg and $HgNH_2Cl$ is sometimes dissolved in $KBrO_3$ + HCl. (a) Write ionic equations for the reactions taking place, assuming the principal products to be NH_4^+, $HgCl_4^=$, and $HgBr_4^=$. (b) How many millimoles of $KBrO_3$ in the presence of acid are theoretically required to dissolve the ppt. obtained by adding an excess of NH_4OH to 1.00 millimole of Hg_2Cl_2?

*A-7. (a) If pptn. of sulfides is carried out in a soln. $0.300 N$ in H^+, what is the pH value, and what is the hydroxyl-ion concn. of the soln.? (b) If 0.100 millimole of $CdSO_4$ is present in 10.0 ml of the acid soln. and H_2S is added to ppt. all the Cd, what would be the pH value of the soln. after filtering off the ppt., boiling out the H_2S, and diluting to 100 ml.?

*A-8. Thioacetamide is sometimes used as a substitute for H_2S in the pptn. of sulfides, and in hot soln. its decomposition can be assumed to be essentially $CH_3CSNH_2 + 2H_2O \longrightarrow H_2S + NH_4^+ + CH_3COO^-$. Each ml of a 5.00% soln. of the amide (sp. gr. of the soln. = 1.01) would provide the equiv. of how many ml of H_2S gas under standard conditions of temp. and pressure?

If a soln. contg. dil. HCl and $CuSO_4$ is treated with thioacetamide and the soln. boiled to ppt. all the Cu and to remove excess H_2S, show from mass-action principles why the pH value of the resulting supernatant liquid would be somewhat greater than it would be if H_2S gas were used as the pptg. agent, all other conditions being the same.

*A-9. If 15.0 ml of a soln. is $2.00 M$ in H^+ ions, is $2.00 M$ in Cl^- ions, and contains 30.0 mg atoms of Bi(III), it is found that the concn. of Bi^{3+} ions is only $1.25 \times 10^{-21} M$ because of the formation of $BiCl_4^-$ ions. (a) What is the dissociation const. of the $BiCl_4^-$ ion? (b) If a soln. of the same acidity were made $0.100 M$ in H_2S, what would be the sulfide-ion concn.?

*A-10. (a) How many ml of H_2SO_4 (sp. gr. 1.14, contg. 19.6% H_2SO_4 by wt.) are theoretically required to ppt. 10.0 mg of Pb^{++}? (b) What is the normality of the above acid, and what is its composition in terms of percentage of combined SO_3? (c) How many f. wts. of ammonium acetate would be required to dissolve the ppt.

of $PbSO_4$?   (d) If the latter soln. were diluted to 50.0 ml, what would be its normality in terms of lead acetate and its molarity in terms of ammonium sulfate?   (e) How many ml of $K_2Cr_2O_7$ (0.100 N as a potassium salt) would be required to convert all the lead acetate to a ppt. of $PbCrO_4$?

*A-11.   Mercuric sulfide dissolves in a soln. of Na_2S + NaOH (HgS + S= $\longrightarrow$ $HgS_2^=$) but not in a soln. of $(NH_4)_2S$ + NH_4OH.   This is due to the difference in the degree of hydrolysis of the sulfide ion: $S^= + H_2O \longrightarrow HS^- + OH^-$.   Calculate the numerical value of the mass-action hydrolysis const. $[HS^-][OH^-]/[S^=]$ by combining appropriate ionization consts.

A-12.   In the pptn. of the copper-tin groups from acid soln. with H_2S, oxidizing agents like permanganate ions and ferric ions are reduced by the H_2S and the H_2S is oxidized to free sulfur.   (a) Write each of these two redox reactions as the difference between two half-cell reactions, and calculate the no. of millimoles and the no. of mg of $KMnO_4$ and of $FeCl_3$ thus reduced by 10.0 ml of H_2S gas (measured under standard conditions).   (b) In a similar reaction of H_2S with hypochlorite ions (which are reduced to chloride ions) write the equations for the half-cell reactions. (c) If the standard potential of chloride-hypochlorite in the presence of acid is A volts, what (in terms of A) is the chloride-hypochlorite potential in a soln. 0.10 M in Cl^-, 0.0010 M in OCl^-, and 0.50 M in H^+?

A-13.   Separation of As_2S_3 from PbS can be effected by a soln. of Na_2S + NaOH. Calculate the no. of millimoles of Na_2S theoretically required if the original mixt. consists of 0.200 millimole of each of the two sulfides.   How many ml of 6.00 N HNO_3 would theoretically be required to dissolve the residual sulfide, assuming reduction of nitrate to NO gas and oxidation of sulfide sulfur to the elementary form.

A-14.   (a) How many ml of 0.100 N $MgCl_2$ soln. are theoretically required to ppt. the As as $MgNH_4AsO_4$ from 10.0 ml of a soln. of Na_3AsO_4 that is 0.100 N as a sodium salt and contains excess NH_4Cl, NH_4OH, and no other solutes?   (b) How many ml of 0.100 M H_2S soln. would be required to ppt. the As as As_2S_5 from a similar soln. after acidification?   (c) How many g of magnesium pyroarsenate can be obtained by igniting the above $MgNH_4AsO_4$ ppt.?

A-15.   (a) Balance the following equation, and express it as the difference between two half-cell reactions: $HgS + ClO_3^- + Cl^- \longrightarrow HgCl_4^= + SO_4^=$.   (b) Assume that 0.233 g of HgS is dissolved according to this equation and the soln. diluted to 50.0 ml.   If excess chloride ions are present in sufficient amt. to make the chloride-ion concn. 0.510 M, how many mg of mercury are present as simple Hg^{++} ions?   (Dissociation const. of $HgCl_4^= = 1.0 \times 10^{-16}$.)

*A-16.   (a) From the soly. products of $Mg(OH)_2$ and $Fe(OH)_3$, calculate the no. of g of Fe^{3+} that can remain dissolved in 100 ml of a soln. of such alkalinity that 243 mg of Mg^{++} will just fail to ppt. as $Mg(OH)_2$.   (b) If, in pptg. the $(NH_4)_2S$ group, the vol. of the soln. is 100 ml and is 0.100 M in dissolved NH_3 and 1.00 M in NH_4^+ ions, how many g of Mg^{++} and of Fe^{3+} can remain unprecipitated as hydroxides?   (c) What is the pH value of the soln., and what color would be given to the soln. by cresol red indicator?

*A-17.   (a) What is the molarity of a soln. of $CrCl_3$ which is 0.10 N as a salt? (b) How many meq. of the salt are present in each ml?   (c) If the Cr is oxidized to dichromate and the vol. of the soln. is twice as great as before, what is the normality as a sodium salt of the $Na_2Cr_2O_7$ present?   (d) How many millimoles of $FeSO_4 \cdot 7H_2O$ are required to reduce the dichromate in 1.00 ml of this soln. to Cr(III) ions in the presence of acid?   (e) Write the ionic equation for the last reaction as the difference between two half-cell reactions.   (f) What (in terms of letters) is the potential between Cr^{3+} ions and $Cr_2O_7^=$ ions in a soln. that is A M in the former, B M in the latter, and C M in H^+ ions?

A-18.   A soln. contains 0.286 g of dissolved $Fe_2(SO_4)_3 \cdot 9H_2O$ in 500 ml.   (a) What is the normality of the soln. as a ferric salt?   (b) What is its normality as a sulfate? (c) How many ml of 3.00 N NH_4OH are required to ppt. all the Fe as $Fe(OH)_3$? (d) How many ml of a soln. contg. 0.333 millimole of $BaCl_2 \cdot 2H_2O$ per ml are required to ppt. all the sulfate?   (e) What is the normality of the $BaCl_2$ soln.?   (f) How many ml of H_2SO_4 (sp. gr. 1.20) are theoretically required to dissolve the pptd. $Fe(OH)_3$? (g) What are the normality and molarity of the H_2SO_4?

A-19.   Starting with 0.010 g ion of Zn^{++}, how many millimoles of NH_3 are theoretically required to form the complex ammonio ion?   If three times this amount of NH_3 is used and the total vol. is 250 ml, what is the molar concn. of Zn^{++}?

A-20.   In the analysis of the $(NH_4)_2S$ group, H_2O_2 is often used in the presence of acid to oxidize ferrous ions and to reduce MnO_2.   (a) Express each reaction as the difference between two half-cell reactions.   (b) In the latter reaction how many ml of O_2 gas (standard conditions) are evolved by excess H_2O_2 on that wt. of MnO_2 that furnishes in the reaction a sufficient amt. of Mn^{++} ions to give with BiO_2 0.0119 g of MnO_4^- ions?   (c) Combine the two half-cell reactions involving H_2O_2 to give the equation for the disproportionation of H_2O_2.

A-21.   (a) If the action of KNO_2 in the presence of acetic acid gives with $CoCl_2$ a ppt. of $K_3Co(NO_2)_6$ plus NO gas, what fraction of the reacting KNO_2 serves as an oxidizing agent?   (b) Express in symbols the soly. product of the ppt. and the dissociation const. of the complex ion present in the soln. of the small amt. of the ppt. that dissolves.

*A-22.   A soln. is 0.030 F in Sr^{++} ions.   (a) What value must the chromate-ion concn. have in order for $SrCrO_4$ to start pptg. (soly. product of $SrCrO_4 = 3.0 \times 10^{-5}$)? (b) How many g of Ba^{++} could remain dissolved in each ml of such a soln. (soly. product of $BaCrO_4 = 3.0 \times 10^{-10}$)?   (c) The mass-action const. for the equilibrium $2CrO_4^= + 2H^+ \rightleftharpoons Cr_2O_7^= + H_2O$ is 4.2×10^{14}. If the above soln. contains sufficient $HC_2H_3O_2$ and $NH_4C_2H_3O_2$ to give a pH value of 5.0, what would be the dichromate-ion concn.?

*A-23.   (a) How many ml of a soln. of $K_2Cr_2O_7$ which is 0.100 N as a K salt would be required to ppt. 0.00100 g atom of Ba as $BaCrO_4$?   (b) If 50 ml of the $K_2Cr_2O_7$ was reduced by SO_2 in the presence of HCl and the resulting soln. diluted to 100 ml, what would be the normality of the soln. as a chromic salt, and what would be the normality of the soln. in sulfate ions that it now contains?

A-24.   (a) How many g of $CaCl_2$ should be taken to prepare 100 ml of 0.20 N soln.? (b) How many millimoles of $H_2C_2O_4 \cdot 2H_2O$ would be required to ppt. all the Ca? (c) How many g atoms of Mg could theoretically be held as $Mg(C_2O_4)_{\overline{2}}$ by this amt. of oxalic acid?   (d) If the Ca ppt. is ignited to $CaCO_3$, how many ml of gas (measured over H_2O at 750 mm and 20°C) would be given off?   (e) If A ml of HCl is required to neutralize the $CaCO_3$ obtained by this ignition, what vol. (in terms of A) of H_2SO_4 of the same normality as the HCl would be required to neutralize the CaO obtained by strong ignition of the $CaCO_3$?

A-25.   (a) How many g of NH_3 would be liberated from 1.00 g equiv. wt. of $(NH_4)_2SO_4$ by the action of NaOH?   (b) If this NH_3 were absorbed in H_2O and diluted to 1 liter, what would be the normality and the approx. sp. gr. of the soln.?   (c) How many ml of 3.40 M H_2SO_4 would it neutralize?

*A-26.   In preparing a soln. for anion analysis, a solid is boiled with Na_2CO_3 soln. (a) If 1.00 g of CaF_2 is so treated with 50 ml of a soln. 3 N in $CO_{\overline{3}}$ ions and then cooled to 20°C and the undecomposed CaF_2 filtered off, what would be the molar concn. of F^- ions in the filtrate?   (b) What percentage of the original salt is shown to have been metathesized?   Assume conditions of equilibrium.

A-27.   (a) Complete and balance the following: $NO_3^- + Al + OH^- \longrightarrow NH_3 + AlO_2^-$.   (b) Also write it as the difference between two half-cell reactions.   (c) If 250 mg of $NaNO_3$ is reduced as above with excess Al in the presence of NaOH, how many ml of $N/2$ H_2SO_4 would be required to neutralize the NH_3 liberated?   (d) How many g atoms of Al are theoretically required for the reduction?

A-28.   (a) If 100 mg of sodium oxalate, $Na_2C_2O_4$, is heated with concd. H_2SO_4, what vol. of mixed gases would be obtained when measured over H_2O at 753 mm pressure and 25°C?   ($Na_2C_2O_4 + H_2SO_4 \longrightarrow Na_2SO_4 + CO + CO_2 + H_2O$.) (b) What vol. of gas would be obtained (under the same conditions of temp. and pressure as above) if the 100 mg of sodium oxalate was treated with excess $KMnO_4$ in the presence of dil. H_2SO_4?

II.   QUANTITATIVE ANALYSIS

WATER.   HYDROGEN PEROXIDE

*A-29.   A manufacturer purchased 130 tons of material at (0.20 × % A) cents/lb, on a guarantee of 10.00% A.   The material was shipped in cars, and on arrival the manufacturer had it analyzed.   The chemist reported 10.46% A but neglected to state that he had dried the sample.   The manufacturer paid on a 10% basis, figuring that he had made money.   In reality he lost $520.   What was the percentage of moisture in the material?

*A-30.   A sample of $BaCl_2 \cdot 2H_2O$ + NaCl loses 10.00% of its wt. on strong ignition. (a) What is the percentage of NaCl in the sample?   (b) If the H_2O from a 0.100-g sample of this material is extracted with CH_3OH and titrated with Karl Fischer reagent, how many mg atoms of I_2 would be used? (*Note:* Reagent is I_2 + methanol + pyridine + SO_2; net titration reaction is $H_2O + I_2 + SO_2 + CH_3OH \longrightarrow 2HI + CH_3HSO_4$.)

A-31. A sample of medicinal hydrogen peroxide has a sp. gr. of 1.010 and is labeled "10 volume," which means that the soln. will give on simple decomposition 10 times its vol. of O_2 gas (standard conditions). (*a*) What is the molarity of the soln.? (*b*) What is its normality as an oxidizing agent and as a reducing agent? (*c*) How many ml of 0.100 N $KMnO_4$ would be required to titrate a diluted 1.00-g sample of the soln. in the presence of acid? (*d*) How many ml of 0.100 M $Na_2S_2O_3$ soln. would be required to titrate the I_2 liberated when excess KI and acid are added to a diluted 1.00-g sample of the soln.? (*e*) If a 1.00-g sample is diluted and treated in the presence of NaOH with three times the theoretical amt. of Na_3AsO_3 required to reduce the H_2O_2, how many ml of 0.100 M KIO_3 would be required to titrate the excess As(III) in the presence of 4 N HCl ($CHCl_3$ indicator)?

SODIUM. POTASSIUM

*A-32. (*a*) How many g of Pt (dissolved in aqua regia) and how many ml of $HClO_4$ (3.00 N as an acid) would theoretically be required to ppt. the K from 0.2123 g of K_3PO_4 without allowing for the customary excess of reagent (see Sec. 8-8)? (*b*) How much would the former ppt. weigh after ignition? (*c*) If the K in a small portion of the sample were determined as sodium-potassium-cobaltinitrite with subsequent titration with 1.00 N $KMnO_4$, what would be the value of each ml of the $KMnO_4$ in terms of mg of K in the portion taken?

*A-33. Caustic potash is to be produced by the electrolysis of a soln. of KCl. A soln. contg. 100 g of KOH per liter is required. An average current of 900 amp is used. At the end of 5 hr, 102 liters of KOH has been produced, and 5.00 ml of the soln., which is removed for analysis, is found to neutralize 7.600 millimoles of potassium biphthalate. (*a*) How much longer should the current be continued in order to produce the desired concn., and (*b*) what is the current efficiency at the cathode?

A-34. In the J. L. Smith method for K (see Sec. 8-8) using a 0.5000-g sample of mineral, the analyst fails to expel all the NH_4Cl from the NaCl + KCl. The ppt. with H_2PtCl_6 weighs 0.08921 g, and on ignition the wt. becomes 0.05969 g. (*a*) What would be the wt. if the ignited ppt. were washed with H_2O and dried, and (*b*) what is the percentage of K_2O in the mineral? (*c*) If 50.0 mg of NaCl was in the chloride mixt., what wt. of $NaMg(UO_2)_3(C_2H_3O_2)_9 \cdot 6\frac{1}{2}H_2O$ would be obtained by the addition of magnesium acetate + uranyl acetate + acetic acid to the filtrate from the chloroplatinate ppt. after removal of the excess chloroplatinic acid by reduction to Pt metal?

AMMONIUM. AMMONIA. NITROGEN

*A-35. A certain vol. of a soln. contg. NO_2^- and NO_3^- requires 5.00 ml of $KMnO_4$ (1.00 ml $\backsimeq$ 0.0500 millimole $Na_2C_2O_4$), and an equal vol. of the soln. requires

15.00 ml of HCl (1.00 ml $\approx$ 0.0106 g Na_2CO_3) to neutralize the NH_3 liberated by the action of Devarda alloy + NaOH. What is the ratio by wt. of nitrate ions to nitrite ions in the soln.?

*A-36. Nitrogen, existing as nitride in a crucible steel, is determined by decomposing a 5.00-g sample with HCl. The resulting NH_4Cl is decomposed with NaOH, and the liberated NH_3 is absorbed in 10.05 ml of H_2SO_4 which is 0.00990 N as an acid. After absorption, the amt. of residual acid is determined by adding an excess of KI and of KIO_3 and titrating with standard $Na_2S_2O_3$ the I_2 liberated (see Prob. A-37). The $Na_2S_2O_3$ is of such concn. that 42.0 ml is equiv. to the I_2 liberated from an excess of KI by 20.0 ml of 0.0258 N $KMnO_4$, and in the above titration 5.14 ml is used. Calculate the percentage of nitrogen in the steel.

*A-37. Potassium biiodate, $KH(IO_3)_2$, serves as a primary standard in acidimetry and in iodimetry. In the following micro-Kjeldahl method, it is used in both capacities.

An organic nitrogenous material is digested as in the regular Kjeldahl method (see Sec. 11-10), and the N is converted to NH_4HSO_4. The NH_3 liberated by the action of NaOH is caught in a 10.0-ml pipetful of $KH(IO_3)_2$ soln. that is 0.0100 N as an acid. Excess KI is added, and the liberated I_2 requires 3.10 ml of thiosulfate soln. A separate 10.0-ml portion of the biiodate when treated with excess KI liberates sufficient I_2 to require 8.65 ml of the thiosulfate. Remembering that the liberation of I_2 from iodate takes place only as long as acid is present (write equation), calculate the no. of mg of N shown to be present in the sample. (The concn. of the thiosulfate is not needed in the calculation.)

A-38. A sample of impure NH_4Cl is dissolved in H_2O, and the soln. is divided into two equal portions. One portion is made alkaline with NaOH, and the liberated NH_3 is distilled into 100 ml of 0.1000 N H_2SO_4, and the excess acid is then found to require 43.90 ml of 0.1320 N NaOH for neutralization. The other portion is treated with sodium hypobromite solution ($2NH_3 + 3OBr^- \longrightarrow 3Br^- + N_2 + 3H_2O$), and the liberated N_2 is found to occupy 51.30 ml when measured over H_2O at 20°C and 753 mm pressure. If the first method gives correct results, what is the percentage error of the gas-volumetric method?

SILVER. MERCURY. GOLD. PLATINUM METALS

*A-39. From a sample contg. Hg^{++}, the Hg is pptd. with periodate as $Hg_5(IO_6)_2$. The ppt. is dissolved in KI + acid, forming $HgI_4^=$ and free I_2. The latter is titrated with $Na_2S_2O_3$ soln. which is 0.100 N as a sodium salt. 10.00 ml is required. Write the equation for the dissolving of the Hg ppt., and calculate the no. of g of Hg present in the sample.

*A-40. A soln. contg. 0.1003 g of Hg(II) is treated with $SnCl_2$, and the pptd. Hg_2Cl_2 is titrated with 0.0200 M KIO_3 in the presence of a high concn. of HCl ($CHCl_3$) indicator (see Sec. 12-8). (*a*) Assuming that the reduction of iodate to free I_2 takes place completely before conversion of the I_2 to ICl_2^- begins, write equations for the two steps in the titration reaction, calculate the vol. of KIO_3 required to give a max. intensity of color to the $CHCl_3$ indicator, and calculate the additional vol. of KIO_3 required to cause the violet color of the $CHCl_3$ to disappear. (*b*) What would be the normality of the KIO_3 soln. when used in ordinary iodimetric work?

*A-41. In the colorimetric detn. of small amts. of Au, measurement is made of the light of appropriate wavelength transmitted through the soln. contg. the colored product formed by the addition of $SnCl_2$. At concn. A of gold, it is found that 70.0% of the light is transmitted through a certain length of soln. If the Lambert-Beer law holds, what would be the percentage transmitted through twice the length of soln. at concn. $0.800A$?

A-42. Mercury, like silver, forms an insoluble thiocyanate [$Hg^{++} + 2CNS^- \longrightarrow Hg(CNS)_2$] and can be determined by titration with standard KCNS. How many ml of 0.08333 N KCNS would be required to titrate the soln. of 0.6000 g of an amalgam consisting of 70.00% Hg and 30.00% Ag?

A-43. The addition of excess NH_4Cl to a soln. of Pt(IV) and Pd(II) ppts. only the former as $(NH_4)_2PtCl_6$. If the two metals are present in the soln. in equal amts. by wt., what would be the ratio of the wt. of the NH_4^+ salt ppt. to that of the yellow ppt. obtained by adding dimethylglyoxime to the acidified filtrate from the Pt pptn.? (*Note:* The formula of the Pd ppt. is [$(CH_3)_2 \cdot CNOH \cdot CNO]_2Pd$.)

HALOGENS. HALOGEN ACIDS. CYANIDE. THIOCYANATE

A-44. In the detn. of fluoride in a given salt mixt. the gas formed by the interaction of the fluoride with SiO_2 is absorbed in water, and the resulting soln. is titrated with NaOH (1.000 ml ≈ 0.01021 g potassium biphthalate). If 20.00 ml of the NaOH is required, what wt. of ppt. would have been obtained if the same wt. of sample had been analyzed for fluoride gravimetrically by pptn. as PbClF?

BARIUM. STRONTIUM. CALCIUM. MAGNESIUM

*A-45. Given the following data: 25.00 ml I_2 soln. ≈ 0.02473 g As_2O_3; 30.00 ml I_2 soln. ≈ 45.00 ml $Na_2S_2O_3$ soln.; 25.00 ml $Na_2S_2O_3$ will reduce the I_2 liberated from an excess of KI by 31.00 ml $KMnO_4$ soln.; 15.00 ml $KMnO_4 \approx 17.00$ ml $KHC_2O_4 \cdot H_2C_2O_4 \cdot 2H_2O$ soln.; 1.000 ml of the tetroxalate ≈ 1.100 ml NaOH soln.; 10.00 ml NaOH ≈ 12.00 HCl soln. How many g of $CaCO_3$ will be reacted upon by 30.0 ml of the HCl soln.?

*A-46. A sample of supposedly pure $MgSO_4 \cdot 7H_2O$ weighs 0.8000 g. The Mg is pptd. as $MgNH_4PO_4$, and the wt. of the product after ignition in air to magnesium pyrophosphate is 0.3900 g. The wt. of $BaSO_4$ obtained from another 0.8000-g sample is 0.8179 g. (*a*) Does the material conform to the given formula? (*b*) If not, in what way and to what degree does if differ? (*c*) What is the percentage of H_2O in the sample?

*A-47. Barium can be determined volumetrically (after pptg. as $BaCrO_4$) either by a permanganate process or by an iodimetric process. In the former, the chromate of the $BaCrO_4$ is reduced by $Fe^{++} + H^+$, and in the latter it is reduced by $I^- +$ acid with the liberation of free I_2. (a) If in the permanganate process 25.00 ml of 0.1000 N ferrous ammonium sulfate was used and the excess ferrous required 10.50 ml of 0.06667 N $KMnO_4$, what wt. of $BaSO_4$ would be pptd. during the titration reactions? (b) If the iodimetric method had been used on the same wt. of sample, how many ml of 0.06667 M $Na_2S_2O_3$ would have been required for the liberated I_2?

A-48. A sample of calcite weighing 1.402 g is titrated with HCl and requires 25.02 ml. (a) What is the alkaline strength of the sample in terms of percentage of CaO if 20.00 ml of the HCl will just neutralize the NH_3 that can be liberated from 4.000 millimoles of $(NH_4)_3PO_4 \cdot 2H_2O$? Show the general form of the titration curve (pH against ml of titrating soln.) obtained in the above titration of (b) the $CaCO_3$, (c) the liberated NH_3.

A-49. Basic magnesium carbonate corresponds approx. to the formula $4MgCO_3 \cdot Mg(OH)_2 \cdot 6H_2O$ (f. wt. = 503.7). A sample weighing 1.000 g is dissolved in 25.00 ml of 1.000 N HCl, and the excess acid requires 5.01 ml of 1.010 N NaOH. (a) Find the percentage purity of the sample in terms of the above theoretical formula, and give reasons to explain why the result is greater than 100%. (b) What would be the loss on ignition of a 1.000-g sample of the pure substance?

A-50. A mineral contg. 34.75% Ca is given to a student for analysis. Using a 1.000-g sample, he reports 35.26% Ca. (a) If the error was due to insufficient ignition of the $CaC_2O_4 \cdot 2H_2O$ ppt. causing contamination of the CaO by $CaCO_3$, what was the percentage of $CaCO_3$ in the ignited product? (b) What was the percentage error? (c) What vol. of H_2SO_4 (sp. gr. 1.060) should be added to this product to convert all the Ca to $CaSO_4$? (d) What would be the new wt. of the ignited product?

LIMESTONE.   LIME.   CEMENT

A-51. A sample of magnesia limestone has the following composition: $SiO_2 = 3.10\%$; $Fe_2O_3 + Al_2O_3 = 0.20\%$; $CaO = 34.10\%$; $MgO = 17.20\%$; $CO_2 = 45.50\%$. In the manufacture of lime from the above, the CO_2 is reduced to 3.00%. (a) How many ml of 0.2500 N $KMnO_4$ will be required to titrate the $CaC_2O_4 \cdot H_2O$ ppt. obtained from a 0.5000-g sample of the lime? (b) Show whether or not the analysis of the original limestone gives indication of isomorphic replacement.

A-52. From the following data, find the percentage of SiO_2, Al_2O_3, MgO, and CaO in a sample of cement weighing 0.6005 g. Wt. of $SiO_2 = 0.1380$ g; wt. of $Fe_2O_3 + Al_2O_3 = 0.1201$ g; wt. of $Mg_2P_2O_7 = 0.0540$ g; vol. of $KMnO_4$ (1.000 ml ≈ 0.007060 g As_2O_3) for the reduced Fe in the above ignited ppt. = 2.05 ml; vol. of the same $KMnO_4$ for the pptd. $CaC_2O_4 \cdot H_2O = 45.12$ ml.

A-53. A certain limestone contains only SiO_2, $FeCO_3$, $CaCO_3$, and $MgCO_3$. From a sample weighing 1.200 g, there were obtained 0.0400 g of Fe_2O_3, 0.5003 g of CO_2, and 0.5007 g of magnesium pyrophosphate. (a) Find the vol. of oxalate soln. [contg. 35.00 g of $(NH_4)_2C_2O_4 \cdot H_2O$ per liter] required to ppt. the Ca as $CaC_2O_4 \cdot H_2O$. (b) Also calculate the normality of the $KMnO_4$ if 38.00 ml was required to titrate the oxalate ppt.

IRON.   ALUMINUM.   BERYLLIUM.   TITANIUM.   ZIRCONIUM

*A-54.   A 1.000-g sample of limonite contg. inactive impurities is dissolved in acid, and the soln. is divided into two equal parts.   One portion is reduced and titrated with $KMnO_4$ (1.000 ml $\approx$ 0.008193 g $H_2C_2O_4 \cdot 2H_2O$).   The other portion is just neutralized, and 40.00 ml of 1.500 N NH_4OH is added to ppt. the Fe as $Fe(OH)_3$. This is in excess of the necessary amt., and the no. of ml in excess is equal to the no. of ml of $KMnO_4$ required in the volumetric process.   What is the percentage of Fe in the sample?

*A-55.   An iodimetric method for determining Zr has been suggested.   The element is pptd. with selenious acid as $ZrOSeO_3$.   The ppt. is dissolved, treated with KI ($SeO_3^= + 4I^- \longrightarrow Se + 2I_2 + 3H_2O$), and the liberated I_2 subsequently titrated with thiosulfate.   If 5.00 ml of 0.08333 N $Na_2S_2O_3$ was required for a given wt. of sample by this method, how many g of residue would be obtained by igniting to ZrO_2 the $ZrOSeO_3$ obtained from another sample of the same wt.?

*A-56.   If 60.00 ml of $BaCl_2$ (0.1000 N as a precipitating agent) is required just to ppt. all the sulfate from a sample of partially dehydrated but otherwise pure $Fe_2(SO_4)_3 \cdot (NH_4)_2SO_4 \cdot 24H_2O$, how many ml of NH_4OH (sp. gr. 0.900) would be required just to ppt. all the Fe as $Fe(OH)_3$ from 100 times that wt. of sample?

*A-57.   After decomposition of a 0.5000-g sample of a certain mineral and the removal of SiO_2, the addition of Br_2 and NH_4OH ppts. $Fe(OH)_3 + Al(OH)_3$.   On ignition, the resulting oxides weigh 0.1205 g.   They are then fused with $KHSO_4$, dissolved in dil. H_2SO_4, passed through amalgamated Zn, and the Fe^{++} titrated with $KMnO_4$ (1.000 ml $\approx$ 0.02500 millimole $Na_2C_2O_4$), requiring 22.46 ml.   (a) What is the percentage of Al_2O_3 and of FeO in the original sample?   (b) How many ml of NH_4OH (sp. gr. 0.970) were required just to ppt. all the ferric iron and aluminum from the soln. after neutralizing the acid?

*A-58.   "Iron by hydrogen" is obtained by reducing pure Fe_2O_3 with H_2.   The resulting material should contain at least 90% metallic Fe and is generally contaminated with Fe_3O_4.   The metallic Fe is soluble in a neutral soln. of $FeCl_3$ (Fe + $2Fe^{3+} \longrightarrow 3Fe^{++}$), and the Fe^{++} is determined by titration with $KMnO_4$.   In an actual analysis, 0.5000 g is weighed into a 100-ml volumetric flask, the air displaced with CO_2, and H_2O is added.   Then 2.500 g (an excess) of anhydrous $FeCl_3$ is added, and the flask is stoppered and shaken.   The soln. is diluted to the mark, mixed, and filtered.   A 20.00-ml portion of the filtrate is acidified, $MnSO_4$ titrating soln. is added, and the soln. titrated with 0.1094 N $KMnO_4$.   If 44.16 ml is required, what is the percentage of metallic Fe in the sample?

*A-59.   Zirconium(IV) can be determined by pptn. with H_2SeO_3.   On long standing, the zirconyl selenite, $ZrOSeO_3$, first formed slowly changes to $Zr(SeO_3)_2$.   This ppt. is filtered, dissolved in NaF + acid [$Zr(SeO_3)_2 + 6F^- \longrightarrow ZrF_6^= + 2SeO_3^=$], and the resulting soln. is treated with KI ($H_2SeO_3 + 4I^- \longrightarrow Se + 2I_2 + 3H_2O$).   The liberated I_2 is titrated with standard thiosulfate.   In this method each ml of $Na_2S_2O_3$ (which is 0.1000 N as a *sodium salt*) is equiv. to how many mg of Zr?

*A-60.   A sample of aluminum sulfate is known to be contaminated with Fe(II) and Mn(II).   The sample weighing 3.362 g is dissolved in dil. acid, and Br_2 + NH_4OH are added to ppt. $Al(OH)_3$, $Fe(OH)_3$, and MnO_2.   Treating the ppt. with concd. HNO_3 dissolves the Al and Fe hydroxides and leaves the MnO_2.   This MnO_2 is ignited in air (forming Mn_3O_4), and the product weighs 0.0363 g.   The HNO_3 soln. is evaporated with H_2SO_4, and the Fe(III) eventually reduced and titrated with 4.90 ml of 0.1020 N $KMnO_4$.   An acid soln. of 3.829 g of the original salt gives with Br_2 + NH_4OH a ppt. that on ignition in air weighs 0.5792 g.   What are the percentages of Al_2O_3, Mn, and Fe in the original material?

*A-61.   The Al in a certain sample is pptd. with oxine, and the ppt. is dissolved in HCl and titrated with standard $KBrO_3$ (+KBr) (see Sec. 12-9).   If an excess of KBr is used and the titration requires 48.0 ml of $KBrO_3$ (of which 1.00 ml will liberate from excess KI in the presence of acid sufficient I_2 to require 1.00 ml of 0.100 N $Na_2S_2O_3$), what wt. of residue would have been obtained if the oxine ppt. had been ignited in air to the oxide?

*A-62.   A silicate rock contains Fe(II), Al(III), and Ti(IV).   A sample weighing 0.6050 g is decomposed by an oxidizing flux, the SiO_2 removed, and NH_4OH added to ppt. the hydroxides of Fe(III), Al, and Ti.   The ignited ppt. weighs 0.5120 g.   It is fused with $K_2S_2O_7$, leached with acid, and the soln. divided into two equal portions.   One portion is poured through amalgamated Zn, and the soln. caught in excess ferric alum soln.   This soln. is titrated with 0.08333 N $KMnO_4$, of which 19.56 ml is required.   The other portion is reduced with $SnCl_2$, the excess stannous is destroyed, and the soln. titrated with the above $KMnO_4$, of which 11.94 ml is required.   Find the percentages of FeO, Al_2O_3, and TiO_2 in the silicate (see note to Prob. A-65).

A-63.   (*a*) How many ml of NH_4OH (sp. gr. 0.946) are required to ppt. the Fe as $Fe(OH)_3$ from that wt. of pure $FeSO_4 \cdot (NH_4)_2SO_4 \cdot 6H_2O$ which requires 0.34 ml of HNO_3 (contg. 55.79% HNO_3 by wt.) for oxidation?   (Assume reduction of the HNO_3 to NO.)   (*b*) How many ml of $KMnO_4$ (contg. 0.03000 millimole of Mn per ml) would be required to oxidize the Fe(II) in an acid soln. of the wt. of sample indicated above?

A-64.   A sample of Ti ore is treated in such a way that all the Fe present is as Fe(II) and all the Ti as Ti(III).   The soln. is then titrated with ferric alum soln. of which 50.00 ml yields 0.4000 g of Fe_2O_3.   If the original sample weighs 0.6000 g and 15.00 ml of ferric alum soln. was used, what is the percentage of TiO_2 in the ore?

A-65.   The Fe(III) in a soln. of a 0.800-g sample of Ti ore was reduced with $SnCl_2$ and then reacted with 26.0 ml of $KMnO_4$ (1.00 ml $\approx$ 0.800 ml of potassium tetroxalate soln. which is 0.0800 N as an acid).   The acid soln. of the same wt. of sample was reduced with Zn, and the reduced soln. was caught in a soln. of ferric alum which then reacted with 48.0 ml of the above $KMnO_4$.   On the assumption that the original mineral was compounded of only Fe_2O_3, TiO_2, and SiO_2, find the percentage of each constituent.   [*Note:* Zn reduces Fe(III) to Fe(II) and Ti(IV) to Ti(III); $SnCl_2$ reduces only Fe(III).]

A-66.   Beryllium can be determined volumetrically by pptg. with oxine and titrating with $KBrO_3$ as in the case of Al.   Using the numerical data given in Prob. A-61, find the wt. of the product obtained by igniting the Be oxine ppt. to BeO.

CERIUM.   THORIUM.   URANIUM.   BISMUTH.   BORON

*A-67.   Anhydrous sodium tetraborate reacts with H_2O according to the following equation: $B_4O_7^= + 5H_2O \longrightarrow 2H_2BO_3^- + 2H_3BO_3$.   The anhydrous salt can be dissolved in H_2O and titrated directly by means of HCl, with methyl orange as indicator, as represented by the following equation: $H_2BO_3^- + H^+ \longrightarrow H_3BO_3$.   After conversion of the sodium tetraborate to boric acid by this titration, a suitable polyhydric alcohol is added, and the first hydrogen of the boric acid is titrated by means of standard NaOH, with phenolphthalein indicator.   The following data were obtained on a sample of tetraborate: Sample = 0.03050 g; vol. of HCl required (methyl orange) = 26.35 ml; vol. of NaOH required to titrate the boric acid = 58.10 ml; normality of NaOH = 0.1030; 40.00 ml NaOH $\approx$ 36.35 ml HCl.   Calculate the percentage of $Na_2B_4O_7$ present in the sample (a) using the data from the acid titration, (b) using the data from the alkali titration.

A-68.   Ce(IV) and Th(IV) can be separated from many other elements by pptn. as iodates.   These are converted to oxalates and then ignited and weighed as oxides $[2Ce(IO_3)_4 + 24H_2C_2O_4 \longrightarrow Ce_2(C_2O_4)_3 + 4I_2 + 42CO_2 + 2H_2O;$ $Th(IO_3)_4 + 2H_2C_2O_4 \longrightarrow Th(C_2O_4)_2 + 4HIO_3;$ $2Ce_2(C_2O_4)_3 + 4O_2 \longrightarrow 4CeO_2 + 12CO_2;$ $Th(C_2O_4)_2 + O_2 \longrightarrow ThO_2 + 4CO_2]$.
If a soln. contains 1.000×10^{-3} g atom of Ce(IV) and 5.000×10^{-4} g atom of Th(IV), (a) how many millimoles of oxalic acid would theoretically be required to react with the pptd. iodates, (b) what wt. of oxide mixt. would be obtained, and (c) how many ml of $FeSO_4$ which is 0.1000 N as a reducing agent would be required to titrate the Ce potentiometrically in the presence of acid?   (d) Show the general appearance of the titration curve (emf against ml).

A-69.   If Bi is determined by pptg. as $(BiO)_2C_2O_4$ and titrating the oxalate with standard $KMnO_4$, what is the value of each ml of $N/10$ $KMnO_4$ in terms of g of Bi_2O_3?

A-70.   Using the data given in Prob. A-68, outline a possible iodimetric method for determining cerium, and indicate the meq. wt. to be used in the calculations.

A-71.   A soln. of uranyl nitrate, $UO_2(NO_3)_2$, is divided into two equal parts.   One portion is evaporated with H_2SO_4, diluted, and passed through a column of Zn which reduces the uranyl ions to uranous ions (U^{4+}).   The soln. then requires 20.50 ml of 0.1200 N $KMnO_4$ to titrate back to UO_2^{++}.   The UO_2^{++} in the other portion is pptd. with NH_4OH as $(NH_4)_2U_2O_7$, and the ppt. is ignited to U_3O_8 and weighed as such.   (a) Write the equation for the titration and for the ignition (NH_3 and N_2 are among the products in the latter case), and (b) calculate the wt. of the oxide obtained.

COPPER.   LEAD.   ZINC.   CADMIUM.   BRASS

*A-72.   What is the percentage of Cu in a steel if with a 5.00-g sample the vol. of H_2S gas (measured under standard conditions) required to ppt. the Cu as CuS is 2.00 ml more than the vol. of 0.100 N $Na_2S_2O_3$ soln. subsequently required for the Cu by the iodimetric method?   (See Sec. 12-7.)

*A-73.   In a certain volumetric method for determining Cu, the element is pptd. as CuCNS and the ppt. is titrated with standard KIO_3 in 4 N HCl soln.   (*a*) If the KIO_3 is of such concn. that 1.00 ml will liberate from excess KI in the presence of acid sufficient I_2 to react with 1.00 ml of 0.1000 N $Na_2S_2O_3$, what is the value of each ml of the KIO_3 in terms of mg of Cu in the above method?   (*b*) If the soln. contains that amt. of Cu to require 5.00 ml of the 0.1000 N $Na_2S_2O_3$ in the common iodimetric method for Cu, how many ml of the above KIO_3 would be required to reach that point in the titration by the iodate method corresponding to the max. intensity of lavender color of the $CHCl_3$ indicator?   Assume that the first reaction in the KIO_3 titration is completed before the second reaction begins.   (See Sec. 12-8.)

*A-74.   Samples of red lead (Pb_3O_4 or $PbO_2 \cdot 2PbO$) are likely to contain excess PbO_2.   When such samples are treated with dil. HNO_3, the monoxide dissolves, leaving a residue of hydrated PbO_2 which can be determined by adding an excess of oxalate and titrating the excess with standard $KMnO_4$.   (See Sec. 12-4.)

A sample weighing 0.7000 g is treated with dil. HNO_3 and subsequently with 5.000 meq. of $Na_2C_2O_4$.   The resulting soln. is diluted, and the excess oxalate is titrated with 0.09987 N $KMnO_4$.   From the fact that 28.56 ml is required, calculate (*a*) the total percentage of PbO_2 (free and combined) in the sample, (*b*) the oxidizing power expressed in terms of percentage of Pb_3O_4, (*c*) on the assumption that the sample is composed only of Pb_3O_4 and PbO_2, the percentage of each.

A-75.   (*a*) How many ml of HNO_3 (sp. gr. 1.130) are theoretically required to dissolve 5.00 g of brass contg. 0.61% Pb, 24.39% Zn, and 75.00% Cu?   Assume reduction of the HNO_3 to NO by each constituent.   (*b*) What fraction of the vol. of acid is used for oxidation?   (*c*) What vol. of H_2SO_4 (sp. gr. 1.420) is required to displace the NO_3^- radical from the mixt. of the salts after evaporating off the free excess HNO_3?

A-76.   A brass weighing 0.800 g contains 75.02% Cu, 23.03% Zn, and 1.95% Pb. (*a*) What vol. of 0.1000 N $Na_2S_2O_3$ would be used in the detn. of Cu by adding KI and titrating the liberated I_2?   (*b*) What vol. of 0.05000 N $KMnO_4$ would be required for the Pb if it is pptd. as $PbCrO_4$, dissolved in acid, reduced with 25.00 ml of 0.04000 N $FeSO_4$, and the excess Fe^{++} titrated with the $KMnO_4$?   (*c*) What wt. of zinc pyrophosphate would be obtained in the detn. of Zn?

A-77.   What wt. of Zn ore should be taken for analysis so that (*a*) the no. of ml of 0.1000 M $K_4Fe(CN)_6$ soln. used in the volumetric method will be equal to the percentage of Zn in the ore, (*b*) the no. of ml of a $K_4Fe(CN)_6$ soln. that is 0.1000 N as a reducing agent will be twice the percentage of Zn in the ore, (*c*) the no. of ml of a $K_4Fe(CN)_6$ soln. that is 0.1000 N as a potassium salt will be one-half the percentage of Zn on the ore?   (See Sec. 14-1.)

A-78. If a copper ore on being analyzed yields 0.235 g of Cu_2S after being heated with S in a stream of H_2, how many g of KIO_3 would react in the iodate method with the same wt. of ore? (See Sec. 12-8.)

A-79. If 0.5000 g of an alloy contg. 25.00% Cu requires 20.00 ml of KCN for titration, what is the equiv. of 1.000 ml of the KCN (*a*) in terms of g of $AgNO_3$ (Liebig method for cyanide) and (*b*) in terms of g of Ni (KI indicator)? (*c*) How many ml of KIO_3 soln. would be required for the same wt. of sample by the iodate method if, with an excess of KI, 15.00 ml of the KIO_3 would have liberated sufficient I_2 to react with a vol. of 0.1000 N thiosulfate equiv. to 0.1000 g of $K_2Cr_2O_7$? (See Secs. 12-8 and 14-1.)

A-80. If in the analysis of a brass contg. 28.00% Zn an error is made in weighing a 2.500-g sample as a result of which 1.0 mg too much is weighed out, (*a*) what percentage error (relative error) in the detn. of Zn would be made? (*b*) What vol. of a soln. contg. 90.0 g of $(NH_4)_2HPO_4$ per liter would be required to ppt. all the Zn as $ZnNH_4PO_4$, and (*c*) what wt. of ignited ppt. of $Zn_2P_2O_7$ would be obtained?

A-81. In the electrolysis of a sample of brass weighing 0.8000 g, there are obtained 0.0030 g of PbO_2 and a deposit of Cu equal in wt. to that of the zinc pyrophosphate subsequently obtained from the residual soln. What is the percentage composition of the brass?

TIN. ANTIMONY. ARSENIC

***A-82.** A sample of type metal weighing 1.100 g is dissolved in concd. H_2SO_4. Concd. HCl is added to the cooled soln., and the soln. is boiled and diluted. At this point the soln. contains Sb(III) and Sn(IV). The Sb(III) is titrated with $KMnO_4$ (1.00 ml $\simeq$ 0.00558 g Fe), requiring 32.80 ml. The soln. is then boiled with powdered Pb, which reduces the Sb(V) to Sb(III) and the Sn(IV) to Sn(II). The Sn(II) is titrated in cold soln. with I_2 (1.00 ml $\simeq$ 0.0500 millimole As_2O_3), requiring 9.27 ml. (*a*) What are the percentages of Sb and Sn in the alloy? (*b*) If the same wt. of alloy had been treated with 6 N HNO_3 and the residual material had been ignited, what wt. of product would have been obtained?

***A-83.** A sample weighing 0.250 g and contg. As is dissolved, and the soln. now contg. As(III) is electrolyzed. AsH_3 is liberated and is conducted into 50.0 ml of 0.125 N I_2. The excess of the latter reacts with 20.0 ml of thiosulfate of which 1.00 ml $\simeq$ 0.00500 g of Cu. Find (*a*) percentage of As_2O_3 in the sample and (*b*) the time required for electrolysis if a current of 3.00 amp is used and only 40.0% of the current is used in reducing the As ($AsH_3 + 4I_2 + 4H_2O \longrightarrow H_3AsO_4 + 8I^- + 8H^+$).

***A-84.** A mixt. of As_2O_3 | As_2O_5 | inert matter is dissolved and titrated in neutral soln. with I_2 [1.00 ml $\simeq$ 1.00 ml $KMnO_4$ $\simeq$ 0.0500 millimole $FeSO_4 \cdot (NH_4)_2SO_4 \cdot 6H_2O$], requiring 20.00 ml. The resulting soln. is acidified, and an excess of KI is added. The liberated I_2 requires 30.50 ml of $Na_2S_2O_3$ of which each ml is equiv. to 0.0100 millimole of $KH(IO_3)_2$. Calculate the wt. of combined $As_2O_3 + As_2O_5$ in the sample.

A-85.   An alloy contg. As weighs 5.10 g.   The As is distilled as $AsCl_3$ from a concd. HCl soln. of the sample and is eventually titrated in neutral soln. with I_2 (1.00 ml $\approx$ 1.00 ml $Na_2S_2O_3$ $\approx$ 0.0024 g Cu).   If 5.00 ml is required, what is the percentage of As in the alloy?   If the As were evolved as arsine and the gas absorbed in excess of 0.100 N I_2, how many ml of 0.0833 N $Na_2S_2O_3$ would be equiv. to the I_2 used up?   (See Prob. A-83.)

CARBON.   CARBON DIOXIDE.   SILICON.   TUNGSTEN.   MOLYBDENUM

*A-86.   A 2.00-g sample of steel is burned in O_2, and the evolved CO_2 after passing through appropriate purifying trains is caught in 100 ml of $Ba(OH)_2$ soln.   The supernatant liquid requires 75.0 ml of HCl [1.00 ml $\approx$ 0.00626 g Na_2CO_3; 1.00 ml $\approx$ 1.12 ml of the $Ba(OH)_2$ soln.].   (a) What is the percentage of carbon in the steel, and (b) what would have been the gain of an Ascarite bulb if a similar sample had been analyzed by the absorption method?

*A-87.   On the assumption that $Mo_{24}O_{37}$ is a mixt. of MoO_3 and Mo_2O_3, (a) what percentage of the total Mo is in the 3-valent state, and (b) what percentage is in the 6-valent state?

A-88.   (a) What vol. of 6.00 N HF is theoretically required to volatilize the SiO_2 from 0.5000 g of $KAlSi_3O_8$?   (b) What vol. of SiF_4 at 29°C and 765 mm pressure is produced?

A-89.   A 3.00-g sample of steel contg. 1.21% Si and 0.23% W is dissolved in concd. HNO_3 and evaporated to dryness.   What should be the wt. of the ignited acid-insoluble residue before and after treatment with HF?

CHROMIUM.   VANADIUM

*A-90.   It is desired to prepare a soln. of chromic acetate to contain the equiv. of 8.00% Cr_2O_3 by wt. for use as a mordant.   A batch of the material is made up to the approx. concn. and is found to have a sp. gr. of 1.195.   A 2.000-ml sample is taken for analysis, and the Cr(III) is oxidized to dichromate.   To one-half of the soln. is added 50.00 ml of $FeSO_4$ soln., and the excess Fe(II) requires 17.32 ml of 0.1334 N $KMnO_4$ for oxidation (25.00 ml $FeSO_4$ soln. $\approx$ 21.73 ml $KMnO_4$ soln.).   How many lb of H_2O must be evaporated from 1 ton of the liquor to give the desired concn.?

*A-91.   A sample of chrome-vanadium steel weighing 2.00 g is dissolved in H_2SO_4 + H_3PO_4, and HNO_3 is added to oxidize the Fe and carbides.   In the presence of Ag^+ catalyst, $(NH_4)_2S_2O_8$ is added to oxidize Cr(III) to dichromate, VO^{++} ions to metavanadate (HVO_3), and Mn^{++} ions to permanganate.   Excess peroxydisulfate is destroyed by boiling, and the MnO_4^- is reduced with a few drops of HCl.   The addition of 25.0 ml of 0.1010 N $FeSO_4$ causes reduction of vanadate and dichromate, and the excess Fe^{++} together with the VO^{++} are titrated with 0.1120 N $KMnO_4$, of which 12.6 ml is required.   A small amt. of $FeSO_4$ is added to reduce the vanadate again, and the excess Fe^{++} is destroyed by oxidation with peroxydisulfate.   The

VO^{++} alone is titrated with the above $KMnO_4$, and 0.86 ml is required.   Calculate the percentage of Cr and of V in the sample.

A-92.   If 0.3938 g of $Na_2V_4O_9$ is reduced and 10.00 ml of $KMnO_4$ (1.000 ml $\simeq$ 0.05360 g $Na_2C_2O_4$) is required to oxidize the V back to vanadic acid, find the oxidation number of the reduced V.

A-93.   The detn. of vanadic acid (HVO_3) in the presence of molybdic acid (H_2MoO_4) depends upon the fact that vanadic acid alone is reduced to VO^{++} by SO_2 in dil. H_2SO_4 and can be reoxidized by standard permanganate soln.   Both vanadic acid and molybdic acid are reduced by amalgamated Zn, the former to V^{++} and the latter to Mo^{3+}.   These reactions are carried out in a Jones reductor, and the reduced constituents oxidized by being passed into an excess of ferric salt and H_3PO_4.   An equiv. reduction of the Fe^{3+} to Fe^{++} takes place.   The Fe^{++} is then titrated with standard permanganate.

Reduction with SO_2		*Reduction with* Zn	
Grams of sample	= 0.4500	Grams of sample	= 0.4500
Normality of $KMnO_4$	= 0.1092	Normality of $KMnO_4$	= 0.1092
Ml $KMnO_4$	= 8.23	Ml $KMnO_4$	= 41.74

(*a*) Complete and balance all the equations in this process.   (*b*) Express the amt. of vanadate as percentage of V and the amt. of molybdate as percentage of Mo.

A-94.   Calculate the percentage of Cr and of V in a chrome-vanadium steel from the following data:
   Chromium.   A sample weighing 2.00 g is dissolved in acid.   Subsequent treatments result in the formation of Fe^{3+}, Mn^{++}, $Cr_2O_7^=$, and VO_3^-.   A 25-ml pipetful of Fe^{++} soln. [39.2 g $FeSO_4 \cdot (NH_4)_2SO_4 \cdot 6H_2O$ per liter] is added.   Cr is thus reduced to Cr^{3+}, and V to VO^{++}.   The soln. is titrated with $KMnO_4$ (1.00 ml $\simeq$ 0.92 ml of the ferrous soln.) and requires 14.28 ml to reach the end point.   Only VO^{++} and the excess Fe^{++} are oxidized in this step.   To correct for overtitration and color interferences, the soln. is boiled until the permanganate color is destroyed, and the soln. is brought to the same shade of color as before with the standard $KMnO_4$, requiring 0.08 ml.
   Vanadium.   The V in the above soln. is now reduced to VO^{++} with dil. $FeSO_4$ soln., and the excess Fe^{++} oxidized with a small amt. of peroxydisulfate (which does not affect the V).   The vanadyl is then titrated back to vanadate with the above $KMnO_4$, requiring 1.10 ml.   It may be assumed that the soln. is overtitrated to the same extent as in the first titration.

*A-95.   A soln. contains $Cr_2(SO_4)_3$, $K_2Cr_2O_7$, free H_2SO_4, and no other active ingredient.   The soln. is diluted to 500 ml and 50-ml-aliquot portions are taken for the following analyses which are designed to determine the quantitative composition of the soln.

In one 50-ml portion the Cr(III) is oxidized in the presence of acid with $NaBiO_3$, and the excess of the latter is filtered off.   The addition of 75.00 ml of 0.09539 N $FeSO_4$ to the filtrate reduces the total Cr(VI), and the excess Fe(II) then requires 7.93 ml of 0.1020 N $KMnO_4$ for oxidation.

In another 50-ml portion the Cr(III) is pptd. with NH_4OH as $Cr(OH)_3$, and after ignition this ppt. yields 0.0812 g of Cr_2O_3.

The filtrate from the $Cr(OH)_3$ ppt. is acidified with HCl, and the sulfate present yields 1.415 g of $BaSO_4$.

Calculate (a) the no. of g of $Cr_2(SO)_4$ (f. wt. = 392.3) and of $K_2Cr_2O_7$ in the 500 ml of original diluted soln. and (b) the amt. of free H_2SO_4 in this soln. expressed as acid normality.

MANGANESE.   COBALT.   NICKEL

*A-96.   If the Mn in 50.0 ml of 0.0833 N $KMnO_4$ soln. was reduced to the manganous condition, how many ml of 0.0833 N $KMnO_4$ would be equiv. to the Mn in the reduced soln. by the (a) Volhard method, (b) bismuthate method, and (c) chlorate method?   (See Sec. 12-4.)

* A-97.   It has been shown that manganous ions can be titrated potentiometrically with standard $KMnO_4$ in nearly neutral pyrophosphate soln. according to the equation $4Mn^{++} + MnO_4^- + 8H^+ + 15H_2P_2O_7^= \longrightarrow 5Mn(H_2P_2O_7)_3^{3-} + 4H_2O$. What is the value of each ml of $KMnO_4$ in terms of g of Mn by this method if each ml of the $KMnO_4$ is equiv. to 0.002040 g of sodium formate, HCO_2Na, when titrated according to the equation $3HCO_2^- + 2MnO_4^- + H_2O \longrightarrow 2\underline{MnO_2} + 3CO_2 + 5OH^-$?

* A-98.   (a) A steel is to be used as a standard in subsequent analyses of other steels for Mn by the persulfate method.   To determine the percentage of Mn in the standard steel, a sample weighing 1.05 g is analyzed by the bismuthate method. A 25-ml pipetful of ferrous ammonium sulfate is used, and the titration requires 13.2 ml $KMnO_4$ (1.00 ml $\backsimeq$ 0.00201 g $Na_2C_2O_4$; 1.00 ml $\backsimeq$ 1.02 ml of the ferrous soln.).   What is the percentage of Mn in the steel?

(b) In the routine analysis of a certain plain carbon steel by the persulfate method, the analysis is run in parallel with a corresponding analysis of the above standard steel. The same wt. of sample is used in the two cases.   The above standard steel requires 10.4 ml of arsenite soln.; the unknown steel requires 17.1 ml.   What is the percentage of Mn in the latter steel?   (c) If in the persulfate method a 1.00-g sample was used and the arsenite soln. contained 1.10 g of As_2O_3 per liter, to what average oxidation no. was the Mn reduced in the titration?   (See Sec. 12-4.)

A-99.   Given the following data in the analysis of pyrolusite by the iodimetric process, (a) find the vol. of phosphate soln. contg. 90.0 g of $Na_2HPO_4 \cdot 12H_2O$ per liter that would be required to ppt. the Mn as $MnNH_4PO_4$ from 0.5000 g of the sample, and (b) find the wt. of the Mn ppt. after ignition to $Mn_2P_2O_7$.   Wt. of sample = 1.000 g; $Na_2S_2O_3$ soln. required = 40.40 ml; the thiosulfate soln. is equiv. in reducing power to a soln. of $SnCl_2$ that contains 29.75 g of Sn per liter.

A-100.   What vol. of bromine water (30.0 g of Br_2 per liter) would theoretically be required to ppt. as MnO_2 all the Mn from an acetic acid soln. of manganous ions if the ppt. gives on subsequent ignition in air 0.1060 g of Mn_3O_4?   (b) How many ml of H_2SO_3 soln. (sp. gr. 1.028, contg. 5.00% SO_2 by wt.) would be required to dissolve the MnO_2 ppt., and (c) what wt. of product would be obtained if the Mn were pptd. with $NH_4Cl + (NH_4)_2HPO_4 + NH_4OH$ and the ppt. ignited in air to Mn pyrophosphate?

A-101.   A sample of ore weighing 0.8900 g yields by electrolysis 0.2670 g of Ni + Co, and from a soln. of the deposited metals a ppt. weighing 0.9405 g is obtained with dimethylglyoxime.   If the Co were pptd. with α-nitroso-β-naphthol, what wt. of Co_3O_4 would be obtained if the ppt. were ignited in O_2?   (Formula of Ni ppt. is $[(CH_3)_2 \cdot CNOH \cdot CNO]_2Ni$.)

PHOSPHORUS

*A-102.   (a) Calculate the percentage of P in a steel from the fact that a 2.00-g sample furnishes a phosphomolybdate ppt. which when dissolved in 20.0 ml of 0.500 N NaOH requires 27.0 ml of 0.333 N HNO_3 to titrate back.   (b) What wt. of steel should be taken for analysis so that every 100 ml of 0.100 N $KMnO_4$ used in the titration by the Blair method will represent directly the percentage of P?   (c) In this last process give the g equiv. wt. of P_2O_5, of Mo and of $Mo_{24}O_{37}$.

*A-103.   A normal ppt. of ammonium phosphomolybdate from a sample of bronze weighing 1.00 g is reduced with Zn.   The reduced soln. requires 21.3 ml of 0.100 N $KMnO_4$ for reoxidation to Mo(VI).   If the alloy contains 0.20% P, to what hypothetical oxide was the Mo reduced by the Zn?

* A-104.   A method for determining phosphate is to titrate it in acetic acid soln. in the presence of NH_4^+ ions with standard uranyl acetate soln. according to the equation $PO_4^{3-} + UO_2^{++} + NH_4^+ \longrightarrow UO_2NH_4PO_4$.   The indicator is ferrocyanide, which gives a brown color with excess UO_2^{++}.   (a) If the standard soln. is 0.100 N as an ordinary acetate salt and 10.0 ml is used in the titration, how many g of combined P_2O_5 are shown to be present?   (b) If the phosphate ppt. was ignited, what would be the wt. of the product?

*A-105.   A soln. contg. H_3PO_4 was treated with $(NH_4)_2MoO_4 + NH_4NO_3$, and an abnormal yellow ppt. was obtained, which after drying may be assumed to have consisted of $[(NH_4)_3PO_4]_x(MoO_3)_y$.   This ppt. was dried, weighed, and dissolved in NH_4OH, and the soln. made up to 500 ml.   Of this, 50.0 ml was taken, made acid with H_2SO_4, reduced with Zn–Hg, and passed directly into an excess of ferric alum soln. which served to oxidize the Mo(III) to Mo(V).   To oxidize the Fe^{++} and bring the Mo to Mo(VI) required a no. of ml of 0.125 N $KMnO_4$ equal to 15.39 times the wt. in g of the original yellow ppt.   Calculate the ratio of y to x in the formula of the yellow ppt.

A-106.   (a) How many ml of magnesia mixt. (1.00 N with respect to $MgCl_2$) are required to ppt. the phosphate from 0.2000 g of $3Ca_3(PO_4)_2 \cdot CaCl_2$?   (b) How many g of $(NH_4)_3PO_4 \cdot 12MoO_3$ could theoretically be obtained from the same wt. of sample?

A-107.   What wt. of steel should be taken for analysis so that the no. of ml of 0.125 N KMnO$_4$ required in the ferric alum method will be 200 times the percentage of P in the steel?

A-108.   A 2.00-g sample of steel is dissolved in HNO$_3$, and the resulting phosphate is pptd. with molybdate as the normal yellow ppt.   The Mo in the ppt. is reduced to a form corresponding to the hypothetical oxide Mo$_{16}$O$_{27}$ and requires 10.0 ml of 0.100 N KMnO$_4$ for reoxidation to Mo(VI).   Find the percentage of P in the steel.

A-109.   A steel is to be used as a standard for phosphorus detns.   It is analyzed by an accurate ("umpire") method in which, from a sample weighing 3.00 g, a phosphomolybdate ppt. is obtained.   This is dissolved, and the P is subsequently pptd. as MgNH$_4$PO$_4$.   On ignition this ppt. yields a pyrophosphate residue weighing 0.0109 g.

In the routine analysis of a plain carbon steel by the alkalimetric method, the analysis is run in parallel with a corresponding analysis of the above standard steel. The same wts. of sample are used in the two cases, and a 25-ml pipetful of standard NaOH is used in each case.   Back titration with HNO$_3$ using phenolphthalein indicator requires 10.2 ml of the acid in the case of the standard steel and 8.6 ml in the case of the unknown steel.   (*a*) If 1.00 ml NaOH $\backsimeq$ 1.08 ml HNO$_3$, what is the percentage of P in the plain carbon steel?   (*b*) If the concn. of the HNO$_3$ were 0.105 N, what wt. of sample must have been taken in each case?

OXYGEN.   SULFUR.   SELENIUM

*A-110.   A sample of pure Fe$_2$(SO$_4$)$_3$·(NH$_4$)$_2$SO$_4$·24H$_2$O is dissolved, and the Fe pptd. with NH$_4$OH.   If the ignited ppt. weighs 0.1597 g, (*a*) what vol. of the NH$_4$OH (sp. gr. 0.900) is theoretically required for the pptn. of the Fe(OH)$_3$, (*b*) how many ml of 0.100 N BaCl$_2$ would be required to ppt. the sulfate from the Fe filtrate, and (*c*) how many ml of 0.100 N Na$_2$S$_2$O$_3$ would be required in the detn. of this amt. of sulfate by the iodimetric (Hinman) method?

*A-111.   In the detn. of S in steel by the "evolution method," the S is evolved as H$_2$S by the action of HCl and is eventually titrated with standard I$_2$ (H$_2$S + I$_2$ $\longrightarrow$ S + 2I$^-$ + 2H$^+$).   Using this method, the following data were obtained: Wt. of sample = 5.03 g; I$_2$ added = 15.6 ml; Na$_2$S$_2$O$_3$ used for back titration = 12.7 ml; 1.00 ml I$_2$ $\backsimeq$ 1.09 ml Na$_2$S$_2$O$_3$; 1.00 ml Na$_2$S$_2$O$_3$ $\backsimeq$ 0.00504 g Cu.   (*a*) Find the percentage of S in the steel.   (*b*) If the evolved H$_2$S had been titrated with a soln. contg. 0.0100 mole of KIO$_3$ and 0.4 mole of KI per liter, what would have been the buret reading?   (See Sec. 12-7.)

*A-112.   A sample of hydrated aluminum sulfate which has lost some of its water of crystallization and is therefore specified as Al$_2$(SO$_4$)$_3$·XH$_2$O is analyzed to determine its approx. composition.   A 0.5000-g sample is dissolved in dil. HCl, and a ppt. of 0.5602 g of BaSO$_4$ is obtained.   Find the value of X to three significant figures.

*A-113.   The amt. of dissolved O$_2$ in a river water is an important factor in determining the sanitary condition of the water.   The Winkler method of analysis has long been used, and the following data were obtained in one such detn.: A bottle of exactly 300.0-ml capacity when stoppered with a glass stopper was completely filled with the sample of water at 20°C. The stopper was inserted, and the overflow discarded. The stopper was removed, and 2.0 ml of a soln. of $MnSO_4$ and 2.0 ml of a soln. of NaOH + KI were run from a pipet to the bottom part of the sample in the bottle. The stopper was inserted, and the overflow of 4.0 ml was discarded. The contents of the bottle were well mixed. The stopper was removed, a 2.0-ml portion of concd. HCl was run in from a pipet as before, the stopper was replaced, and the overflow discarded. The bottle was shaken until the ppt. dissolved and the soln. was homogeneous. A 100.0-ml pipetful was removed and titrated with 0.0100 N $Na_2S_2O_3$ (starch indicator). 8.88 ml was required to decolorize the soln. At 20°C water satd. with O_2 contains 9.19 p.p.m. by wt. of that gas. Calculate the degree of saturation of the water sample. The essential chemical changes taking place in the procedure are as follows: (1) $Mn^{++} + OH^- \longrightarrow Mn(OH)_2$; (2) $Mn(OH)_2 + O_2 \longrightarrow MnO_2$; (3) $MnO_2 + H^+ + I^- \longrightarrow Mn^{++} + I_2$; (4) $I_2 + S_2O_3^= \longrightarrow I^- + S_4O_6^=$.

*A-114.   It is desired to prepare a soln. of I_2 of such concn. that each ml will be equiv. to 0.010% S when the latter is determined on a 5.00-g sample by the evolution method (see Prob. A-111). The I_2 soln. is to be prepared in the following way: A certain vol. of 0.105 N $KMnO_4$ is to be run from a buret into an aq. soln. contg. an excess of KI, and the soln. is to be acidified and diluted to 1,000 ml. What vol. of the $KMnO_4$ should be used?

*A-115.   The H_2S in a sample of illuminating gas is determined by passing 10.0 cu ft of the gas through an absorbing agent and oxidizing the H_2S to sulfate. By the Hinman method 12.00 ml of thiosulfate soln. is used having two-thirds the normality as a reducing agent as a certain potassium tetroxalate soln. (See Prob. A-110.) If it is known that 6.00 ml of the tetroxalate will reduce in acid soln. 3.00 ml of a $KMnO_4$ soln. contg. 6.32 g of the salt per liter, what is the H_2S content of the gas in p.p.t. (by vol.)?

*A-116.   The Norris and Fay method for determining selenium is to titrate with standard $Na_2S_2O_3$ according to the equation $H_2SeO_3 + 4Na_2S_2O_3 + 4HCl \longrightarrow Na_2S_4SeO_6 + Na_2S_4O_6 + 4NaCl + 3H_2O$.
     The Jamieson method for determining arsenic is to titrate with standard KIO_3 according to the equation $2AsCl_3 + KIO_3 + 5H_2O \longrightarrow 2H_3AsO_4 + KCl + ICl + 4HCl$.
     If the above KIO_3 is of such concn. that 3.00 ml will liberate from excess KI in the presence of acid that amt. of I_2 which reacts with 3.00 ml of the above $Na_2S_2O_3$, and 3.00 ml of the $Na_2S_2O_3$ will react with 3.00 ml of 0.100 N I_2, (a) what is the value of 1.00 ml of the KIO_3 in terms of g of As, and (b) what is the value of 1.00 ml of the $Na_2S_2O_3$ in terms of g of Se?

A-117.   A soln. of a mixt. of H_2S and NaHS is acidified with a ml of $N/10$ HCl, and the total H_2S then present is determined by adding b ml of $N/10$ I_2 and titrating back with c ml of $N/10$ $Na_2S_2O_3$. The acidity at the end of the titration is measured by d ml of $N/10$ NaOH. Show that the no. of g of H_2S present in the original soln. is given by the formula $[c + 2d - (b + 2a)]0.001704$.

A-118. A sample is prepared for student analysis by mixing pure $FeSO_4 \cdot (NH_4)_2SO_4 \cdot 6H_2O$ with an inert substance. Using a sample weighing 0.7650 g, a student correctly obtains 0.1263 g of Fe_2O_3. (*a*) What vol. of soln. contg. 25.00 g of $BaCl_2 \cdot 2H_2O$ per liter would be necessary to ppt. all the sulfate from the filtrate? (*b*) What is the percentage of inert material in the sample?

A-119. A soluble sulfate weighing 0.9261 g yields a ppt. with $BaCl_2$ which on ignition weighs 1.3724 g. On further ignition the wt. increases to 1.3903 g owing to the fact that the ppt. as first weighed had been partly reduced to BaS which on further ignition was reoxidized to $BaSO_4$. (*a*) Calculate the true percentage of S in the original sample. (*b*) What fraction of the total S in the first ignition product is present in the form of sulfide sulfur?

*A-120. Chlorosulfonic acid ($SO_3 \cdot HCl$) is prepared by passing Cl_2 into concd. H_2SO_4 under proper conditions, and the product normally contains excess H_2SO_4 as well as some free SO_3. In contact with water it decomposes vigorously into H_2SO_4 and HCl.

   In the analysis of a certain sample of the material, a sealed glass tube contg. 4.217 g is broken under water contg. 50.00 ml of 1.104 N NaOH. The acid still present in excess then requires 44.82 ml more of the NaOH for a neutralization titration. The chloride in the neutralized soln. is then determined by titrating a $\frac{1}{5}$-aliquot portion with 0.1314 N $AgNO_3$ (K_2CrO_4 indicator), and a vol. of 43.65 ml is required. Calculate the percentages of the three components ($SO_3 \cdot HCl$, H_2SO_4, and free SO_3) in the original sample.

A-121. In Prob. A-120, assuming the wt. of sample and the normalities of the standard solns. to be as therein stated, what total vol. of the NaOH and what vol. of the $AgNO_3$ should be used in order for the data to apply to a mixt. of 78.8% $SO_3 \cdot HCl$, 15.2% H_2SO_4, and 6.0% free SO_3?

*A-122. Ammonium peroxysulfate, $(NH_4)_2S_2O_8$, is used as an oxidizing agent and is normally reduced to sulfate. A sample of the powder contg. only inert impurities weighs 0.3000 g. It is dissolved in water, acidified, and treated with excess KI. The liberated I_2 requires 24.42 ml of 0.1023 M $Na_2S_2O_3$ for titration. (*a*) Calculate the percentage purity of the sample. (*b*) In hot aq. soln. peroxysulfate slowly decomposes to sulfate and O_2. If the above sample were completely decomposed in this way, what would be the no. of meq. gain or loss in acidity?

*A-123. A certain oleum consists of a mixt. of H_2SO_4, SO_3, and SO_2. A sample weighing 3.926 g is dissolved in water ($SO_3 + H_2O \longrightarrow H_2SO_4$; $SO_2 + H_2O \longrightarrow H_2SO_3$) and a $\frac{1}{5}$-aliquot portion is titrated with 0.5132 N NaOH with methyl orange indicator, requiring 34.01 ml for the color change. (Methyl orange changes at the point of complete neutralization of H_2SO_4 but, unlike phenolphthalein, only at the point where H_2SO_3 has been converted to HSO_3^-). Another $\frac{1}{5}$ portion requires 4.93 ml of 0.1032 N I_2 to give a blue color with starch indicator. (*a*) Calculate the percentages of the three components of the sample. (*b*) What vol. of the NaOH would have been used if phenolphthalein had been substituted for the methyl orange?

A-124.   A certain oleum consists of free SO_3 and SO_2 dissolved in H_2SO_4.   A sample weighing 0.7850 g is dissolved in water ($SO_3 \longrightarrow H_2SO_4$; $SO_2 \longrightarrow H_2SO_3$). With phenolphthalein indicator 17.70 meq. of NaOH are required for complete neutralization of the products.   Another sample weighing 0.7500 g requires 0.4870 meq. of I_2 to give a blue color with starch indicator.   (a) What is the percentage composition of the oleum, and (b) how many meq. of NaOH would have been used in the titration if methyl orange were the indicator?   (Methyl orange changes color at the point of conversion of H_2SO_3 to HSO_3^-.)

***A-125.**   Commercial hydrofluoric acid is approx. a 50% aq. soln. of the acid, but it is often contaminated with H_2SiF_6, H_2SO_4, and H_2SO_3.   Given such a soln., calculate the percentage of each of the above four acidic components from the following data:
(a) A sample weighing 2.012 g is run under the surface of a cold concd. soln. of KNO_3 contg. 50.00 ml of 0.5927 N NaOH.   The weakly acidic hydrofluorsilicic acid reacts as follows: $H_2SiF_6 + 2KNO_3 \longrightarrow K_2SiF_6 + 2HNO_3$.   The HNO_3 formed, together with the other acids present, is titrated to a phenolphthalein end point with 47.20 ml more of the NaOH.   The soln. is heated, and an additional 3.07 ml of the NaOH is required to reach the end point ($K_2SiF_6 + 4NaOH \longrightarrow 4NaF + 2KF + SiO_2 + 2H_2O$).
(b) Another sample of the original material weighing 12.43 g is evaporated to a small vol. to remove volatile acids (H_2SiF_6 decomposes to $2HF + SiF_4$).   The residual acid then requires 13.80 ml of the above standard NaOH for neutralization.
(c) Another sample of the original material weighing 15.21 g is titrated with 0.1292 N I_2, requiring 8.07 ml to give a blue color with starch indicator.

GENERAL AND TECHNICAL ANALYSES

***A-126.**   A sample of pyrolusite analyzes as follows: $MnO_2 = 75.00\%$; $CaO = 5.60\%$; $MgO = 4.00\%$; $SiO_2 = 15.40\%$.   A sample weighing 1.000 g is dissolved in HCl, and the silica is removed in the regular way.   The soln. is neutralized, and the Mn pptd. with $NH_4OH + Br_2$ ($MnCl_2 + Br_2 + 4NH_4OH \longrightarrow MnO_2 + NH_4Cl + 2NH_4Br + 2H_2O$).   From the filtrate the Ca is pptd. as oxalate, and the ppt. is dissolved and titrated with $KMnO_4$.   The Mg is pptd. with phosphate in the regular way, and the ppt. is ignited and weighed.   Calculate to three significant figures (a) the no. of ml of 3.00 N NH_4OH and (b) the no. of ml of 3.00% Br_2 soln. (sp. gr. 1.10) required to ppt. the Mn according to the above equation, (c) the total no. of ml of 1.00 N $Na_2C_2O_4$ soln. to form $Mg(C_2O_4)_2^=$ and ppt. all the Ca, (d) the no. of ml of 0.100 M $KMnO_4$ to titrate the pptd. Ca, (e) the wt. of the ignited Mg ppt., and (f) the percentage of Mn in the material obtained by strongly igniting a sample of the original pyrolusite in air, assuming conversion of MnO_2 to Mn_3O_4 and no other changes.

***A-127.**   A certain mineral has the following composition: $FeO = 14.41\%$; $MnO = 7.12\%$; $CaO = 28.00\%$; $MgO = 3.89\%$; $SiO_2 = 2.98\%$; $CO_2 = 43.60\%$.   A 1.000-g sample is decomposed without oxidizing the Fe(II) and is put through a systematic analysis.   Calculate to three significant figures (a) no. of ml of 6.00 N HF theoretically required to volatilize the silica, (b) no. of ml of bromine water (sp. gr. 1.100, contg. 3.00% Br_2 by wt.), and (c) no. of ml of 3.00 N NH_4OH to ppt. the Fe and Mn together according to the equations $2Fe^{++} + Br_2 + 6NH_4OH \longrightarrow 2Fe(OH)_3 + 2Br^- + 6NH_4^+$; $Mn^{++} + Br_2 + 4NH_4OH \longrightarrow \underline{MnO_2} + 2Br^- + 4NH_4^+ + 2H_2O$, (d) wt. of this ppt. after ignition in air, (e) total no. of ml of 0.100 N $H_2C_2O_4$ soln. to form the complex $Mg(C_2O_4)_{\overline{2}}$ and ppt. all the Ca, (f) wt. of the material obtained by pptg. the Mg with $(NH_4)_2HPO_4$ in the regular way and igniting the ppt., and (g) no. of ml of $KMnO_4$ required to titrate the Fe^{++} in a 1.000-g sample of the original mineral after decomposition without oxidation.   Each ml of the $KMnO_4$ is equiv. to 0.006802 g of HCO_2Na in the following titration: $3HCO_2^- + 2MnO_4^- + H_2O \longrightarrow 2MnO_2 + 3CO_2 + 5OH^-$.

*A-128.   A sample of meat scrap is submitted for analysis. The material consists principally of a mixt. of beef and bone that has been processed by heating, and the sample has been ground to a fairly fine consistency.   Material of this type is used commercially as an important component of poultry food, dog biscuits, and similar products.

The scrap from which the sample was taken was sold under the following specifications: Protein: not less than 45%, ash: not greater than 35%, bone phosphate: within the limits of 25 to 33%, fat: not greater than 10%, free fatty acid: not greater than 10% of the fat, moisture: not greater than 9%, crude fiber: not greater than 2%.

The following numerical data represent the averages of duplicate detns. in each case.   (a) Calculate the analysis of the material as indicated.   (b) Does it conform to specifications?

Protein.   A 2.000-g sample was analyzed by the Kjeldahl method.   The evolved NH_3 was caught in a 5% soln. of H_3BO_3 and titrated with HCl, requiring 19.40 ml.   The HCl was standardized against the NH_3 liberated from pure $(NH_4)_2SO_4$ [1.000 ml $\simeq$ 0.03490 g $(NH_4)_2SO_4$].   Arbitrary factor for converting percentage of N to percentage of protein = 6.25.

Moisture.   A sample weighing 5.000 g was dried to const. wt. at 105°C. Wt. of dried material = 4.638 g.

Ash.   The material from the moisture detn. was ignited at dull red heat. Wt. of residue = 1.611 g.

Bone Phosphate.   This means phosphate expressed as $Ca_3(PO_4)_2$.   The ash obtained above was dissolved in HNO_3, the soln. evaporated dry, and the residue taken up in dil. HNO_3.   The soln. was filtered and a $\frac{1}{40}$-aliquot portion was treated with $(NH_4)_2MoO_4$.   The yellow phosphomolybdate ppt. was filtered and dissolved in NH_4OH, and the phosphate was then pptd. as $MgNH_4PO_4$ and ignited.   Wt. of $Mg_2P_2O_7$ = 0.0250 g.

Fat.   A 3.000-g sample of the original material was dried and extracted with anhydrous ether.   The ether extract was evaporated.   Wt. of residue = 0.2700 g.

Crude Fiber.   The fat-free material was digested with dil. H_2SO_4 and then with dil. NaOH according to exact specifications of procedure.   The residue was filtered off on an alundum crucible and dried at 105°C.   Wt. of residue (= fiber + inorganic material) plus crucible = 11.8366 g.   The crucible plus residue was then ignited at dull red heat.   Wt. of residue (inorganic material) plus crucible = 11.8016 g.

Free Fatty Acid.   The fat from the above ether extraction was heated with alcohol and titrated with NaOH, using phenolphthalein indicator.   Vol. of 0.05050 N NaOH required = 2.16 ml.   Free fatty acid is usually expressed as percentage of oleic acid (meq. wt. = 0.282) present in the fat rather than in the original material.

*A-129.   It is proposed to discharge the spent dye liquor from a dyehouse, amounting at times to 126 gal/min, into a neighboring stream.   Laboratory tests indicate that this can be done satisfactorily if the vol. of the stream is sufficient to dilute the dye liquor 1,000 times.   Tests of the stream flow are made by adding to the stream a soln. of NaCl at the rate of 1.00 gal in 24 sec.   The chloride in the stream above the point of dosing is found by titrating 100 ml with 0.01156 N AgNO$_3$, 1.10 ml of the AgNO$_3$ being required.   A 100-ml sample taken below the point of dosing required 1.22 ml of the same soln.   Each ml of the dosing soln. required 73.17 ml of AgNO$_3$.   (*a*) What is the stream flow in gal per min?   (*b*) What is the normal chloride content of the stream in p.p.m.?   (*c*) What dilution would be obtained for the max. discharge of dye liquor?

*A-130.   "Bisulfite liquor" is an aq. soln. of calcium and magnesium bisulfites [Ca(HSO$_3$)$_2$ and Mg(HSO$_3$)$_2$] and excess free sulfurous acid.   It is made by passing SO$_2$ gas through a suspension of Ca(OH)$_2$ and Mg(OH)$_2$ and generally contains a small amt. of sulfate because of the presence of SO$_3$ in the gas.   The liquor is used in the sulfite digestion process for the production of paper pulp; it disintegrates the wood chips by rendering the noncellulose parts soluble.

For control tests in the mill, a volumetric method is usually sufficient.   Gravimetric methods are used for a complete and more precise analysis.

Determination of Specific Gravity.   By means of a Westphal balance, determine the sp. gr. of the liquor.   Value obtained = 1.050.

Into a 100-ml volumetric flask, transfer a 10-ml pipetful of the liquor, dil. to the mark, and mix.

Determination of Total SO$_2$.   Titrate with standard iodine a 10-ml pipetful of the above prepared soln.   Vol. of 0.1010 N I$_2$ required = 10.05 ml.   (HSO$_3^-$ + I$_2$ + H$_2$O $\longrightarrow$ HSO$_4^-$ + 2I$^-$ + 2H$^+$.)

Determination of Available SO$_2$.   Titrate with standard NaOH (using phenolphthalein) a 10-ml pipetful of the prepared soln.   Vol. of 0.1100 N NaOH required = 6.04 ml.   (HSO$_3^-$ + OH$^-$ $\longrightarrow$ SO$_3^=$ + H$_2$O.)

Determination of Silica.   Evaporate a 25-ml pipetful of the original liquor with HCl to dryness.   Dehydrate, dissolve in HCl, filter, and ignite residue in the regular way.   Wt. of residue = 0.0027 g.

Determination of Fe$_2$O$_3$ + Al$_2$O$_3$.   Use the filtrate from the silica detn. and ppt. with NH$_4$OH.   Filter and ignite in the regular way.   Wt. of ignited ppt. = 0.0051 g.

Determination of CaO *and of* MgO.   Evaporate a 25-ml pipetful of the original liquor with H$_2$SO$_4$ to dryness.   Wt. of CaSO$_4$ + MgSO$_4$ = 0.5875 g.   Dissolve in

HCl, add NH_4OH and $(NH_4)_2C_2O_4$.   Filter the pptd. CaC_2O_4 and ignite.   Wt. of $CaO = 0.2225$ g.

Determination of SO_3.   Pipet 100 ml of the original liquor into a flask, add HCl, and boil out the SO_2 in a current of CO_2 to exclude air.   Ppt. the sulfate with $BaCl_2$.   Wt. of $BaSO_4 = 0.0330$ g.

"Available SO_2" is the free H_2SO_3 plus one-half the SO_2 in the calcium and magnesium bisulfites and indicates the SO_2 in excess of the amt. necessary to form neutral sulfites.   It is given by the titration with NaOH.   "Total SO_2" is given by the iodine titration.   "Combined SO_2" is represented by one-half the SO_2 in the bisulfites of calcium and magnesium and is found by subtracting "available SO_2" from "total SO_2."

(*a*) From the volumetric analysis, calculate the percentages of "available SO_2," "total SO_2" and "combined SO_2."   (*b*) From these values, find the percentage of "free SO_2" (i.e., as free H_2SO_3).   (*c*) From the gravimetric analysis, calculate the percentages of SiO_2, $Fe_2O_3 + Al_2O_3$, and SO_3.   (*d*) From the gravimetric analysis of calcium and magnesium, calculate the wt. of SO_2 combined as $Ca(HSO_3)_2$ and $Mg(HSO_3)_2$.   One-half of this is "combined SO_2."   Calculate this percentage, and compare with the value obtained volumetrically.

NINE
Answers to Problems

Answers
to Problems

1-1. (*a*) three; (*b*) seven; (*c*) four.   **1-2.**   332.0.   **1-3.**   1.860 ×
10⁵ miles/sec.   **1-4.**   (*a*) 6.5 p.p.t.; (*b*) 33.91%; (*c*) 0.12%; (*d*) 3.5 p.p.t.
1-5.   (*a*) 24 p.p.t. each; (*b*) no.   **1-6.**   167.0.   **1-7.**   (*a*) 0.2555;
(*b*) 0.00023; (*c*) 0.00012; (*d*) 0.39 p.p.t.   **1-8.**   (*a*) no; (*b*) 0.212 and 0.056;
(*c*) 22.813; (*d*) 0.022; (*e*) 0.028; (*f*) 22.83; (*g*) 14 p.p.t.; (*h*) 8.5 p.p.t.
1-9.   slide rule, 7.4 × 10⁻⁴.   **1-10.**   0.784.   **1-23.**   (*a*) 2.5884;
(*b*) $\overline{4}$.9679 or 6.9679 − 10; (*c*) $\overline{2}$.2789 or 8.2789 − 10; (*d*) 1.2216; (*e*) 280.2;
(*f*) 0.0001490; (*g*) 0.001610.   **1-24.**   (*a*) 0.005864; (*b*) 0.0009005;
(*c*) 0.01308; (*d*) 0.4564.   **1-25.**   0.03061.

2-1.   (*a*) +3; (*b*) +3, −2; (*c*) +3; (*d*) +1, +2, +3; (*e*) 0; (*f*) +3, −3; (*g*) +2,
+3, +2, −3; (*h*) +2, +1; (*i*) +4, +5; (*j*) +2, +5; (*k*) +6, +7.

3-1.   (*a*) 0.0781 g; 0.0359 g; (*b*) 39.1 g; 48.0 g.   **3-2.**   (*a*) 0.00997 g;
(*b*) 0.131 g; (*c*) 15.8%.   **3-3.**   (*a*) 0.686 g; (*b*) 13.5%.   **3-4.**   (*a*) 0.500;
(*b*) 17.0 g; (*c*) 44.8 ml.   **3-5.**   (*a*) CaO = 0.500 lb; K_2CO_3 = 1.23 lb;
(*b*) $Na_2SO_4 \cdot 10H_2O$ = 1.38 lb; $Ba_3(PO_4)_2$ = 0.860 lb.   **3-6.**   (*a*) 2.00;
(*b*) 0.0556; (*c*) 2.10 g; (*d*) 4.48 g.   **3-7.**   (*a*) 2.00; (*b*) 176 g; (*c*) 7.27;
(*d*) 89.6 ml.   **3-8.**   (*a*) 0.200; (*b*) 2.50; (*c*) 0.0286; (*d*) 0.633 g.
3-9.   (*a*) 0.0723 g; (*b*) 0.0348 g, 22.8 ml.

4-1.   (*a*) 1/2,000; (*b*) 1/2,000; (*c*) 1/6,000.   **4-2.**   (*a*) 0.871 g; (*b*) 5.00 millimoles.   **4-3.**   (*a*) 15.0 *N*; (*b*) 17.3 ml; (*c*) 325 ml; (*d*) 1.29.   **4-4.**   (*a*) 7.22 *N*;
(*b*) 3.61 *M*.   **4-5.**   (*a*) 36.7 g; (*b*) 0.275 *F*, 11.0 ml.   **4-6.**   (*a*) 66.67 ml;
(*b*) 40.0 ml.   **4-7.**   (*a*) 3.00 *M*; (*b*) 3.39 molal.   **4-8.**   (*a*) 0.365 *N*;
(*b*) 0.750 *N*; (*c*) 9.30 ml; (*d*) 558 ml.

5-1.   52.0.   **5-2.**   306.0.   **5-3.**   (*a*) 32.2; (*b*) 29.7.   **5-4.**   − 7.0 kg-cal.
5-5.   483.3 kg-cal.   **5-6.**   39.59.   **5-13.**   228 min.   **5-14.**   (*a*) 158 mm;

(*b*) 200 mm; (*c*) 187.5 mm.   **5-15.**   29.9 ml.   **5-16.**   (*a*) 90.0 min;
(*b*) 48.2 min.   **5-17.**   1,733 years.   **5-18.**   (*a*) 6.25%; (*b*) 14.3%.
5-19.   (*a*) 2*A* min; (*b*) 6.65*A* min.   **5-20.**   14.41 ml.   **5-21.**   10.5 min.
5-22.   3.18°.   **5-23.**   137 min.   **5-34.**   (*a*) 2.55, acid; (*b*) 1.5×10^{-10},
alkaline.   **5-35.**   (*a*) 2.0; (*b*) 13.43; (*c*) -0.90.   **5-36.**   3.6 *M*.
5-37.   (*a*) 3.5×10^{-11}, 2.9×10^{-4}, 3.54; (*b*) 1.8×10^{-13}, 12.75; 1.25.
5-42.   (*a*) 3.2×10^{-8}; (*b*) 7.49.   **5-43.** 8.9×10^{-3} *M*.   **5-44.** $[H^+] =$
0.00096 *M*; $[C_2H_3O_2^-] = 0.00096$ *M*; $[HC_2H_3O_2] = 0.049$ *M*.   **5-45.**   (*a*) 0.019 *M*;
(*b*) 0.70 *M*.   **5-46.**   (*a*) 2.1×10^{-4}, 6.5%; (*b*) 3.68.   **5-47.** 2.2×10^{-6} *M*.
5-48.   0.015%.   **5-49.**   (*a*) 11.36; (*b*) 8.64.   **5-50.**   8.0 g.
5-51.   (*a*) decrease; (*b*) increase.   **5-52.**   (*a*) 1.0×10^{-14}; (*b*) 2×10^{-7};
(*c*) 9.1×10^{-13}; (*d*) 1.8×10^{-5}; (*e*) 7.2×10^{-20}; (*f*) the fourth.   **5-53.**   900 ml.
5-54.   (*a*) 2.00; (*b*) 12.00; (*c*) 3.00; (*d*) 6.00; (*e*) 5.95; (*f*) 6.05.   **5-55.** $1.2 \times$
10^{-5} *M*, 8×10^{-5} *M*.   **5-56.** 5.5×10^{-17} *M*.   **5-57.** 2.9×10^{-8} *M*,
5.8×10^{-8} *M*.   **5-58.** $[Na^+] = 0.040$ *M*; $[Cd^{++}] = 6.4 \times 10^{-5}$ *M*; $[CN^-] =$
2.5×10^{-4} *M*; $[Cd(CN)_4^=] = 0.020$ *M*.   **5-59.** 1.06×10^{-9} *M*.
5-60. 2.0×10^{-9} *M*.   **5-84.** 1.7×10^{-6}.   **5-85.**   9.69.
5-86. 2.15×10^{-4} *M*.   **5-87.** 1.7×10^{-6}; 5.77.   **5-88.** 9.4×10^{-14};
13.03.   **5-89.**   96%.   **5-90.** 3.4×10^{-13}.   **5-91.**   (*a*) 228 mg;
(*b*) 0.0032 mg.   **5-92.**   (*a*) 3.7×10^{-4} g, 4.6×10^{-4} g; (*b*) 1.8×10^{-3} *M*,
3.6×10^{-3} *N*.   **5-93.**   (*a*) 4.6×10^{-5}; (*b*) 0.90 mg.   **5-94.** 1.4×10^{-21}.
5-95. 9.3×10^{-14}.   **5-96.** $\sqrt{8B^3/A}$.   **5-97.** 7.0×10^{-5}.
5-98. $432A^4$; 6*A*.   **5-99.** $\sqrt[5]{72A}$.   **5-100.**   13.7 mg.   **5-101.** $1.2 \times$
10^{-19} mg.   **5-102.**   1.3 mg.   **5-103.**   (*a*) 6.5×10^3; (*b*) 3.1×10^{-5};
(*c*) 4.6×10^8; (*d*) 1.2×10^8.   **5-104.** 1.6×10^{-49}.   **5-105.** 3.0×10^{-10}.
5-106.   (*a*) 1.6×10^{-6}, 1.1×10^{-10}; (*b*) sulfate, 0.027 mg.   **5-131.** $2.4 \times$
10^{-4} g, 68 g.   **5-132.**   0.094 mg.   **5-133.**   29.0 g, 1.5×10^{-4} g.
5-134. 1.5×10^{-72}.   **5-135.**   0.0034 f. wt.   **5-136.** 2.3×10^{-4} f. wt.
5-137.   0.16 g.   **5-138.** 1.2×10^{-20} *M*.

6-1.   (*a*) $+0.764$ volt; (*b*) -0.295 volt; (*c*) $+1.257$ volts; (*d*) $+0.781$ volt.
6-2. $PbO_2 + 2Br^- + 4H^+ \longrightarrow Pb^{++} + Br_2 + 2H_2O$; $(PbO_2 + 4H^+ + 2e \rightleftharpoons$
$Pb^{++} + 2H_2O) - (Br_2 + 2e \rightleftharpoons 2Br^-)$.   **6-3.**   (*a*) $2Ag^+ + Cu(s) \longrightarrow$
$Ag(s) + Cu^{++}$; (*b*) $MnO_2(s) + H_2O_2 + 2H^+ \longrightarrow Mn^{++} + O_2 + 2H_2O$.
6-4.   (*a*) $SbO^+ + 2H^+ + 3e \rightleftharpoons Sb + H_2O$; (*b*) $NO_3^- + 3H^+ + 2e \rightleftharpoons HNO_2 +$
H_2O; (*c*) $HAsO_2 + 3H^+ + 3e \rightleftharpoons As + 2H_2O$; (*d*) $Bi_2O_4(s) + 4H^+ + 2e \rightleftharpoons$
$2BiO^+ + 2H_2O$; (*e*) $2BrO_3^- + 12H^+ + 10e \rightleftharpoons Br_2 + 6H_2O$.
6-5.   (*a*) $ZnO_2^= + 2H_2O + 2e \rightleftharpoons Zn + 4OH^-$; (*b*) $HCO_3^- + 2H_2O + 2e \rightleftharpoons$
$HCHO + 3OH^-$; (*c*) $Sn(OH)_6^= + 2e \rightleftharpoons HSnO_2^- + 3OH^- + H_2O$;
(*d*) $P + 3H_2O + 3e \rightleftharpoons PH_3 + 3OH^-$; (*e*) $Ag_2O + H_2O + 2e \rightleftharpoons 2Ag + 2OH^-$.
6-6.   (*a*) 0.15 volt; (*b*) right to left.   **6-7.**   (*a*) 1.590 volts; (*b*) left to right;
(*c*) $Zn \longrightarrow Zn^{++} + 2e$; $2Ag^+ + 2e \longrightarrow 2Ag$; $Zn + 2Ag^+ \longrightarrow Zn^{++} + 2Ag$;
(*d*) 3.7×10^{-28} *M*.   **6-8.**   (*a*) 0.740 volt, left to right; (*b*) 0.0340 volt, right to left;
(*c*) 0.56 volt, left to right; (*d*) 1.31 volts, right to left; (*e*) 0.567 volt, left to right.
6-9. 4.7×10^{-9} *M*.   **6-10.** -0.62 volt.   **6-11.**   0.062 volt.

6-12. −0.50 volt.   **6-13.** (a) 160; (b) +0.85 volt.   **6-14.** +1.51 volts.
6-15. +1.46 volts.   **6-16.** 1.8×10^{-5}.   **6-17.** 8.5×10^{-28} M.
6-18. 1.5×10^{-16} M.   **6-19.** (a) 1.7×10^{37}; (b) 0.34; (c) 6.3×10^{-37};
(d) 7.0×10^{56}; (e) 2.0×10^{-11}.

7-1. 5.5.   **7-2.** 4.2 divisions.   **7-3.** 10.1226 g.   **7-4.** 34.9969 g.
7-5. 12.3408 g.   **7-6.** 16.0006 g.   **7-7.** 12.8161 g.
7-8. (a) 0.99991 g; (b) 35.0031 g.   **7-9.** −0.2 mg.

8-1. (a) 0.5884; (b) 0.6990; (c) 0.3623; (d) 0.3399; (e) 1.032.
8-2. (a) 0.07666; (b) 0.7492; (c) 0.8480; (d) 2.739; (e) 0.03782.
8-3. 0.7793 g.   **8-4.** 1.897 g.   **8-5.** 94.85%.   **8-6.** (a) 1.28%;
(b) 43.32%; (c) 1.60%; (d) 0.4236 g.   **8-7.** 0.3852 g.   **8-8.** (a) 69.58% Cu,
0.31% Pb, 30.11% Zn; (b) 0.3508 g.   **8-9.** 8.10%.   **8-10.** 5.043%.
8-11. (a) 42.21%; (b) 0.2670 g.   **8-12.** (a) 12.48%; (b) 7.67%.
8-25. 31.01.   **8-26.** 79.916.   **8-27.** 56.66, 55.035, 54.931.
8-28. (a) 69.9609%; (b) 74.961.   **8-33.** 0.1558 g.   **8-34.** 1.000 g.
8-37. (a) 4.82 ml; (b) 0.71 ml.   **8-38.** (a) 13.99 ml; (b) 4.86 ml.
8-39. 18.26 ml.   **8-40.** 18.3 ml.   **8-41.** 3.56 ml.
8-42. (a) 39.0 ml; (b) 59.9 ml; (c) 4.33 ml.   **8-43.** 1.24 ml of NH_4OH.
8-44. 16.6 ml.   **8-45.** 11.6 ml.   **8-46.** (a) 8.68 ml; (b) 0.3065 g;
(c) 1.372 g.   **8-47.** (a) 19.8%; (b) 1.14.   **8-48.** A/B = 1/0.581;
A/B = 1/0.444.   **8-49.** 281 g.   **8-50.** (a) 18.8%, (b) 19.1%.
8-51. 5.75 g.   **8-52.** (a) 26.7%.   **8-68.** 33.54%.   **8-69.** 8.72% K_2O,
8.59% Na_2O.   **8-70.** (a) 10.42% Na_2O, 6.11% K_2O; (b) 1.1349 g.
8-71. 21.3%.   **8-72.** 2.54%.   **8-73.** 23.4%.   **8-74.** 0.179 g.
8-75. 17.8% Ca, 67.3% Ba.   **8-76.** 7.32% Na_2O, 10.26% K_2O.
8-77. 0.212 g.   **8-78.** 25.0%.   **8-79.** 19.8%.   **8-80.** 72.5%.

9-1. 39.76%.   **9-2.** 17.49%.   **9-3.** 44.33%.   **9-4.** 77.67% CaO,
16.35% MgO, 2.22% SiO_2, 1.65% Fe_2O_3, 1.08% CO_2, 1.00% H_2O.
9-5. 76.14% CaO, 18.51% MgO, 4.00% SiO_2, 1.37% CO_2.   **9-6.** 16.6% ZnO,
34.4% lithopone, 15.7% $BaCrO_4$, 33.3% oil.   **9-7.** 0.15%.
9-8. (a) 18.11%; (b) 0.9062A dollars/ton.   **9-9.** (a) 27.61% Al_2O_3,
65.05% SO_3, 7.36% H_2O; (b) 1.805A cents/lb.   **9-10.** 56.32%.
9-11. 59.35%.   **9-12.** 56.27%.   **9-21.** C_2H_7N.   **9-22.** $Ca(H_2PO_2)_2$.
9-23. $C_7H_6O_2$.   **9-25.** $H_2C_2O_4$.   **9-26.** $C_{12}O_9$.   **9-27.** (a) 34.0;
(b) H_2O_2.   **9-28.** $C_3H_6O_2$.   **9-29.** N_2H_4.   **9-30.** $C_4H_4N_2$.
9-31. (a) $C_6H_{12}O_6$; (b) −0.558°C.   **9-32.** Si_2H_6.   **9-33.** $C_{10}H_8$.
9-34. $C_{16}H_{10}O_2N_2$.   **9-35.** $H_2Ca_2Al_2Si_3O_{12}$.   **9-37.** $KAlSi_2O_6$.
9-38. $Na_2CaS_2O_8$.   **9-39.** $Cu_2(OH)_2CO_3$.   **9-40.** $2Bi_2(CO_3)_3 \cdot 6Bi_2O_3 \cdot 9H_2O$.
9-41. $Ca(Mg,Fe)(SiO_3)_2$.   **9-42.** $H_4(Ca,Na_2)Al_2(SiO_3)_6 \cdot 4H_2O$.
9-43. $(Mn,Ca)SiO_3$.   **9-44.** $(K,Na)AlSi_3O_8$.   **9-45.** $HCa_2(Fe,Mn)Al_2B(SiO_4)_4$.
9-46. $(H,K)_2(Mg,Fe)_2AlSi_3O_{12}$.

10-1.   249.38 g.   **10-2.**   10.1.   **10-3.**   (a) 0.016%; (b) 497.96 g.
10-4.   750.06 ml.   **10-5.**   5.9 mm below.

11-1.   (a) 136.2 g; (b) 72.49 g; (c) 54.01 g; (d) 34.81 g; (e) 57.46 g; (f) 50.01 g.
11-2.   (a) 0.04069; (b) 0.1578; (c) 0.1271; (d) 0.1703; (e) 0.2124.
11-3.   (a) 0.1382 g; (b) 49.00 g; (c) 16.99 g.   **11-4.**   (a) 126.1 g; (b) 12.61 g;
(c) 0.2804 g; (d) 0.008589 g.   **11-5.**   2.301 g.   **11-6.**   (a) 0.197 N;
(b) 2.14 N; (c) 0.3000 N.   **11-7.**   (a) 3.524 N; (b) 2.643.   **11-14.**   0.267 N.
11-15.   1.699 N.   **11-16.**   0.935 N.   **11-17.**   0.3994 N.
11-20.   2,057 ml.   **11-21.**   667 ml of 6 N and 333 ml of 3 N.
11-22.   1,048 ml.   **11-23.**   158 ml.   **11-24.**   (a) 3,040 ml; (b) 5.26 g;
(c) 0.04167 mole, 0.0833.   **11-25.**   (a) 0.719 N; (b) 20.1 ml.
11-26.   292 ml.   **11-33.**   13.25 ml.   **11-34.**   (a) 1.622 ml; (b) 1.622;
(c) 3.244 ml.   **11-35.**   0.1414 N.   **11-36.**   (a) acid; (b) 6.87 ml of alkali.
11-37.   (a) 53.34; (b) 1.905 N.   **11-42.**   (a) 0.6617; (b) 0.6617; (c) 0.6617 N.
11-43.   0.4000 N.   **11-44.**   (a) 53.45 ml; (b) 84.61 ml.
11-45.   0.08125 millimole.   **11-46.**   0.2367 N.   **11-47.**   (a) 0.1045 N;
(b) 0.1045 N.   **11-48.**   0.4605 N HCl, 0.4704 N NaOH.   **11-49.**   0.2282 N.
11-50.   (a) 0.4983 N; (b) 40.10 ml; (c) 51.61 ml.   **11-51.**   0.03329 N.
11-52.   0.6669 N H_2SO_4, 0.6513 N NaOH.   **11-53.**   1.00 ml of NaOH.
11-54.   95.02% CaO, 2.19% CO_2.   **11-64.**   34.66%.   **11-65.**   95.50%.
11-66.   23.55%.   **11-67.**   (a) 0.05300 g; (b) 0.04710 g; (c) 0.05004 g,
0.02200 g, 0.05550 g; (d) 0.08473 g.   **11-68.**   34.59%.   **11-69.**   76.94%.
11-70.   (a) $2NaHg_2 + 2H_2O \longrightarrow 2NaOH + 4Hg + H_2$; (b) 2.00%.
11-71.   18.14 ml.   **11-72.**   53.21%.   **11-73.**   3.30%.
11-74. $(2AB - 3CD)(0.08501)$ g.   **11-83.**   0.3173 N.   **11-84.**   41.25 ml.
11-85.   0.1605 N.   **11-86.**   (a) 3.59 N; (b) 0.647 N.   **11-87.**   (a) 1.550 g;
(b) 0.5167 g; (c) 4.650 g; (d) 0.5167 g; (e) 1.033 g.   **11-91.**   71.26%, 5.40%.
11-92.   0.719 g.   **11-93.**   (a) 0.180 g; (b) 0.647 g; (c) 0.218 g.
11-94.   0.217 g LiOH, 0.057 g KOH, 0.226 g $Ba(OH)_2$.   **11-95.**   33.82%;
0.5678 g.   **11-96.**   37.8%.   **11-97.**   87.1%.   **11-98.**   0.850.
11-99.   22.4% SO_3, 75.6% H_2SO_4.   **11-106.**   (a) 6.62; (b) yellow; (c) yellow.
11-107.   (a) 7.08×10^{-6}; (b) methyl red.   **11-108.**   pH $= 14 + \log K_b$.
11-109. 2.7×10^{-11}.   **11-110.**   (a) 2.50; (b) 3.10; (c) 8.16.
11-111.   (a) 10.57; (b) 5.62; (c) methyl red.   **11-112.**   0.032%.
11-113.   4.5%.   **11-114.**   (a) 11.07, 1.2×10^{-3}, 1.2%; (b) 6.51.
11-115. 1.6×10^{-5}.   **11-116.**   (a) 5.05%; (b) 8.82; (c) yes.
11-117. 1.6×10^{-5}.   **11-118.**   8.50.   **11-119.**   (a) 10.82, 9.24, 5.44;
(b) methyl red.   **11-120.**   (a) 2.22×10^{-4}; (b) 7.97; (c) cresol red.
11-139.   61.24% NaOH, 35.32% Na_2CO_3.   **11-140.**   53.84% Na_2CO_3,
36.92% $NaHCO_3$.   **11-141.**   (1) 64.44% Na_2CO_3; (2) 80.80% $NaHCO_3$;
(3) 40.51% Na_2CO_3, 37.59% $NaHCO_3$; (4) 39.96% NaOH.   **11-142.**   23.28%.
11-143.   75.0%.   **11-144.**   4.20.   **11-145.**   % KOH $= \dfrac{5.611(b - d)c}{a}$;

% $K_2CO_3 = \dfrac{13.82cd}{a}$.   **11-146.**   % $Na_2CO_3 - \dfrac{10.60bc}{a}$; % $NaHCO_3 =$

$$\frac{8.401(d - b)c}{a}.$$ **11-147.**   (a) 0.9877 N; (b) 0.9689 N.   **11-153.**   13.8%

$NaH_2PO_4 \cdot H_2O$, 83.6% $Na_2HPO_4 \cdot 12H_2O$.   **11-154.**   0.135 g HCl, 0.481 g H_3PO_4.
11-155.   (a) $B > A$, but $B < 2A$; (b) $B > 2A$; (c) $B = 2A$.

12-1.   (a) 1; (b) $\frac{1}{4}$; (c) $\frac{1}{4}$; (d) $\frac{1}{2}$; (e) 1; (f) $\frac{1}{6}$.   **12-2.**   (a) 0.1000 N; (b) 0.2998 N;
(c) 0.3336 ml.   **12-3.**   100 ml.   **12-4.**   0.04734 N.   **12-5.**   1.608.
12-6.   350 ml.   **12-7.**   25.00 ml.   **12-8.**   0.1266 N.   **12-9.**   1 : 0.6458.
12-10.   0.5723 N, 0.7094 N.   **12-11.**   (a) 342.8 g; (b) 0.01760 g;
(c) 20.00 ml.   **12-19.**   (a) 0.1100 N; (b) 0.04314 g; (c) 0.005440 g;
(d) 0.007047 g; (e) 0.001871 g; (f) 0.02366 g.   **12-20.**   (a) 0.01597 g;
(b) 0.04000 millimole.   **12-21.**   4.214 g.   **12-22.**   0.3000 N.
12-23.   A/B = 1.574.   **12-24.**   (a) 24.00; (b) 0.1699 N.   **12-25.**   19.11 g.
12-26.   1.714 g.   **12-27.**   1.437 g.   **12-28.**   (a) 0.02200 M;
(b) 0.02200 N; (c) 0.1100 N; (d) 0.01793 g.   **12-29.**   (a) 0.2400 N;
(b) 0.4000 millimole.   **12-30.**   84.33%.   **12-31.**   (a) 34.67%; (b) 20.00 ml.
12-32.   0.0800 N, 31.34 mg.   **12-33.**   27.73%.   **12-34.**   0.1000 N.
12-35.   (a) 0.2300 N; (b) 62.07 ml.   **12-36.**   (a) 0.00758 g; (b) 0.00594 g.
12-37.   0.00071 g.   **12-38.**   (a) 0.02234 g; (b) 0.2000 millimole; (c) 0.01122 g;
(d) 0.006593 g.   **12-39.**   (a) 0.002004 g; (b) 0.002804 g; (c) 0.005004 g.
12-40.   (a) 55.96%; (b) 71.99%; (c) 80.01%.   **12-41.**   (a) 99.44%;
(b) 70.78 ml.   **12-42.**   0.6429 g.   **12-43.**   +0.85 volt.
12-44.   (a) 5.60 ml; (b) 0.238 millimole.   **12-45.**   (a) 0.5880 N; (b) 0.2940
millimole.   **12-46.**   (a) 0.2000 N; (b) 0.4647 g.   **12-47.**   2.745 g.
12-48.   (a) 1.39 g; (b) 2.50 millimoles.   **12-49.**   (a) 4.467 g; (b) 0.2004 mg
atom; (c) 0.00007514 mole, 0.1503 meq.   **12-50.**   (a) 30.8 ml; (b) 4.37 ml;
(c) 0.600%.   **12-51.**   4.124 g.   **12-52.**   (a) 0.09293 N; (b) 29.40 g;
(c) 61.91%.   **12-53.**   83.67%.   **12-54.**   92.5%.   **12-55.**   92.37%.
12-56.   0.4167A ml.   **12-85.**   (a) 0.003978 g; (b) 0.005095 g; (c) 0.01963 g;
(d) 0.004651 g.   **12-86.**   (a) 0.002542 g; (b) 0.009839 N.
12-87.   0.2494 g.   **12-88.**   0.009384 g.   **12-89.**   (a) 0.06161 N,
0.06161 M; (b) 0.002003 g.   **12-90.**   0.02491 g.   **12-91.**   (a) 0.1752 N,
0.02223 g; (b) 0.1769 N.   **12-92.**   0.0577%.   **12-93.**   0.3154 g.
12-94.   (a) 0.2831 g; (b) 50.00 millimoles.   **12-95.**   25.67%.
12-96.   (a) 0.36%, 0.09964 N; (b) 3.6 ml.   **12-97.**   96.39%.
12-98.   (a) 5.51 ml; (b) 0.0300 N; (c) 33.6 g.   **12-99.**   0.0125 g.
12-100.   68.28%.   **12-101.**   0.030%.   **12-102.**   0.2498 g.
12-103.   11.0% Cr, 20.5% Mn.   **12-104.**   26.15 ml.   **12-105.**   11A.
12-106.   (a) 4.00%; (b) 70.0%.   **12-107.**   37.68%.   **12-108.**   (a) 95.03%;
(b) 2.498 meq. gain.   **12-109.**   38.24%.   **12-126.**   0.0126 g, 0.0266 g.
12-127.   0.51 g.   **12-128.**   0.003040.   **12-129.**   0.5571 g.

12-130.   2 : 3.   **12-131.** $\dfrac{(4C - A)}{2A}$.   **12-132.**   0.05094 g.

13-1. 15.14 ml.   **13-2.** (*a*) 48.00 ml; (*b*) 0.04167 *M*.   **13-3.** 24.92 ml.
13-4. (*a*) 0.07473 *N*; (*b*) 0.03737 *N*; (*c*) 55.43 ml.   **13-5.** (*a*) 32.91 ml;
(*b*) 0.2667 *N*.   **13-6.** 0.08343 *N*.   **13-7.** 11.3 ml.   **13-8.** (*a*) 60.07 ml;
(*b*) 19.93 ml.   **13-9.** 49.95%, 3.75%.   **13-10.** 0.1482 g.
13-11. 44.61%.   **13-12.** 0.03008 *N*.   **13-13.** 6.34%.
13-14. (*a*) 99.13% KCN; (*b*)1.20% KCl.   **13-15.** 96.35%.

14-1. 50.00 ml.   **14-2.** 4.00 millimoles KCN, 1.00 millimole KCl.
14-3. (*a*) 30.71 ml; (*b*) 19.62 ml.   **14-4.** 21.53% KCN, 10.22% KCNS.
14-5. (*a*) 0.002452 g; (*b*) 0.009807 g.   **14-6.** 0.85 g KCl, 1.83 g KCN,
6.73 g KCNS.   **14-7.** $A = 2.50, B = 9.17, C = 5.83.$ **14-8.** 11.67 ml.
14-9. 26.3%.   **14-10.** 271 p.p.m.   **14-11.** 407.6 p.p.m.
14-12. 20.38 ml.   **14-13.** 1.412×10^{-2} *M*.   **14-14.** 5.36%.
14-15. 4.66%.   **14-16.** 2.694×10^{-2} *M*.

15-1. 0.953 g.   **15-2.** 18.6 min.   **15-3.** (*a*) 327.5 coul; (*b*) 0.2684 amp;
(*c*) 0.090926 g.   **15-4.** (*a*) 1,174 joules; (*b*) 770 joules.   **15-5.** (*a*) 170
joules; (*b*) 5,100 coul; (*c*) 7.75%.   **15-6.** (*a*) 965 coul; (*b*) 9,650 coul, (*c*) 258
coul.   **15-7.** 57.4 min.   **15-8.** (*a*) 0.02694 *M*; (*b*) 0.05388 *N*.
15-9. 0.040 g equiv. lost.   **15-10.** (*a*) 94.5 ml; (*b*) 0.034 *N*.
15-11. (*a*) 0.0009652 mole; (*b*) 0.00835 mole; (*c*) 0.00835 mole; (*d*) 108.9 ml.
15-12. 2×10^{-45} *M*.   **15-13.** 0.250 volt.   **15-14.** (*a*) 0.373 volt;
(*b*) 0.009 volt.   **15-15.** (*a*) 1.97 volts; (*b*) 2.00 volts; (*c*) 2.03 volts; (*d*) 2.06
volts; (*e*) $H_2O \longrightarrow \frac{1}{2}O_2 + 2H^+ + 2e$.   **15-16.** (*a*) 1.28 volts; (*b*) 2.27 volts.
15-17. (*a*) Ag; (*b*) 0.985 volt.   **15-18.** (*a*) yes; (*b*) -0.919 volt; (*c*) 20.0 min.
15-19. 1.1×10^{-5} *M*.

16-1. (*a*) 9.14; (*b*) 1.38×10^{-5} *M*.   **16-2.** (*a*) 11.56; (*b*) 0.429 volt.
16-3. (*a*) 0.237 volt; (*b*) 0.041 volt.   **16-4.** (*a*) 1.83×10^{-4}; (*b*) 0.280 volt.
16-5. 1.07×10^{-7} *M*.   **16-6.** $E = 1.112 + 0.0591K_b$.   **16-7.** 0.59 volt.
16-8. 0.188 volt.   **16-9.** (*a*) 15.49 ml; (*b*) 15.65 ml; (*c*) 8.29; (*d*) 576 mv;
(*e*) 1.2×10^{-5}; (*f*) 0.657 *N*; (*g*) 0.0631%.   **16-10.** (*a*) 41.1% Na_2CO_3,
29.4% $NaHCO_3$, 29.5% inert; (*c*) 0.515 volt.   **16-11.** (*a*) 12.3; (*b*) 8.29;
(*c*) 3.39, 4.1×10^{-4}; (*d*) 4.0×10^{-3} *M*, 0.039 *M*; (*e*) 0.598 g.   **16-12.** 49.
16-13. (*a*) 1.35 volts; (*b*) 0.522 volt; (*c*) 5×10^{-18} *M*; (*d*) 3×10^{-16} *M*.
16-14. 72%.   **16-15.** 0.352 volt.   **16-16.** -1.07 volts.
16-17. -0.98 volt.   **16-18.** (*a*) 1.14 volts; (*b*) 0.504 volt.
16-19. (*a*) 0.238 volt; (*b*) 1.36 volts; (*c*) 0.151 volt; (*d*) 0.302 volt.
16-20. (*a*) $+0.414$ volt; (*b*) $+0.146$ volt; (*c*) -0.036 volt.
16-21. (*a*) 0.018 volt; (*b*) 0.045 volt; (*c*) 0.218 volt; (*d*) 0.388 volt.
16-22. 19.8%.   **16-23.** 45% A, 42% B.   **16-24.** 93%.
16-25. 8.9 p.p.m.

17-1.   396 ohms^{-1}.   **17-2.**   141.7 ohms^{-1}.   **17-3.**   (a) 139.9; (b) 115.0; (c) 233.5; (a) 139.9; (b) 126.4; (c) 256.3 (all in ohms^{-1}).   **17-4.**   0.127 g.
17-5.   0.820 g.   **17-6.**   (a) 0.057 g HCl; (b) 0.035 g HC$_2$H$_3$O$_2$.
17-7.   (a) 6.75 meq.   **17-8.**   0.214 g.   **17-9.**   3.03 $\times$ 10^{-4} g/50 ml.
17-10.   (a) 342.

18-1.   11.3 mg.   **18-2.**   2:1.   **18-3.**   9.75 μa.   **18-4.**   1.53.
18-5.   (b) 97.5%.   **18-6.**   (b) 3.6 $\times$ 10^{-4} M.   **18-7.** $D = 6.50 \times$ 10^{-5} cm/sec.   **18-8.**   0.810 M.   **18-9.**   (a) 16; (b) 5.29 $\times$ 10^{-5} M.
18-10.   4.02 $\times$ 10^{-2} M.   **18-11.**   1.59 $\times$ 10^{-3} M.   **18-12.**   1.30 $\times$ 10^{-2} M.
18-13.   1.12%.   **18-14.**   7.29 $\times$ 10^{-4} M.

19-1.   (a) 0.00124 N; (b) 0.35 ml.   **19-2.**   5.08 $\times$ 10^{-10} g.
19-3.   (a) 4.23 min.   **19-4.**   (a) 4.94 $\times$ 10^{-5}%.   **19-5.**   9.60 $\times$ 10^{-2}%.
19-6.   2.48%.

20-1.   (a) 6.67%; (b) 0.477.   **20-2.**   0.08 p.p.m.   **20-3.**   (a) 0.335%.
20-4.   0.806.   **20-5.**   51.3%.   **20-6.**   65.4 mg/l.   **20-7.**   68.5%.
20-8.   53.3%.   **20-9.**   A:B = 1.00:0.83.   **20-10.**   (a) 30.0; (b) 0.602.
20-11.   0.800.   **20-12.**   5.73 $\times$ 10^3.   **20-13.**   [P] = 8.21 $\times$ 10^{-5}; [R] = 1.75 $\times$ 10^{-4}.   **20-14.**   8.54 $\times$ 10^{-2}%.   **20-15.**   (a) 8.04 $\times$ 10^{-4} M; (b) 9.56 $\times$ 10^{-2} mg/ml.   **20-16.**   0.703.   **20-17.**   (a) yes; (b) 1.1 $\times$ 10^{-4} M.
20-18.   1.92 $\times$ 10^{-2}%.   **20-19.**   (b) 1.56 $\times$ 10^{-3}.   **20-20.**   0.182 g/l.
20-21.   4.02 $\times$ 10^{-5} M.   **20-22.**   6.65 $\times$ 10^{-5} M.   **20-23.**   343.
20-24.   159.   **20-25.**   4.3.   **20-26.**   pKa = 2.85; Ka = 1.41 $\times$ 10^{-3}.
20-27.   4.11, 4.11.   **20-28.**   7.5.   **20-29.**   (a) 2:1.   **20-30.**   2:1.
20-31.   4:1.   **20-32.**   2:1.   **20-33.**   13.1%; 18.4%.   **20-34.**   1.72%.
20-35.   0.248 mg/ml.   **20-36.**   7.54 $\times$ 10^{-2}%.   **20-37.**   2.9%.
20-38.   15.5%.   **20-39.**   1.1.   **20-40.**   (a) 0.94%.   **20-41.**   6.5 p.p.m.
20-42.   yes.   **20-43.**   (a) 1,250 p.p.m.; (b) 0.125%.   **20-44.**   0.460 p.p.m.
20-45.   (a) 4.3 p.p.m.; (b) 0.065%.

21-1.   2.7 p.p.m.   **21-2.**   2.8 p.p.m.   **21-3.**   4.95 p.p.m.
21-4.   30.4 p.p.m.   **21-5.**   9.1 p.pm.   **21-6.**   8.74 $\times$ 10^{-3}%.
21-7.   B = 4113.3 Å, A = 4140.0 Å.   **21-8.**   Mn, W, and Zn.
21-9.   (a) 2624 Å; (b) no.   **21-10.**   3582.6 Å.   **21-11.**   2.25 p.p.m.
21-12.   5.05 p.p.m.   **21-13.**   0.16% Cd.   **21-14.**   0.121% Mn.
21-15.   6.40 $\times$ 10^{-2}% Fe.   **21-16.**   0.24% X.   **21-17.**   0.49% Si.
21-18.   0 to 25 p.p.m.; yes.   **21-19.**   3.1 p.p.m.   **21-20.**   (a) 16.0 mg/100 ml; (b) 32 mg/100 ml.   **21-21.**   2.33 $\times$ 10^{-3}% Se.
21-22.   0.23 p.p.m.   **21-23.**   (a) 1:1 ratio; (b) 0.34 $\times$ 10^{-5} M in the metal.
21-24.   (a) Child 2, 5; (b) 1.02 mg/ml.   **21-25.**   1.72 $\times$ 10^{-3}%.

22-1.   3.96.   **22-2.**   0.93%.   **22-4.**   0.23%.   **22-5.**   0.07 in.
22-6.   0.25%.   **22-7.**   0.21%.

23-1.   6.9% 1-butanol, 5.9% 3-butanol, 2.1% 2-butanol.   **23-2.**   6.14% H.
23-3.   9.25% I, 13.0% II.   **23-4.**   24.6% F.   **23-5.**   0.41%.
23-6.   (a) 9; (b) 1.83.   **23-7.**   8.2% cis, 3.5% trans.

24-1.   39.947.   **24-2.**   (a) and (b) A = 15.7, B = 24.2, C = 6.5, D = 53.6
(mole percents); (c) yes.   **24-3.**   A = 7.5, B = 20.8, C = 48.4, D = 23.3 (mole
percents).   **24-5.**   (a) m/e values: A = 108, B = 127, C = 168, D = 145.
(b) mole-percent values: A = 3.6, B = 5.2, C = 89.3, D = 1.9.
24-6.   (a) mole-percent values: A = 2.4, B = 4.7, C = 91.0, D = 1.9.
24-7.   1.5 mole %.   **24-8.**   (a) 2.98%; (b) 3.02%.

25-1.   1.3775.   **25-2.**   46.9% toluene, 53.1% aminotoluene.
25-3.   4.18%.   **25-4.**   31.1% heptanoic, 68.9% pentanoic.
25-5.   (a) 29.2 g/100 ml; (b) g/100 ml.   **25-6.**   26.8 g/100 ml.
25-7.   −85.0°; 27.0 g/100 ml.   **25-8.**   (a) linear; (b) A = 5.27, B = 0.85.
25-9.   (a) parabola; (b) A = 37, B = 0.00482, C = 0.00013.   **25-10.**   90.7%.
25-11.   0.188 g/liter.

26-1.   92.   **26-2.**   8,108 ± 93 cpm.   **26-3.**   (a) ±89 cpm, ±178 cpm,
±267 cpm; (b) 1.13%, 2.25%, 3.38%.   **26-4.**   (a) 11,600 ± 110 cpm;
(b) 75 cpm.   **26-5.**   1.25%.   **26-6.**   (a) no.   **26-7.**   yes.
26-8.   (a) N = 90,000; (b) t = 25 sec.   **26-9.**   17.2%.   **26-10.**   68%.
26-11.   (a) 2.14×10^5; (b) 7.42×10^5; (c) 8.71×10^2.   **26-12.**   (a) $5.65 \times$
10^{-11} g; (b) 4.60×10^{-9} g; (c) 1.50×10^{-8} g.   **26-13.** 1.19×10^{-8}%.
26-14.   (a) 1,110 cpm; (b) 560 cpm; (c) 11 cpm.   **26-15.** 2.21×10^8 dps.
26-16. 8.48×10^{-4}.   **26-17.** 2.56×10^{-2}%.   **26-18.**   0.561%.
26-19. 8.5×10^{-3} M.   **26-20.**   3.09.   **26-21.**   (a) 0.803 g; (b) $3.82 \times$
10^{-3} M.   **26-22.**   562 μg.   **26-23.** 1.78×10^{-3} M.   **26-24.** $6.88 \times$
10^{-15}%.   **26-25.**   Compd. 1—$10\frac{1}{2}$ min; compd. 2—58 min.   **26-26.**   0.70%.
26-27.   (a) 6.65×10^6 c/hr/g; (b) 3.04×10^6 c/hr/g.   **26-28.**   Compd. 1—
1.22; compd. 2—0.569.   **26-29.** 1.95×10^{-8} g.

27-1.   91.56%.   **27-2.**   0.023 M.   **27-3.** 2.42×10^{-2} M.
27-4.   98.7%.   **27-5.**   (a) 35.2%, 34.3%.   **27-6.**   1.23%.
27-7.   0.478 millimoles/g.

28-1.   (a) 0.159 sec; (b) 1.16 sec; (c) 7.68 sec.   **28-2.** 1.15×10^{-2} sec⁻¹.
28-3.   500.   **28-4.**   3.6 p.p.m.   **28-5.**   30.5 p.p.m.   **28-6.**   (a) 20.8

p.p.m.; (*b*) 2.08 × 10⁻³%.   **28-7.**   (*b*) 27.2%.   **28-8.**   0.35%.
28-9.   (*a*) 0.206 sec; (*b*) 0.700%; (*d*) no.   **28-10.**   (*a*) 61%; (*b*) 4.65 ×
10⁻³ min⁻¹; (*c*) 990 min; (*d*) 1.85 × 10⁻¹ min⁻¹.

29-1.   6.   **29-3.**   (*a*) 1,830 ml; (*b*) 4.   **29-5.**   7.   **29-6.**   (*a*) 173;
(*b*) 173.   **29-7.**   (*a*) 90.9% A, 9.09% B; (*b*) 99.2% A, 17.4% B; (*c*) no;
(*d*) 82.7% A, 0.8% B; (*e*) yes.   **29-8.**   (*a*) 19:1; (*b*) 90.5%.   **29-9.**   44.5.
29-10.   (*a*) 2.08; (*b*) 67.5%; (*c*) yes.   **29-11.**   39.2.   **29-12.**   (*a*) 66.7 ml;
(*b*) 22.0 ml; (*c*) 1.2; (*d*) 2.5.   **29-13.**   3.90%.

30-1.   (*a*) 19.7%; (*b*) 17.4%; (*c*) 57.4%; (*d*) 5.5%.   **30-2.**   A = 10.1%,
B = 17.9%, C = 17.9%, D = 2.0%, E = 10.8%, F = 17.9%, G = 5.5%, H = 17.9%.
30-3.   (*a*) A = 7.9%, B = 58.0%, C = 34.1%.   **30-5.**   (*a*) 82.4% ethanol;
(*b*) 76.7% ethanol.   **30-6.**   4.88 mg/ml.   **30-7.**   2,3-xylenol = 6.93%;
3,5-xylenol = 9.00%; 3,4-xylenol = 4.17%.   **30-8.**   (*a*) 0.055% benzoic,
0.076% phenylacetic; (*b*) 9.25 cm² benzoic, 36.1 cm² phenylacetic.
30-10.   0.416% Al, 0.252% Ga, 0.950% In.   **30-11.**   1.17 × 10⁻² p.p.m.
30-12.   0.074%.   **30-13.**   0.292 g in 25 ml.   **30-14.**   (*a*) A = 625,
B = 610, C = 635; (*b*) 623; (*c*) 1.16 in.

31-1.   (*a*) 440 ml; (*b*) 431 ml.   **31-2.**   26°C.   **31-3.**   (*a*) 230 ml;
(*b*) 264 ml.   **31-4.**   (*a*) 0.285 mole, 9.12 g; (*b*) 729 mm; (*c*) 741 mm; (*d*) 92°C.
31-5.   (*a*) 3.3 × 10¹² molecules; (*b*) 5.5 × 10⁻¹² mole; (*c*) 1.6 × 10⁻¹⁰ g.
31-6.   (*a*) 23.1 g; (*b*) 1.78 g.   **31-7.**   1.00 g.   **31-8.**   0.188 g.
31-9.   (*a*) 0.18 ml; (*b*) 970 ml.   **31-10.**   (*a*) 52.4 cu ft; (*b*) 49.5 cu ft.
31-11.   8.5% CO₂, 10.1% O₂, 0.3% CO, 81.1% N₂.   **31-12.**   (*a*) 80.7 ml;
(*b*) 77.1 ml; (*c*) 76.5 ml.   **31-13.**   (*a*) 21.0% H₂, 79.0% N₂; (*b*) 71.9 ml.
31-14.   66.7% H₂, 33.3% N₂.   **31-15.** 25.0%.   **31-16.**   38.1% H₂,
45.7% CO, 16.2% CH₄.   **31-17.**   36.5%.   **31-18.**   33.3% CO, 33.3% C₂H₆,
33.3% N₂.   **31-19.**   (*a*) 39.0% H₂, 49.3% N₂, 11.7% CO; (*b*) 164.6 ml.
31-20.   35.7% C₂H₆, 28.6% H₂, 21.4% CO, 14.3% N₂.   **31-21.**   2.2% CO₂,
4.2% unsat. compds., 0.5% O₂, 8.5% CO, 42.8% CH₄, 38.6% H₂, 3.3% N₂.
31-22.   26.7% CO, 49.3% CH₄, 24.0% C₂H₂.   **31-23.**   59.5% H₂, 21.0% CH₄,
3.0% C₂H₆, 1.5% illuminants, 5.5% CO, 3.3% CO₂, 6.0% N₂, 0.2% O₂.

32-1.   (*a*) 19.0%; (*b*) 0.100 *N*.   **32-3.**   0.875 millimole.   **32-5.**   (*a*) 90.0%.
32-7.   63.2 ml.   **32-8.**   2.02 g.   **32-9.**   0.0294 g.   **32-10.**   93.0.
32-12.   0.250 g.   **32-14.**   (*a*) 90; (*b*) 10.   **32-15.**   0.184 g.
32-17.   8.00%.   **32-18.**   0.444 millimole.

A-1.   (*a*) 0.500 meq., 0.000500 g ion, 0.0177 g; (*b*) 0.107 ml; (*c*) 5.59 *N*; (*d*) √*A*.
A-2.   (*a*) 0.20 ml; (*b*) 5.00 ml; (*c*) 0.30 ml; (*d*) 4*A*³.   **A-7.**   (*a*) 0.522;

3.33×10^{-14}; (b) 1.50.   **A-8.**   15.1 ml.   **A-9.**   (a) 1.00×10^{-20};
(b) 2.75×10^{-24}.   **A-10.**   (a) 0.0212 ml; (b) 4.56 N, 16.0%; (c) 0.0000966 f. wt.;
(d) 0.00193 N, 0.000966 M; (e) 0.483 ml.   **A-11.**   8.3.   **A-16.**   (a) 9.8×10^{-22} g; (b) 27 g, 1.15×10^{-18} g; (c) 8.24, orange.   **A-17.**   (a) 0.0333 M;
(b) 0.10 meq; (c) 0.0167 N; (d) 0.050 millimole.   **A-22.**   (a) 1.0×10^{-3} M;
(b) 4.1×10^{-8} g; (c) 0.042 M.   **A-23.**   (a) 10.0 ml; (b) 0.15 N, 0.15 N.
A-26.   (a) 0.055 M; (b) 10.7%.   **A-29.**   14.0%.   **A-30.**   (a) 32.20%;
(b) 1.11.   **A-32.**   (a) 0.2926 g, 1.00 ml; (b) 0.5163 g; (c) 0.711 mg.
A-33.   (a) 52.3 min; (b) 92.3%.   **A-35.**   14.8:1.00.   **A-36.**   0.0102%.
A-37.   0.898 mg.   **A-39.**   0.03134 g.   **A-40.**   (a) 5.00 ml, 1.25 ml;
(b) 0.120 N.   **A-41.**   56.5%.   **A-45.**   0.008093 g.   **A-46.**   (c)47.27%.
A-47.   (a) 0.1400 g; (b) 27.00 ml.   **A-51.**   (a) 43.29 ml.   **A-54.**   46.10%.
A-55.   0.01284 g.   **A-56.**   30.05 ml.   **A-57.**   (a) 6.16% Al_2O_3,
16.14% FeO; (b) 1.24 ml.   **A-58.**   89.94%.   **A-59.**   0.5701 mg.
A-60.   12.86% Al_2O_3, 0.78% Mn, 0.83% Fe.   **A-61.**   0.0204 g.
A-62.   23.63% FeO, 41.59% Al_2O_3, 16.77% TiO_2.   **A-67.**   (a) 98.7%;
(b) 98.5%.   **A-72.**   0.205%.   **A-73.**   (a) 0.6051 mg; (b) 42.0 ml.
A-74.   (a) 36.79% PbO_2; (b) 105.2% Pb_3O_4; (c) 97.23% Pb_3O_4, 2.77% PbO_2.
A-82.   (a) 18.2% Sb, 10.0% Sn; (b) 0.392 g.   **A-83.**   (a) 23.1%; (b) 282 sec.
A-84.   0.2023 g.   **A-86.**   (a) 0.507%; (b) 37.1 mg.   **A-87.**   (a) 97.22%
Mo(III); (b) 2.78% Mo(VI).   **A-90.** $151\frac{1}{2}$ lb.   **A-91.**   0.966% Cr, 0.245% V.
A-95.   (a) 2.090 g $Cr_2(SO_4)_3$, 1.540 g $K_2Cr_2O_7$; (b) 0.1785 N.
A-96.   (a) 33.3 ml; (b) 50.0 ml; (c) 20.0 ml.   **A-97.**   0.004393 g.
A-98.   (a) 0.355%; (b) 0.584%; (c) 3.42.   **A-102.**   (a) 0.0674%; (b) 0.886 g;
(c) 2.05, 32.9, 41.3.   **A-103.** MO_8O_{13}.   **A-104.**   (a) 0.03549 g; (b) 0.1785 g.
A-105.   12.9.   **A-110.**   (a) 0.401 ml; (b) 80.0 ml; (c) 120.0 ml.
A-111.   (a) 0.109%; (b) 5.70 ml.   **A-112.**   15.7.   **A-113.**   78.9%.
A-114.   297 ml.   **A-115.**   0.0211 p.p.t.   **A-116.**   (a) 0.0025 g;
(b) 0.00197 g.   **A-120.**   79.25% $SO_3 \cdot HCl$, 16.60% H_2SO_4, 4.15% SO_3.
A-122.   (a) 95.03%; (b) 2.498 meq. gain.   **A-123.**   (a) 55.77% H_2SO_4,
42.15% SO_3, 2.08% SO_2; (b) 34.51 ml.   **A-125.**   55.02% HF, 3.27% H_2SiF_6,
3.24% H_2SO_4, 0.28% H_2SO_3.   **A-126.**   (a) 11.5 ml; (b) 41.8 ml; (c) 5.97 ml;
(d) 4.00 ml; (e) 0.111 g; (f) 52.2%.   **A-127.**   (a) 0.333 ml; (b) 9.70 ml;
(c) 3.33 ml; (d) 0.236 g; (e) 140 ml; (f) 0.113 g; (g) 6.00 ml.
A-128.   (a) 44.85% protein, 7.24% moisture, 32.22% ash, 27.87% bone phosphate, 9.00% fat, 1.17% crude fiber, 11.40% free fatty acid.
A-129.   (a) 153,000 gal; (b) 4.51 p.p.m.; (c) 1,214 times.   **A-130.**   (a) 2.03%,
3.10%, 1.07%; (b) 0.96%; (c) 0.010%, 0.019%, 0.011%; (d) 0.5581 g, 1.063%.

Appendix

Table 6   **Density of water at temperatures 15 to 30°C**

Temp. °C	Density (unit = wt in vacuo of 1 ml water at 4°C)	Weight of 1 ml water, in glass container, in air against brass weights, g
15	0.99913	0.99793
16	0.99897	0.99780
17	0.99880	0.99766
18	0.99862	0.99751
19	0.99843	0.99735
20	0.99823	0.99718
21	0.99802	0.99700
22	0.99780	0.99680
23	0.99757	0.99660
24	0.99732	0.99638
25	0.99707	0.99615
26	0.99681	0.99593
27	0.99654	0.99569
28	0.99626	0.99544
29	0.99597	0.99518
30	0.99567	0.99491

Table 7 Vapor pressure of water

Temp. °C	Pressure mm	Temp. °C	Pressure mm
0	4.6	21	18.5
1	4.9	22	19.7
2	5.3	23	20.9
3	5.7	24	22.2
4	6.1	25	23.6
5	6.5	26	25.0
6	7.0	27	26.5
7	7.5	28	28.1
8	8.0	29	29.8
9	8.6	30	31.6
10	9.2	31	33.4
11	9.8	32	35.4
12	10.5	33	37.4
13	11.2	34	39.6
14	11.9	35	41.9
15	12.7	40	55.0
16	13.5	50	92.2
17	14.4	60	149.2
18	15.4	70	233.8
19	16.4	80	355.5
20	17.4	90	526.0

Table 8 Specific gravity of strong acids at $\frac{15°}{4°}$ in vacuo

(According to G. Lunge)

Specific gravity at $\frac{15°}{4°}$ (vacuo)	Percent by weight			Specific gravity at $\frac{15°}{4°}$ (vacuo)	Percent by weight	
	HCl	HNO$_3$	H$_2$SO$_4$		HNO$_3$	H$_2$SO$_4$
1.000	0.16	0.10	0.09	1.220	35.28	29.84
1.005	1.15	1.00	0.95	1.225	36.03	30.48
1.010	2.14	1.90	1.57	1.230	36.78	31.11
1.015	3.12	2.80	2.30	1.235	37.53	31.70
1.020	4.13	3.70	3.03	1.240	38.29	32.28
1.025	5.15	4.60	3.76	1.245	39.05	32.86
1.030	6.15	5.50	4.49	1.250	39.82	33.43
1.035	7.15	6.38	5.23	1.255	40.58	34.00
1.040	8.16	7.26	5.96	1.260	41.34	34.57
1.045	9.16	8.13	6.67	1.265	42.10	35.14
1.050	10.17	8.99	7.37	1.270	42.87	35.71
1.055	11.18	9.84	8.07	1.275	43.64	36.29
1.060	12.19	10.68	8.77	1.280	44.41	36.87
1.065	13.19	11.51	9.47	1.285	45.18	37.45
1.070	14.17	12.33	10.19	1.290	45.95	38.03
1.075	15.16	13.15	10.90	1.295	46.72	38.61
1.080	16.15	13.95	11.60	1.300	47.49	39.19
1.085	17.13	14.74	12.30	1.305	48.26	39.77
1.090	18.11	15.53	12.99	1.310	49.07	40.35
1.095	19.06	16.32	13.67	1.315	49.89	40.93
1.100	20.01	17.11	14.35	1.320	50.71	41.50
1.105	20.97	17.89	15.03	1.325	51.53	42.08
1.110	21.92	18.67	15.71	1.330	52.37	42.66
1.115	22.86	19.45	16.36	1.335	53.22	43.20
1.200	23.82	20.23	17.01	1.340	54.07	43.74
1.125	24.78	21.00	17.66	1.345	54.93	44.28
1.130	25.75	21.77	18.31	1.350	55.79	44.82
1.135	26.70	22.54	18.96	1.355	56.66	45.35
1.140	27.66	23.31	19.61	1.360	57.57	45.88
1.145	28.61	24.08	20.26	1.365	58.48	46.41
1.150	29.57	24.84	20.91	1.370	59.39	46.94
1.155	30.55	25.60	21.55	1.375	60.30	47.47
1.160	31.52	26.36	22.19	1.380	61.27	48.00
1.165	32.49	27.12	22.83	1.385	62.24	48.53
1.170	33.46	27.88	23.47	1.390	63.23	49.06
1.175	34.42	28.63	24.12	1.395	64.25	49.59
1.180	35.39	29.38	24.76	1.400	65.30	50.11
1.185	36.31	30.13	25.40	1.405	66.40	50.63
1.190	37.23	30.88	26.04	1.410	67.50	51.15
1.195	38.16	31.62	26.68	1.415	68.63	51.66
1.200	39.11	32.36	27.32	1.420	69.80	52.15
1.205	....	33.09	27.95	1.425	70.98	52.63
1.210	....	33.82	28.58	1.430	72.17	53.11
1.215	....	34.55	29.21	1.435	73.39	53.59

Source: From Treadwell and Hall, "Analytical Chemistry," vol. II, published by John Wiley & Sons, Inc., by permission.

Table 8   Specific gravity of strong acids at $\frac{15°}{4°}$ in vacuo *(Continued)*

Specific gravity at $\frac{15°}{4°}$ (vacuo)	Percent by weight		Specific gravity at $\frac{15°}{4°}$ (vacuo)	Percent by weight H_2SO_4	Specific gravity at $\frac{15°}{4°}$ (vacuo)	Percent by weight H_2SO_4
	HNO_3	H_2SO_4				
1.440	74.68	54.07	1.595	68.26	1.750	81.56
1.445	75.98	54.55	1.600	68.70	1.755	82.00
1.450	77.28	55.03	1.605	69.13	1.760	82.44
1.455	78.60	55.50	1.610	69.56	1.765	83.01
1.460	79.98	55.97	1.615	70.00	1.770	83.51
1.465	81.42	56.43	1.620	70.42	1.775	84.02
1.470	82.90	56.90	1.625	70.85	1.780	84.50
1.475	84.45	57.37	1.630	71.27	1.785	85.10
1.480	86.05	57.83	1.635	71.70	1.790	85.70
1.485	87.70	58.28	1.640	72.12	1.795	86.30
1.490	89.90	58.74	1.645	72.55	1.800	86.92
1.495	91.60	59.22	1.650	72.96	1.805	87.60
1.500	94.09	59.70	1.655	73.40	1.810	88.30
1.505	96.39	60.18	1.660	73.81	1.815	89.16
1.510	98.10	60.65	1.665	74.24	1.820	90.05
1.515	99.07	61.12	1.670	74.66	1.825	91.00
1.520	99.67	61.59	1.675	75.08	1.830	92.10
1.525	....	62.06	1.680	75.50	1.835	93.56
1.530	....	62.53	1.685	75.94	1.840	95.60
1.535	....	63.00	1.690	76.38	1.8405	95.95
1.540	....	63.43	1.695	76.76	1.8410	96.38
1.545	....	63.85	1.700	77.17	1.8415	97.35
1.550	....	64.26	1.705	77.60	1.8410	98.20
1.555	....	64.67	1.710	78.04	1.8405	98.52
1.560	....	65.20	1.715	78.48	1.8400	98.72
1.565	....	65.65	1.720	78.92	1.8395	98.77
1.570	....	66.09	1.725	79.36	1.8390	99.12
1.575	....	66.53	1.730	79.80	1.8385	99.31
1.580	....	66.95	1.735	80.24		
1.585	....	67.40	1.740	80.68		
1.590	....	67.83	1.745	81.12		

Table 9   Specific gravity of potassium and sodium hydroxide solutions at 15°C

Specific gravity	Percent KOH	Percent NaOH	Specific gravity	Percent KOH	Percent NaOH
1.007	0.9	0.61	1.252	27.0	22.64
1.014	1.7	1.20	1.263	28.2	23.67
1.022	2.6	2.00	1.274	28.9	24.81
1.029	3.5	2.71	1.285	29.8	25.80
1.037	4.5	3.35	1.297	30.7	26.83
1.045	5.6	4.00	1.308	31.8	27.80
1.052	6.4	4.64	1.320	32.7	28.83
1.060	7.4	5.29	1.332	33.7	29.93
1.067	8.2	5.87	1.345	34.9	31.22
1.075	9.2	6.55	1.357	35.9	32.47
1.083	10.1	7.31	1.370	36.9	33.69
1.091	10.9	8.00	1.383	37.8	34.96
1.100	12.0	8.68	1.397	38.9	36.25
1.108	12.9	9.42	1.410	39.9	37.47
1.116	13.8	10.06	1.424	40.9	38.80
1.125	14.8	10.97	1.438	42.1	39.99
1.134	15.7	11.84	1.453	43.4	41.41
1.142	16.5	12.64	1.468	44.6	42.83
1.152	17.6	13.55	1.483	45.8	44.38
1.162	18.6	14.37	1.498	47.1	46.15
1.171	19.5	15.13	1.514	48.3	47.60
1.180	20.5	15.91	1.530	49.4	49.02
1.190	21.4	16.77	1.546	50.6	
1.200	22.4	17.67	1.563	51.9	
1.210	23.3	18.58	1.580	53.2	
1.220	24.2	19.58	1.597	54.5	
1.231	25.1	20.59	1.615	55.9	
1.241	26.1	21.42	1.634	57.5	

Source: From Treadwell and Hall, "Analytical Chemistry," vol. II, published by John Wiley & Sons, Inc., by permission.

Table 10   Specific gravity of ammonia solutions at 15°C
(According to Lunge and Wiernik)

Specific gravity	Percent NH_3	Specific gravity	Percent NH_3
1.000	0.00	0.940	15.63
0.998	0.45	0.938	16.22
0.996	0.91	0.936	16.82
0.994	1.37	0.934	17.42
0.992	1.84	0.932	18.03
0.990	2.31	0.930	18.64
0.988	2.80	0.928	19.25
0.986	3.30	0.926	19.87
0.984	3.80	0.924	20.49
0.982	4.30	0.922	21.12
0.980	4.80	0.920	21.75
0.978	5.30	0.918	22.39
0.976	5.80	0.916	23.03
0.974	6.30	0.914	23.68
0.972	6.80	0.912	24.33
0.970	7.31	0.910	24.99
0.968	7.82	0.908	25.65
0.966	8.33	0.906	26.31
0.964	8.84	0.904	26.98
0.962	9.35	0.902	27.65
0.960	9.91	0.900	28.33
0.958	10.47	0.898	29.01
0.956	11.03	0.896	29.69
0.954	11.60	0.894	30.37
0.952	12.17	0.892	31.05
0.950	12.74	0.890	31.75
0.948	13.31	0.888	32.50
0.946	13.88	0.886	33.25
0.944	14.46	0.884	34.10
0.942	15.04	0.882	34.95

Source: From Treadwell and Hall, "Analytical Chemistry," vol. II, published by John Wiley & Sons, Inc., by permission.

Table 11   Ionization constants, 25°C

Acids

	Constant for 1st hydrogen	Constant for 2d hydrogen	Constant for 3d hydrogen
Acetic acid, $HC_2H_3O_2$	1.86×10^{-5}		
Arsenic acid, H_3AsO_4	5×10^{-3}	4×10^{-5}	6×10^{-10}
Benzoic acid, $HC_7H_5O_2$	6.6×10^{-5}		
Boric acid, H_3BO_3	5.5×10^{-10}		
Carbonic acid, H_2CO_3	3.3×10^{-7}	5×10^{-11}	
Chloracetic acid, $HC_2H_2O_2Cl$	1.6×10^{-3}		
Citric acid, $H_3C_6H_5O_7$	8×10^{-4}		
Formic acid, $HCHO_2$	2.1×10^{-4}		
Hydrocyanic acid, HCN	7.2×10^{-10}		
Hydrogen sulfide, H_2S	9.1×10^{-8}	1.2×10^{-15}	
Hypochlorous acid, HClO	4.0×10^{-8}		
Lactic acid, $HC_3H_5O_2$	1.6×10^{-1}		
Nitrous acid, HNO_2	4.5×10^{-4}		
Oxalic acid, $H_2C_2O_4$	3.8×10^{-2}	4.9×10^{-5}	
Phosphoric acid, H_3PO_4	1.1×10^{-2}	2.0×10^{-7}	3.6×10^{-13}
Phosphorous acid, H_3PO_3	5×10^{-2}	2×10^{-5}	
Selenious acid, H_2SeO_3	3×10^{-3}	5×10^{-8}	
Sulfurous acid, H_2SO_3	1.7×10^{-2}	5×10^{-6}	
Tartaric acid, $H_2C_4H_4O_6$	1.1×10^{-3}	6.9×10^{-5}	

Bases | ### Complex ions

Bases		Complex ions	
Ammonium hydroxide, NH_4OH	1.75×10^{-5}	$Ag(NH_3)_2^+$	6.8×10^{-8}
Aniline, $C_6H_5NH_2$	4×10^{-10}	$Cd(NH_3)_4^{++}$	2.5×10^{-7}
Diethyl amine, $(C_2H_5)_2NH$	1.3×10^{-3}	$Co(NH_3)_6^{3+}$	2×10^{-34}
Dimethyl amine, $(CH_3)_2NH$	7.4×10^{-4}	$Cu(NH_3)_4^{++}$	4.6×10^{-14}
Ethyl amine, $C_2H_5NH_2$	5.6×10^{-4}	$Ni(NH_3)_4^{++}$	5×10^{-8}
Methyl amine, CH_3NH_2	4.4×10^{-4}	$Zn(NH_3)_4^{++}$	3×10^{-10}
Pyridine, C_5H_5N	2.3×10^{-9}	$Ag(CN)_2^-$	1.0×10^{-21}
		$Cd(CN)_4^=$	1.4×10^{-17}
		$Cu(CN)_3^=$	5.0×10^{-28}
		$Fe(CN)_6^{4-}$	1.0×10^{-36}
		$Hg(CN)_4^=$	4.0×10^{-42}
		$Ni(CN)_4^=$	1.0×10^{-22}
		$HgI_4^=$	5.0×10^{-31}
		$HgS_2^=$	2.0×10^{-55}
		$Ag(S_2O_3)_2^{3-}$	4.0×10^{-14}

Table 12   Solubility Products
(Approximately 25°C)

Aluminum hydroxide, $Al(OH)_3$	3.7×10^{-15}
Barium carbonate, $BaCO_3$	8.1×10^{-9}
chromate, $BaCrO_4$	3.0×10^{-10}
fluoride, BaF_2	1.7×10^{-6}
iodate, $Ba(IO_3)_2$	6.0×10^{-10}
oxalate, BaC_2O_4	1.7×10^{-7}
sulfate, $BaSO_4$	1.1×10^{-10}
Bismuth sulfide, Bi_2S_3	1.6×10^{-72}
Cadmium sulfide, CdS	3.6×10^{-29}
Calcium carbonate, $CaCO_3$	1.6×10^{-8}
chromate, $CaCrO_4$	2.3×10^{-2}
fluoride, CaF_2	3.2×10^{-11}
iodate, $Ca(IO_3)_2$	6.4×10^{-9}
oxalate, CaC_2O_4	2.6×10^{-9}
sulfate, $CaSO_4$	6.4×10^{-5}
Cobalt sulfide, CoS	3.0×10^{-26}
Cupric sulfide, CuS	8.0×10^{-45}
Cuprous chloride, $CuCl$	1.0×10^{-6}
bromide, $CuBr$	4.1×10^{-8}
iodide, CuI	5.0×10^{-12}
sulfide, Cu_2S	1.0×10^{-46}
thiocyanate, $CuCNS$	1.6×10^{-11}
Ferric hydroxide, $Fe(OH)_3$	1.1×10^{-36}
Ferrous hydroxide, $Fe(OH)_2$	1.6×10^{-14}
sulfide, FeS	1.5×10^{-19}
Lead carbonate, $PbCO_3$	5.6×10^{-14}
chloride, $PbCl_2$	2.4×10^{-4}
chromate, $PbCrO_4$	1.8×10^{-14}
fluoride, PbF_2	3.7×10^{-8}
iodate, $Pb(IO_3)_2$	9.8×10^{-14}
iodide, PbI_2	2.4×10^{-8}
oxalate, PbC_2O_4	3.3×10^{-11}
phosphate, $Pb_3(PO_4)_2$	1.5×10^{-32}
sulfate, $PbSO_4$	1.1×10^{-8}
sulfide, PbS	4.2×10^{-28}

Magnesium carbonate, $MgCO_3$	2.6×10^{-5}
fluoride, MgF_2	6.4×10^{-9}
hydroxide, $Mg(OH)_2$	3.4×10^{-11}
oxalate, MgC_2O_4	8.6×10^{-5}
Manganese hydroxide, $Mn(OH)_2$	4.0×10^{-14}
sulfide, MnS	1.4×10^{-15}
Mercurous chloride, Hg_2Cl_2	1.1×10^{-18}
bromide, Hg_2Br_2	1.4×10^{-21}
iodide, Hg_2I_2	1.2×10^{-28}
sulfide, HgS	1.0×10^{-50}
Nickel sulfide, NiS	1.4×10^{-24}
Silver bromate, $AgBrO_3$	5.0×10^{-5}
bromide, $AgBr$	5.0×10^{-13}
carbonate, Ag_2CO_3	6.2×10^{-12}
chloride, $AgCl$	1.0×10^{-10}
chromate, Ag_2CrO_4	9.0×10^{-12}
cyanide, $Ag_2(CN)_2$	1.2×10^{-12}
hydroxide, $AgOH$	1.5×10^{-8}
iodate, $AgIO_3$	2.0×10^{-8}
iodide, AgI	1.0×10^{-16}
nitrite, $AgNO_2$	7.0×10^{-4}
oxalate, $Ag_2C_2O_4$	1.3×10^{-11}
phosphate, Ag_3PO_4	1.8×10^{-18}
sulfate, Ag_2SO_4	7.0×10^{-5}
sulfide, Ag_2S	1.6×10^{-49}
thiocyanate, $AgCNS$	1.0×10^{-12}
Strontium carbonate, $SrCO_3$	1.6×10^{-9}
chromate, $SrCrO_4$	3.0×10^{-5}
fluoride, SrF_2	2.8×10^{-9}
oxalate, SrC_2O_4	5.6×10^{-8}
sulfate, $SrSO_4$	2.8×10^{-7}
Zinc carbonate, $ZnCO_3$	3.0×10^{-8}
hydroxide, $Zn(OH)_2$	1.8×10^{-14}
sulfide, Ag_2S	1.6×10^{-40}

Table 13   Standard potentials

(Temperature $= 25°C$. Substances in solution are at unit activity but may be taken as 1 M in concentration unless otherwise specified. Gases are at 1 atm pressure.)

Half-reaction	E, volts
$F_2 + 2e \rightleftharpoons 2F^-$	+2.65
$O_3 + 2H^+ + 2e \rightleftharpoons O_2 + H_2O$	+2.07
$S_2O_8^= + 2e \rightleftharpoons 2SO_4^=$	+2.01
$H_2O_2 + 2H^+ + 2e \rightleftharpoons 2H_2O$	+1.77
$MnO_4^- + 4H^+ + 3e \rightleftharpoons MnO_2 + 2H_2O$	+1.695
$Ce^{4+} + e \rightleftharpoons Ce^{3+}$	+1.61
$MnO_4^- + 8H^+ + 5e \rightleftharpoons Mn^{++} + 4H_2O$	+1.51
$Au^{3+} + 3e \rightleftharpoons Au$	+1.50
$PbO_2 + 4H^+ + 2e \rightleftharpoons Pb^{++} + 2H_2O$	+1.46
$BrO_3^- + 6H^+ + 6e \rightleftharpoons Br^- + 3H_2O$	+1.45
$Cl_2 + 2e \rightleftharpoons 2Cl^-$	+1.359
$Cr_2O_7^= + 14H^+ + 6e \rightleftharpoons 2Cr^{3+} + 7H_2O$	+1.33
$MnO_2 + 4H^+ + 2e \rightleftharpoons Mn^{++} + 2H_2O$	+1.23
$O_2 + 4H^+ + 4e \rightleftharpoons 2H_2O$	+1.229
$IO_3^- + 6H^+ + 6e \rightleftharpoons I^- + 3H_2O$	+1.087
$Br_2(l) + 2e \rightleftharpoons 2Br^-$	+1.065
$OP + e \rightleftharpoons OP'$ (orthophenanthroline)	+1.06
$AuCl_4^- + 3e \rightleftharpoons Au + 4Cl^-$	+1.00
$NO_3^- + 4H^+ + 3e \rightleftharpoons NO + 2H_2O$	+0.96
$2Hg^{++} + 2e \rightleftharpoons Hg_2^{++}$	+0.920
$Hg^{++} + 2e \rightleftharpoons Hg$	+0.854
$Cu^{++} + I^- + e \rightleftharpoons CuI$	+0.85
$DPS + e \rightleftharpoons DPS'$ (diphenylamine sulfonate)	+0.84
$\frac{1}{2}O_2 + 2H^+(10^{-7}\ M) + 2e \rightleftharpoons H_2O$	+0.815
$Ag^+ + e \rightleftharpoons Ag$	+0.799
$Hg_2^{++} + 2e \rightleftharpoons 2Hg$	+0.789
$Fe^{+3} + e \rightleftharpoons Fe^{++}$	+0.771
$OBr^- + H_2O + 2e \rightleftharpoons Br^- + 2OH^-$	+0.76
Q(satd. soln.) $+ 2H^+ + 2e \rightleftharpoons H_2Q$(satd. soln.)	
(quinhydrone electrode)	+0.700
$O_2 + 2H^+ + 2e \rightleftharpoons H_2O_2$	+0.682
$2HgCl_2 + 2e \rightleftharpoons Hg_2Cl_2 + 2Cl^-$	+0.63
$H_3AsO_4 + 2H^+ + 2e \rightleftharpoons H_3AsO_3 + H_2O$	+0.559
$I_2(I_3^-) + 2e \rightleftharpoons 2I^-$	+0.535
$Fe(CN)_6^{3-} + e \rightleftharpoons Fe(CN)_6^{4-}$	+0.36
$Cu^{++} + 2e \rightleftharpoons Cu$	+0.337
$UO_2^{++} + 4H^+ + 2e \rightleftharpoons U^{4+} + 2H_2O$	+0.334
$BiO + 2H^+ + 3e \rightleftharpoons Bi + H_2O$	+0.32
$Hg_2Cl_2 + 2e \rightleftharpoons 2Hg + 2Cl^-$ (1 M KCl) (calomel half-cell)	+0.285
$Hg_2Cl_2 + 2e \rightleftharpoons 2Hg + 2Cl^-$ (satd. KCl) (calomel half-cell)	+0.246

(handwritten annotation:) most powerful oxid. agent

Table 13   Standard potentials (*Continued*)

Half-reaction	E, volts
$AgCl + e \rightleftharpoons Ag + Cl^-$	+0.222
$SbO^+ + 2H^+ + 3e \rightleftharpoons Sb + H_2O$	+0.212
$S_4O_6^= + 2e \rightleftharpoons 2S_2O_3^=$	+0.17
$SO_4^= + 4H^+ + 2e \rightleftharpoons H_2SO_3 + H_2O$	+0.17
$Sn^{4+} + 2e \rightleftharpoons Sn^{++}$	+0.15
$TiO^{++} + 2H^+ + e \rightleftharpoons Ti^{3+} + H_2O$	+0.1
$AgBr + e \rightleftharpoons Ag + Br^-$	+0.095
$2H^+ + 2e \rightleftharpoons H_2$	+0.000
$Pb^{++} + 2e \rightleftharpoons Pb$	−0.126
$Sn^{++} + 2e \rightleftharpoons Sn$	−0.136
$AgI + e \rightleftharpoons Ag + I^-$	−0.151
$Ni^{++} + 2e \rightleftharpoons Ni$	−0.24
$Co^{++} + 2e \rightleftharpoons Co$	−0.28
$Cd^{++} + 2e \rightleftharpoons Cd$	−0.403
$Cr^{3+} + e \rightleftharpoons Cr^{++}$	−0.41
$2H^+(10^{-7} M) + 2e \rightleftharpoons H_2$	−0.414
$Fe^{++} + 2e \rightleftharpoons Fe$	−0.440
$2CO_2 + 2H^+ + 2e \rightleftharpoons H_2C_2O_4$	−0.49
$S + 2e \rightleftharpoons S^=$	−0.51
$AsO_4^{3-} + 3H_2O + 2e \rightleftharpoons H_2AsO_3^- + 4OH^-$	−0.67
$Cr^{3+} + 3e \rightleftharpoons Cr$	−0.74
$Zn^{++} + 2e \rightleftharpoons Zn$	−0.763
$Mn^{++} + 2e \rightleftharpoons Mn$	−1.18
$Al^{3+} + 3e \rightleftharpoons Al$	−1.67
$AlO_2^- + 2H_2O + 3e \rightleftharpoons Al + 4OH^-$	−2.35
$Mg^{++} + 2e \rightleftharpoons Mg$	−2.37
$Na^+ + e \rightleftharpoons Na$	−2.714
$Ca^{++} + 2e \rightleftharpoons Ca$	−2.87
$Sr^{++} + 2e \rightleftharpoons Sr$	−2.89
$Ba^{++} + 2e \rightleftharpoons Ba$	−2.90
$K^+ + e \rightleftharpoons K$ ← Most preferred. Agent	−2.925

Table 14   Abbreviations

(The abbreviations in the first group are of units of measurement and conform mostly to the recommendations of the United States of America Standards Institute. With the exception of "in." for "inches" they are used without periods and usually only in conjunction with numerical values.   The abbreviations in the second group conform mostly to those used in *Chemical Abstracts*.   They are used extensively in the problems, but only sparingly in the main text and illustrative material.)

I

Å	angstrom units	in.	inch(es)
amp	ampere(s)	kg-cal	kilogram-calorie(s)
atm	atmosphere(s)	lb	pound(s)
c	curie(s)	M	molar
cal	calorie(s)	ma	milliampere(s)
cg	centigram(s)	mc	millicurie(s)
cm	centimeter(s)	mg	milligram(s)
coul	coulomb(s)	min	minute(s)
cpm	counts per minute	ml	milliliter(s)
cu ft	cubic feet	mm	millimeter(s)
°C	degrees centigrade (or	mμ	millimicron(s)
	Celcius)	mv	millivolt(s)
F	formal	N	normal
g	gram(s)	μa	microampere(s)
gal	gallon(s)	μg	microgram(s)
hr	hour(s)	μl	microliter(s)
°K	degrees Kelvin (absolute	sec	second(s)
	scale)		

II

amt.	amount	min.	minimum
approx.	approximate(ly)	mixt.	mixture
aq.	aqueous	mol. wt.	molecular weight
at. wt.	atomic weight	no.	number
compd.	compound	p.p.t.	parts per thousand
concd.	concentrated	p.p.m.	parts per million
concn.	concentration	ppt.	precipitate
const.	constant	pptd.	precipitated
contg.	containing	pptn.	precipitation
detn.	determination	satd.	saturated
dil.	dilute	soln.	solution
emf	electromotive force	soly.	solubility
equiv.	equivalent	sp. gr.	specific gravity
f. wt.	formula weight	temp.	temperature
insol.	insoluble	vol.	volume
max.	maximum	wt.	weight
meq. wt.	milliequivalent weight		

Table 15   Minerals and technical products

(This table gives the essential composition of minerals and technical products frequently encountered in the problems in this book.)

Apatite	$Ca_3(PO_4)_2 \cdot Ca(Cl,F)_2$
Calcite	$CaCO_3$
Chromite	$Fe(CrO_2)_2$
Dolomite	$(Ca,Mg)CO_3$
Feldspar	$KAlSi_3O_8$
Lime	CaO
Limestone	$CaCO_3$
Limonite	Fe_2O_3
Magnetite	Fe_3O_4
Pearl ash	K_2CO_3
Pyrolusite	MnO_2
Red lead	Pb_3O_4
Siderite	$FeCO_3$
Soda ash	Na_2CO_3
Spathic iron ore	$FeCO_3$
Stibnite	Sb_2S_3

Table 16   Formula weights

(These weights cover most of the elements and compounds encountered in the problems of this text.)

Ag	107.87	Bi_2S_3	514.15
Ag_3AsO_4	462.53	Br	79.91
AgBr	187.78	Br_2	159.82
$AgBrO_3$	235.78	Ca	40.08
AgCl	143.32	$CaCl_2$	110.99
AgI	234.77	$CaCl_2 \cdot 2H_2O$	147.02
$AgNO_3$	169.87	$CaCO_3$	100.09
Ag_3PO_4	418.58	CaF_2	78.08
Ag_2SO_4	311.80	$Ca(NO_3)_2$	164.09
Al	26.98	CaO	56.08
$AlBr_3$	266.71	$Ca(OH)_2$	74.09
Al_2O_3	101.96	$Ca_3(PO_4)_2$	310.18
$Al(OH)_3$	78.00	$3Ca_3(PO_4)_2 \cdot CaCl_2$	1041.53
$Al_2(SO_4)_3$	342.15	$CaSO_4$	136.14
$Al_2(SO_4)_3 \cdot 18H_2O$	666.43	Ce	140.12
As	74.92	CeO_2	172.12
As_2O_3	197.84	$Ce(SO_4)_2 \cdot 2(NH_4)_2SO_4 \cdot 2H_2O$	632.56
As_2O_5	229.84	C	12.01
As_2S_3	246.04	CH_3COOH (acetic acid)	60.05
B	10.81	$(CH_3CO)_2O$ (acetic anhydride)	102.09
B_2O_3	69.62	CO_2	44.01
Ba	137.34	$CO(NH_2)_2$ (urea)	60.06
$Ba_3(AsO_4)_2$	689.86	$CS(NH_2)_2$ (thiourea)	76.12
$BaBr_2$	297.16	Cl	35.45
$BaCl_2$	208.25	Cl_2	70.90
$BaCl_2 \cdot 2H_2O$	244.28	Co	58.93
$BaCO_3$	197.35	Cr	52.00
BaC_2O_4	225.36	$CrCl_3$	158.35
BaF_2	175.34	Cr_2O_3	151.99
BaI_2	391.15	$Cr_2(SO_4)_3$	392.18
$Ba(IO_3)_2$	487.15	Cu	63.54
BaO	153.34	CuO	79.54
$Ba(OH)_2$	171.36	$Cu_2(OH)_2CO_3$	221.11
$Ba(OH)_2 \cdot 8H_2O$	315.48	CuS	95.60
$Ba_3(PO_4)_2$	601.96	Cu_2S	159.14
$BaSO_4$	233.40	$CuSO_4 \cdot 5H_2O$	249.68
Be	9.01	F	19.00
BeO	25.01	F_2	38.00
Bi	208.98	Fe	55.85
$Bi(NO_3)_3 \cdot 5H_2O$	485.07	$FeCl_3$	162.21
BiO_2	240.97	$FeCl_3 \cdot 6H_2O$	270.30
Bi_2O_3	465.96	$FeCO_3$	115.85
$BiOHCO_3$	285.99		

Table 16   Formula weights *(Continued)*

$Fe(CrO_2)_2$	223.84	KCNS	97.18
$Fe(NO_3)_3 \cdot 6H_2O$	349.95	K_2CO_3	138.21
FeO	71.85	K_2CrO_4	194.20
Fe_2O_3	159.69	$K_2Cr_2O_7$	294.19
Fe_3O_4	231.54	$K_3Fe(CN)_6$	329.26
$Fe(OH)_3$	106.87	$K_4Fe(CN)_6 \cdot 3H_2O$	422.41
FeS_2	119.98	$KHC_4H_4O_6$ (tartrate)	188.18
Fe_2Si	139.78	$KHC_8H_4O_4$ (phthalate)	204.23
$FeSO_4 \cdot 7H_2O$	278.05	$KHCO_3$	100.12
$Fe_2(SO_4)_3$	399.87	KHC_2O_4	128.11
$Fe_2(SO_4)_3 \cdot 9H_2O$	562.01	$KHC_2O_4 \cdot H_2O$	146.13
$FeSO_4 \cdot (NH_4)_2SO_4 \cdot 6H_2O$	392.14	$KHC_2O_4 \cdot H_2C_2O_4 \cdot 2H_2O$	254.20
H	1.008	$KH(IO_3)_2$	389.92
H_2	2.016	$KHSO_4$	136.17
HBr	80.92	KI	166.01
$HCHO_2$ (formic acid)	46.03	KIO_3	214.00
$HC_2H_3O_2$ (acetic acid)	60.05	$KMnO_4$	158.04
$HC_7H_5O_2$ (benzoic acid)	122.12	$KNaC_4H_4O_6 \cdot 4H_2O$	282.19
HCl	36.46	$KNaCO_3$	122.10
$HClO_4$	100.46	KNO_2	85.11
$H_2C_2O_4 \cdot 2H_2O$ (oxalic acid)	126.07	KNO_3	101.11
HCOOH (formic acid)	46.03	K_2O	94.20
HNO_3	63.01	KOH	56.11
H_2O	18.02	K_3PO_4	212.28
H_2O_2	34.02	K_2PtCl_6	486.01
H_3PO_3	82.00	K_2SO_4	174.27
H_3PO_4	98.00	$K_2SO_4 \cdot Al_2(SO_4)_3 \cdot 24H_2O$	948.78
H_2S	34.08	$K_2SO_4 \cdot Cr_2(SO_4)_3 \cdot 24H_2O$	998.82
H_2SO_3	82.08	Li	6.94
$HSO_3 \cdot NH_2$ (sulfamic acid)	97.09	LiCl	42.39
H_2SO_4	98.08	Li_2CO_3	73.89
Hg	200.59	Li_2O	29.88
Hg_2Br_2	561.00	LiOH	23.95
Hg_2Cl_2	472.09	Mg	24.31
Hg_2I_2	654.99	$MgCl_2$	95.22
HgO	216.59	$MgCO_3$	84.32
I	126.91	$MgNH_4AsO_4$	181.27
I_2	253.82	$MgNH_4PO_4$	137.32
K	39.10	MgO	40.31
$KAl(SO_4)_2 \cdot 12H_2O$	474.39	$Mg(OH)_2$	58.33
K_3AsO_4	256.23	$Mg_2P_2O_7$	222.57
$KBrO_3$	167.01	$MgSO_4$	120.37
KCl	74.56	$MgSO_4 \cdot 7H_2O$	246.48
$KClO_3$	122.56	Mn	54.94
$KClO_4$	138.56	MnO	70.94
KCN	65.12	MnO_2	86.94

Table 16 Formula weights (Continued)

Mn_2O_3	157.87	Na_2O_2		77.98
Mn_3O_4	228.81	NaOH		40.00
$Mn_2P_2O_7$	283.82	Na_3PO_4		164.11
Mo	95.94	$Na_3PO_4 \cdot 12H_2O$		380.12
MoO_3	143.94	Na_2S		78.04
$Mo_{24}O_{37}$	2894.56	Na_2SO_3		126.04
MoS_3	192.13	$Na_2SO_4 \cdot 10H_2O$		322.19
N	14.007	$Na_2S_2O_3$		158.11
N_2	28.02	$Na_2S_2O_3 \cdot 5H_2O$		248.18
NH_3	17.03	Ni		58.71
NH_4Cl	53.49	$NiC_8H_{14}O_4N_4$ (Ni dimethyl-		
$(NH_4)_2C_2O_4 \cdot H_2O$	142.11	glyoxime)		288.94
$(NH_4)_2HPO_4$	132.05	O		16.00
NH_4OH	35.05	O_2		32.00
$(NH_4)_3PO_4 \cdot 12MoO_3$	1876.37	P		30.97
$(NH_4)_2PtCl_6$	443.89	P_2O_5		141.94
$(NH_4)_2SO_4$	132.14	Pb		207.19
NO	30.01	$PbCl_2$		278.10
NO_2	46.01	PbClF		261.64
N_2O_3	76.01	PbC_2O_4		295.21
Na	22.99	$PbCrO_4$		323.18
Na_3AsO_3	191.89	PbI_2		461.00
Na_3AsO_4	207.89	$Pb(IO_3)_2$		557.00
$Na_2B_4O_7$	201.22	$Pb(NO_3)_2$		331.20
$Na_2B_4O_7 \cdot 10H_2O$	381.37	PbO		223.19
NaBr	102.90	PbO_2		239.19
$NaBrO_3$	150.90	Pb_2O_3		462.38
$NaCHO_2$ (formate)	68.01	Pb_3O_4		685.57
$NaC_2H_3O_2$ (acetate)	82.03	$Pb_3(PO_4)_2$		811.51
NaCl	58.44	$PbSO_4$		303.25
NaCN	49.01	S		32.064
Na_2CO_3	105.99	SO_2		64.06
$Na_2C_2O_4$	134.00	SO_3		80.07
Na_2HAsO_3	169.90	Sb		121.75
$NaHCO_3$	84.00	Sb_2O_3		291.50
$NaHC_2O_4$	112.01	Sb_2O_4		307.52
Na_2HPO_4	142.04	Sb_2O_5		323.50
$Na_2HPO_4 \cdot 12H_2O$	358.14	Sb_2S_3		339.69
NaHS	56.06	Si		28.09
NaH_2PO_4	119.98	$SiCl_4$		169.90
$NaH_2PO_4 \cdot H_2O$	137.99	SiF_4		104.08
NaI	149.89	SiO_2		60.08
$NaKCO_3$	122.10	Sn		118.69
$NaNO_2$	69.00	$SnCl_2$		189.60
$NaNO_3$	84.99	$SnCl_4$		260.50
Na_2O	61.98			

Table 16   Formula weights *(Continued)*

SnO_2	150.69	W	183.85
Sr	87.62	WO_3	231.85
$SrCl_2 \cdot 6H_2O$	266.62	Zn	65.37
$SrCO_3$	147.63	$ZnNH_4PO_4$	178.38
SrO	103.62	ZnO	81.37
$SrSO_4$	183.68	$Zn_2P_2O_7$	304.68
Ti	47.90	$ZnSO_4$	161.43
TiO_2	79.90	$ZnSO_4 \cdot 7H_2O$	287.54
U	238.03	Zr	91.22
UO_3	286.03	ZrO_2	123.22
U_3O_8	842.09		

Partial list of atomic weights, 1961 (Based on C-12)

(Only those elements more commonly encountered in analytical chemistry are included.   In the case of a few of the atomic weight values, a slight variation in the last significant figure may occur either because of experimental uncertainty or because of natural variation in isotopic composition.)

Element	Symbol	Atomic weight	Element	Symbol	Atomic weight
Aluminum	Al	26.9815	Nickel	Ni	58.71
Antimony	Sb	121.75	Niobium	Nb	92.906
Arsenic	As	74.9216	Nitrogen	N	14.0067
Barium	Ba	137.34	Osmium	Os	190.2
Beryllium	Be	9.0122	Oxygen	O	15.9994
Bismuth	Bi	208.980	Palladium	Pd	106.4
Boron	B	10.811	Phosphorus	P	30.9738
Bromine	Br	79.909	Platinum	Pt	195.09
Cadmium	Cd	112.40	Potassium	K	39.102
Calcium	Ca	40.08	Rhodium	Rh	102.905
Carbon	C	12.01115	Rubinium	Rb	85.47
Cerium	Ce	140.12	Ruthenium	Ru	101.07
Cesium	Cs	132.905	Selenium	Se	78.96
Chlorine	Cl	35.453	Silicon	Si	28.086
Chromium	Cr	51.996	Silver	Ag	107.870
Cobalt	Co	58.9332	Sodium	Na	22.9898
Copper	Cu	63.54	Strontium	Sr	87.62
Fluorine	F	18.9984	Sulfur	S	32.064
Gold	Au	196.967	Tantalum	Ta	180.948
Hydrogen	H	1.00797	Tellurium	Te	127.60
Iodine	I	126.9044	Thallium	Tl	204.37
Iridium	Ir	192.2	Thorium	Th	232.038
Iron	Fe	55.847	Tin	Sn	118.69
Lead	Pb	207.19	Titanium	Ti	47.90
Lithium	Li	6.939	Tungsten	W	183.85
Magnesium	Mg	24.312	Uranium	U	238.03
Manganese	Mn	54.9380	Vanadium	V	50.942
Mercury	Hg	200.59	Zinc	Zn	65.37
Molybdenum	Mo	95.94	Zirconium	Zr	91.22

Logarithms of numbers

Natural numbers	0	1	2	3	4	5	6	7	8	9	1	2	3	4	5	6	7	8	9
											*Proportional parts*								
10	0000	0043	0086	0128	0170	0212	0253	0294	0334	0374	4	8	12	17	21	25	29	33	37
11	0414	0453	0492	0531	0569	0607	0645	0682	0719	0755	4	8	11	15	19	23	26	30	34
12	0792	0828	0864	0899	0934	0969	1004	1038	1072	1106	3	7	10	14	17	21	24	28	31
13	1139	1173	1206	1239	1271	1303	1335	1367	1399	1430	3	6	10	13	16	19	23	26	29
14	1461	1492	1523	1553	1584	1614	1644	1673	1703	1732	3	6	9	12	15	18	21	24	27
15	1761	1790	1818	1847	1875	1903	1931	1959	1987	2014	3	6	8	11	14	17	20	22	25
16	2041	2068	2095	2122	2148	2175	2201	2227	2253	2279	3	5	8	11	13	16	18	21	24
17	2304	2330	2355	2380	2405	2430	2455	2480	2504	2529	2	5	7	10	12	15	17	20	22
18	2553	2577	2601	2625	2648	2672	2695	2718	2742	2765	2	5	7	9	12	14	16	19	21
19	2788	2810	2833	2856	2878	2900	2923	2945	2967	2989	2	4	7	9	11	13	16	18	20
20	3010	3032	3054	3075	3096	3118	3139	3160	3181	3201	2	4	6	8	11	13	15	17	19
21	3222	3243	3263	3284	3304	3324	3345	3365	3385	3404	2	4	6	8	10	12	14	16	18
22	3424	3444	3464	3483	3502	3522	3541	3560	3579	3598	2	4	6	8	10	12	14	15	17
23	3617	3636	3655	3674	3692	3711	3729	3747	3766	3784	2	4	6	7	9	11	13	15	17
24	3802	3820	3838	3856	3874	3892	3909	3927	3945	3962	2	4	5	7	9	11	12	14	16
25	3979	3997	4014	4031	4048	4065	4082	4099	4116	4133	2	3	5	7	9	10	12	14	15
26	4150	4166	4183	4200	4216	4232	4249	4265	4281	4298	2	3	5	7	8	10	11	13	15
27	4314	4330	4346	4362	4378	4393	4409	4425	4440	4456	2	3	5	6	8	9	11	13	14
28	4472	4487	4502	4518	4533	4548	4564	4579	4594	4609	2	3	5	6	8	9	11	12	14
29	4624	4639	4654	4669	4683	4698	4713	4728	4742	4757	1	3	4	6	7	9	10	12	13
30	4771	4786	4800	4814	4829	4843	4857	4871	4886	4900	1	3	4	6	7	9	10	11	13
31	4914	4928	4942	4955	4969	4983	4997	5011	5024	5038	1	3	4	6	7	8	10	11	12
32	5051	5065	5079	5092	5105	5119	5132	5145	5159	5172	1	3	4	5	7	8	9	11	12
33	5185	5198	5211	5224	5237	5250	5263	5276	5289	5302	1	3	4	5	6	8	9	10	12
34	5315	5328	5340	5353	5366	5378	5391	5403	5416	5428	1	3	4	5	6	8	9	10	11
35	5441	5453	5465	5478	5490	5502	5514	5527	5539	5551	1	2	4	5	6	7	9	10	11
36	5563	5575	5587	5599	5611	5623	5635	5647	5658	5670	1	2	4	5	6	7	8	10	11
37	5682	5694	5705	5717	5729	5740	5752	5763	5775	5786	1	2	3	5	6	7	8	9	10
38	5798	5809	5821	5832	5843	5855	5866	5877	5888	5899	1	2	3	5	6	7	8	9	10
39	5911	5922	5933	5944	5955	5966	5977	5988	5999	6010	1	2	3	4	5	7	8	9	10
40	6021	6031	6042	6053	6064	6075	6085	6096	6107	6117	1	2	3	4	5	6	8	9	10
41	6128	6138	6149	6160	6170	6180	6191	6201	6212	6222	1	2	3	4	5	6	7	8	9
42	6232	6243	6253	6263	6274	6284	6294	6304	6314	6325	1	2	3	4	5	6	7	8	9
43	6335	6345	6355	6365	6375	6385	6395	6405	6415	6425	1	2	3	4	5	6	7	8	9
44	6435	6444	6454	6464	6474	6484	6493	6503	6513	6522	1	2	3	4	5	6	7	8	9
45	6532	6542	6551	6561	6571	6580	6590	6599	6609	6618	1	2	3	4	5	6	7	8	9
46	6628	6637	6646	6656	6665	6675	6684	6693	6702	6712	1	2	3	4	5	6	7	7	8
47	6721	6730	6739	6749	6758	6767	6776	6785	6794	6803	1	2	3	4	5	5	6	7	8
48	6812	6821	6830	6839	6848	6857	6866	6875	6884	6893	1	2	3	4	4	5	6	7	8
49	6902	6911	6920	6928	6937	6946	6955	6964	6972	6981	1	2	3	4	4	5	6	7	8
50	6990	6998	7007	7016	7024	7033	7042	7050	7059	7067	1	2	3	3	4	5	6	7	8
51	7076	7084	7093	7101	7110	7118	7126	7135	7143	7152	1	2	3	3	4	5	6	7	8
52	7160	7168	7177	7185	7193	7202	7210	7218	7226	7235	1	2	2	3	4	5	6	7	7
53	7243	7251	7259	7267	7275	7284	7292	7300	7308	7316	1	2	2	3	4	5	6	6	7
54	7324	7332	7340	7348	7356	7364	7372	7380	7388	7396	1	2	2	3	4	5	6	6	7

Logarithms *(Continued)*

Natural numbers	0	1	2	3	4	5	6	7	8	9	*Proportional parts*								
											1	2	3	4	5	6	7	8	9
55	7404	7412	7419	7427	7435	7443	7451	7459	7466	7474	1	2	2	3	4	5	5	6	7
56	7482	7490	7497	7505	7513	7520	7528	7536	7543	7551	1	2	2	3	4	5	5	6	7
57	7559	7566	7574	7582	7589	7597	7604	7612	7619	7627	1	2	2	3	4	5	5	6	7
58	7634	7642	7649	7657	7664	7672	7679	7686	7694	7701	1	1	2	3	4	4	5	6	7
59	7709	7716	7723	7731	7738	7745	7752	7760	7767	7774	1	1	2	3	4	4	5	6	7
60	7782	7789	7796	7803	7810	7818	7825	7832	7839	7846	1	1	2	3	4	4	5	6	6
61	7853	7860	7868	7875	7882	7889	7896	7903	7910	7917	1	1	2	3	4	4	5	6	6
62	7924	7931	7938	7945	7952	7959	7966	7973	7980	7987	1	1	2	3	3	4	5	6	6
63	7993	8000	8007	8014	8021	8028	8035	8041	8048	8055	1	1	2	3	3	4	5	5	6
64	8062	8069	8075	8082	8089	8096	8102	8109	8116	8122	1	1	2	3	3	4	5	5	6
65	8129	8136	8142	8149	8156	8162	8169	8176	8182	8189	1	1	2	3	3	4	5	5	6
66	8195	8202	8209	8215	8222	8228	8235	8241	8248	8254	1	1	2	3	3	4	5	5	6
67	8261	8267	8274	8280	8287	8293	8299	8306	8312	8319	1	1	2	3	3	4	5	5	6
68	8325	8331	8338	8344	8351	8357	8363	8370	8376	8382	1	1	2	3	3	4	4	5	6
69	8388	8395	8401	8407	8414	8420	8426	8432	8439	8445	1	1	2	2	3	4	4	5	6
70	8451	8457	8463	8470	8476	8482	8488	8494	8500	8506	1	1	2	2	3	4	4	5	6
71	8513	8519	8525	8531	8537	8543	8549	8555	8561	8567	1	1	2	2	3	4	4	5	5
72	8573	8579	8585	8591	8597	8603	8609	8615	8621	8627	1	1	2	2	3	4	4	5	5
73	8633	8639	8645	8651	8657	8663	8669	8675	8681	8686	1	1	2	2	3	4	4	5	5
74	8692	8698	8704	8710	8716	8722	8727	8733	8739	8745	1	1	2	2	3	4	4	5	5
75	8751	8756	8762	8768	8774	8779	8785	8791	8797	8802	1	1	2	2	3	3	4	5	5
76	8808	8814	8820	8825	8831	8837	8842	8848	8854	8859	1	1	2	2	3	3	4	5	5
77	8865	8871	8876	8882	8887	8893	8899	8904	8910	8915	1	1	2	2	3	3	4	4	5
78	8921	8927	8932	8938	8943	8949	8954	8960	8965	8971	1	1	2	2	3	3	4	4	5
79	8976	8982	8987	8993	8998	9004	9009	9015	9020	9025	1	1	2	2	3	3	4	4	5
80	9031	9036	9042	9047	9053	9058	9063	9069	9074	9079	1	1	2	2	3	3	4	4	5
81	9085	9090	9096	9101	9106	9112	9117	9122	9128	9133	1	1	2	2	3	3	4	4	5
82	9138	9143	9149	9154	9159	9165	9170	9175	9180	9186	1	1	2	2	3	3	4	4	5
83	9191	9196	9201	9206	9212	9217	9222	9227	9232	9238	1	1	2	2	3	3	4	4	5
84	9243	9248	9253	9258	9263	9269	9274	9279	9284	9289	1	1	2	2	3	3	4	4	5
85	9294	9299	9304	9309	9315	9320	9325	9330	9335	9340	1	1	2	2	3	3	4	4	5
86	9345	9350	9355	9360	9365	9370	9375	9380	9385	9390	1	1	2	2	3	3	4	4	5
87	9395	9400	9405	9410	9415	9420	9425	9430	9435	9440	0	1	1	2	2	3	3	4	4
88	9445	9450	9455	9460	9465	9469	9474	9479	9484	9489	0	1	1	2	2	3	3	4	4
89	9494	9499	9504	9509	9513	9518	9523	9528	9533	9538	0	1	1	2	2	3	3	4	4
90	9542	9547	9552	9557	9562	9566	9571	9576	9581	9586	0	1	1	2	2	3	3	4	4
91	9590	9595	9600	9605	9609	9614	9619	9624	9628	9633	0	1	1	2	2	3	3	4	4
92	9638	9643	9647	9652	9657	9661	9666	9671	9675	9680	0	1	1	2	2	3	3	4	4
93	9685	9689	9694	9699	9703	9708	9713	9717	9722	9727	0	1	1	2	2	3	3	4	4
94	9731	9736	9741	9745	9750	9754	9759	9763	9768	9773	0	1	1	2	2	3	3	4	4
95	9777	9782	9786	9791	9795	9800	9805	9809	9814	9818	0	1	1	2	2	3	3	4	4
96	9823	9827	9832	9836	9841	9845	9850	9854	9859	9863	0	1	1	2	2	3	3	4	4
97	9868	9872	9877	9881	9886	9890	9894	9899	9903	9908	0	1	1	2	2	3	3	4	4
98	9912	9917	9921	9926	9930	9934	9939	9943	9948	9952	0	1	1	2	2	3	3	4	4
99	9956	9961	9965	9969	9974	9978	9983	9987	9991	9996	0	1	1	2	2	3	3	3	4

Antilogarithms

Logarithms	0	1	2	3	4	5	6	7	8	9	1	2	3	4	5	6	7	8	9
															Proportional parts				
.00	1000	1002	1005	1007	1009	1012	1014	1016	1019	1021	0	0	1	1	1	1	2	2	2
.01	1023	1026	1028	1030	1033	1035	1038	1040	1042	1045	0	0	1	1	1	1	2	2	2
.02	1047	1050	1052	1054	1057	1059	1062	1064	1067	1069	0	0	1	1	1	1	2	2	2
.03	1072	1074	1076	1079	1081	1084	1086	1089	1091	1094	0	0	1	1	1	1	2	2	2
.04	1096	1099	1102	1104	1107	1109	1112	1114	1117	1119	0	1	1	1	1	2	2	2	2
.05	1122	1125	1127	1130	1132	1135	1138	1140	1143	1146	0	1	1	1	1	2	2	2	2
.06	1148	1151	1153	1156	1159	1161	1164	1167	1169	1172	0	1	1	1	1	2	2	2	2
.07	1175	1178	1180	1183	1186	1189	1191	1194	1197	1199	0	1	1	1	1	2	2	2	2
.08	1202	1205	1208	1211	1213	1216	1219	1222	1225	1227	0	1	1	1	1	2	2	2	3
.09	1230	1233	1236	1239	1242	1245	1247	1250	1253	1256	0	1	1	1	1	2	2	2	3
.10	1259	1262	1265	1268	1271	1274	1276	1279	1282	1285	0	1	1	1	1	2	2	2	3
.11	1288	1291	1294	1297	1300	1303	1306	1309	1312	1315	0	1	1	1	2	2	2	2	3
.12	1318	1321	1324	1327	1330	1334	1337	1340	1343	1346	0	1	1	1	2	2	2	2	3
.13	1349	1352	1355	1358	1361	1365	1368	1371	1374	1377	0	1	1	1	2	2	2	3	3
.14	1380	1384	1387	1390	1393	1396	1400	1403	1406	1409	0	1	1	1	2	2	2	3	3
.15	1413	1416	1419	1422	1426	1429	1432	1435	1439	1442	0	1	1	1	2	2	2	3	3
.16	1445	1449	1452	1455	1459	1462	1466	1469	1472	1476	0	1	1	1	2	2	2	3	3
.17	1479	1483	1486	1489	1493	1496	1500	1503	1507	1510	0	1	1	1	2	2	2	3	3
.18	1514	1517	1521	1524	1528	1531	1535	1538	1542	1545	0	1	1	1	2	2	2	3	3
.19	1549	1552	1556	1560	1563	1567	1570	1574	1578	1581	0	1	1	1	2	2	3	3	3
.20	1585	1589	1592	1596	1600	1603	1607	1611	1614	1618	0	1	1	1	2	2	3	3	3
.21	1622	1626	1629	1633	1637	1641	1644	1648	1652	1656	0	1	1	2	2	2	3	3	3
.22	1660	1663	1667	1671	1675	1679	1683	1687	1690	1694	0	1	1	2	2	2	3	3	3
.23	1698	1702	1706	1710	1714	1718	1722	1726	1730	1734	0	1	1	2	2	2	3	3	4
.24	1738	1742	1746	1750	1754	1758	1762	1766	1770	1774	0	1	1	2	2	2	3	3	4
.25	1778	1782	1786	1791	1795	1799	1803	1807	1811	1816	0	1	1	2	2	2	3	3	4
.26	1820	1824	1828	1832	1837	1841	1845	1849	1854	1858	0	1	1	2	2	3	3	3	4
.27	1862	1866	1871	1875	1879	1884	1888	1892	1897	1901	0	1	1	2	2	3	3	3	4
.28	1905	1910	1914	1919	1923	1928	1932	1936	1941	1945	0	1	1	2	2	3	3	4	4
.29	1950	1954	1959	1963	1968	1972	1977	1982	1986	1991	0	1	1	2	2	3	3	4	4
.30	1995	2000	2004	2009	2014	2018	2023	2028	2032	2037	0	1	1	2	2	3	3	4	4
.31	2042	2046	2051	2056	2061	2065	2070	2075	2080	2084	0	1	1	2	2	3	3	4	4
.32	2089	2094	2099	2104	2109	2113	2118	2123	2128	2133	0	1	1	2	2	3	3	4	4
.33	2138	2143	2148	2153	2158	2163	2168	2173	2178	2183	0	1	1	2	2	3	3	4	4
.34	2188	2193	2198	2203	2208	2213	2218	2223	2228	2234	1	1	2	2	3	3	4	4	5
.35	2239	2244	2249	2254	2259	2265	2270	2275	2280	2286	1	1	2	2	3	3	4	4	5
.36	2291	2296	2301	2307	2312	2317	2323	2328	2333	2339	1	1	2	2	3	3	4	4	5
.37	2344	2350	2355	2360	2366	2371	2377	2382	2388	2393	1	1	2	2	3	3	4	4	5
.38	2399	2404	2410	2415	1421	2427	2432	2438	2443	2449	1	1	2	2	3	3	4	4	5
.39	2455	2460	2466	2472	2477	2483	2489	2495	2500	2506	1	1	2	2	3	3	4	5	5
.40	2512	2518	2523	2529	2535	2541	2547	2553	2559	2564	1	1	2	2	3	4	4	5	5
.41	2570	2576	2582	2588	2594	2600	2606	2612	2618	2624	1	1	2	2	3	4	4	5	5
.42	2630	2636	2642	2649	2655	2661	2667	2673	2679	2685	1	1	2	2	3	4	4	5	6
.43	2692	2698	2704	2710	2716	2723	2729	2735	2742	2748	1	1	2	3	3	4	4	5	6
.44	2754	2761	2767	2773	2780	2786	2793	2799	2805	2812	1	1	2	3	3	4	4	5	6
.45	2818	2825	2831	2838	2844	2851	2858	2864	2871	2877	1	1	2	3	3	4	5	5	6
.46	2884	2891	2897	2904	2911	2917	2924	2931	2938	2944	1	1	2	3	3	4	5	5	6
.47	2951	2958	2965	2972	2979	2985	2992	2999	3006	3013	1	1	2	3	3	4	5	5	6
.48	3020	3027	2034	3041	3048	3055	3062	3069	3076	3083	1	1	2	3	4	4	5	6	6
.49	3090	3097	3105	3112	3119	3126	3133	3141	3148	3155	1	1	2	3	4	4	5	6	6

Logarithms	0	1	2	3	4	5	6	7	·8	9	Proportional parts								
											1	2	3	4	5	6	7	8	9
.50	3162	3170	3177	3184	3192	3199	3206	3214	3221	3228	1	1	2	3	4	4	5	6	7
.51	3236	3243	3251	3258	3266	3273	3281	3289	3296	3304	1	2	2	3	4	5	5	6	7
.52	3311	3319	3327	3334	3342	3350	3357	3365	3373	3381	1	2	2	3	4	5	5	6	7
.53	3388	3396	3403	3412	3420	3428	3436	3443	3451	3459	1	2	2	3	4	5	6	6	7
.54	3467	3475	3483	3491	3499	3508	3516	3524	2532	3540	1	2	2	3	4	5	6	6	7
.55	3548	3556	3565	3573	3581	3589	3597	3606	3614	3622	1	2	2	3	4	5	6	7	7
.56	3631	3639	3648	3656	3664	3673	3681	3690	3698	3707	1	2	3	3	4	5	6	7	8
.57	3715	3724	3733	3741	3750	3758	3767	3776	3784	3793	1	2	3	3	4	5	6	7	8
.58	3802	3811	3819	3828	3837	3846	3855	3864	3873	3882	1	2	3	4	4	5	6	7	8
.59	3890	3899	3908	3917	3926	3936	3945	3954	3963	3972	1	2	3	4	5	5	6	7	8
.60	3981	3990	3999	4009	4018	4027	4036	4046	4055	4064	1	2	3	4	5	6	6	7	8
.61	4074	4083	4093	4102	4111	4121	4130	4140	4150	4159	1	2	3	4	5	6	7	8	9
.62	4169	4178	4188	4198	4207	4217	4227	4236	4246	4256	1	2	3	4	5	6	7	8	9
.63	4266	4276	4285	4295	4305	4315	4325	4335	4345	4355	1	2	3	4	5	6	7	8	9
.64	4365	4375	4385	4395	4406	4416	4426	4436	4446	4457	1	2	3	4	5	6	7	8	9
.65	4467	4477	4487	4498	4508	4519	4529	4539	4550	4560	1	2	3	4	5	6	7	8	9
.66	4571	4581	4592	4603	4613	4624	4634	4645	4656	4667	1	2	3	4	6	7	8	9	10
.67	4677	4688	4699	4710	4721	4732	4742	4753	4764	4775	1	2	3	4	5	6	7	9	10
.68	4786	4797	4808	4819	4831	4842	4853	4864	4875	4887	1	2	3	4	5	7	8	9	10
.69	4898	4909	4920	4932	4943	4955	4966	4977	4989	5000	1	2	3	5	6	7	8	9	10
.70	5012	5023	5035	5047	5058	5070	5082	5093	5105	5117	1	2	4	5	6	7	8	9	11
.71	5129	5140	5152	5164	5176	5188	5200	5212	5224	5236	1	2	4	5	6	7	8	10	11
.72	5248	5260	5272	5284	5297	5309	5321	5333	5346	5358	1	2	4	5	6	7	9	10	11
.73	5370	5383	5395	5408	5420	5433	5445	5458	5470	5483	1	3	4	5	6	8	9	10	11
.74	5495	5508	5521	5534	5546	5559	5572	5585	5598	5610	1	3	4	5	6	8	9	10	12
.75	5623	5636	5649	5662	5675	5689	5702	5715	5728	5741	1	3	4	5	7	8	9	10	12
.76	5754	5768	5781	5794	5808	5821	5834	5848	5861	5875	1	3	4	5	7	8	9	11	12
.77	5888	5902	5916	5929	5943	5957	5970	5984	5998	6012	1	3	4	5	7	8	10	11	12
.78	6026	6039	6053	6067	6081	6095	6109	6124	6138	6152	1	3	4	6	7	8	10	11	13
.79	6166	6180	6194	6209	6223	6237	6252	6266	6281	6295	1	3	4	6	7	9	10	11	13
.80	6310	6324	6339	6353	6368	6383	6397	6412	6427	6442	1	3	4	6	7	9	10	12	13
.81	6457	6471	6486	6501	6516	6531	6546	6561	6577	6592	2	3	5	6	8	9	11	12	14
.82	6607	6622	6637	6653	6668	6683	6699	6714	6730	6745	2	3	5	6	8	9	11	12	14
.83	6761	6776	6792	6808	6823	6839	6855	6871	6887	6902	2	3	5	6	8	9	11	13	14
.84	6918	6934	6950	6966	6982	6998	7015	7031	7047	7063	2	3	5	6	8	10	11	13	15
.85	7079	7096	7112	7129	7145	7161	7178	7194	7211	7228	2	3	5	7	8	10	12	13	15
.86	7244	7261	7278	7295	7311	7328	7345	7362	7379	7396	2	3	5	7	8	10	12	13	15
.87	7413	7430	7447	7464	7482	7499	7516	7534	7551	7568	2	3	5	7	9	10	12	14	16
.88	7586	7603	7621	7638	7656	7674	7691	7709	7727	7745	2	4	5	7	9	11	12	14	16
.89	7762	7780	7798	7816	7834	7852	7870	7889	7907	7925	2	4	5	7	9	11	13	14	16
.90	7943	7962	7980	7998	8017	8035	8054	8072	8091	8110	2	4	6	7	9	11	13	15	17
.91	8128	8147	8166	8185	8204	8222	8241	8260	8279	8299	2	4	6	8	9	11	13	15	17
.92	8318	8337	8356	8375	8395	8414	8433	8453	8472	8492	2	4	6	8	10	12	14	15	17
.93	8511	8531	8551	8570	8590	8610	8630	8650	8670	8690	2	4	6	8	10	12	14	16	18
.94	8710	8730	7850	8770	8790	8810	8831	8851	8872	8892	2	4	6	8	10	12	14	16	18
.95	8913	8933	8954	8974	8995	9016	9036	9057	9078	9099	2	4	6	8	10	12	15	17	19
.96	9120	9141	9162	9183	9204	9226	9247	9268	9290	9311	2	4	6	8	11	13	15	17	19
.97	9333	9354	9376	9397	9419	9441	9462	9484	9506	9528	2	4	7	9	11	13	15	17	20
.98	9550	9572	9594	9616	9638	9661	9683	9705	9727	9750	2	4	7	9	11	13	16	18	20
.99	9772	9795	9817	9840	9863	9886	9908	9931	9954	9977	2	5	7	9	11	14	16	18	20

Index